METABOLIC DISEASE

A Guide to Early Recognition

ROBERT M. COHN, M.D.

Associate Professor, Department of Pediatrics,
University of Pennsylvania School of Medicine;
Senior Physician, Division of Metabolism,
and Associate Director of Clinical Laboratories,
Children's Hospital of Philadelphia

KARL S. ROTH, M.D.

Associate Professor and Chief, Section of
Genetics, Endocrinology, and Metabolism,
Department of Pediatrics
Medical College of Virginia, Richmond

W. B. SAUNDERS COMPANY *1983*

Philadelphia • London • Toronto • Mexico City • Rio de Janeiro • Sydney • Tokyo

W. B. Saunders Company: West Washington Square
                           Philadelphia, PA 19105

                           1 St. Anne's Road
                           Eastbourne, East Sussex BN21 3UN, England

                           1 Goldthorne Avenue
                           Toronto, Ontario M8Z 5T9, Canada

                           Apartado 26370—Cedro 512
                           Mexico 4, D.F., Mexico

                           Rua Coronel Cabrita, 8
                           Sao Cristovao Caixa Postal 21176
                           Rio de Janeiro, Brazil

                           9 Waltham Street
                           Artarmon, N.S.W. 2064, Australia

                           Ichibancho, Central Bldg., 22-1 Ichibancho
                           Chiyoda-Ku, Tokyo 102, Japan

Library of Congress Cataloging in Publication Data

Cohn, Robert M.
    Metabolic disease.

    1. Metabolism—Disorders—Diagnosis.   I. Roth,
Karl S.   II. Title.   [DNLM: 1. Metabolism, Inborn
errors—Diagnosis.   2. Metabolic diseases—Diagnosis.
WD 200 C67m]
RC627.54.C64   1983   616.3'9   82-48508
ISBN 0-7216-2652-1

Metabolic Disease: A Guide to Early Recognition   ISBN   0-7216-2652-1

Last digit is the print number: 9   8   7   6   5   4   3   2   1

CONTRIBUTORS

HAROLD FINKEL, D.O.

Clinical Practice of Pediatric Neurology, Detroit, Michigan; Formerly Fellow in Pediatric Neurology, Children's Hospital of Philadelphia

JOHN FORMAN, M.D.

Assistant Professor of Pediatrics, University of Pennsylvania School of Medicine; Assistant Physician, Division of Nephrology and Metabolic Diseases, Children's Hospital of Philadelphia; Acting Director, Division of Nephrology, Children's Hospital of Philadelphia

PETER JEZYK, Ph.D., D.V.M.

Assistant Professor of Medicine in Medical Genetics, University of Pennsylvania School of Veterinary Medicine; Director of Metabolic Screening Laboratory, Children's Hospital of Philadelphia

MIKE PALMIERI, Ph.D.

Assistant Professor of Pediatric Research, University of Pennsylvania School of Medicine

MARC YUDKOFF, M.D.

Associate Professor of Pediatrics, University of Pennsylvania School of Medicine; Senior Physician, Division of Metabolic Diseases, Children's Hospital of Philadelphia

FOREWORD

An earlier companion to this volume presented the basic principles of metabolic control.[1] That book was intended to fulfill the varied needs of the graduate student, physician, and biochemist as well as selected undergraduates and medical students who wish to augment their understanding of the principles that underlie metabolic regulation. The current volume undertakes the task of relating these principles of metabolism to medicine, health, and disease.

In 1657, William Harvey stated that nature might display her secret mysteries:

> . . . in cases where she shows traces of her workings apart from the beaten path; nor is there any better way to advance the proper practice of medicine than to give our minds to the discovery of the normal laws of nature by careful investigation of cases of rarer forms of disease. For it has been found in almost all things that what they contain of useful or applicable nature is hardly perceived unless we are deprived of them or they become deranged in some way.[2]

Harvey's prophetic words, now more than 300 years old, anticipated the career of Sir Archibald Garrod, who is regarded by many as the father of the precepts of inborn errors of metabolism. In his Croonian Lectures of 1908 Garrod advanced these ideas further in his studies of alkaptonuria.

> Actual derangements of the metabolic processes follow almost any deviations from the normal of health, but our interpretation of the urinary changes which result is, in many instances, greatly hampered by the scantiness of our knowledge of the intermediate steps of the paths of metabolism. Such knowledge as we have of these steps is derived from casual glimpses afforded when as the outcome of one of Nature's experiments, some particular line is interfered with and intermediate products are excreted incompletely burnt.[3]

During the ensuing decades, and especially in the past thirty years, many such "intermediate products" have been characterized and a large number of metabolic pathways have been well defined through intensive study in both the normal and disease states. Technological advances, often the work of clinical investigators interested in these problems, made it possible to recognize and measure a vast array of chemical compounds and enzymatic and transport transactions in the tissues of the body. It has often been necessary to render certain formidable instruments of research into more readily applicable methods of clinical testing in order to arrive at a precise diagnosis and to derive and to apply possible forms of therapy. There has been much emphasis on enzymatic derangements during these processes; where some pathways have been systematically studied, defects at each step have been described. However, this is not the entire story. We know that mutations resulting in the alteration of protein structure affect cell membranes and their function of transport, specific membrane receptors, and cytosol receptors for some types of chemical messengers. At present the interaction of the latter with regions of the nuclear chromatin is poorly understood.

The contemporary student of medicine must understand the connections between metabolism and disease, perceive the basic biochemical transactions of life, their pathophysiology, and their relevance to clinical derangements. Only through such study will it be possible to recognize certain categories of disease and to arrive at precise diagnoses. In some instances today, appropriate treatment introduced early in life is ameliorative. So, too, prenatal diagnosis, detection of heterozygosity, and genetic counseling may be skillfully employed. It should not be assumed that these matters lie within the realm of exotica. The principles discussed in this volume are responsible for the very maintenance of life. And they have a certain poetry as well as scientific and medical validity. In presenting the biochemical bases of metabolic disease, the authors speak of the ordered state of life and point out that all living systems age and die. That discourse concerns life, organization, disease, disorganization, aging, and death. Furthermore, there is a patent link between these matters and those that concern the more common diseases of man. The infectious diseases are modified by variations in individual susceptibility. There is increasing evidence of an association between susceptibility to infection and metabolic defects, and infections indirectly disrupt the ordered state of living systems, as for example in acid-base regulation.

Because the primary basic disturbances are often discerned at birth, it is not surprising that an increasing number of investigators have addressed themselves to the study of the infant. And it is no surprise that the authors of this volume have chosen to direct their efforts primarily within the field of pediatrics. But this is not to suppose that some of the disturbances are always apparent early in life rather than first displaying themselves at a later age. The recognition of disorganization at the earliest possible moment in life is necessary to circumvent the immediate ravages. The recognition of more subtle and perhaps partial derangements is equally important, in order to offset the clinical consequences in later life. Especially valuable therefore are the presentations concerning catastrophic diseases presenting during infancy and the relationships of derangements to human growth and development. The clinical and chemical implements for the identification of an array of important disorders are well integrated. The design here is to correlate thoroughly clinical medicine with basic scientific knowledge. As noted by Sir William Osler in 1895 ". . . the physician without physiology and chemistry flounders along in an aimless fashion, never able to gain any accurate conception of disease. . . ."[4] So much more legitimate is this observation today!

REFERENCES

1. Herman, R.H., Cohn, R.M., McNamara, P.D.: Principles of Metabolic Control In Mammalian Systems. New York and London, Plenum Press, 1980.
2. Harvey, W., cited by Garrod, A.E.: Lancet 1:1055, 1928.
3. Garrod, A.E.: Inborn errors of metabolism (Croonian Lectures). Lancet 2:1–7; 73–79; 142–148; 214–220, 1908.
4. Osler, W.: Teaching and thinking: The two functions of a medical school. Montreal Med. J. 23:561–72, 1895.

ALFRED M. BONGIOVANNI, M.D.
Professor of Pediatrics and
Professor of Pediatrics in
  Obstetrics and Gynecology
School of Medicine, University
of Pennsylvania.

The Pennsylvania Hospital and
The Children's Medical Center
of Philadelphia.

PREFACE

Biochemistry provides the foundation for understanding metabolic disease. In reality all clinical disease is the expression of underlying disordered biochemistry and physiology. In this book we wish to develop an approach to metabolic diseases that embodies the mind-liberating concepts derived from biochemistry. Physicians need not rely on memory when basic science can clarify common and uncommon clinical problems.

In organizing the material in this book, we have directed our major efforts toward making the presumptive diagnosis of metabolic disease as clinical an endeavor as possible. It has been our experience in teaching medical students and house staff that metabolic causes frequently are not considered in the differential diagnosis, perhaps because of discomfiture with biochemistry. We believe that in order to arrive at the definitive diagnosis of a metabolic disorder a careful history and physical examination, which represent the cornerstone of the clinical method, must also be utilized here. In considering the pathogenesis of these disorders we have elected to present as coherent a picture as possible while neglecting to document point by point the experimental bases for the picture we draw. We have done this in recognition of the fact that this book must serve the needs of the busy clinician. By including adequate references, we provide access to relevant and usually exhaustive discussions of important evidence and research. Nonetheless, we believe that the second chapter of this book, Biochemistry in Metabolism and Medicine, will provide any reader, regardless of sophistication, with the biochemical perspective so essential to understanding the disease process.

In the clinical sections we have tried to provide references that furnish additional background and greater details of therapy than we feel are appropriate in this book. Therapy of a metabolic disorder is not to be undertaken lightly. Not only is a clear understanding of the deranged biochemistry essential, but one must also be able to monitor readily biochemical parameters in the patient. As the title indicates, this is a book primarily concerned with recognizing and understanding metabolic disorders. We believe it is the responsibility of the physician to suspect an inborn error of metabolism in the appropriate clinical setting and then to obtain further expert help in diagnosing and managing such a patient. The requirement for specialized studies in no way diminishes the need for the judicious use of the clinical method, which acts as a guide to when to seek metabolic consultation. Very often it will entail transfer of the patient—most particularly the catastrophically ill newborn—to a center specifically equipped to deal with metabolic diseases.

While the book is directed primarily to the general clinician we believe that individuals expert in metabolic disease will also find it useful. The major works in this area furnish little diagnostic aid for the consultant and for those undergoing postdoctoral training in inborn errors. Further, we believe that it is useful to have a "bite-size" view of biochemistry and metabolic disorders that can be read and assimilated in a relatively short time. Such a view of the subject will render the major works more useful as the reference works that they were intended to be. Moreover, we feel that such a view will document the utility of studying inborn errors of metabolism for the light that they shed on the understanding of acquired disease. It is through cultivation of the fields of inborn errors that important advances in our understanding of acquired disease have emerged and will continue to emerge. We hope heightened awareness will reduce the suffering and improve the lives of individuals afflicted with inborn errors of metabolism.

We would not have undertaken this task were it not for Dr. Stanton Segal, Director of the Division of Biochemical Development and Molecular Diseases, Children's Hospital of Philadelphia, who trained us and encouraged us to write this book. In addition, we were fortunate to have a group of dedicated, highly competent and imperturbable secretaries, who accepted each task with relish. They are Karen Gunn, Marie Lanzilotta, Clara Polaski, Linda Braxton, and Edith Mayes. Susan Thomas of W. B. Saunders Company made the transition from manuscript to text an enjoyable and educational experience.

We are delighted and honored that Dr. Alfred M. Bongiovanni consented to contribute the Foreword to this book.

Notwithstanding the aforementioned individuals, our deepest appreciation must be reserved for Roberta Kangilaski, Medical Editor at the W. B. Saunders Company, who entered as a catalyst but emerged as our friend. Her skill, patience, good counsel, and good humor will always be appreciated.

CONTENTS

I

METABOLISM AND MEDICINE

Catastrophic Metabolic Diseases Presenting in the Newborn Period

This century has witnessed the full flowering of Archibald Garrod's concept of inborn errors of metabolism. Painstaking clinical observation, combined with unusual insight, led him to propose at the turn of the century that the clinical manifestations of albinism, alcaptonuria, cystinuria, and pentosuria were the result of a defect in enzyme activity, itself the result of a defect in the heredity of the individual. In effect, before the concept of the gene had emerged, he had proposed that a defect in the gene would cause a defect in an enzyme.

Subsequent research in laboratories throughout the world has given considerable flesh to these bare bones. In the next chapter we will consider these insights in much greater detail. Here we will summarize them so that we may apply them directly to the matter of inborn errors of metabolism presenting in the neonatal period. Proteins (of which enzymes are a subset) are the functional devices of life, carrying out the chemical reactions required by living cells as well as fulfilling a myriad of structural and transport functions. Deoxyribonucleic acid (DNA), the macromolecule that comprises the genes, directs the linear sequence of amino acids comprising these molecules. A mutation in the informational content of DNA can alter the sequence of the resulting protein and thereby alter or abolish its function. Hence, the linear sequence in DNA directs the linear sequence in proteins, with an informational correspondence that is one to one.

It follows that inborn errors of metabolism result from a defect in the genetic material. While defective enzymes are the best-known causes for inborn errors of metabolism, these disorders are not limited to this class of proteins only. Defects in structural proteins, transport proteins, and subunits of functioning proteins account for other inborn errors. Nonetheless, those inborn errors that present in the neonatal period appear to be limited to defects in enzymes.

Recognition of disease in the newborn infant rests on an awareness of the limited number and relative nonspecificity of clinical signs and symptoms. Such symptoms include lethargy, irritability, and hyperactivity. Failure to feed well is also a cardinal manifestation of disease in the newborn. Others include fever or hypothermia, cyanosis, convulsions, vomiting, and the early or prolonged presence of jaundice during the neonatal period. Diarrhea and abdominal distention may also be indicative of severe disease in the newborn.

Any or all of these symptoms may be present in a child who suffers from an infection during the newborn period. Consequently it is essential that the alert physician suspect the diagnosis of sepsis neonatorum with this kind of nonspecific presentation. At the time an infectious etiology is being considered for this array of symptoms, however, it is equally important that the prudent physician consider metabolic causes.

The accumulation of substances toxic to the infant can account for these findings, although the mechanisms are poorly understood. The symptom triad of vomiting, lethargy, and poor feeding can be caused by disturbances in carbohydrate, fat, or protein metabolism. If the substance is delivered in or derived from the diet, then its elimination or reduction (or the provision of a cofactor needed by the infant for its metabolism) may bring about remission (see Chapter 37). On the other hand, if the substance is of endogenous origin, alterations in diet will have little effect. Such substances

Table 1-1   CATASTROPHIC METABOLIC DISEASE MASQUERADING AS NEONATAL SEPSIS*

	Neurologic Findings†	Acidosis	Renal Dysfunction	Liver Dysfunction	Other	Definitive Diagnosis
Organic Acidemias						
Maple Syrup Urine Disease	1,2,4,5	+	—	—	Bone marrow depression, ↑lactate, hypoglycemia, hyperammonemia	See Chapter 34
Propionic acidemia	1,2,4,5	+	—	—		
Isovaleric acidemia	1,2,4,5	+	—	—		
Methylmalonic acidemia	1,2,4,5	+	—	—		
Holocarboxylase synthase deficiency‡	1	+	—	—		
HMG CoA lyase deficiency‡	1,2,4,5	+	—	—		
Other organic acidemias (see Chapter 34)						
Congenital lactic acidemia (see Chapter 29)						
Urea Cycle Defects						
Congenital hyperammonemia	1,2,5	±	—	+		
Carbamyl phosphate synthetase deficiency						
Ornithine transcarbamylase deficiency	1,2,5	±	—	+	Orotic acid crystals	See Chapter 22
Citrullinemia	1–3,5	+	—	+		
Argininosuccinic aciduria	2,3	±	—	+		
Other urea cycle defects (see also Chapter 11)						
Carbohydrate Disorders						
Galactosemia	1	+	+	+	Jaundice	See Chapter 26
Hereditary fructose intolerance§	1,2	+	+	+	Decreased serum Pi	
Aminoacidopathies						
Hereditary tyrosinemia	1,5	+	+	+	Abnormalities of porphyrins and coagulation	See Chapter 22
Homocystinuria (remethylation)	1,2	—	—	—	Hypsarrhythmia	
Nonketotic hyperglycinemia	1,2,4	—	—	—		
Endocrinopathies						
Congenital adrenal hyperplasia	1,2	±	—	—	Postnatal virilization, hyperkalemia	↑—17 Ketosteroids, ↑pregnanetriol, ↓aldosterone
Congenital diabetes mellitus	1	+	—	—	Hyperglycemia, acetonuria, tachypnea, ketonemia	Blood sugar, urine ketones, +nitroprusside

*Failure to thrive is universal and mental retardation is common (save for fructose intolerance and tyrosinemia), as are diverse neurologic findings. Deterioration in association with feeding is frequent, with vomiting a major clinical problem.

†Neurologic Findings: 1—lethargy, coma; 2—seizures; 3—spasticity; 4—abnormal reflexes; 5—respiratory center symptoms.

‡Erythematous, exfoliative dermatitis.

§Seen only in neonates or infants receiving sucrose-containing formula.

4

may have been cleared antenatally by the placenta. Consequently infants in whom they accumulate after birth may appear normal in the early neonatal period.

Response to diet may be an important modality of diagnostic evaluation and may suggest the need for further evaluation. For example, in an infant who has been vomiting for several days, the following clearly indicate the need for immediate observations: the baby shows no improvement after the administration of sugar-electrolyte mixture; the baby must be roused for feedings; the parents report weight loss or the infant has sunken eyes or dry mucous membranes; dyspnea, tachypnea, or other alterations in respirations are present; the baby is yellow, blue, or pale; no stools have been passed and there is abdominal distention; the baby has not voided; tremors, seizures, or stiffness is present. Dehydration and disturbances of acid-base balance must be attended to promptly. Vomiting in the immediate neonatal period is likely to occur under close medical scrutiny, and so rarely should dehydration supervene before evaluation begins.

Table 1–1 lists the major metabolic causes of catastrophic illness in neonates. Except when an odor is produced as a consequence of the metabolic block, there are few pathognomonic findings of these disorders in the neonatal period. Cataracts may be present in young infants with galactosemia, giving the lens a bubbly or grapelike appearance. This may be associated as well with hepatomegaly and positive reducing substance in the urine. Many of these conditions are associated with an anion-gap acidosis, and a few are associated with a hyperchloremic acidosis (see Chapter 3). Hence, measurement of serum electrolytes and calculation of the data with particular reference to the contribution of chloride are important simple modalities in the evaluation of any gravely ill newborn. At the same time cultures are being collected for the work-up of possible sepsis, urine should be collected before a potentially toxic nutrient is removed from the diet. The urine should then be promptly sent to a laboratory that provides screening tests for possible metabolic diseases. These tests are discussed extensively in Chapter 38. Immediate further evaluation of the sick infant with a positive test for urine ferric chloride, ketonuria, or increased reducing substances is imperative. The disorders suggested by these results can be fulminant and fatal in young infants unless appropriately treated. Positive tests may indicate galactosemia, branched-chain ketoacid problems, ketotic hyperglycinemia, or methylmalonic acidemia.

Orange staining of the diaper due to urate crystals may, with vomiting, be the first manifestation of Lesch-Nyhan syndrome and should be followed up by serum uric acid determination. Crystalluria in a lethargic infant may indicate hereditary orotic aciduria, and measurement of urinary orotic acid should be requested. Orotic aciduria is also seen in ornithine transcarbamylase deficiency, a disorder of the urea cycle. Vomiting, poor feeding, and irritability may indicate renal colic secondary to stone formation in hyperoxaluria or cystinuria. Usually, however, cystinuria does not cause problems until much later in life. Urine amino acid determinations or a cyanide nitroprusside test can establish the presence of cystine. Other nonspecific abnormalities encountered in these disorders include neutropenia, which may indicate branched-chain amino acid or urea cycle disorders, anemia, and thrombocytopenia.

Hypernatremic dehydration, particularly in the absence of diarrhea and with a history of polyuria going back to the neonatal period, suggests excessive renal water loss, which may be due to nephrogenic diabetes insipidus, particularly in males. Hypercalcemia, hypophosphatemia, failure to acidify the urine, and generalized amino aciduria are other findings suggestive of renal tubular disorders; all may present with vomiting, lethargy, and poor feeding (see Chapter 37). Hyponatremia and hyperkalemia with dehydration suggest congenital adrenal hyperplasia. Young female infants with this disorder show ambiguous genitalia, including clitoral enlargement. Hypoglycemia is associated with vomiting, lethargy, and poor feeding and may indicate galactosemia, hereditary fructose intolerance, or branched-chain amino acid disorders (see Chapter 22). Abnormalities of liver function as manifested by hyperbilirubinemia or by elevation of serum liver enzymes usually indicate hepatitis, but galactosemia, hereditary fructose intolerance, disorders of the urea cycle, or hereditary tyrosinemia may also be the cause (see Chapter 22).

Measurement of a postprandial plasma ammonia is key in any child who appears to have deteriorated as a consequence of feeding, particularly if it is apparent that protein has been the causative agent. Hyperammonemia is commonly seen in disorders of the urea cycle and of branched-chain amino acid metabolism.

Odors are exceedingly important features of differential diagnosis in the catastrophically ill newborn or young infant. They can be noted in soiled diapers, breath, cerumen, saliva, and sweat. Odor can reveal diseases such as maple syrup urine disease, isovaleric acidemia, holocarboxylase synthetase deficiency, and disorders of methionine metabolism (see Chapter 34).

During the authors' training in metabolic disease, one mentor coined the dictum "smell a baby; save a life." We have found this waggish comment to be among the most useful clinical approaches in our dealings with gravely ill infants.

In this overview we have tried to stress the importance of considering an inherited metabolic disorder in the differential diagnosis of a very sick infant. These diseases, although individually uncommon, constitute in the aggregate a considerable incidence in the newborn infant population. Furthermore, advances in their diagnosis and treatment are being made rapidly, so that diagnosis of an affected infant, even post-mortem, may make it possible to avoid a second family tragedy by prenatal testing.

2

Biochemistry in Metabolism and Medicine

INTRODUCTION

Living systems epitomize a level of complexity and order without counterpart in the nonliving world. This order depends upon an enormous information store, which is miniaturized at the level of biological macromolecules, and upon the maintenance of structural and functional complexity by the expenditure of energy. That life's processes can be explained in terms of chemistry and physics, i.e., in terms of matter and energy, is a basic tenet of biochemistry. Such a point of view enables us to focus on life in terms of transformations of chemical substrates, mediated by enzymes (organic catalysts). These reactions occur within the organized complex of the cell, the simplest living entity.

Mammalian cells exist within an extracellular environment that must be maintained relatively constant. Alterations of pH, temperature, or ionic concentration, for example, engender a response by the cell to return the intracellular environment to its original conditions. When the cell is unable to adjust to such changes, the normal conduct of metabolism is disrupted, leading to disordered functioning at the level of the organism. Indeed, without the capacity of intracellular machinery to adjust in turn to various physiological and pathological changes, cell damage or death is likely. Clearly the cornerstone of life must then be the *control mechanisms* for intermediary metabolism, which allow the cell to withstand altered intracellular and extracellular environmental changes. Hence, we may say that disease begins at the level of a response of intracellular components to a perturbation, be it inherited or acquired. As such, all *disease is the result of disordered cellular function*.

Overview of the Consequences of Inborn Errors of Metabolism

It is clear that the genetic endowment of the host is the crucial determinant of the individual's response to an environmental perturbation. At present, the complexity of the components of the genome that govern the responses of the host to an external stress (acquired disease) is poorly understood. However, in the group of diseases known as "inborn errors of metabolism," the relationship between a defect in the genetic endowment of the individual and the inability to cope with some environmental factor is, on the surface, more direct. For example, there are well over 100 electrophoretic variants of hemoglobin, but only a few of them are associated with clinical disease. Hence, there must be far more variation in the structure of proteins within the body than there are clinical diseases. Stated differently, there are many variations in amino acid sequence that are compatible with retention of biological functions, since the shape of the protein is altered minimally. As presently understood, inborn errors of metabolism are the result of an absence of or a diminution in the biologic activity of a protein, whether the protein is actually missing or simply defective in its biological function. Most of these defects involve enzymes. When an enzyme normally present in a particular metabolic pathway is functionally absent, we may expect either the

7

accumulation of substrate involved in the abnormal enzyme step or the absence or reduced formation of a product of that particular enzyme step. Indeed, both possibilities often materialize. Concomitantly, one often finds unusual metabolites, rarely encountered in normal individuals, as the body attempts to rid itself of the substrate accumulating as a result of the defect. In fact, in many of the inborn errors of metabolism, the identification of some unusual metabolite is the means by which the diagnosis is suggested, if not actually proved.

In addition to defects in enzyme activity, there are a number of genetic disorders that involve defects in the active transport of key substrates across cell membranes. This is to be expected, since all available evidence supports the view that these carrier proteins act in a stereospecific fashion: being protein in nature they must also be synthesized according to the information in the amino acid code.

It is difficult to overstate the importance of Garrod's concept of inborn errors of metabolism. Long before biochemistry had come of age as a science he had proposed that inherited diseases were biochemical and that the response to all external disease-producing factors was biochemical as well. In fact, in 1908 he wrote, "The existence of chemical individuality follows of necessity from chemical specificity, but we should expect the differences between individuals to be still more subtle and difficult of detection." Today we are reaping the intellectual and therapeutic harvest of his genius.

Order in Life and Disease

It is impossible to overemphasize the role control plays in the life process. Control mechanisms are found at every level of biological function, beginning with enzymatic processes. Such mechanisms provide for the proper function of metabolic pathways and of cells within a tissue (and so on), providing ultimately for the ability of the organism to adapt to its environment. Control, in the biochemical sense, connotes the ability to use *information* from within and without the cell. Since all physiological function rests ultimately upon biochemical function, it follows that the most decisive control resides at the level of enzymes, the functional entities that carry out the chemical reactions of intermediary metabolism. Derangements of enzyme function or control therefore will lead to disease or even death.

The relationship between the sequence of bases in DNA and the sequence of amino acids in proteins was one of the major factors in the emerging recognition that in living systems *structure mandates function*. An inherited defect in the DNA code will be translated into a protein of altered amino acid composition. If this change occurs at a site that affects the shape (highly ordered three-dimensional structure) of the protein, its activity may be modified or abolished, resulting in an inborn error.

In living systems enzymes provide the mechanism by which matter is consumed, providing the energy to poise the system in its essential state, far from equilibrium. These proteins possess tremendous specificity and prodigious efficiency, permitting them to carry out the reactions of intermediary metabolism within the rapid time frame necessary for life to exist.

To sustain life the cell must generate adenosine triphosphate (ATP) at a rate that will ensure the synthesis of the structural and functional macromolecules of the cell, the maintenance of the cellular organization against the relentless drive toward increasing entropy, and the maintenance of transmembrane ionic gradients. These broad categories of energy-requiring processes maintain the cell in a state far from equilibrium.

How Macromolecules Work

The Need for Flexibility

Large molecules and supramolecular structures (e.g., membranes and multienzyme complexes) are indispensable components of the cell and extracellular structures (e.g., collagen fibrils). While

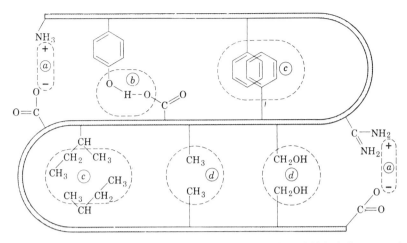

Figure 2–1 Weak or noncovalent forces, which provide for the flexibility of biological macro-molecules: (*a*) salt bridges or electrostatic interactions; (*b*) hydrogen bonding; (*c*) hydrophobic interactions; (*d*) van der Waals interactions. (From Anfinsen, C.B.: The Molecular Basis of Evolution. New York, John Wiley and Sons, 1959.)

covalent forces, in the range of 50 to 100 kcal/mole, are essential to the structural integrity of these entities, it is the weak or noncovalent forces, in the range of 1 to 5 kcal/mole, that confer upon these molecules and life itself the flexibility that permits them to respond to perturbations in their environment (Fig. 2–1).

Many factors operate to disrupt the ordered state of life, and if left unopposed, they would render the system malfunctional. Ultimately, all living systems age and die as they become less organized. In particular, proteins and lipids in cell membranes may be denatured or oxidized within the membrane. For example, proteins may be denatured by a host of environmental factors (ionizing radiation, temperature, pH, and so on) as well as by their own substrates or products, and lipids may undergo peroxidative destruction.

Here we want to emphasize the role of *noncovalent forces* in the life process (Table 2–1). Organic chemistry, which deals with carbon and covalent bonds, provides the basis for a thorough understanding of the nature of chemical processes occurring both in the laboratory and in the cell. Nonetheless, we must have recourse to noncovalent bonds to achieve an understanding of the life process. Indeed, it is because of the great strength of covalent bonds, essential to the formation of the polymeric substances (proteins, glycosaminoglycans, membranes) encountered in living systems, that these bonds are not able to provide for flexibility in response to environmental perturbations. Substances like horn and wood that are predominantly covalent do not possess those attributes that we intuitively associate with living systems. Thus, it is necessary to understand weaker, noncovalent forces, which can account for the immense variety of biochemical reactions and changes in the three-dimensional configuration of protein and nucleic acids. Noncovalent forces account for this flexibility or plasticity, being quite responsive to fluctuations within the environment. Enzymes act largely by virtue of these noncovalent forces, which include the following: hydrogen bonding, electrostatic interactions, van der Waals' interactions, and hydrophobic bonding. Such forces ac-

Table 2–1 CLASS OF WEAK (NONCOVALENT)
CHEMICAL INTERACTIONS

Interaction	Approximate Bond Energies (Kcal/mole)
Electrostatic	5
Hydrogen Bonds	2–5
Hydrophobic	0.3–3
Van der Waals forces	1

Table 2–2 STRUCTURES AND
FUNCTIONS DEPENDENT ON WEAK
FORCES

1. Secondary, tertiary, and quaternary protein structures
2. Enzyme-substrate complex
3. Membrane structure and membrane receptor-ligand interactions
4. Higher order structure of water
5. Nucleic acid interactions with other nucleic acids or proteins

count for the high degree of organization of proteins and nucleic acids as well as the binding of compounds and effectors to proteins, be they enzymes, immunoglobulins, or membrane receptors (see Table 2–2).

While these weaker forces provide for the plasticity of the living organism in response to environmental conditions, they also introduce instability into protein structure and, consequently, into protein function. Thus, proteins may undergo denaturation by thermal agitation, with the evolution of heat leading to the disruption of the noncovalent bonds. A short discussion on noncovalent forces is presented here; the reader desiring a more detailed account should consult the references at the end of the chapter.

The Nature of Noncovalent Bonds

The strength of chemical bonds correlates directly with length; two atoms bound covalently are closer than two bound noncovalently. Nonetheless, when two molecules possess structures that permit a complementary interaction (e.g., jigsaw puzzle pieces) the cumulative effect of their noncovalent interactions can be appreciable. Indeed, when these weak forces come into play in the environment of macromolecules and supramolecules, their cumulative contribution can be significant and, indeed, as regards specificity, decisive.

Hydrogen Bonding (Fig. 2–2)

When hydrogen forms a covalent bond with an electronegative atom like nitrogen or oxygen, the bonding electrons are attracted toward the electronegative atom. As a consequence, the proton remains at the outer end of the covalent bond, its charge unbalanced, forming a dipole in which one atom has a slight positive charge and the other a slight negative charge. The proton is able to attract an external, negatively charged group on another molecule in an essentially ionic interaction that represents bond energy of about 3 to 5 kcal/mole. Protein side-chains can often engage in hydrogen bonding, and groups with this ability usually complete their potential to do so. While hydrogen bonds play an important role in stabilizing the structures of proteins (through interpeptide, interside chains, and side-chain–peptide hydrogen bonds) and nucleic acids (through base-pair hy-

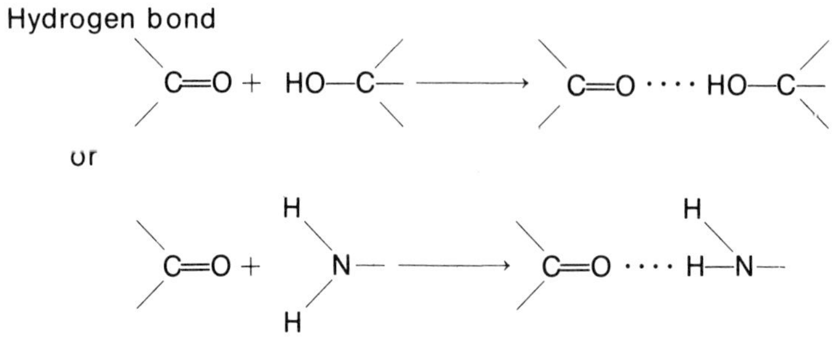

Hydrogen bond

Figure 2–2 Examples of hydrogen bonding. (From Villee, C., and Dethier, V.C.: Biological Principles and Processes. 2nd ed. Philadelphia, W.B. Saunders Co., 1976.)

drogen bonds), they only come into play after covalent forces (peptide bonds, disulfide bonds) and noncovalent forces (hydrophobic bonds) have generated the general form of the three-dimensional structure. This is so because hydrogen bonds are highly directional in nature and therefore require complementary structures for their full potential to be realized. If a mutation affects the ability of a protein to assume its normal structure, then such complementary interactions cannot occur.

Salt Bridges or Electrostatic Interactions (see Fig. 2–1)

Fixed positive charges, e.g., a positively charged amino group from the N-terminal residue of lysine or arginine, may attract and be attracted by negatively charged groups such as the carboxylate group in the side-chain of glutamic and aspartic acid residues of a protein.

Van der Waals' Interactions (see Fig. 2–1)

Van der Waals' interactions are relatively weak forces, often termed "nonbonded interactions," existing between otherwise nonattracting atoms. They are generated by the fluctuating dipole moments associated with all atoms. The temporary moment induced can polarize another atom with which it comes in contact, causing an attraction between them. Once such polarization is established the atoms interact as if they were dipoles; hence, the interaction may be viewed as that occuring between transient dipoles. The force of attraction is inversely proportional to the sixth power of the distance. Hence this interaction requires close approximation for optimal attraction. As with hydrogen bonding, this is achieved when a complementary structure exists.

Hydrophobic Bonding (see Fig. 2–1)

The essential feature of hydrophobic bonding resides in the inability of water to solubilize nonpolar residues, with the hydrophobic molecules interacting with each other rather than with water. By forming an oil droplet-like structure, the hydrophobic side-chains avoid the increased order (unfavorable decreased entropy) that would occur were they to be incorporated into the water lattice. Since "likes dissolve in likes," the apolar residues turn away from water and do not impose an orderly arrangement on the water molecules in their immediate vicinity. Hence, the driving force for this interaction is essentially entropic, since the disorganization of water increases when the hydrophobic molecules coalesce.

Hydrophobic forces, being nondirectional, contribute to the stabilization of the general three-dimensional protein structure but are unlikely to contribute much to specificity in terms of recognition and binding. Rather it is the van der Waals', electrostatic, and hydrogen bonds which, requiring complementary surfaces and proximity, are the decisive factors in binding substances to proteins.

Water and the Life Process

On earth, water is the essential ingredient required for the functioning of all biological systems. Proteins (enzymes) require an aqueous environment for development of their biological activity. The hydrophobic interaction discussed above is one of the most important forces in stabilizing the three-dimensional structures of proteins. The driving force for these interactions appears to be largely based on the formation of oil-like enclaves by which hydrophobic side-chains of amino acids, within the protein, coalesce. Thus, they do not impose a local ordering on the surrounding water (and an unfavorable decrease in entropy), which would occur were they to be incorporated into a water lattice. On a more macroscopic level certain properties of water make essential contributions to the success of life. These include the high heat capacity, the high heat of vaporization, and the wide range between freezing and boiling points as well as solubilizing ability, high dielectric constant, ionizing ability, and high surface tension of water. All of these properties relate to the hydrogen-bonding ability of water.

THE ROLE OF MACROMOLECULES IN THE LIFE PROCESS

Types of Macromolecules

As we have noted, the structural and functional hierarchy of life depends on the special properties of certain classes of macromolecules, in particular, proteins, nucleic acids, and polysaccharides. In the proteins and nucleic acids, the structures are precise. Proteins have a linear sequence of amino acids, defined by the nucleotide triplet code, which also specifies the three-dimensional shape that the protein will assume in an aqueous environment.

All three classes of macromolecules are chain polymers formed by a condensation process during which a molecule of water is eliminated for each two building blocks that condense (Fig. 2–3). The precursors, in each case, are small molecules which are intermediates of metabolic sequences and are therefore constantly replenished. Proteins are formed by condensation reactions between the amino and carboxyl groups of amino acids, forming the so-called "peptide bond." The analogous condensation product of nucleic acids is the phosphodiester bond, involving the phosphate group and a hydroxyl group on the pentose of an adjacent nucleotide. At one end of the nucleic acid chain is a pentose in which the 3' position is free, while at the other end the 5' position of a pentose is not involved in the condensation process.

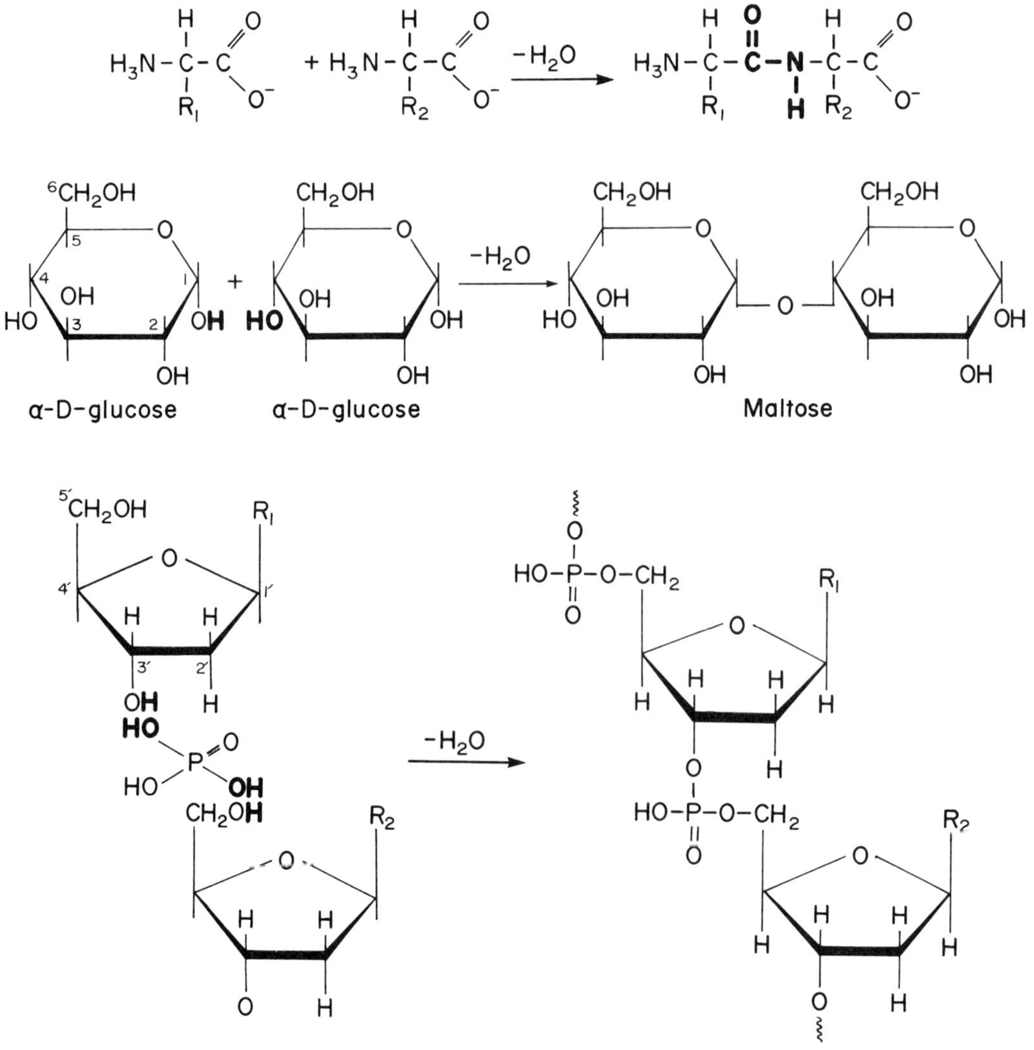

Figure 2–3 Formation of biological polymers by a condensation process that eliminates one molecule of water per bond. *A*, Peptide bond; *B*, glycosidic bond; *C*, phosphodiester bond.

Lastly, the polysaccharides (of which we will have more to say when we consider glycogen storage diseases) consist of sugars condensed through their hydroxyl group, to form a glycosidic linkage.

Protein Structure

The linear sequence in nucleic acids and proteins is stringently controlled by virtue of precise recognition of base sequences by DNA polymerase, RNA polymerases, and t-RNA aminoacyl synthetases. Such recognition depends upon structural and electronic complementarity, as discussed above. This tight control is essential, since, as emphasized before, the relationship between structure and function is so close that changes at crucial positions in the sequence will change the three-dimensional structure and thereby alter the biological activity of a protein. Herein lies the essence of an inborn error of metabolism.

Proteins are the most abundant and variegated macromolecules in the body, usually being composed of hundreds of amino acids. While individual molecules possess molecular weights in the range of 10,000 to 50,000, formation of higher order structures results in entities with molecular weights greater than 1,000,000.

The side-chains, which remain chemically unaltered after peptide bond formation between amino acids, are responsible for the structural and functional characteristics of the resulting protein molecule. Certain amino acids possessing either an aromatic ring or a long side-chain engage in hydrophobic interactions. Approximation of residues in space can be achieved by these hydrophobic interactions, so dependent on the aqueous environment, permitting individual van der Waals' and other short-range forces to come into play. Complementary structural interactions may aid attainment of the final structure as well.

There are four levels of protein structure. The *primary* structure is the unique linear sequence of amino acids determined by the genetic code (Fig. 2–4). Since this linear sequence, in an aqueous

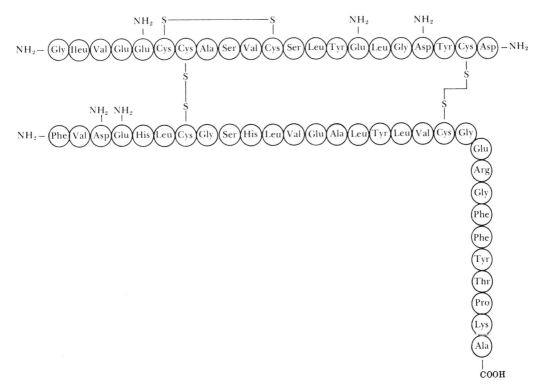

Figure 2–4 The linear sequence (primary structure) of the peptide chains comprising the insulin molecule. Chain A (top) contains 21 amino acid residues and is bound covalently to chain B (bottom), which contains 30 residues. Disulfide bridges provide the covalent links. (From Villee, C., and Dethier, V.C.: Biological Principles and Processes. 2nd ed. Philadelphia, W.B. Saunders Co., 1976.)

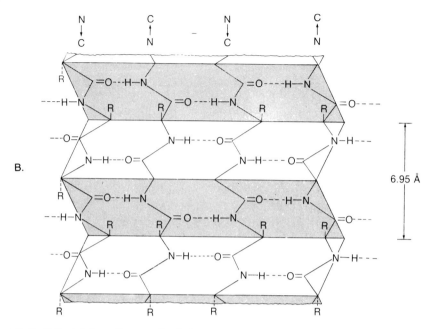

Figure 2–5 β-Pleated sheet. Hydrogen bonds impart stability to the extended polypeptide chains that run in opposite directions, allowing a stacked structure to form. (From Flickinger, C.A., Brown, J.C., Kutchai, H.C., and Ogilvie, J.W.: Medical Cell Biology. Philadelphia, W.B. Saunders Co., 1979.)

environment, will direct the shape of the final three-dimensional structure of the protein, the relationship between linear sequence to structure and structure to function of a protein is highlighted. In other words, changes at crucial points in the linear sequence of a protein can have far-reaching effects on form and function. Such changes, as for example in hemoglobin S, must account for many inborn errors of metabolism.

The *secondary* structure refers to the spiral course traversed by the polypeptide chain, first delineated by x-ray diffraction in studies undertaken by Pauling and Corey (1951). The α-helix is a right-handed helix that has 3.6 amino acid residues per turn and owes its stability to hydrogen bonds between a carbonyl group of one residue and an $-NH$ group of another. Since these two groups are covalently bound and are therefore relatively fixed in place, one would expect them to generate a recurring structure such as the α-helix. Other noncovalent forces may contribute as well. Another secondary structure is the β-pleated sheet shown in Figure 2–5.

X-ray diffraction studies indicate that most proteins are compact, possessing a structure akin to a tightly packed crystal. Such a formation cannot be accounted for by the secondary structure but requires recourse to a *tertiary* structure, usually stabilized by noncovalent interactions (Fig. 2–6). This term denotes the three-dimensional structure of a single polypeptide chain called the *conformation;* most enzymes possess a globular tertiary structure with a polar surface and a hydrophobic interior. This is to be expected because of the axial role water plays in directing the hydrophobic interactions of macromolecules. Indeed, a polypeptide (one dimension) does not become a protein (three dimensions) until placed in an aqueous environment.

The final level, the *quaternary* structure, refers to the interaction of individual polypeptide chains, each with their own tertiary structure, to form a larger (polymeric) protein molecule composed of subunits. Hemoglobin, the most extensively studied protein, possesses a quaternary structure composed of two alpha and two beta chains, designated α_2 and β_2 (Fig 2–7). As a general rule, most proteins with molecular weights greater than 20,000 are composed of more than one polypeptide chain.

As the protein assumes its native or fully active form it is reasonable to assume that longer-range forces, particularly hydrophobic interactions, will play an important role early on as water is excluded. With the general form of the protein defined by these hydrophobic interactions, disulfide

Figure 2-6 Larger figure shows 1 of 4 chains comprising hemoglobin molecule. Smaller figure depicts the 4 polypeptide chains. The folding of the chain creates the unique three-dimensional conformation that underlies its structure and function. (From Moore, J.A., and Barton, T.J.: Organic Chemistry—an Overview. Philadelphia, W.B. Saunders, 1978.)

bonds, hydrogen bonds, and van der Waals' interactions can be brought into play as the interbond distances are diminished.

The peptide bond, which links C-2 atoms of adjoining amino acids, is the most important covalent bond determining the linear sequence (primary structure) of a protein. There is, however, another covalent bond in proteins, the *disulfide* bond, formed by the oxidation of two cysteine residues to form cystine. It is found most frequently in cross-links between different parts of the

Figure 2-7 Interaction of the four polypeptide chains of hemoglobin to create the quaternary structure. (Based on Dickerson, R.E.: Ann Rev Biochem 71:820, 1972; from Flickinger, C.A., Brown, J.C., Kutchai, H.C., and Ogilvie, J.W.: Medical Cell Biology. Philadelphia, W.B. Saunders Co., 1979.)

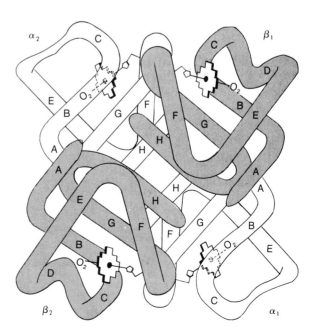

polypeptide chain and between different polypeptide chains. These covalent bridges can stabilize the three-dimensional structure (tertiary structure), since they are much stronger than noncovalent bonds. However, as with all covalent bonds they are very short-range, since even a slight extension breaks them completely. Hence, they will come into play only after other interactions have generated the general three-dimensional structure that the protein will assume. In other words, the cysteine residues must be brought together by other forces before such a bond can form and act to fix the final conformation.

Nucleic Acid Structure

The four nucleotide subunits that comprise the nucleic acids are shown in Figure 2–8. A mononucleotide consists of a ring compound known as a base (called heterocyclic because it contains atoms other than carbon and hydrogen) linked to a sugar to which is attached a phosphate group. The nucleotide base–sugar combination without the phosphate group is a nucleoside.

The phosphodiester bond is analogous to the peptide bond of proteins and is formed by the esterification of two of the three hydroxyl groups of phosphoric acid by the hydroxyl groups on the pentose sugar. The remaining hydroxyl can donate a proton, accounting for the designation nucleic "acids."

As with polypeptides, the hydrophobic properties of the bases play an important role in the structure assumed by nucleic acid polymers. The planar aromatic rings exclude water, seeking instead hydrophobic interactions with other bases as they stack together. The hydrogen-bonding properties of the bases have been the subject of great interest because of their role in purine-pyrimidine interaction to form the double helix characteristic of DNA. The carbonyl and amino groups of the bases are able to form hydrogen bonds both with water and with corresponding groups on other bases.

Indeed, one way to account for the capacity of a linear sequence to direct formation of other linear sequences is a helix (as in the protein α-helix). Here the effects of intramolecular forces arrayed in regular sequence can be employed to transmit information. While the hydrophobic interaction accounts for the majority of the 1000 calories/mole/base pair that holds the double helix together, it is the hydrogen-bonded base pairing that ultimately determines the stability of the structure. In other words, hydrophobic interactions must first eliminate water between the helices before the hydrogen bonds provide the crucial contribution to the stability of this ordered structure.

Having gone to great lengths to store hereditary information as a helix, expression of this information in DNA demands that the double helix unwind. This is not a trifle, since separation of the components of a single pair of bases requires 1000 calories/mole. Since nucleic acids may

BASE	CYTOSINE	URACIL	THYMINE	ADENINE	GUANINE
	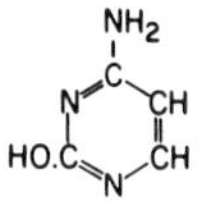	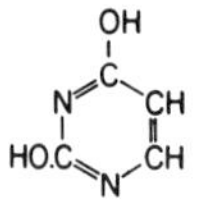	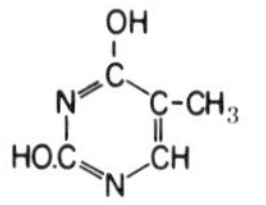	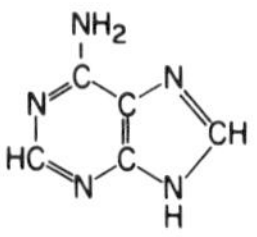	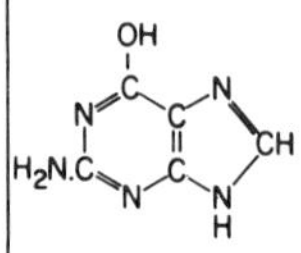
+ SUGAR	RIBOSE	RIBOSE	DEOXYRIBOSE	RIBOSE	RIBOSE
NUCLEOSIDE	CYTIDINE	URIDINE	THYMIDINE	ADENOSINE	GUANOSINE
+ PHOSPHATE NUCLEOTIDE	CYTIDYLIC ACID	URIDYLIC ACID	THYMIDYLIC ACID	ADENYLIC ACID	GUANYLIC ACID

Figure 2–8 Purine and pyrimidine bases, which are components of the nucleic acids, are shown along with the nomenclature employed for the units as they are built up. (From Weissman, S.M.: Gene structure and function. *In* Bondy, P.K., and Rosenberg, L.E.: Metabolic Control and Disease. 8th ed. Philadelphia, W.B. Saunders Co., 1980.)

possess thousands of such base pairs, unwinding them would require an enormous outlay of energy. However, this dilemma of energetics is avoided in an economical fashion. During replication and transcription only a limited section of the helix unwinds at a time. Just a few base pairs are separated briefly and are rejoined as contiguous base pairs unwind. What we have then is the propagation down the double helix of a sequential unwinding-rewinding phenomenon that involves only a few bases at a time. In this manner the energy requirement is kept within tolerable limits: once unwinding commences, much of the energy required to separate the bases is furnished by that made available by bases reuniting.

We have remarked earlier that the base pairing implicit in the double helical structure explains the mechanism by which DNA serves its role in reproduction. Here hydrogen binding provides for optimal fit of certain base pairs, a purine with a pyrimidine (G-C and A-T), so that once the sequence of one strand is specified so is the complementary sequence of the other strand. In this manner the replication of DNA and the transcription of DNA into the various RNA species— messenger, ribosomal and transfer—is directed by one strand of the DNA helix. These are enzyme-mediated processes, which are carried out by DNA polymerase in the case of replication and by RNA polymerases in the case of transcription.

The Function of Nucleic Acids in Biochemical Information Transfer

As noted before, the use of the term "information" in conjunction with a nucleic acid is synonymous with the word "sequence," since the double helix is functionally a linear chain containing four major nucleotide components. The code for amino acids and for RNA sequences resides in the order of these four units, so that we can view the molecular language of the nucleic acids as consisting of a four-letter alphabet. Perhaps a punched tape in a computer conveys the visual picture more vividly.

DNA must carry out two functions. First, it must reproduce itself during cell division so that its information can be transmitted precisely to daughter cells. Second, the cells must express this information by controlling the metabolism of the cell. The latter is accomplished through regulation of the supply of enzymes. In the presence of enzymes chemical reactions proceed readily; in their absence these reactions proceed very slowly. Additionally, enzymes are sites of control for the rate of chemical reactions.

The use of nucleic acid macromolecules as the repository for the genetic information underscores the key to information transfer in living systems; that is, the linear sequence in the nucleic acids, present as triplets of the four nucleotide bases, is amplified and diversified when it is expressed as proteins composed of 20 amino acids. By the process of translation a protein is created on the basis of a 20-letter alphabet. This amplification of building blocks creates hydrophobic, hydrophilic, and charged environments and enables proteins to serve as enzymes or structural elements. Nucleic acids cannot form such complex structures.

The linear sequence of DNA directs the linear sequence (primary structure) of proteins and thereby controls all the functional and structural proteins of the cell. Since the amino acid sequence determines the folding characteristics of a particular protein as it assumes its higher order structure, it is clear that a change in that sequence in a position essential for this structure can result in a protein whose functional capability is severely impaired. Such a change is caused by a mutation in the genome and is the basis for many inherited defects. The information present in the triplet code of the DNA is utilized to transcribe complementary (cognate) messenger RNA, ribosomal RNA, and transfer RNA molecules, which will either direct or be utilized in the process of protein synthesis (Fig. 2–9). Recognition and information transfer involve codon-anticodon pairing through hydrogen bonding.

A point mutation in the linear sequence of a protein can have profound effects on protein structure and consequently function. Such structural lability underscores the relationship of a defect in the genetic information (DNA) to the formation of an abnormal protein, which may then function in an abnormal fashion, thus defining the biochemical basis for an inherited disease.

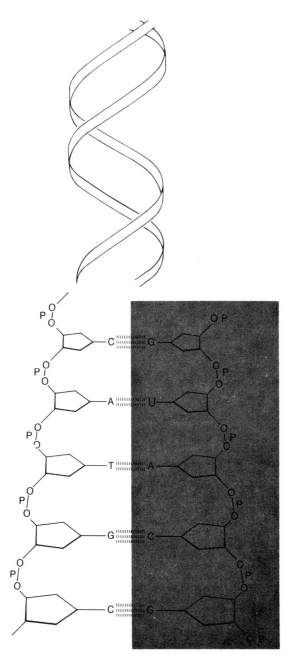

Figure 2–9 Double helical structure underlies the means by which the information in one strand of DNA is read by DNA-dependent RNA polymerase to generate a complementary RNA molecule. (From Villee, C., and Dethier, V.C.: Biological Principles and Processes. 2nd ed. Philadelphia, W.B. Saunders Co., 1976.)

ENZYME FUNCTIONS

The Nature of Catalysis

Enzymes are the catalysts of the cell. They accelerate the approach of a chemical reaction to thermodynamic equilibrium. They do so by providing an alternate pathway that possesses a lower energy of activation than the uncatalyzed reaction. The enormous capability these catalysts possess for stereospecific recognition and rate acceleration provides for the brisk conduct of the thousands of chemical reactions constituting what we term "intermediary metabolism." Indeed, intermediary metabolism forms the roadways of life's processes, and in this section we wish to consider how enzymes carry out their indispensable biological activities.

Without enzymes, life as we know it would not be possible. Why is this so? Enzymes possess great stereochemical specificity, which permits them to bind a compound (the substrate) to the so-called active site. This specificity is a direct consequence of complementary surfaces between the substrate and the enzyme, as in a jigsaw puzzle. The forces involved are noncovalent. In addition to their specificity, enzymes are able to accelerate the rate of the reaction they mediate to a degree not possible by inorganic catalysts acting under the constraints of body temperature and ionic (particularly hydrogen ion) concentrations characteristic of living cells. In other words, living cells cannot raise their temperature appreciably or change the ionic composition of the medium, as may be done in the organic chemistry laboratory.

The tenuous poising of the living system requires a brisk conduct to the whole of intermediary metabolism. This requirement can only be met by the ability of enzymes to accelerate chemical reactions. Indeed, enzymes can mediate the transformation of anywhere from 1000 to 1 million moles of substrate per minute per mole of enzyme. As we shall see, enzymes act by lowering the energy of activation of the reaction that they catalyze, i.e., they provide an alternative mechanism for achieving the formation of products from reactants. How they do this will be the major focus of this section.

However, before we discuss that aspect of enzyme function, we want to note here a third attribute of enzymes, one that is uniquely in keeping with the properties of a living system. These macromolecules have the ability to receive information by binding *effector* or *signal molecules,* which provide information to the enzymes and thereby permit the enzymes to modify the rate at which they carry out the reactions that they catalyze. Defects in such binding sites can be another cause of an inborn error of metabolism.

Enzyme Mechanism of Action

We must remind ourselves here that a chemical reaction involves attraction between opposite charges, with movement of electrons, as bonds are broken and others form between the participating atoms. Hence, a chemical reaction is said to have taken place when the electrons that maintain the structure of compound A undergo a permanent change in configuration, forming a new molecular entity that possesses a unique geometry, that of compound B. Because covalent forces are strong, compounds A and B are usually stable and isolatable and, indeed, can often be purchased from a biochemical supply house. The same cannot be said for noncovalent aggregates, e.g., the enzyme-substrate complex that is unstable and transient in existence.

Originally, enzymes and their substrates were viewed as interacting as a lock does with its key. More recently, studies demonstrating changes in the conformation of enzymes as they bind their substrates make this view of enzymes no longer completely adequate. Nonetheless, both the static "template" and "induced-fit" flexible enzyme models assume that the *active site* of an enzyme possesses electric charges or dipoles that complement those of the reactants. This active site is located in the interior of the globular or ellipsoid protein and is thus isolated from the surrounding aqueous environment. In consequence of this protected status, charged molecules are able to interact without hindrance from water, which, with its high dielectric constant, would diminish charge attraction between charged groups in the substrate and the enzyme. Thus, the interior of the enzyme molecule may be considered to be "waxlike," while the exterior of the protein may be considered to be "soaplike." The molecule thus has the properties of a micelle (Fig. 2–10), so that it can exist simultaneously in the aqueous and hydrophobic environment.

X-ray diffraction studies have demonstrated that the protein's active site is comprised of functional groups brought together from different regions of the primary sequence. As a result, only a small percentage of the total number of amino acid side-chains contribute to the catalytic or active site. Functionally, the active site represents those amino acid side-chains and cofactors that are involved in the chemical transformation. These include sites that provide the actual catalytic mechanism to mediate the chemical reaction as well as those that provide for the specificity of the reaction through stereospecific binding of substrates. As emphasized above, enzymes lower the free energy of activation of the reaction they catalyze.

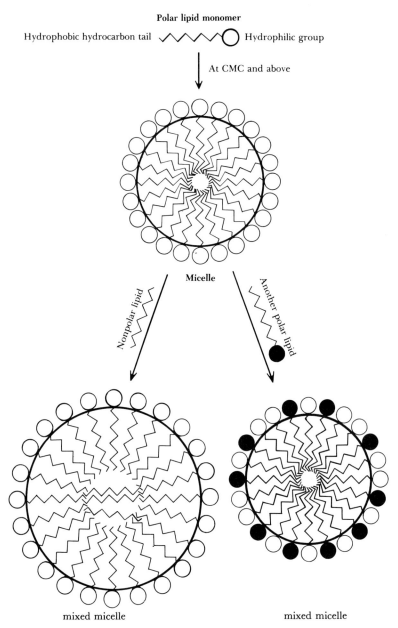

Figure 2–10 Micelles are detergent-like, since they are able to exist in an aqueous environment while possessing an interior that is lipid-soluble. Enzymes have a similar (but more complicated) division of reactive domains. (From Masoro, E.J.: Physiological Chemistry of Lipids in Mammals. Philadelphia, W.B. Saunders Co., 1968.)

Approximation and Orientation

Without recourse to sophisticated arguments, it appears likely that by approximating reactants at the active site and placing them in correct orientation for reactions, the essential ingredients for the successful outcome of an enzyme-mediated reaction are immediately at hand. As we noted above, the first step of an enzyme-mediated reaction is the binding of substrates to the enzyme in the noncovalent "enzyme-substrate complex." When the substrate binds to the enzyme, its freedom to move is severely restricted. Hence, the degree of order of this microsystem is increased, and the entropy of the enzyme-substrate complex is lowered, making collision and subsequent reaction more probable. This aspect of catalysis is termed *"approximation"* or *"propinquity."* It assumes as well

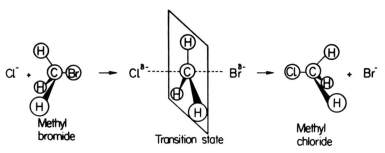

Figure 2–11 Formation of a transition state, with bonds in the midst of being broken and new ones being formed. (From Ferdinand, W.: The Enzyme Molecule. New York, John Wiley & Sons, Inc., 1976. Reprinted by permission of John Willey & Sons, Inc.)

that the catalytic groups of the active site of the enzyme are oriented precisely as regards the substrate, allowing for key groups in the enzyme to interact with the substrate.

As a chemical reaction progresses the reactants enter into a very short-lived state termed the *"transition state,"* which represents a molecule in which covalent bonds are in the midst of being formed and destroyed (Fig. 2–11). Over 30 years ago, Pauling suggested that an enzyme would bind more strongly to a molecular aggregation akin to the transition state than it would to either substrates or products. The reason for this affinity was the greater complementarity in structure between the transition state and the active site. That powerful insight has been supported by data that show that when a substrate binds to the active site, a portion of the energy of binding is utilized to strain the substrate complex toward the geometry of the transition state. Accordingly, the separation between enzyme specificity and catalytic efficiency is an artificial one, since when the enzyme binds the substrate, a considerable portion of the reaction rate enhancement is brought about. This accounts for the large size of enzyme molecules, since the substrates and their enzyme will interact at multiple sites to bring about complementary binding as the energy of interaction is used to force the substrate into the molecular geometry of the transition state. This optimization of binding interaction characterizes the interaction of coenzymes (cofactors) as well.

General Acid-Base Catalysis

We have cautioned earlier that while acid or base can be used in the laboratory to prepare a molecule to react, wide variations in hydrogen ions or hydroxyl ions are incompatible with life. Since the hydrogen is a small naked charge, it polarizes other groups easily, an ability that is exploited readily in the laboratory. Remembering that delocalization of electrons (resonance) brings about increased stability, it follows that localization of electrons can destabilize a molecule, preparing it to react further. Through general acid catalysis, a weak acid functions by inducing polarization, through hydrogen bonding, and thus acts in a manner analogous to that of the proton itself. Hence, general acid-base catalysis may serve to prime a reactant for further chemical modification. The side chains of glutamic and aspartic acids, histidine, tyrosine, and cysteine have considerable acidic or basic character and are likely to function in a general acid-base role in the cell.

Covalent Catalysis

A number of enzymes are able to catalyze a chemical reaction by use of a limited number of the side-chains remaining after peptide bond formation has taken place. Predominant among the side-chain residues that serve such a role are those of the amino acids histidine, serine, cysteine, lysine, glutamate, and aspartate. Often this involves formation of a covalent intermediate with a group in the substrate, permitting the formation of a new structure with greater reactivity than that present in the starting substrate. Such intermediates are key in the mechanism of extracellular proteases (chymotrypsin, trypsin, elastase, and thrombin) as well as aldolases and decarboxylases.

A *nucleophile* is an atomic center with a strong tendency to donate an electron pair, and it follows that in nucleophilic catalysis rate enhancement is brought about when the enzyme donates an electron pair to the substrate.

An *electrophile* is an electron-seeking center, and electrophilic catalysis involves removal of an electron pair from the substrate by a group in the enzyme. The most common form of electrophiles in biology are the coenzymes pyridoxal phosphate and thiamine and metal ions. The most common type of electrophilic mechanism involves the creation of a positive nitrogen, which acts as an "electron sink," or a free nitrogen, which donates an electron pair. Despite the limited tendency of nitrogen to draw electrons to it (electronegativity), it is easily protonated, thereby facilitating its role as an electron sink.

Role of Certain Functional Groups in the Protein

With the foregoing discussion it should be obvious that a number of enzymes furnish the key nucleophilic, basic, or acidic groups from the side-chains of certain amino acids. Hydrolytic cleavages (e.g., chymotrypsin) represent the most well-studied examples of such a role for protein functional groups. These groups include the carboxyl, thiol, and imidazole of histidine as well as the serine hydroxyl. The imidazole and thiol groups can act as nucleophiles, while the carboxylate anion functions in general base catalysis.

Detailed studies of the mechanism of action of chymotrypsin, lysozyme, and ribonuclease have led to the following generalizations: (1) for the optimal energy interactions between substrate and enzyme, binding must be exact; (2) incorrect binding will not permit key functional groups in the enzyme to adopt the complementary orientation with respect to substrate; and (3) stabilization of the transition state is an important aspect of the catalytic mechanism.

Further details of this fascinating subject may be found in the references at the end of this chapter.

Coenzymes

As noted before, the active site is composed of side-chains remaining from amino acids after condensation to form peptide bonds. While these functional groups can engage in a number of catalytic roles, the needs of metabolism have required an increase in the repertoire available to proteins. These diverse and expanded roles are subserved by vitamins, which by conversion to coenzymes and incorporation into enzymes through either noncovalent or covalent means can augment the capability of the protein. In what follows, we review briefly the chemical mechanism of action of coenzymes in terms that are relevant to our later considerations about vitamin therapy (see Chapter 37). A fuller account of the coenzymes can be found in the discussion by Lowe and Ingraham.

Enzymes may, by attaching certain specific cofactors, dramatically increase their capability for bonding of substrates. From a general point of view coenzymes are ring structures bearing close resemblance to the purines and pyrimidines of the nucleic acids. Such molecules are capable of stabilizing transition states by electronic delocalization, transmission of electronic perturbations over several atoms, and facilitation of electron mobility. Additionally, they may provide for optimal binding interaction with specific subsites on the enzymes, thereby contributing to approximation and orientation at the active site of the enzyme.

Enzymes devoid of any coenzyme or metal cofactor may carry out hydrolytic reactions, as exemplified by chymotrypsin. However, with provision of a coenzyme the variety of reaction types susceptible to catalysis is greatly expanded to include oxidation-reduction, decarboxylation, condensation, elimination, transamination, and carboxylation, as well as oxidation of α-keto acids (e.g., pyruvate), a notoriously difficult reaction. Table 2–3 lists the metabolic role served by each of the coenzymes.

Most enzymes require cofactors or coenzymes to provide specific chemical properties not attainable by amino acid residues alone. Abnormal binding of a cofactor to its enzyme may be responsible for an inborn error of metabolism.

Table 2–3   COENZYME FUNCTIONS

Coenzyme	Function
Coenzymes Engaged in Oxidation Reduction Reactions	
NAD	Dehydrogenases
FAD, FMN	Dehydrogenases
	Oxidation and acyl group transfer
Hemoproteins	Cytochromes, catalase, peroxidase
B_{12}	Hydrogen transfer (isomerization of L-methyl-malonyl CoA to succinyl CoA)
	Methyl group-THF-homocysteine
Vitamin C	Reducing agent
Coenzymes Catalyzing Other Reactions	
Thiamine	Oxidative decarboxylation-α-keto acids (scission C-C bonds)
Pyridoxal Phosphate	Transamination, racemization, decarboxylation
Folic Acid	Transfer of 1-carbon units
Biotin	Carboxylation
Coenzyme A	Transfer of acyl groups by forming thiol esters
Purine and Pyrimidine Phosphates	Purines—driving force for biochemical reactions; pyrimidines—transfer of glycosyl groups as in glycoprotein synthesis
S-Adenosylmethionine	Biological methyl donor

Evolution of Enzyme Function

Koshland (1976) has proposed that the first step in the development of a precursor to the protein catalyst must have been a structure capable of attracting substrates and catalytic groups in a complementary interaction. Specificity would then follow, since it was needed to ensure that each enzyme catalyzed a particular reaction with a limited group of substrates. In this view, a static enzyme (template) would allow complementary interactions but would be liable to bind the water molecule. In reactions involving hydroxyl groups, e.g., carbohydrates, water present in much greater concentration could supplant the "substrate." Flexibility in the enzyme, permitting a change in three-dimensional configuration when the substrate binds, must then have been an essential factor in the development of specificity. Such "induced fit" would require a minimum of sites at which the substrate binds to bring about a particular alignment of catalytic groups and force the substrate into the conformation of the transition state complex. Lastly, a flexible enzyme presents the possibility, through addition of subunits, of regulation of the enzyme by modifiers that are not substrates for the enzyme. Thus, ability to bind modifiers could then affect the kinetic behavior of the enzyme.

Summary of Enzyme Action

1. Enzymes, because they are macromolecules, present specific binding and catalytic sites that recognize and interact with substrates in a precise manner based upon complementary interactions.

2. Enzymes, as they bind the substrate, cause the latter to be strained or deformed into the conformation of the transition state (activated complex). By this means the starting state is made more labile and therefore more likely to react. In actuality, the conformation of the enzyme changes as well. In somewhat simplified terms the interaction between enzyme and substrate has the effect of transferring some of the conformational energy of the enzyme to the substrate, thereby raising the energy of the substrate.

3. In addition, the orientation effects spoken of earlier, coupled with the ability of enzymes to set up regions of unusual reactivity within the hydrophobic interior of its structure, also contribute to the enhancement of chemical reactions mediated by enzymes.

4. It follows that a mutation in DNA could alter or abolish the activity of the protein it specifies by altering the folding of the protein. This could lead to the clinical expression of an inborn error of metabolism. More detailed considerations of enzyme action are listed in the references at the end of this section.

REGULATION OF INTERMEDIARY METABOLISM

Levels of Control

The highly organized state of life demands close control. This in turn requires a hierarchy of sites at which control can be exercised. In addition to the ability to catalyze reactions, enzymes can be controlled. Control at any level must be based on the ability to obtain information and use that information to alter metabolic phenomena appropriately. Often this is accomplished by changing the rate at which a reaction is catalyzed. Within the cell there is a remarkable multiplicity of controls that provide for the brisk and usually faultless conduct of intermediary metabolism. Inasmuch as intermediary metabolism must provide both adequate ATP and other high-energy compounds as well as intermediates needed to construct other molecules and macromolecules, regulation must coordinate disparate reactions and pathways. By ensuring that a proper balance of all precursors exists, synthesis of the complex structural elements of the cell, e.g., membranes, is assured.

We want to concentrate here on those aspects of regulation that are essential to an understanding of the disordered biochemistry that is the basis of disease. The means available to the cell to regulate intermediary metabolism may be discussed on the basis of the physical or chemical transformations that the enzymes undergo and the time scales in which they occur. The following mechanisms may be distinguished: (1) *Noncovalent* interactions, which are rapid and freely reversible and occur within milliseconds. These bring about a change in enzyme conformation when the substrate or modifier, such as H^+ or other ions, binds to key control sites or changes the state of ionization of groups that determine the conformation of the protein. (2) *Covalent modifications,* which are enzyme mediated and change the catalytic or regulatory properties of the enzyme being acted on. Such modifications occur over a longer time frame than do noncovalent modifications (which depend on equilibrium binding) and are more decisive. Moreover, they can be either irreversible or reversible. In the former category, an enzyme stored in an inactive state (e.g., a zymogen) is not activated until it is needed. In the latter category, a regulatory signal may be transmitted and amplified (e.g., glucagon) that acts through the stimulation of cyclic AMP formation. Through the binding of the hormone to a specific receptor in the cell membrane, the first step in the information process is amplified into a cascade of subsequent enzyme reactions. (3) *De novo synthesis,* a relatively slow process in comparison to the other two but one of greater overall effect. Since this process involves the entire protein biosynthetic apparatus, the energy cost is greater, which is consistent with the more definitive result achieved.

Noncovalent Regulatory Mechanisms

Modulation of Enzyme Activity by Substrate and Product Concentration: Hyperbolic Kinetics

Substrate availability is one way in which a metabolic pathway could be controlled. When substrate concentration falls, enzyme activity would likewise decrease, diminishing the rate of the entire pathway. In actuality, substrate levels in vivo show little fluctuation, and it is thought that while such a mechanism may be important for single enzymes, it is not the decisive factor that controls entire pathways in higher animals.

A hyperbolic response of velocity to changing substrate concentration characterizes so-called classical Michaelis-Menten kinetics (Fig. 2–12). Such enzymes are most responsive to changes in substrate concentration in the range from zero to the K_m, the latter defined as the substrate concentration at which 1/2 maximal velocity is achieved. While the enzyme may still be able to respond rapidly to a small change in substrate concentration at the K_m, when substrate levels fall far below the K_m the catalytic ability of the enzyme would be unrealized—a wasteful situation. Hence it is likely that intracellular levels of most substrates are near the K_m for the enzyme. Such a system places constraints on the ability of the enzyme to respond to substrate concentrations outside of the range of the K_m. Hence for enzymes to adjust reaction rates quickly it is preferable that their substrates remain in the range of the K_m.

Figure 2–12 Plot of velocity of enzyme-catalyzed reaction versus substrate concentration. The K_m (or $S_{0.5}$) is a measure of the affinity of the enzyme for its substrate. When the K_m is too high, affinity is low; thus substrate concentrations must be high to carry out the reaction at a brisk rate. Coversely, when the K_m is too low, affinity is high. In this case, the enzyme's active site will be saturated at low concentrations and further increases in substrate will not increase the rate of reaction. (From Hochachka, P.W., and Somero, G.L.: Strategies of Biochemical Adaptation. Philadelphia, W.B. Saunders Co., 1973.)

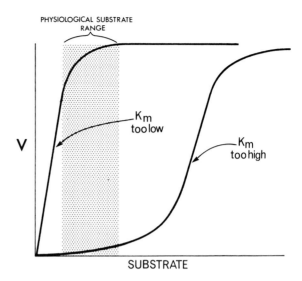

Hepatic glucokinase is an instructive example of the significance of the K_m in hyperbolic kinetic responses. For this enzyme the K_m (10 mM) exceeds the usual glucose level, but this ability to function efficiently at a high glucose concentration permits the enzyme to respond to the postabsorptive influx of glucose that follows ingestion of a carbohydrate-containing meal.

Cooperativity

As we have discussed, enzymes with a hyperbolic response curve (which defines a decreasing responsiveness to increasing substrate concentration) have a limited ability to maintain substrate levels within small tolerances. Enzymes that have a role in controlling the flux through a pathway usually have greater flexibility in their response to substrate, demonstrating the phenomenon of *cooperativity*. Such enzymes are often polymeric and have more than one catalytic site, usually located on separate polypeptides. Most importantly these sites communicate their status to each other by engendering a conformational change in the enzyme structure. In this manner a macromolecule composed of subunits can receive and respond to information.

Two forms of cooperativity have been described, both usually being found in enzymes composed of subunits (Fig. 2–13). With *positive cooperativity,* when substrate binds to one catalytic site on the enzyme, the activity of other sites is enhanced by augmenting either the binding affinity for the substrate or the catalytic activity. These enzymes have a velocity-substrate profile that describes a sigmoid curve. As substrate concentration increases, additional sites are occupied, accen-

Figure 2–13 Idealized plots of velocity versus substrate concentration for enzymes demonstrating (*a*) hyperbolic behavior, (*b*) positive cooperativity, and (*c*) negative cooperativity. (From Cohn, R.M., and Yandrasitz, J.R.: Modulation of enzyme activity. *In* Herman, R.H., Cohn, R.M., and McNamara, P.D. (eds.): Principles of Metabolic Control in Mammalian Systems. New York, Plenum Press, 1980.)

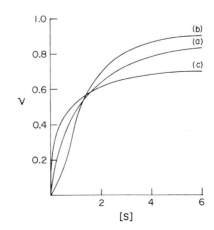

tuating the activity of the remaining sites until all the sites are fully active and velocity no longer increases. In contrast to hyperbolic enzymes, when the substrate concentration permitting half maximal ($S_{0.5}$) velocity is approached, the velocity curve becomes nearly vertical. Hence, small changes in substrate concentration in the region of $S_{0.5}$ bring about significant rate changes.

On the other hand, *negative cooperativity* is shown by enzymes whose velocity-substrate profiles show even less variability than do those of hyperbolic enzymes (Fig. 2–13). An extreme example of negative cooperativity is called "half-of-the-sites reactivity," in which binding at the initial half of the sites renders the remaining half of the sites virtually inactive.

What do these control mechanisms achieve? Positive cooperativity facilitates a rapid response to increasing substrate concentration, thereby attenuating fluctuations in substrate levels. Negative cooperativity permits constancy of enzyme activity (rather than substrate concentration, as with positive cooperativity) as substrate concentration fluctuates. In particular, by optimizing the binding of a cofactor, e.g., NAD, such an enzyme will be able to compete successfully when such a key metabolite or coenzyme is in short supply. Once the catalytic sites are saturated further binding is unnecessary, so the enzyme binds at additional sites with a low affinity.

Modulation of Enzyme Activity by Binding of Small Molecules to Regulatory Sites—Allosterism

We have considered modulation of enzyme activity by substrate and product interaction at the active or catalytic site of the enzyme. Additionally, enzyme activity may be regulated by compounds bearing no chemical resemblance to the substrate (termed allosteric). Such metabolites or modifiers have been shown to bind at sites that are distinct from the catalytic site: the phenomenon is called *allostery,* and the site at which the modifier binds, the *allosteric site.* The distinctive nature of the catalytic and allosteric sites can be demonstrated by chemicals that eliminate the allosteric control while leaving catalytic activity unchanged (Fig. 2–14).

In terms of information reception and response this binding causes a conformational change in the enzyme, with the result that enzyme activity is changed. This capacity to be regulated by a product of a biosynthetic pathway is termed *"feedback inhibition."* Although it is usually the final product of the pathway that inhibits the activity of the first enzyme of that pathway, metabolites from other pathways that may share common cofactors (e.g., ATP, NAD) can also act in such a servomechanism. A particularly good example of this is furnished by the purine synthetic pathway. Feedback inhibition must be distinguished from repression of enzyme synthesis. The former reversibly abolishes the activity of an enzyme, while the latter involves inhibition of protein synthesis. Loss of feedback inhibition has been implicated in the pathogenesis of the porphyrias, familial hypercholesterolemia, and several causes of hyperuricemia.

Covalent Regulation of Enzyme Activity

In this form of regulation, a covalent change in the enzymes brings about a change in conformation of the enzyme; one form is active and the other is inactive. Such a change is brought about by another enzyme and so takes longer than equilibrium binding, as occurs in noncovalent modu-

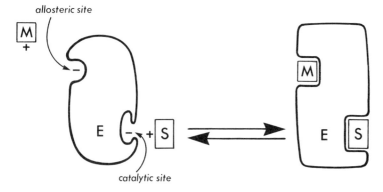

Figure 2–14 The distinct locations of the allosteric (regulatory) site and the active site of the enzyme are shown. When the modulator binds to the allosteric site it generates a conformational change in the enzyme, as seen in the figure. When the structure of the enzyme is changed, its function is modified as well. (From Hochachka, P.W., and Somero, G.L.: Strategies of Biochemical Adaptation. Philadelphia, W.B. Saunders Co., 1973.)

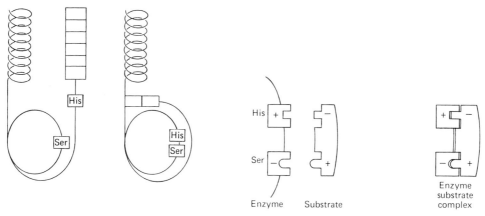

Figure 2–15 Removal of a segment, shown as blocks of amino acids, from the zymogen permits the enzyme to assume the active conformation. The histidine and serine residues (shaded blocks), which function in the catalytic mechanism, are approximated. From Burton, D.J., and Routh, J.I.: Essentials of Organic and Biochemistry. Philadelphia, W.B. Saunders Co., 1974.)

lation. Moreover, energy (ATP) is often expended, stacking the cards, so to speak, to assure the outcome.

Modulation by Reversible Covalent Action

Certain key intracellular enzymes can undergo reversible phosphorylation/dephosphorylation, which stabilizes the configuration of the active site. Four such examples of phosphorylation have been discovered, all of which involve the addition of phosphate to specific serine residues. Covalent modification differs from noncovalent by persistence of the response even after the triggering signal has disappeared. The mammalian systems involved in phosphorylation regulation include the pyruvate dehydrogenase multienzyme complex, triglyceride lipase, acetyl CoA carboxylase, and glycogen phosphorylase-glycogen synthetase. The last-named enzyme system is the axial system involved in glycogen metabolism and the locus of disorders resulting in the "glycogen storage diseases." The mechanism of action and regulation of these enzymes is discussed in the section dealing with those inborn errors in Part III of this book.

Control by Irreversible Covalent Interconversions

Gastrointestinal proteases exist in an inactive form (*zymogen* or *proenzyme*), which can be converted into the active form when an amino acid or small peptide group is removed (Fig. 2–15). Such a system protects the mucosa of the gut from damage by an enzyme that has no normal substrate present. Hormone production, the coagulation cascade, fibrinolysis, and complement reactions are all examples of such irreversible conversions.

PROTEIN SYNTHESIS

Enzyme "Death"

We have noted before that it is necessary to synthesize proteins continually because of their liability to constant degradation. Further, we have observed that enzymes function by virtue of their ability to undergo conformational changes employing noncovalent forces. These weak forces are used to effect substrate binding and product release as well as to bring about the covalency changes required for chemical reactions. As a consequence of this conformability, enzymes are liable to denaturation and consequent loss of function. Hence, they are semistable. A balance between functionality and denaturation is maintained by protein synthesis on the one hand and degradation of denatured enzymes on the other. Since enzymes make life possible, they must be continually renewed or life would cease. Synthesis and degradation of proteins (and enzymes) continue incessantly, maintaining the entire metabolic network far from equilibrium, in a condition that reflects its highly ordered (negative entropic) state. As emphasized earlier, this nonequilibrium state constitutes the "poising" of the life process.

A moment's reflection will reveal that were an enzyme to be totally stable, it would have no catalytic function, since it acts by virtue of its ability to bind other molecules and respond to environmental changes. It would be in effect a "dud." However, a highly unstable enzyme would then be too transient in its existence to act, thus blocking a particular metabolic step. Hence, enzyme catalysis requires that the protein be flexible, implying, therefore, inherent instability.

Overview of Protein Synthesis

Some of the information contained in the genome is expressed by the synthesis of proteins. In addition, the genes contain information for their own replication, for the synthesis of complementary nucleic acids, and for the binding of informational molecules (e.g., hormones), which have a control function in protein biosynthesis. So profound has been the impact of the information explosion in molecular biology that now high school students are taught that the genes are polymers of purine and pyrimidine nucleoside triphosphates arranged to form deoxyribonucleic acid (DNA). Further, the double-stranded nature of DNA, with each strand joined with its partner in an anticomplementary helical fashion is now a part of the general fund of information at that level of schooling. Attached to the double-stranded DNA are histones (basic proteins) and nuclear acidic proteins which constitute the chromatin of the nucleus. These proteins are believed to have a role in the structure of the chromatin as well as in modulating the transcription of DNA into RNA.

The general sequence of protein synthesis begins with the unfolding of the double-stranded DNA in a circumscribed region (see Fig. 2–10). A DNA-dependent RNA polymerase uses the unfolded strand as a template to polymerize purine and pyrimidine nucleoside triphosphates into a messenger RNA (mRNA). The messenger RNA so formed is further modified by addition of poly A at the 3' and of a cap at the 5' (Fig. 2–16). The purine and pyrimidine bases in messenger RNA are arrayed in a sequence that is anticomplementary to the sequence in the unwound strand of DNA. Thus, the sequence of bases in the messenger RNA mirrors the sequence of bases in the gene. Ribosomal RNA and transfer RNA are synthesized from their specific genes through the action of a DNA-dependent RNA polymerase as well. The various tRNA species undergo covalent modification in a phenomenon termed *"processing."* These tRNAs with their attached amino acids are polymerized into polypeptides on the ribosomes according to the information contained in the messenger RNAs. The sequence of the amino acids in each polypeptide therefore depends on the ordering of the tRNAs in accordance with the sequential arrangement of the bases in the messenger RNAs. The *initiation, elongation,* and *termination* of the polypeptide chain is under the control of a multiplicity of protein factors assumed to be enzymatic in function but as yet incompletely characterized and understood.

Translation from the linear sequence of mRNA to proteins is a tightly controlled and complex process, consistent with the fidelity requirements of a process that forms the basis of life. Translation hinges upon the tRNA molecules, which are akin to the Rosetta stone. These specific adaptor molecules align the amino acids with the mRNA code and thus read the information in mRNA and in amino acids.

The triplet codons represent a prescription for pairing between the tRNA-amino acid moieties and the mRNA transcript of the genome. Here, as with transcription, the code functions through antiparallel recognition between codon and its anticodon. They act with a group of specific enzymes, the aminoacyl tRNA synthetases. The ribosomes are elaborate supramolecular structures in which protein synthesis takes place.

Messenger RNA attaches to the protein as they are brought to the synthetic apparatus by the various tRNA-amino acid species. The anticodon in tRNA corresponds to a particular triplet code in mRNA and so specificity for amino acid selection is provided by complementary base recognition. When the polypeptide chain is completed, it detaches from the ribosome and assumes its

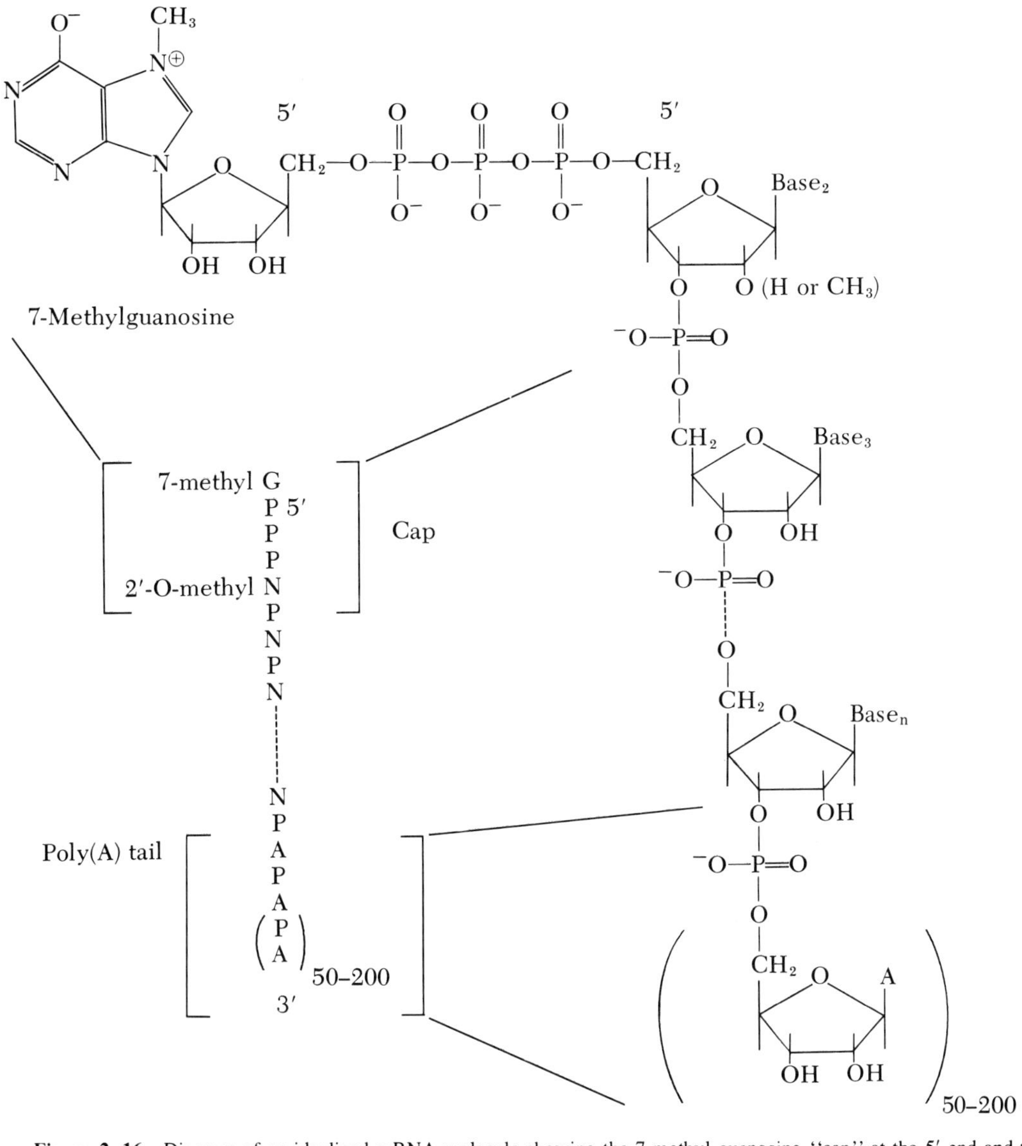

Figure 2–16 Diagram of an idealized mRNA molecule showing the 7-methyl guanosine "cap" at the 5' end and the polyadenylic acid "tail" at the 3' end. (From Flickinger, C.A., Brown, J.C., Kutchai, H.C., and Ogilvie, J.W.: Medical Cell Biology. Philadelphia, W.B. Saunders Co., 1979.)

unique three-dimensional structure. At this stage it can combine with other polypeptide chains to form a protein with quaternary structure.

This process is exceedingly complex and is shown diagrammatically in Figure 2–17. Further details may be found in any of the major biochemistry texts or references listed at the end of this chapter.

Mutations: Alteration in DNA

Since the information for all of the proteins of the cell is contained in the DNA sequences and since each amino acid is determined by a triplet of nucleotide bases, it follows that alteration in that sequence can have profound effects on the resulting protein synthesized. Such errors can come about either through mistakes during DNA replication, with substitution of the incorrect base, or through radiation or chemical modification, or most commonly through errors in crossing over. All

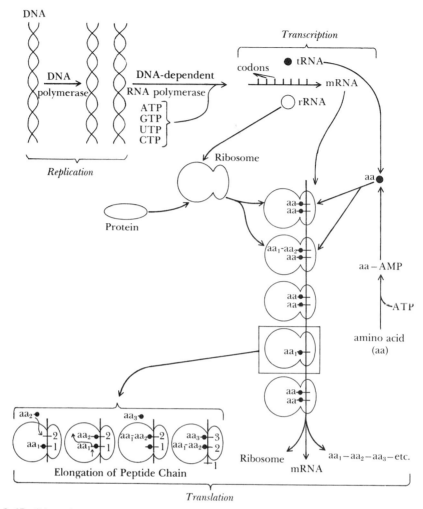

Figure 2–17 Schematic representation of processes involved in polypeptide synthesis, including DNA replication, formation of mRNA from the DNA template, and translation of the information in the triplet nucleotide code into the linear sequence of amino acids. (From Villee, D.B.: Human Endocrinology: A Developmental Approach. Philadelphia, W.B. Saunders Co., 1975.)

such heritable defects are termed mutations. These may lead to *misreading* of the code with the *deletion* of a key amino acid, a *substitution* of one amino acid for another, premature cessation of protein synthesis, or *addition* of amino acid sequences past the point of correct termination. Considering that the linear sequence of amino acids directs the folding of the protein into its three-dimensional structure, any of these defects may profoundly affect protein structure and therefore its function. Nonetheless, many variations (e.g., hemoglobin) are detected by laboratory techniques only and do not have uniformly deleterious effects on function. The key then lies in the location of the change in the primary structure. If the amino acid position affected is crucial in directing the folding or in forming part of a binding/catalytic site or increases the in vivo lability of a protein then the mutation will be serious and is likely to manifest as clinical disease.

THE ORGANIZATION OF METABOLIC PROCESSES

Strategies of Metabolism

Krebs and Kornberg (1957) have divided metabolism into three phases (Fig. 2–18). In the first phase, a high molecular weight nutrient undergoes digestion or hydrolysis, being broken down into smaller units, which are then absorbed into the cell. Little, if any, energy is recovered during that step. Indeed, an energy-requiring *priming reaction* is usually required before further metabolism can occur. For example, in the case of the fatty acids, combination with coenzyme A to form the fatty acyl coenzyme A derivative is required. This reaction also requires the expenditure of ATP. In the case of glucose the first step involved in its catabolism involves the formation of a phosphorylated derivative prior to entry into the glycolytic sequence. During the *second stage* of catabolism, substrates undergo *partial oxidation,* with the formation of acetyl coenzyme A, α-ketoglutaric acid, and oxaloacetic acids. During this phase, approximately a third of the available energy in the chemical bonds is recovered. In the *final phase* of catabolism, *complete oxidation* of the metabolic endproducts of the previous step are carried through the so-called metabolic mill, i.e., the citric acid cycle with coupling of the energy released to the formation of ATP. This latter process is termed *oxidative phosphorylation.*

Intermediary Metabolism

Intermediary metabolism involves the graded changes that biochemical compounds, residing within the cell, undergo as they are transformed through chemical reactions into other molecules. As we have discussed earlier, these reactions are mediated by enzymes. We may ask why it takes so many steps to metabolize a particular compound, e.g., glucose into the final product of glycolysis (pyruvate). There are several answers to this key question. In the first place the brisk conduct of the chemical reactions that constitute the life process requires that enzymes carry out their chemical conversions rapidly. Enzyme-substrate interaction involves binding of the substrate to the enzyme and subsequently transformation of the substrate into its product. Having reviewed the nature of catalysis, it is clear that it is easier to bring about a minor rather than a major structural change in a compound in a short time. In addition, we must remember that enzymes have developed as a result of evolutionary pressure. Consequently, modest changes in the configuration of a particular compound are probably more easily achieved than major ones. In the second place, intermediary metabolism must accomplish two crucial functions responsible for the maintenance of the living

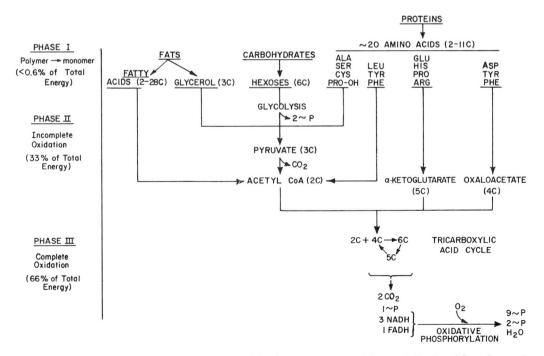

Figure 2–18 Overview of the strategies by which substrates are sequentially metabolized to CO_2 and water in a process that captures the energy as ATP. (From Hoch, F.L.: Energy Transformations in Mammals: Regulatory Mechanisms. Philadelphia, W.B. Saunders Co., 1971.)

process: the storage of chemical energy in the form of ATP and the provision of building blocks for the macromolecules composing the highly organized structures of the cell.

A final consideration is that the highly organized nature of the life process demands tiers of control. Thus, dividing the metabolic sequence into a multiplicity of steps provides for the possibility of multiple controls and redundancy of control.

Metabolic pathways have traditionally been divided into three types: *catabolic, anabolic,* and *amphibolic.* Degradative pathways in which substrates are broken down into products, with the storage of liberated energy in the form of ATP, are termed catabolic pathways. Synthetic pathways whereby small precursors coalesce into larger molecules, with energetic coupling being provided by ATP, are termed anabolic pathways. Amphibolic pathways serve both of the above functions; such a pathway is the tricarboxylic acid cycle.

Cellular Structure

For us to speak realistically of the life process, we must recognize that the physiological chemical reactions, both enzymatic and nonenzymatic, and the binding reactions associated with life must occur within a given bounded volume, i.e., the cell. The cell is the basic unit of life and is made up of subcellular organelles and cytoplasm maintained in a highly compartmentalized array

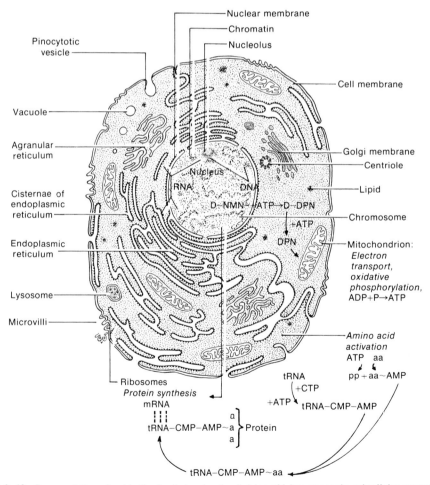

Figure 2–19 Representation of an idealized cell showing the division of labor among the subcellular organelles. (From Villee, C., Dethier, V.C.: Biological Principles and Processes. 2nd ed. Philadelphia, W.B. Saunders Co., 1976.)

Table 2–4 STRUCTURES AND FUNCTIONS OF THE CELL

Organelle	Functions Served or Carried Out Within or by the Organelle	Importance in Metabolic Diseases
Cell membrane (plasma membrane)	Selective permeability to ions, nutrients Acidification of urine by tubular membranes Absorption of digested products of hydrolysis of polymers in diet	Renal tubular disorders—primary, e.g., RTA secondary to toxins—Wilson's, hereditary fructose intolerance, galactosemia Gastrointestinal absorptive disorders—primary congenital lactase deficiency, glucose-galactose absorptive defect Secondary—malabsorptive
Cytosol	Contains many metabolic sequences with enzymes highly ordered plus other organelles (see below) Glycolysis	Red cell metabolic defects
Mitochondria	Furnaces of the cell—carry out citric acid cycle, β-oxidation, and oxidative phosphorylation	
Lysosomes	Single-membrane vesicles which contain hydrolytic enzymes which break down complex lipids, membrane fragments, and mucopolysaccharides	Lysosomal storage diseases: e.g., glycosphingolipidoses, mucopolysaccharidoses, mucolipidoses
Endoplasmic reticulum and ribosomes	Protein synthesis at direction of mRNA made according to instructions in DNA	
Golgi apparatus	Stacked vesicles that are involved in secretion of polymers (often glycoproteins) made in cell to the exterior	Glycosylated proteins—many lysosomal enzymes and immunoglobulins are partially formed in the Golgi apparatus

(Fig. 2–19). The cell is bounded by a plasma membrane and contains cytoplasm (cytosol) and a number of specialized structures, which are listed in Table 2–4 along with the functions they serve and their importance in metabolic disorders. The ability to form membranes is the key to the formation of the cell and its subcellular organelles. This ability depends on the physicochemical properties of hydrophobic phospholipids, which aggregate to form vesicles. It depends as well on the insertion of hydrophobic proteins into this membrane, which are thus able to provide for substrate transport into and out of the cell.

When a series of enzymatic reactions occurs in sequence, we have a *metabolic pathway,* with the product of each reaction serving as substrate for the next. The output of each pathway can become the input for the next, serving to link otherwise disparate metabolic routes. In many cases the linking reactions must traverse organellar membrane barriers, so that compartmentalization imposes spatial order and temporal control.

When the enzymes and resulting intermediates in a metabolic pathway coexist in a fluid medium (e.g., the cytosol), the number of times each enzyme and substrate can come into contact depends statistically upon their concentrations. For optimal flux through a pathway, each substrate must find its enzyme quickly and effectively. Organizing enzymes in a sequence through attachment to the matrix of the cytosol, as has been shown with the glycolytic pathway enzymes, can account for the rapidity with which a metabolic sequence is traversed in vivo.

Metabolic Control Principles

The fact that a series of chemical reactions can form a metabolic pathway with an ordered sequence presupposes both organization and control. Metabolic pathways must proceed at a rate that is "just right." Operation at maximal rates would exhaust substrates or cause accumulation of toxic levels of one or more intermediates. Additionally, competition among various pathways for sparse intermediates might render one pathway nonfunctional. Were metabolic pathways to operate at minimal rates, the incessant production of ATP necessary to maintain energy-requiring processes would be insufficient and life would cease. Moreover, the ability to adjust to changing intracellular conditions would no longer be possible.

Table 2-5 MAJOR HORMONAL EFFECTS ON METABOLISM

	Insulin	Glucagon	Corticosteroids	HGH	Thyroid	Catecholamines
Protein Metabolism	Promotes cellular uptake of amino acids by muscle, liver and other tissues—↓plasma amino acid concentration. Stimulates protein synthesis (↑syn enz. of glycolysis, ↓syn enz. of gluconeogenesis). Inh ibits protein degradation	In liver: Stimulates transport of amino acids. Inhibits protein synthesis. Accelerates protein degradation. Stimulates gluconeogenesis (from amino acids) and ureogenesis	Stimulates catabolism in muscle and synthesis in liver (enzymes included include: tryptophan pyrolase, tyrosine transaminase, gluconeogenic enzymes). Stimulates synthesis of all RNA species in liver	↑ Nitrogen retention by muscle. ↑Protein synthesis—stimulates synthesis of RNA polymerases. ↑Cellular uptake amino acids	Acute: ↑liver protein. Chronic: ↓peripheral and liver protein. Stimulates activity of carbamyl phosphate synthetase	Epinephrine inhibits incorporation of amino acids into protein
Carbohydrate Metabolism	Stimulates glucose transport into muscle, adipose tissue (uptake by liver not insulin dependent)—there glucose can serve energy needs or be conserved. ↑Glycolysis in muscle. ↑Glucokinase activity in liver	Provides glucose as an energy source. Stimulates glycogenolysis and gluconeogenesis. Inhibits glycolysis: secreted when glucose availability↓—e.g., starvation, exercise, hypoglycemia	Stimulates gluconeogenesis. Acts in concert with glucagon	↑Glycogenolysis. ↑Glucose uptake by cells	Stimulates glycogenolysis and gluconeogenesis—acts in concert with catecholamines. Stimulation of protein breakdown augments substrate supply to liver	Muscle—stimulates glycogenolysis. Liver—stimulates glycogenolysis and gluconeogenesis
Fat Metabolism	Acute: ↓lipolysis and ↑lipogenesis. Chronic: ↑activities of lipogenic enzymes. In fasting insulin↓, glucagon ↑→lipid mobilization. Stimulates FA synthesis in liver; opposes ketogenic effect glucagon (mole for mole more potent than glucagon). FA's transported to adipose tissue (as CM + VLDL) are hydrolyzed by LPL (insulin dependent)—↑activity LPL→uptake FA into adipose tissue. In adipose tissue insulin stimulates re-esterification of FFA and inhibits depot fat lipase	Stimulates triglyceride hydrolysis in adipose tissue. In liver stimulates FA oxidation and ketogenesis (↑ cytoplasmic carnitine). Inhibits triglyceride release	Has a permissive effect on lipolysis; inhibits lipogenesis	Stimulates lipid mobilization from adipose tissue—acts synergistically with corticosteroids. Stimulates ketogenesis	Stimulates mobilization of FFA from adipose tissue; ↑FA oxidation	Stimulates triglyceride hydrolysis; conversion of glucose to lipids; hepatic cholesterol synthesis

An inborn error of metabolism may result in the accumulation of certain intermediates proximal to a metabolic block or lack of production of a key intermediate distal to that block. Such changes can have profound consequences on the conduct of a pathway as well as on other metabolic sequences that depend upon an intermediate from the genetically deranged pathway.

Endocrine Organization

Just as the coordinated activity of metabolic sequences within the cellular microcosm requires the constant input of information to ensure the optimal activity of the component enzymes, the macrocosm of an organ needs an information system to integrate its activities with those of the various other organs. As is to be expected, the level at which this control is felt initially is at the biochemical level, i.e., at the *cell receptor*. The endocrine system is able to orchestrate the conduct of metabolic processes by coordinating the activity of millions of cells so that the biochemical response engendered finds expression at a physiologic level (Table 2–5). Today it is clear that almost every tissue elaborates at least one hormone. The corollary of this synthetic capability is that almost all organs are acted upon by at least one hormone.

The coordinated activity of the components of the organism is attained by the correlation and interplay of two major systems: the endocrine system and the autonomic nervous system. Nerve endings release chemical transmitters, acetylcholine, and norepinephrine, which are often found in the blood, so that they may be thought of as hormones as well. The unique inter-relationships between these systems is most striking at the level of the hypothalamus. This center is the site at which the activities of both the autonomic and the endocrine systems merge, producing several hormones that act upon other endocrine glands as well as carry out neurotransmission.

Feedback and feedforward controls, as discussed for control of enzyme activity, play an important role in the transfer of information to endocrine glands. To receive such information, cells that respond to a hormonal stimulus have specific hormonal receptors either upon or within particular cells. These receptors must possess discriminating ability based on the principles of complementary interaction, so important in enzyme action. Only proteins possess the capability for stereospecific binding, and proteins alone are coded for by the DNA. Hence, we can expect that certain inherited endocrine conditions will depend upon abnormalities in receptor structure or function. Once the hormone interacts with its receptor, the information is transduced into *second* or *intracellular messengers* through activation of a membrane-bound enzyme that forms cyclic AMP or through stimulation of DNA transcription into mRNA. As this ordered sequence of response continues, intracellular targets (usually enzymes) mediate the biochemical response that brings about the action associated with the hormone. Feedback control, through servomechanism organization, ensures the capacity to modulate the response and correct for overshoot. Hence, control at the biochemical level gains expression at the physiological level.

Plasma Membrane-Mediated Systems

A number of the polypeptide hormones and catecholamines engender a series of events, which begin with binding of the hormone to the external surface of the plasma membrane at a specific hormone receptor. This brings about activation of an effector (usually adenylate cyclase), with a subsequent increase in intracellular concentration of a signal molecule second messenger (usually cyclic adenosine-3′,5′-monophosphate-cyclic AMP, Fig. 2–20). The second messenger then mediates intracellular effects that permit expression of specific tissue responses.

The best-known action of cyclic AMP is the activation of specific intracellular protein kinases, by binding to the regulatory portion of a specific protein kinase complex. cAMP binding brings about dissociation of the regulatory subunit from the catalytic portion, thereby activating it. Activated protein kinase phosphorylates other proteins (some of which are also protein kinase), with the terminal phosphate of ATP being transferred to specific serine or threonine hydroxyl groups. Phosphorylation of various proteins can bring about either enzyme activation or enzyme inactivation.

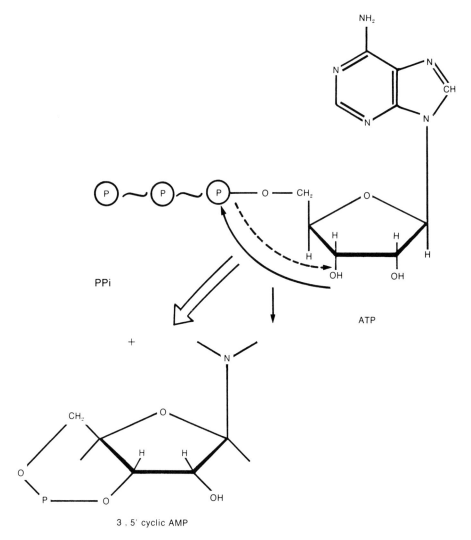

Figure 2–20 Formation of 3',5' cyclic adenosine monophosphate (cAMP) from ATP by the enzyme adenylate cyclase. (From Villee, C., Dethier, V.C.: Biological Principles and Processes. 2nd ed. Philadelphia, W.B. Saunders Co., 1976.)

Other effects depend upon the protein phosphorylated and include alteration in messenger RNA, alterations in enzyme synthesis, and changes in membrane permeability. By phosphorylating key proteins, protein kinases translate information received at the plasma membrane into specific responses of specific functional proteins.

Hormones Employing Intracellular Binding Proteins

In contrast to polypeptide hormones and catecholamines, steroid and thyroid hormones do not act at the cell membrane; rather they traverse the cell membrane and bind to an intracellular binding protein (Fig. 2–21). This noncovalent complex then gains entrance into the nucleus where it stimulates protein synthesis by actions (not well understood) on the chromatin or DNA itself, which lead to synthesis of specific mRNA's. Intracellular binding proteins have been described for estrogens, progesterone, dihydrotestosterone, cortisol, aldosterone, 1,25-dihydroxycholecalciferol, and triiodothyronine. These hormone receptors are proteins that possess a high binding affinity for their specific hormones.

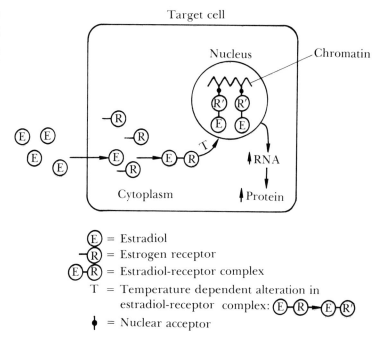

Figure 2–21 Scheme showing the mechanism of action of estradiol as a representative of the mode of action of steroid hormones. (From Villee, D.B.: Human Endocrinology: A Developmental Approach. Philadelphia, W.B. Saunders Co., 1975.)

(E) = Estradiol
(R) = Estrogen receptor
(E)-(R) = Estradiol-receptor complex
T = Temperature dependent alteration in estradiol-receptor complex: (E)-(R) → (E)-(R')
⭍ = Nuclear acceptor

ETIOLOGY OF GENETIC DEFECTS

Although this book focuses on the role of mutations as the cause of genetic defects, we must remember that mutations may act as the progenitors of variation within the genome, allowing for evolution of biochemical capability. Serving in both roles, mutations constitute a double-edged sword. A point mutation affects a single nucleotide and may cause either a replacement of one of the bases or an insertion or loss of a single base. Such mutations are termed mis-sense or no-sense mutations; in the former instance, a different amino acid is substituted at a given site in the protein, while in the latter the change of base sequence is such that protein synthesis ceases when that nucleotide sequence is reached. A mutation may alter the properties of an enzyme so profoundly that it no longer manifests any catalytic activity, or it may become particularly susceptible to environmental denaturation or enzymatic destruction. Despite these dire possibilities, most mutations result in a substitution or replacement of a conservative nature, so that little or no functional or physical change is discerned in the final gene product. For example, in the case of the hemoglobin variants, those associated with disease are small in number compared with those that are distinguished from hemoglobin A only on the basis of electrophoretic or other laboratory analysis.

Mis-sense mutations are termed CRM-positive, while no-sense mutations are CRM-negative. CRM ("krim") means *cross-reactive material* and indicates the presence of a protein that shows immunologic reactivity with antibodies developed against the normal enzyme. Of course, immunologic reactivity is not synonymous with catalytic activity: such a reaction distinguishes immunologic determinants from the unique three-dimensional configuration that constitutes the active site of the enzyme.

More complex kinds of mutations and control errors are possible, but an exhaustive discussion of these possibilities is beyond the scope of this book. These possibilities are thoroughly discussed in the general references at the end of Part I.

Human Inheritance

Genes are located either on the autosomal chromosomes or on the sex chromosomes. Sex-linked genes reside almost exclusively on the X chromosome, since only one or two traits are known to be associated with the Y. Different templates of the same gene occurring at the same locus on homologous chromosomes are termed *alleles*. A homozygote possesses two identical alleles at a given gene locus, while a heterozygote has nonidentical alleles at the same locus. Hemizygotes have only one allele, for example, in an X-linked trait such as hemophilia.

When a trait is expressed in a heterozygote, it is presumed to be *dominant*, while a double dose is called *recessive* and is expressed in the homozygote only. Depending on the means of uncovering a particular trait, even a single dose of a recessive condition may be found to have biochemical stigmata. For example, heterozygotes for cystinosis are always asymptomatic, but quantitation of intracellular cystine levels will reveal 8- to 10-fold greater than normal amounts of cystine (homozygotes have levels 100-fold greater than normal), so that the abnormal trait is being partially expressed.

The underlying genetic complement is known as the genotype, while the overt expression of interaction of the genotype and the environment is the *phenotype*. Depending on the nature and the degree of environmental stress, certain traits may be more or less expressible. The term *penetrance* denotes the percentage of individuals possessing a particular gene who manifest it under ordinary circumstances. Variability of expression of a given trait is the rule and is partially accounted for by the interaction of the genotype with the environment.

Autosomal Dominant Inheritance

Certain general rules characterize classic autosomal dominant inheritance, but they are not invariant. According to statistical predictions, males and females should be equally affected, with an affected individual having at least one parent with the trait. It follows then that each sibling of an affected person has a 50 percent risk of manifesting the trait and similarly each child of an affected person has a 50 percent chance.

There are several circumstances under which these rules are violated:

1. The sex ratio of those affected may not be equal, owing to greater lethality of the mutation in one sex.

2. New mutations may account for affected children with normal parents. Such a situation is exemplified by achondroplasia. However, children with achondroplasia due to a new mutation will transmit the trait in a dominant fashion, so that their children have a 50-50 chance of being affected.

3. Penetrance may be so low as to be subclinical in an affected individual.

In general, autosomal dominant traits are expressed in two ways: structural defects caused by abnormalities in embryogenesis and late-onset functional disorders without apparent early warning. Two embryogenetic defects are achondroplasia and cleft lip and palate with pits of the lower lip. Huntington's chorea is the classic illustration of an autosomal dominant disorder with delayed onset and one that has received considerable public attention. Acute intermittent porphyria and hypercholesterolemia also have delayed onsets with dominant transmission.

In contrast to autosomal recessive disorders, the basic biochemical defects have been elucidated in very few autosomal dominant diseases. Possibilities include defects in structural proteins, defects in activity of rate-limiting enzymes, and membrane receptor defects. In early-onset hypercholesterolemia the homozygous offspring of two parents heterozygous for this trait do not possess cell-surface receptors for low-density lipoproteins (LDL), while their heterozygous parents have a partial deficiency for the LDL receptor.

A structurally altered protein can account for some other autosomal dominant conditions. Examples are provided by certain hemoglobinopathies, such as hemoglobin C, in which there is a substitution of lysine for glutamine on the β-chain of the globin molecule.

Generally, autosomal dominant traits are less severe than autosomal recessive ones, since in the former there is a normal allele present that modifies the phenotypic expression of the abnormal allele. This phenomenon is known as *co-dominance*, without which most autosomal dominant traits would be lethal in utero. On the other hand, autosomal recessive traits are phenotypically expressed only in the absence of a normal allele, as we will see below.

Autosomal Recessive Inheritance

This mode of inheritance is characterized by equal representation between male and female, with unaffected parents and a 25 percent chance in any pregnancy of an offspring being affected. It follows that children of a parent who is affected with an autosomal recessive disorder must all be heterozygous carriers of the abnormal gene.

As with the other genetic rules, deviation from what might be expected is often encountered. Since heterozygotes possess approximately half the normal complement of enzyme activity, they are free of symptoms, but they may show abnormal handling of a metabolite with a loading test. However, routine screening tests are unlikely to uncover an abnormality, since rarely do recessively inherited defects affect rate-limiting enzymes. It is important to note that while the disease may be rare, the carrier state may be not at all uncommon. For example, phenylalanine hydroxylase deficiency (classic PKU) has a frequency of approximately 1 in 10,000 with a carrier frequency of about 1 in 50.

X-Linked Inheritance

We come finally to sex-linked inheritance. In X-linked recessive inheritance males are affected, while both their mother and carrier sisters are usually asymptomatic. There is a 50 percent chance of any male offspring born to a heterozygous mother being affected.

In sex-linked inheritance, examination of a pedigree usually reveals an affected maternal uncle whose asymptomatic sister transmitted the disorder to her son. Male-to-male transmission is never encountered. As noted above, while males with X-linked traits tend to be uniformly affected, female carriers are usually free of symptoms. However, this is not without exception. For example, girls with vitamin D-resistant rickets may be mildly affected. Women are genetic mosaics, due to X inactivation (Lyon hypothesis—see below), and as a consequence, some carriers do show mild manifestations. A case in point is the carrier for Duchenne's muscular dystrophy; some females show an elevated serum creatine phosphokinase level and may also have mild muscle dysfunction.

With X-linked dominant inheritance, females as well as males are affected and either affected parent can transmit the disorder to offspring. This form of inheritance resembles autosomal dominant inheritance. However, the two are distinguished by the fact that while the mother will transmit the disorder to half of her sons or daughters, the father will transmit it to all of his daughters and none of his sons.

Lyon Hypothesis

For a number of years, mammalian geneticists were puzzled by the fact that females who were homozygous for an X-linked disorder often manifested an attenuated clinical picture when compared with their hemizygous male counterparts. Contrary to expectation, a female hemophiliac patient, for example, does not manifest a more severe coagulopathy than a male hemophiliac with the same specific gene disorder, although the former carries a double dose of the abnormal gene. Conversely a heterozygous female may occasionally be as severely affected as a hemizygous male, although this is far less common. These extraordinary observations have been explained by the Lyon hypothesis, which simply states that only one X chromosome expresses its information in the mature cell. Hence, the number of active X chromosomes within a mature mammalian cell is always one regardless of the number of X chromosomes. As a consequence, the number of Barr bodies in the cell is equal to the number of inactive X chromosomes.

According to the Lyon hypothesis, selection of a functional X chromosome from the total available occurs randomly within each cell during embryologic development. Once inactivation of the remaining X chromosome(s) has occurred, all daughter cells will possess the same active X chromosome as their parent cells. It follows from the principle of random selection that statistically it is most likely that in a cell mass derived from an XX heterozygote embryo 50 percent of the cells will contain a normal active X and 50 percent will have the abnormal X active. Variations of random distribution about the mean will produce the clinical discrepancies mentioned earlier.

REFERENCES

Order in Life and Disease

Cohn, R. M., Palmieri, M.J., and McNamara, P.D.: Nonequilibrium thermodynamics, noncovalent forces, and water. *In* Herman, R.H., Cohn, R.M., and McNamara, P.D. (eds.): Principles of Metabolic Control in Mammalian Systems. Plenum Press, New York, 1980, p. 63.
Nicolis, G., and Prigogine, I.: Self-organization in Nonequilibrium Systems: From Dissipative Structures to Order through Fluctuations. John Wiley & Sons, New York, 1977.
Schroedinger, E.: What Is Life? Cambridge University Press, Cambridge, 1944.
Weiss, P.: Dynamics of Development: Experiments and Inferences. Academic Press, New York, 1968.

How Macromolecules Work

Franks, F. (ed.): Water—A Comprehensive Treatise. 5 Volumes Plenum Press, New York, 1975.
Lewin, S.: Displacement of Water and Its Control of Biochemical Reactions. Academic Press, New York, 1974.
Tanford, C.: The hydrophobic effect and the organization of living matter. Science 200:1012, 1978.
Tanford, C.: The Hydrophobic Effect: Formation of Micelles and Biological Membranes. 2nd ed. Wiley-Interscience, New York, 1980.

The Role of Macromolecules in the Life Process

Cantor, C.R., and Schimmel, P.R.: Biophysical Chemistry. Part I. The Conformation of Biological Macromolecules. W.H. Freeman, San Francisco, 1980.
Dickerson, R.E., and Geis, I.: The Structure and Action of Proteins. Harper & Row, New York, 1969.
Pauling, L., and Corey, R.B.: Atomic coordinates and structure factors for two helical configurations of polypeptide chains. Proc. Natl. Acad. Sci. USA. 37:235, 1951.
Rees, D.A.: Polysaccharide Shapes. Halsted Press, New York, 1977.
Rossman, M.G., and Argos, P.: Protein folding. Ann. Rev. Biochem. 50:497, 1981.
Schulz, G.E., and Schirmer, R.H.: Principles of Protein Structure. Springer-Verlag, New York, 1979.

Enzyme Functions

Bell, R.M., and Koshland, D.E., Jr.: Covalent enzyme-substrate intermediates. Science 172:1253, 1971.
Cohn, R.M.: Enzymes and coenzymes: A mechanistic view. *In* Herman, R.H., Cohn, R.M., and McNamara, P.D. (eds.): Principles of Metabolic Control in Mammalian Systems. Plenum Press, New York, 1980, p. 93.
Dugas, H., and Penney, C.: Bioorganic Chemistry. Springer-Verlag, New York, 1981.
Fersht, A.: Enzyme Structure and Mechanism. W.H. Freeman, San Francisco, 1977.
Jencks, W.P.: Binding energy, specificity and enzymatic catalysis: The Circe effect. Adv. Enzymol. 43:219, 1975.
Koshland, D.E., Jr.: The evolution of function in enzymes. Fed. Proc. 35:2104, 1976.
Lowe, J.N., and Ingraham, L.L.: An Introduction to Biochemical Reaction Mechanisms. Prentice-Hall, Englewood Cliffs, New Jersey, 1974.
Pauling, L.: Chemical achievement and hope for the future. Am. Sci. 36:51, 1948.
Walsh, C.: Enzymatic Reaction Mechanisms. W.H. Freeman, San Francisco, 1979.

Regulation of Intermediary Metabolism

Cohn, R.M., and Yandrasitz, J.R.: Modulation of enzyme activity. *In* Herman, R.H., Cohn, R.M., and McNamara, P.D. (eds.): Principles of Metabolic Control in Mammalian Systems. Plenum Press, New York, 1980, p. 135.
Uy, R., and Wold, F.: Posttranslational covalent modification of proteins. Science 198:890, 1977.
Chock, P., Rhee, S., and Stadtman, E.R.: Interconvertible enzyme cascades in cellular regulation. Ann. Rev. Biochem. 49:813, 1980.
Krebs, E.G., and Beavo, J.A.: Phosphorylation-dephosphorylation of enzymes. Ann. Rev. Biochem. 48:923, 1979.
Freedman, R.B., and Hawkins, A.C. (eds.): The Enzymology of Post-translational Modifications of Proteins. Academic Press, New York, 1980.

Protein Synthesis

Breathnach, R., and Chambon, P.: Organization and Expression of Eucaryotic Split Genes Coding for Proteins. Ann. Rev. Biochem. 50:349, 1981.
Cohn, R.M., McNamara, P.D., and Herman, R.H.: Regulation of Protein Biosynthesis. *In* Herman, R.H., Cohn, R.M., and McNamara, P.D. (eds.): Principles of Metabolic Control in Mammalian Systems. Plenum Press, New York, 1980, p. 171.
Goldberger, R.F. (ed.): Biological Regulation and Development. Vol. I. Gene Expression. Plenum Press, New York, 1979.
Lake, J.A.: The ribosome. Sci. Am. 245(2):84, 1981.
Thomas, A.A.M., Benne, R., and Voorma, H.O.: Initiation of eukaryotic protein synthesis. FEBS Lett. 128:177, 1981.
Weissbach, H., and Pestka, S.: Molecular Mechanism of Protein Biosynthesis. Academic Press, New York, 1977.
Vogel, H.J. (ed.): Nucleic Acid-Protein Recognition. Academic Press, New York, 1977.

The Organization of Metabolic Processes

Krebs, H.A., and Kornberg, H.L.: Energy Transformations in Living Matter. Springer-Verlag, Berlin, 1957.
McGilvery, R.: Biochemistry: A Functional Approach. W.B. Saunders, Philadelphia, 1979.
Spiegel, A.M., and Downs, R.W., Jr.: Guanine nucleotides: Key regulations of hormone receptor-adenylate cyclase inter-action. Endocrine Reviews 2:275, 1981.
Stryer, L.: Biochemistry. 2nd ed. W.H. Freeman, San Francisco, 1981.
Williams, R.H. (ed.): Textbook of Endocrinology. W.B. Saunders, Philadelphia, 1981.

Etiology of Genetic Defects

Bondy, P. and Rosenberg, L. (eds.): Metabolic Control and Disease. W.B. Saunders, Philadelphia, 1980.
Danks, D.M.: Inborn errors of metabolism—A review of some general concepts. Aust. N. Z. J. Med. 11:309, 1981.
Garrod, A.E.: Inborn errors of metabolism. Lancet 2:1,73,142,214, 1908.
Stanbury, J., Wyngaarden, J., and Fredrickson, D., et al. (eds.): The Metabolic Basis of Inherited Disease. McGraw-Hill, New York, 1982.

II

PATHOPHYSIOLOGY AND DIFFERENTIAL DIAGNOSIS OF CLINICAL DERANGEMENTS

3

Acid-Base Physiology in Health and Disease

John W. Foreman

The blood hydrogen ion concentration (pH) is one of the most tightly regulated physiological variables in the body. In health, blood pH varies between 7.45 and 7.35, which represents a shift in hydrogen ion concentration of only 10 nEq/l. Limits of pH compatible with life are generally stated to be from 7.8 to 7.0, which represents a change in hydrogen ion concentration of only 86 nEq/l. Thus, the body is 100,000 times more sensitive to changes in the extracellular hydrogen ion concentration than to changes in the potassium concentration and a million times more sensitive than to changes in the sodium concentration.

BODY BUFFERS

The body is able to maintain this tight regulation of blood pH by means of several buffer systems that are combinations of a weak acid or base and its conjugate salt. An acid, according to the Lowry-Brönsted definition, is a proton (H^+) donor, while a base is a proton acceptor. Hence, carbonic acid, carbon dioxide, ammonium ion (NH_4^+), organic acids, and dihydrogen phosphate anion ($H_2PO_4^-$) are acids, while HCO_3^-, OH^-, NH_3, hydrogen phosphate anion ($HPO_4^=$), and proteins, especially hemoglobin, are bases. "Strength" of an acid or a base refers to the degree of ionization in an aqueous solution. There are all gradations of strength, from HCl, which is a strong acid and virtually completely ionized, to acetic acid, which is a weak acid and minimally ionized. Strength can be measured in terms of the equilibrium constant, K_a, for the following reaction:

$$HA \rightleftharpoons H^+ + A^- \qquad (1)$$

$$\text{where } K_a = \frac{[H^+][A^-]}{[HA]} \qquad (2)$$

Taking the negative logarithm of both sides,

$$pK_a = pH - \log \frac{[A^-]}{[HA]} \qquad (3)$$

$$\text{or}$$

$$pH = pK_a + \log \frac{[A^-]}{[HA]} \qquad (4)$$

A buffer is an aqueous solution to which the addition of an acid or a base causes a much smaller shift in the pH than would be the case with pure water. The simplest buffer solution consists of a weak acid (HA) and a neutral salt of its conjugate base (NaA). When a strong acid is added to a buffer solution, most of the resulting H^+ is combined with the conjugate base (A^-) to form the undissociated weak acid (HA), effectively reducing the number of free H^+ ions and the shift in pH as shown in reaction 5. When a base is added to a buffer solution, most of the H^+ ions consumed by the added OH^- ions to form water are regenerated by the dissociation of the weak acid shown by reaction 6. Again, there is little change in the pH.

$$A^- + H^+ + Cl^- \rightleftharpoons HA + Cl^- \tag{5}$$

$$HA + Na^+ + OH^- \rightleftharpoons H_2O + Na^+ + A^- \tag{6}$$

A buffer solution is most effective at mitigating pH shifts when the initial pH of the solution is equal to the pK_a of the buffer. This can be seen from equation 4. If the initial pH is one unit greater than the pK_a, then the ratio of $[A^-]/[HA]$ would be 10/1, seriously limiting the ability of the buffer solution to dampen pH changes with the addition of hydroxyl ions. If the pH is one unit less than the pK_a, then the ratio of $[A^-]/[HA]$ would be 1/10, limiting the ability of the buffer solution to handle H^+ ions.

The major buffer system of blood is the HCO_3^-–H_2CO_3 system. The pK_a of this system, at body temperature and the usual ionic strength of plasma, is 6.1. As noted above, a buffer with this pK_a would be normally ineffective at body pH, which is 7.4. However, the uniqueness of the HCO_3^-–H_2CO_3 buffer system in the body is that it is not a closed system, but rather an open system. That is, H_2CO_3 is in equilibrium with the CO_2 dissolved in blood by means of the enzyme carbonic anhydrase that resides in many tissues, especially RBC's. Carbonic anhydrase catalyzes the reaction:

$$H_2CO_3 \rightleftharpoons CO_2 + H_2O$$

the equilibrium of which strongly favors the formation of CO_2. The importance of this reaction is that the excretion of CO_2 by the lungs makes the HCO_3^-–H_2CO_3 buffer system an open and extremely effective one in spite of the pK_a of 6.1. This can be seen from the Henderson-Hasselbalch equation,

$$pH = pK_a + \log \frac{\text{(ionized form)}}{\text{(nonionized form)}} \tag{7}$$

which for the HCO_3^- – H_2CO_3 system is

$$pH = 6.1 + \log \frac{(HCO_3^-)}{(H_2CO_3)} \frac{\text{(kidney)}}{\text{(lungs)}} \tag{8}$$

However, H_2CO_3 is in equilibrium with dissolved CO_2, and dissolved CO_2 is equal to pCO_2 times a solubility factor (0.03 mmoles/l per unit of Torr), so that the Henderson-Hasselbalch equation becomes

$$pH = 6.1 + \log \frac{(HCO_3^-)}{(0.03 \, pCO_2)} \tag{9}$$

Therefore, if 10 mEq of a strong acid were added to each liter of extracellular fluid, the HCO_3^- concentration would fall from a normal of 24 mEq/l to 14 and the blood pH would drop to 6.20 in the closed system described by equation 8. But since H_2CO_3 is in equilibrium with pCO_2, with the lungs maintaining the pCO_2 around 40 Torr, the denominator of equation 9 is essentially unchanged and the pH falls only to 7.17. Thus, because the lungs make this an open system by eliminating CO_2, the HCO_3^-–H_2CO_3 system becomes a very effective buffering system indeed.

Protein constitutes the other major body buffer. Plasma proteins (e.g., hemoglobin) and intracellular proteins can act as buffers by virtue of the side-chains of certain amino acids such as the free basic group of lysine, arginine, and histidine; the free carboxyl group of glutamate and aspartate; the sulfhydryl group of cysteine; and the phenolic group of tyrosine. The terminal anion and carboxyl groups of the proteins also act as buffers. Since the pK_a of these varied ionizable groups covers a wide range of pH, proteins constitute a buffering system of large capacity and effective dynamic range.

Most clinical laboratories report the acid-base status of the blood not in terms of the hydrogen ion concentration ($[H^+]$), but rather as the negative logarithm of $[H^+]$ or pH. Occasionally, it is useful in clinical medicine to know the actual $[H^+]$, but converting pH to $[H^+]$ can be cumbersome. Recently, Meeroff et al. described a rapid method of converting pH to $[H^+]$ over wide physiologic range without the use of logarithm tables. Their method is based on the fact that

$$pH_1 - pH_2 = -\log ([H^+]_1 \div [H^+]_2) \text{ and} \tag{10}$$

$$[H^+]_1 = [H^+]_2 \times 10^{-(pH_1 - pH_2)} = [H^+]_2 \times 10^{-\Delta pH} \tag{11}$$

Substituting F for $10^{-\Delta pH}$ simplifies equation (11) to

$$[H^+]_1 = [H^+]_2 \times F \tag{12}$$

Values of F for convenient pH differences are:

ΔpH	F
1.0	0.1
0.7	0.2
0.3	0.5
0.1	0.8
0.05	0.9

In order to use equation (12), reference values for $[H^+]_2$ must also be known. Since pH $6 = 1000$ nEq/l and pH $7 = 100$ nEq/l, values for $[H^+]_2$ are readily inserted into the equation. In order to find the corresponding hydrogen ion concentration for pH 7.65, convert 7.65 to a sum of a reference pH value plus convenient "ΔpHs":

$$pH\ 7.65 = 7.00 + 0.3 + 0.3 + 0.05 \tag{13}$$

Substituting the hydrogen ion concentration corresponding to the reference pH and multiplying it by the F values for the "ΔpHs" gives

$$[H^+]_1 = (100)\ (0.5)\ (0.5)\ (0.9) = 22.5 \text{ nEq/l} \tag{14}$$

for a pH of 7.65. For a pH of 6.85,

$$pH\ 6.85 = 6.00 + 0.7 + 0.1 + 0.05 \tag{15}$$

$$[H^+]_1 = (1000)\ (0.2)\ (0.8)\ (0.9) = 144 \text{ nEq/l} \tag{16}$$

As can be seen, this method allows relatively accurate conversion of pH to $[H^+]$ without resorting to logarithm tables. Interpolation is necessary to find values of $[H^+]$ corresponding to pH units smaller than 0.05.

Disturbances in body pH have been categorized into four major types. *Metabolic acidosis* occurs with the gain of an acid, other than carbonic, or with the loss of bicarbonate from the extracellular fluid. *Metabolic alkalosis* occurs with the gain of exogenous bicarbonate or the loss of H^+ from the extracellular fluid. *Respiratory acidosis* occurs with a primary decrease in alveolar ventilation leading to a rise in pCO_2. *Respiratory alkalosis* occurs with a primary increase in alveolar ventilation with a decrease in pCO_2. In a clinical setting combinations of the foregoing simple types are quite frequent.

Buffer Capacity

The effectiveness and contribution of the various body buffers to neutralizing disturbances in pH has been elucidated in a number of now classic experiments. Swan and Pitts infused HCl in nephrectomized dogs to study the nature of acute buffering in metabolic acidosis. They found that 57 percent of the infused acid was buffered by intracellular buffers and 43 percent by extracellular buffers, mainly HCO_3^-. It is worth emphasizing the importance of intracellular buffers (mainly proteins) in the acute buffering of an acid load. They demonstrated that acid was buffered by intracellular proteins by means of an exchange of intracellular Na^+ for extracellular H^+ and a similar exchange of intracellular K^+ for extracellular H^+. A smaller fraction of intracellular buffering was the result of an extracellular Cl^- for intracellular HCO_3^- exchange.

An important factor mitigating the fall in pH during the acid load in these dogs, and in patients, is the increased pulmonary elimination of CO_2, which lowers the pCO_2 and thereby the H_2CO_3 concentration. Referring back to the Henderson-Hasselbalch equation, one can readily appreciate the importance of this respiratory compensation. Normally, the ratio of $HCO_3^-/0.03pCO_2$ is 24/1.2 or 20/1. If the HCO_3^- concentration drops to 7 mEq/l after the acid infusion but the pCO_2 remains constant, the pH would fall to 6.8, since $pH = 6.1 + \log 7/1.2 = 6.8$. But with hyperventilation, the pCO_2 would fall to 23 Torr and the pH to 7.1. This would be a severe acidosis, but it is more likely to be compatible with survival than a pH of 6.8.

Pitts and his group also examined the nature of body buffering during the infusion of alkali in nephrectomized dogs as a model of metabolic alkalosis. With alkali infusion, only 32 percent of the load was buffered by intracellular mechanisms. The major intracellular mechanism was the exchange of intracellular H^+ dissociated from proteins for extracellular Na^+. A smaller amount was buffered by the efflux of lactic acid from cells and the exchange of intracellular Cl^- for extracellular HCO_3^- mainly by the RBC. In striking contrast to acid infusion only 1 per cent of the alkali was buffered by extracellular mechanisms, and this was only by the dissociation of H^+ from plasma proteins; the majority of the infused alkali was retained in the extracellular fluid. While respiratory compensation can attenuate the pH change by retaining CO_2, such compensation, by alveolar hypoventilation, is limited by the overriding need to maintain tissue oxygenation.

Renal Regulation of Acid-Base Balance (see also Chapter 14)

The major end-product of metabolism is CO_2. In normal man, this amounts to 13,000 mmoles/day, which constitutes an enormous acid load that would be rapidly fatal if the lungs were not so efficient in excreting CO_2.

In addition to this large quantity of volatile acid, small quantities of nonvolatile acid are formed as a consequence of intermediary metabolism (Table 3–1). In the adult about a third of this nonvolatile acid arises from the catabolism of proteins and the sulfur-containing amino acids, methionine and cysteine, which generate sulfuric acid. Incomplete oxidation of fat, generating β-hydroxybutyric and acetoacetic acid, and of carbohydrate, generating lactic acid, constitutes about a third of the nonvolatile acid formed. The ingestion of potential nonvolatile acid in the form of phosphoproteins and phospholipids and foodstuffs containing an excess of inorganic anions over inorganic cations (thereby containing an excess of organic cations such as arginine-HCl, which liberates H^+ with catabolism) accounts for another third of the daily nonvolatile acid production in the adult and older child. In the adult, this amounts to 50 to 70 mEq/day depending on the diet. Diets containing large amounts of meat and eggs will generate more nonvolatile acid, while diets containing predominantly fruits and vegetables will generate less nonvolatile acid and even possibly net alkali.

In the infant, especially the actively growing premature infant, this partition of nonvolatile acids does not pertain. Because of the rapid growth rate, net protein catabolism is minimal and the contribution of sulfuric acid to the total nonvolatile acid is negligible. Also, formula and breast milk, which constitute the diet in this age group, supply net alkali as opposed to the mixed diet of older children and adults, which supplies net acid. Organic acids formed from the incomplete oxidation of fat and carbohydrate constitute a large fraction of the total nonvolatile acids. The other major source is the formation of bone because the synthesis of the hydroxyapatite of bone is asso-

Table 3–1 THE SOURCES OF ACID AND ALKALI PRODUCTION

Sources	Added H^+ or HCO_3^- and Mechanism
1. Cellular Metabolism of Dietary and Tissue Constituents	
Carbohydrates	Glucose $\xrightarrow{\;O_2\;}$ 2 lactate$^-$ + 2 H
Fats	Triglycerides $\xrightarrow{\;O_2\;}$ acetoacetate$^-$ + H^+
Nucleoproteins	Nucleic acids $\xrightarrow{\;O_2\;}$ urate$^-$ + H^+
Sulfur-containing amino acids	Methionine $\xrightarrow{\;O_2\;}$ urea + CO_2 + H_2O + $SO_4^=$ + 2 H^+
Hydroxyapatite formation	$10Ca^{++} + 4.8HPO_4^= + 1.2H_2PO_4^- + H_2O \rightarrow (Ca_3(PO_4)_2)_3 \cdot Ca(OH)_2 + 9.2\ H^+$
2. Dietary Intake of Preformed or Potential Acid or Alkali	
Phosphoproteins	Phosphoserine $\xrightarrow[\text{at pH 7.4}]{H_2O}$ ROH + $\dfrac{0.8\ HPO_4^=}{0.2\ H_2PO_4^-}$ + 1.8 H^+
Phospholipids	Lecithin $\xrightarrow[\text{at pH 7.4}]{H_2O}$ ROH + $\dfrac{0.8\ HPO_4^=}{0.2\ H_2PO_4^-}$ + 1.8 H^2
Metabolizable cations (NH_4Cl, arginine—HCl, etc.)	R—NH_2^+ Cl^- $\xrightarrow{\;O_2\;}$ urea + CO_2 + Cl^- + H^+
Metabolizable anions (K^+ citrate, Na^+ lactate, etc.)	R—COO^- K^+ $\xrightarrow{\;O_2\;}$ urea + CO_2 + K^+ + HCO_3^-
3. Fecal loss of Actual or Potential Alkali	Fecal loss of K^+ HCO_3^- or of K^+ acetate$^-$, propionate$^-$, butyrate$^-$, etc.

*Modified from Harrington, J.T., and Lemann, J., Jr.: The metabolic production and disposal of acid and alkali. Med. Clin. North Am. 54:1543, 1970.

ciated with the release of nonvolatile acid. These sources of nonvolatile acid give rise to 1 to 2 mEq/kg/day of H^+ in the infant and younger child that must be excreted by the kidney. From infancy to adolescence, the proportion of the total nonvolatile acid production due to bone formation diminishes and the proportion due to dietary intake and sulfur amino acid catabolism increases.

This need to excrete the nonvolatile acids formed by metabolism cannot be met by the lung and must be performed by the kidney. First the kidney has to reclaim the continuously filtered plasma bicarbonate before net acid can be excreted. This amounts to 4500 mEq/day of HCO_3^- that must be restored to the plasma to prevent severe depletion of body buffer stores. The bulk of this filtered HCO_3^- is reabsorbed in the proximal tubule. However, HCO_3^- is not reabsorbed as such directly, but by a process that involves the secretion of H^+ (Fig. 3–1). Sodium bicarbonate enters the lumen of the proximal tubule, where Na^+ is driven into the renal tubule cell by a favorable electrochemical gradient in exchange for H^+. There H^+ combines with HCO_3^- in the lumen to form H_2CO_3, which is dehydrated by carbonic anhydrase situated on the luminal membrane of the proximal tubule cell. The resulting CO_2 produced by the dehydration of H_2CO_3 diffuses freely into the cytosol, where it is rehydrated into H_2CO_3 by a cytosolic carbonic anhydrase. The H_2CO_3 formed dissociates again into H^+ and HCO_3^-. The HCO_3^- thus formed accompanies the previously reabsorbed Na^+ as it is actively extruded across the basolateral membrane by the enzyme Na^+, K^+-ATPase. The H^+ formed is then available again for secretion into the lumen for reclamation of more filtered HCO_3^-. By this mechanism, the proximal convoluted tubule can reabsorb 80 to 90 per cent of the filtered $NaHCO_3$, yet net secretion of H^+ does not occur in this segment. Recently, it has been shown that the pars recta of the proximal tubule is capable of reabsorbing $NaHCO_3$ directly and may account for 10 to 15 per cent of the total $NaHCO_3$ reabsorbed, since only 1 to 5 per cent of the filtered load of $NaHCO_3$ is presented to the distal tubule.

Several factors act to alter HCO_3^- reabsorption by the proximal tubule. One of the major factors influencing renal HCO_3 handling is pCO_2. With a rise in pCO_2, enhanced proximal HCO_3^- reabsorption occurs, raising the plasma HCO_3^- concentration, and with a fall in pCO_2 the converse occurs. This alteration in HCO_3^- reabsorption is related to change in pCO_2 and not to a change in extracellular pH. Evidence for this comes from infusion of HCO_3^- to normalize serum pH in the

PROXIMAL TUBULE

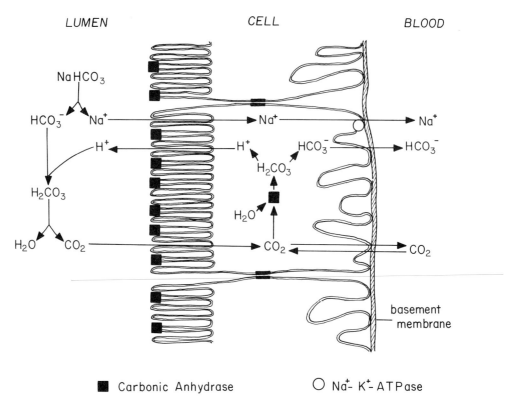

Figure 3–1 Bicarbonate reclamation in the proximal tubule.

face of a raised pCO_2, which still leads to enhanced HCO_3^- reabsorption proximally. A change in intracellular pH may mediate this alteration in HCO_3^- handling related to pCO_2, since intracellular pH is a function of intracellular HCO_3^- and pCO_2.

Potassium and phosphate may also exert their effect on proximal HCO_3^- reabsorption via alterations in intracellular pH. Potassium deficiency leads to intracellular acidosis and enhanced proximal HCO_3^- reabsorption. Phosphate depletion is associated with depressed proximal HCO_3^- reabsorption and raised intracellular pH. Phosphate excess, as occurs in hypoparathyroidism, can lead to an augmented HCO_3^- reabsorption and metabolic alkalosis, which may be related to a fall in intracellular pH.

Parathyroid hormone also influences proximal HCO_3^- handling. Hyperparathyroidism occasionally is associated with a metabolic acidosis. Infusion of parathyroid hormone has been shown to depress proximal HCO_3^- reabsorption. Parathyroid hormone acts directly on adenyl cyclase to raise the concentration of adenosine 3′,5′-cyclic monophosphate (cyclic AMP) inside the proximal renal tubule cell, which may, in turn, exert an effect on HCO_3^- reabsorption. Parathyroid hormone also increases serum calcium and lowers serum phosphate, which, in turn, may also affect HCO_3^- reabsorption.

Extracellular fluid volume, more specifically effective arterial blood volume, can also alter proximal HCO_3^- reabsorption. A variety of solutes, such as glucose, amino acids, and phosphate, but particularly sodium salts, are transported by active processes from the proximal tubule lumen into the lateral intercellular spaces (Fig. 3–2). This establishes an osmotic gradient for the reabsorption of water from the lumen through the "tight" junctions. The fluid and solute now present in the intercellular spaces can either enter the peritubular capillaries and effect net reabsorption or leak back into the proximal tubule lumen, depending on the balance of the Starling forces.

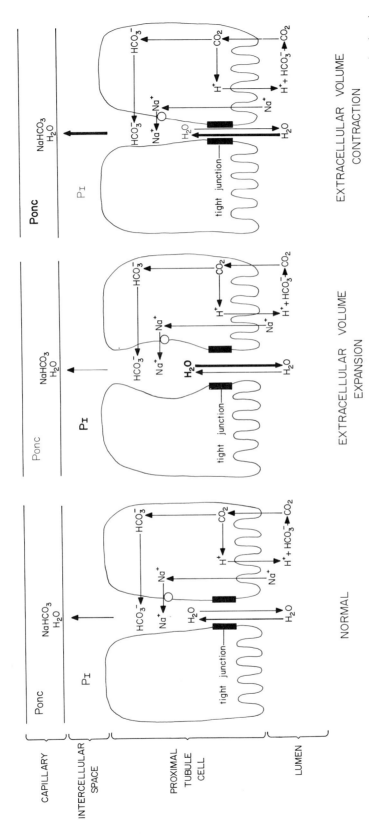

Figure 3–2 Influence of the state of the extracellular volume on sodium bicarbonate and water reabsorption in the proximal tubule. With extracellular volume expansion there is an increase in intercellular hydrostatic pressure (Pi) and a decrease in peritubular capillary oncotic pressure (P_{onc}) such that there is an increase in the backleak of water and sodium bicarbonate into the proximal tubule lumen. With extracellular volume contraction there is an increase in peritubular capillary oncotic pressure and a decrease in intercellular hydrostatic pressure such that there is a decrease in backleak and an increase in sodium bicarbonate and water reabsorption.

51

DISTAL TUBULE

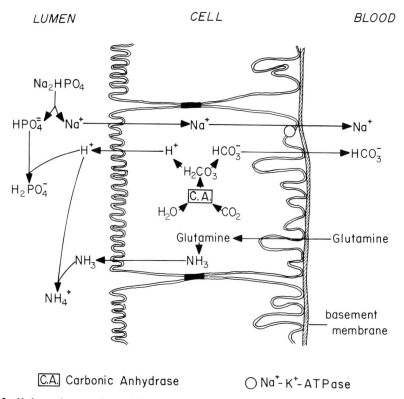

C.A. Carbonic Anhydrase   ○ Na$^+$-K$^+$-ATPase

Figure 3–3   Hydrogen ion secretion and bicarbonate generation in the distal tubule. Hydrogen ion is excreted in conjunction with the urinary buffers NH_3 and $HPO_4^=$.

During extracellular volume contraction there is an increase in the plasma protein concentration from hemoconcentration. In addition, there is a greater fall in the renal plasma flow than in the glomerular filtration rate, resulting in an increase in the filtration fraction (that fraction of plasma delivered to the kidney that enters the proximal tubule). Since the plasma proteins do not traverse the glomerular membrane, they remain in the postglomerular plasma entering the peritubular capillaries. An increase in the filtration fraction will increase the plasma leaving the glomerular capillaries, further concentrating the plasma proteins. This leads to increased peritubular capillary oncotic pressure and enhanced fluid uptake from the intercellular space. Increased fluid uptake will also enhance solute uptake because of solvent drag. The opposite set of events occurs during extracellular volume expansion. With diminished peritubular capillary oncotic pressure, less fluid is taken up from the intercellular spaces, and the interstitial hydrostatic pressure will increase, leading to the backleak of fluid and solute through the tight junctions and into the proximal tubule lumen. The net effect is to diminish fluid and solute (such as $NaHCO_3$) reabsorption from the proximal tubule.

In the distal and collecting tubules, the final 1 to 5 per cent of filtered bicarbonate is reabsorbed, permitting net H^+ ion secretion to occur, resulting in a fall in urine pH below 5.5. This fall in pH permits the titration of the major urinary buffers—$HPO_4^=$ and NH_3—and the excretion of the nonvolatile acid load. The presumed mechanism of H^+ secretion in the distal tubule is shown in Figure 3–3. Here, cytosolic carbonic anhydrase combines CO_2 and H_2O, forming H_2CO_3 that rapidly decomposes into H^+ and HCO_3^-. The newly formed hydrogen ion is then secreted into the lumen in exchange for Na$^+$. This exchange of H^+ and Na$^+$ may not be direct exchange, but is probably only "loosely coupled" by the need to maintain electroneutrality. However, Na$^+$ delivery to the distal tubule is necessary for H^+ secretion. Again, as in the proximal tubule, the secreted H^+

combines with HCO_3^- to form H_2CO_3. However, in the distal tubule, there is no carbonic anhydrase associated with the luminal membrane to facilitate rapid equilibration of H_2CO_3 and CO_2. Because of this, the urine is slightly more acid than it would be if H_2CO_3 and CO_2 were in equilibration. This difference is termed the "disequilibrium pH." In spite of the lack of luminal membrane carbonic anhydrase, the final 1 to 5 per cent of the filtered HCO_3 is reabsorbed in the distal tubule from H^+ secretion. However, the bicarbonate reabsorptive capacity of the distal tubule is limited in comparison with that of the proximal.

With complete reabsorption of HCO_3^-, further secretion of H^+ allows the distal luminal pH to fall. In contrast to the proximal tubule, the distal tubule and collecting duct can effectively lower the urine pH to 4.5, which represents a 1000-fold increase in the H^+ ion concentration over the blood. This occurs because the distal tubule and collecting duct can secrete H^+ against a gradient and these nephron segments have "nonleaky" tight junctions between cells, permitting maintenance of this 1000-fold concentration gradient. Also, these tight junctions allow the maintenance of the large potential difference, with the lumen negative, facilitating H^+ secretion into the lumen.

Other Factors in Renal Acidification

The generation of the hydrogen ion gradient is not only dependent on the complete reabsorption of HCO_3^-, an intact H^+ secretory mechanism, and "nonleaky" tight junctions, but it is also dependent on the delivery of sodium to the distal tubule, the "avidity" of the distal tubule for sodium, and the presence of aldosterone. The importance of sodium delivery and the "avidity" of the distal tubule for sodium reabsorption was clearly demonstrated by De Sousa et al. (1974). These investigators administered equimolar amounts of H^+ chronically as HCl, H_2SO_4, or HNO_3. They found that after two weeks the serum HCO_3^- level was the lowest in those dogs given HCl, while those given a comparable amount of H^+ as HNO_3 had normal serum HCO_3^- concentrations. Dogs given H_2SO_4 had intermediate levels.

The explanation for these findings involves first the delivery of sodium to sites of Na^+–H^+ exchange in the distal tubule and second the avidity of this nephron segment for sodium reabsorption. Little sulfate and even less nitrate are absorbed proximally, and therefore both easily pass into the distal tubule in the company of sodium. Initially, the distal tubule is unable to conserve this increased sodium delivery fully and sodium excretion rises. With the continued loss of sodium, the avidity of the distal tubule for sodium reabsorption in exchange for H^+ excretion increases and allows removal of the exogenous acid load. With administration of HCl, the permeant anion, Cl^-, is easily reabsorbed proximally and does not allow the necessary increment in distal sodium delivery. Only after significant chloride retention does sufficient distal sodium delivery occur. By this time a state of severe metabolic acidosis has developed.

Another important observation from this study is the relative unimportance of systemic pH for acidification of the urine. After two weeks of acid administration in these dogs, all three groups were excreting similar amounts of urinary acid, but systemic pH varied from normal to low. Schwartz and Cohen have gone so far as to postulate that the regulation of renal acidification is not related to changes in systemic pH but rather to changes in distal tubular sodium handling. Whether their formulation is correct or not, it is clear that the kidney increases acid excretion with an increased acid load even if only indirectly.

In addition to distal sodium delivery, aldosterone appears necessary for the excretion of acid. Deficiency of aldosterone leads to metabolic acidosis from impaired hydrogen ion secretion in the distal portions of the nephron. It appears from experimental evidence using isolated perfused cortical collecting tubules that aldosterone is necessary for the development of large negative transtubular potential differences in the distal portions of the nephron. These potential differences would facilitate H^+ secretion and may explain the acidosis associated with aldosterone deficiency.

In spite of this 1000-fold increase in luminal H^+ concentration, only trivial amounts of acid would be excreted if this were the only mechanism for urinary acid excretion. With a urine pH of 4.5 only 0.00006 mEq of H^+ is excreted in 1½ liters of urine without buffer. This would lead to a severe acidosis, since about 50 to 80 meq/day of H^+ is generated from a normal diet. However, urine does contain several buffers, which permit the excretion of large amounts of H^+ without requiring the pH to fall below 4.4. One group of these urinary buffers requires the urine pH to fall below 6 for their titration with H^+. Hydrogen ion excretion by these buffers has been termed "titratable acidity." The major urinary buffer in this group is $HPO_4^=$ with a pK_a of 6.8, which is rapidly converted to $H_2PO_4^-$ when the urine pH descends below 6. Others, although of lesser importance, are creatinine with a pK_a of 4.97 and β-hydroxybutyrate with a pK_a of 4.7. Not surprisingly, during diabetic ketoacidosis when large amounts of β-hydroxybutyrate are excreted in the urine, β-hydroxybutyrate accounts for a large fraction of the H^+ excreted. The amount of H^+ excreted in association with these buffers, the "titratable acidity," is equal to the amount of alkali necessary to titrate the urine pH back to 7.4.

The major vehicle of acid excretion by the kidney is ammonia. The pK_b* for the formation of the ammonium ion (NH_4^+) from ammonia is 9.4. Thus, at physiologic pH over 99 percent of the ammonia formed would be protonated. The other important feature of ammonia as a urinary buffer is that the nonionized form (NH_3) is freely diffusible across cell membranes, while the ionized form (NH_4^+) is not. Therefore, the highly diffusible NH_3 can move from basic areas to be trapped in relatively acidic areas as NH_4^+. This would allow more NH_3 to be formed in basic areas, which could then be trapped in more acidic regions. Thus, the distribution of the ammonium ion among blood, cell, and tubular fluid depends on the relative pH of each compartment. As the urine pH falls, increasing amounts of ammonia can be trapped as NH_4^+, facilitating H^+ excretion.

Ammonia for acidification is formed from amino acid precursors, mainly glutamine, in both the proximal and distal tubules. While ammonia is not formed in the medulla, the loop of Henle may have an important role to play in ammonia excretion. Ammonia that is made in the proximal tubule cell diffuses into the lumen where it is trapped in the proximal tubule fluid, which is relatively acidic (7.0 to 6.6) from the reabsorption of the bulk of the filtered HCO_3^-. The proximal tubule fluid then enters the descending limb of the loop of Henle where the tubule fluid is slightly alkalinized by the removal of H_2O, which concentrates the HCO_3^- that has escaped reabsorption in the proximal tubule. This relative alkalinization shifts the NH_4^+/NH_3 equilibrium slightly towards NH_3, which freely diffuses throughout the medulla and is trapped in the acidic fluid of the collecting tubule. This allows more NH_4^+ to become NH_3 in the descending limb for further entrapment in the collecting tubule. In this manner, proximal tubule ammonia production adds to the final excretion of hydrogen ion.

As mentioned earlier, glutamine is the major precursor of urinary ammonia, accounting for two-thirds of the total excreted. Glycine, alanine, and glutamic acid add a smaller but still significant amount, and preformed arterial ammonia accounts for just over a quarter of the excreted ammonia. The formation of ammonia from glutamine occurs by means of several metabolic pathways, as shown in Figure 3–4.

The major pathway for ammoniagenesis from glutamine occurs intramitochondrially. Glutamine entering the inner mitochondrial matrix is deaminated by glutaminase I, which is activated by phosphate (thus the name phosphate-dependent glutaminase), to glutamate and NH_3. The resulting glutamate is deaminated by glutamate dehydrogenase to α-ketoglutarate and NH_3. This reaction appears to be at equilibrium in vivo, and therefore removal of the products would be important for cycling further glutamate through this enzyme step. Alpha-ketoglutarate can be removed by either oxidizing it to CO_2 and H_2O or by formation of glucose via the cytosolic gluconeogenic pathway. This major pathway allows the formation of two moles of NH_3 for each mole of glutamine.

Several minor pathways for ammoniagenesis have also been described. One of these involves the transamination of α-ketoglutarate back to glutamate with its subsequent deamination via glutamate dehydrogenase. This would allow the formation of NH_3 from the nitrogen of other amino acids. Glutamine can be transaminated in the cytosol by glutamine keto-acid aminotransferase to α-

---

*The pK_b is the negative logarithm of the base dissociation constant. A buffer is half protonated when the pH of a solution equals the pK_b. At a pH lower than the pK_b, a greater proportion of the buffer is protonated.

AMMONIAGENESIS IN THE NEPHRON

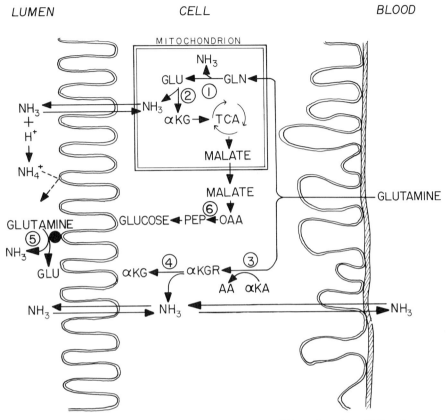

Figure 3–4 Ammoniagenesis in the nephron. Abbreviations: GLN, glutamine; GLU, glutamate; αKG, α-ketoglutarate; αKGR, α-ketoglutaramate; OAA, oxaloacetate; PEP, phosphoenolpyruvate; αKA, α-ketoacid; AA, amino acid; TCA, tricarboxylic acid cycle. Enzymes: (*1*) glutaminase I; (*2*) glutamate dehydrogenase; (*3*) glutamine ketoacid transaminase; (*4*) ω-amidase; (*5*) λ-glutamyltranspeptidase; (*6*) phosphoenolypyruvate carboxykinase.

ketoglutaramate with subsequent deamidation by ω-amidase. Glutamine can also be acted on by the phosphate-independent glutaminase, which probably reflects the glutaminase activity of γ-glutamyl-transpeptidase, to form one mole of NH_3 for each mole of glutamine.

The remarkable feature of the ammonia urinary buffer system is the response, in terms of ammonia excretion, by the body to various signals. Plasma (and probably more importantly intracellular) potassium and hydrogen ion concentrations are the two major factors controlling ammonia formation. Urinary ammonia excretion correlates inversely with the plasma potassium concentration and pH. This can amount to as much as a tenfold increase in ammonia excretion with a concomitant increase in hydrogen ion excretion. Increased ammonia excretion during acidosis is due, in part, to increased trapping of NH_3 as NH_4^+ from the augmented H^+ excretion but also to increased formation of NH_3.

Several sites have been proposed as the locus controlling this increased formation of NH_3, but the precise regulatory step is not yet known. It is clear that plasma glutamine, which is continuously replenished by muscle, and its entry in the renal tubule cell are not rate limiting. Mitochondrial uptake is increased with the onset of acidosis, and this may play a role in augmenting ammonia production. However, it is not clear whether this increased glutamine uptake is related, in part or entirely, to glutamine metabolism and not solely to mitochondrial transport. Glutaminase I activity in vitro under optimal conditions has been shown to increase in the rat with acidosis, but increased ammoniagenesis can be demonstrated prior to increased enzymatic activity, and increased ammoniagenesis occurs in the dog without any demonstrable increase in glutaminase I. However, in vivo modification of glutaminase I activity by such substances as phosphate, H^+, and glutamate may occur and may not be detected by in vitro techniques.

Glutamate dehydrogenase activity also rises in rats with acidosis but, like glutaminase I, it does not rise in dogs. The products of this reaction, NH_3 and α-ketoglutarate, are at nearly equilibrium levels, so that their removal would increase flux through this pathway. Acidification of the urine, as occurs in acidosis, would facilitate ammonia trapping and its removal from the mitochondria. Alpha-ketoglutarate can either be oxidized to CO_2 and H_2O or converted to glucose via gluconeogenesis. A critical enzymatic step for either fate of α-ketoglutarate is the formation of phosphoenolpyruvate by phosphoenolpyruvate carboxykinase. Increased glucose production during acidosis has been demonstrated and inhibition of phosphoenolpyruvate carboxykinase has abolished enhanced ammonia formation in acidotic rats, implying that this may be an important regulatory site. However, enhanced ammonia production by isolated mitochondria from acidotic rats suggests that this is not the sole regulatory step.

In summary, the kidney maintains acid-base balance by first reclaiming filtered bicarbonate in the proximal tubule via H^+ secretion. The magnitude of this process is modulated by the state of the extracellular volume, serum potassium, and pCO_2. Hydrogen ion secretion proximally does not result in net secretion, since all the H^+ is used to reclaim HCO_3^-. Net hydrogen ion secretion does occur distally and is used to titrate the urinary buffers NH_3 and $HPO_4^=$ by increasing the urine hydrogen ion concentration 1000-fold. Distal hydrogen ion secretion is influenced by sodium delivery, potassium concentration, and aldosterone secretion from the adrenal cortex. The other major urinary buffer is ammonia, which accounts for the bulk of H^+ secretion during chronic acidosis. Urinary ammonia excretion is influenced by the urine pH, plasma potassium concentration, and plasma pH.

CLINICAL DISORDERS OF ACID-BASE BALANCE

As mentioned previously, there are four primary acid-base disturbances. If the primary abnormality in pH is due to an alteration in pCO_2, then the disturbance is classified as respiratory, whereas if the primary abnormality is due to an alteration in plasma HCO_3^-, then the disturbance is labeled as metabolic. Besides the initial buffering done by bicarbonate and proteins, both of these primary acid-base disturbances call into play a secondary set of mechanisms, termed compensation, that tend to minimize the shift in pH. However, these compensatory mechanisms cannot normalize the pH. With any primary disturbance in pCO_2, the compensatory mechanism is a secondary change in the renal handling of HCO_3^- and the excretion of acid and ammonia that will tend to normalize the blood pH. With any primary alteration in HCO_3^- concentration, a secondary change in the pulmonary excretion of CO_2 will occur, again tending to normalize the blood pH. Thus, the lungs compensate for metabolic disturbances and the kidneys compensate for respiratory disturbances. However, respiratory compensation occurs much more rapidly than renal compensation.

Metabolic Acidosis

Metabolic acidosis can be divided into two major categories based on the anion gap or delta. The anion gap is the difference between the sum of the plasma Na^+ and K^+ concentrations and the sum of the plasma Cl^- and HCO_3^-. Since K^+ varies only slightly compared with the other ions, the anion gap is expressed as:

$$A.G. = ([Na^+]) - ([Cl^-] + [HCO_3^-])$$

which is usually 12 ± 4 mEq/l. Actually, because the law of electroneutrality must be satisfied, there is not a true gap between cations and anions but only an apparent one, because certain anions are not routinely measured. A large portion of this gap is made up by the negative charges on plasma proteins, with a lesser portion from phosphate, sulfate, and organic anions.

Increased anion gap or delta acidosis occurs with the gain by the body of strong organic acids. A raised anion gap may in certain clinical settings be the only clue to the presence of an organic acidemia. These strong acids titrate body buffers, leading to a fall in plasma bicarbonate that is replaced by the anion of the acid. The classic example of this type of acidosis is diabetic ketoacidosis. In diabetic ketoacidosis, the ketone bodies, acetoacetic and β-hydroxybutyric acid formed from the incomplete oxidation of fat, rapidly dissociate at body pH. This leads to the titration of $NaHCO_3$ to H_2CO_3, then to CO_2, which is eliminated by the lungs, leaving behind the sodium salt of these two ketoacids. The net result of this is a fall in plasma HCO_3^- concentration that is replaced by the anions of the ketoacids. This, in turn, raises the apparent anion gap, since the sodium and chloride concentrations are unchanged.

Table 3–2 lists the major diseases associated with a raised anion-gap acidosis. Many of these illnesses are caused by inborn errors of metabolism leading to the generation of strong organic acids. Diarrhea in infancy typically leads to anion-gap acidosis from starvation ketosis, formation of strong organic acids by bacteria in the gastrointestinal tract acting on undigested food, and decreased acid excretion by kidney due to dehydration. Renal failure causes anion-gap acidosis from retention of phosphate and sulfate anions and an inability to excrete the daily acid load from the diet. This usually does not occur until the glomerular filtration rate has fallen to a quarter of normal. The major cause of the diminished H^+ ion excretion is related to reduced ammonium ion excretion. This is not from diminished ammonia trapping, since an acid urine can usually be elaborated, except in some forms of interstitial renal disease. Reduced ammonium ion excretion appears to arise from diminished production from a reduced functioning nephron mass, although individual functioning nephrons are synthesizing ammonia maximally. Uremic acidosis is usually associated with a fall in serum HCO_3^- to 12 to 16 mEq/1, without further diminution thereafter. This probably occurs because bone salts buffer a significant portion of the daily acid production. Thus, there is a "trade-off" of progressive acidemia for renal osteodystrophy as proposed by Bricker (see Chapter 14).

Several poisons can lead to raised anion-gap acidosis. Of these, salicylates are probably the most common offenders in the pediatric age group. The raised anion gap is related mainly to increased organic acid production, especially ketone bodies, from an altered metabolism due to the salicylates. Part of the raised anion gap may also be due to the salicylate anion itself in severe

Table 3–2 CAUSES OF A RAISED ANION-GAP ACIDOSIS	Table 3–3 CAUSES OF NORMAL ANION-GAP ACIDOSIS
Shock	Renal tubular acidosis
Diabetes Mellitus	Diarrhea—older children and adults
Renal Failure	Enterostomies
Diarrhea of Infancy	Pancreatic fistula
Inborn Errors of Metabolism	Cholestyramine
Maple syrup urine disease	Hyperalimentation
Propionic acidemia	Synthetic diets
Methylmalonic acidemias	Ureterosigmoidostomy
Isovaleric acidemia	Sulfamylon
β-Methylcrotonic aciduria	Acidifying agents
Glutaric aciduria	$CaCl_2$
Pyruvate dehydrogenase deficiency	NH_4Cl
Pyruvate carboxylase deficiency	Arginine HCl
Glycogen storage disease, Type I	Lysine HCl
Pyroglutamic aciduria	
Poisonings	
Salicylates	
Ethanol	
Methanol	
Ethylene Glycol	

poisonings. The alcohols, methanol, ethanol, and ethylene glycol, can cause an anion gap acidosis by altering intermediary metabolism, leading to the formation of lactic acid and ketone bodies. Metabolism of methanol to formic acid and ethylene glycol to oxalic and glyoxalic acid also accounts for a significant fraction of the acid load.

The other major category of metabolic acidosis is nondelta or normal anion-gap acidosis. In this form of metabolic acidosis, the reduced plasma HCO_3^- concentration is balanced by a raised Cl^- concentration leading to hyperchloremia. Table 3–3 lists the major causes of this form of metabolic acidosis. Gastrointestinal bicarbonate loss from diarrhea in the older child or adult or pancreatic fistula can produce this type of acidosis. The accompanying volume contraction will give rise to an enhanced NaCl reabsorption by the kidney and hyperchloremia. Large doses of $CaCl_2$ can lead to hyperchloremic metabolic acidosis by intraluminal formation of insoluble calcium salts with intestinally secreted HCO_3^-, leading to depletion of plasma HCO_3^-. Chloride ion is absorbed, generating hyperchloremia. Cholestyramine can also cause nondelta acidosis in a somewhat similar fashion. Other acidifying salts, such as NH_4Cl, arginine HCl, and lysine HCl, yield HCl upon catabolism of the cationic portion of the molecule. In a similar manner, hyperalimentation solutions can lead to a normal anion-gap acidosis from the catabolism of the hydrochloride salts of the basic amino acids. Nondelta acidosis has also been observed in infants fed synthetic amino acid diets for the treatment of inborn errors of metabolism. Synthetic diets can contain an excess of inorganic anions over inorganic cations and therefore a net excess of organic or unmeasured cations over organic or unmeasured anions. Catabolism of these organic ions will generate more H^+ than HCO_3^-, leading to acidosis.

Another major cause of hyperchloremic metabolic acidosis is renal tubular acidosis (RTA). Renal tubular acidosis can also be divided into two major types based on whether the defect is primarily bicarbonate wastage or defective acid secretion. In distal RTA, or Type I, the distal nephron is unable to generate a large hydrogen ion gradient, which is manifested clinically by the inability to lower the urine pH below 6. This leads to ineffective titration of urinary buffers and ultimately to retention of the endogenous acid load with consequent systemic acidosis. Some of the causes of distal RTA can be seen in Table 3–4. Idiopathic distal RTA can be genetically transmitted

Table 3–4 CAUSES OF DISTAL RENAL TUBULAR ACIDOSIS	Table 3–5 CAUSES OF PROXIMAL RENAL ACIDOSIS
Sporadic	Transient
Hereditary	Idiopathic or genetically transmitted
Sickle cell anemia	Acetazolamide
Ehlers-Danlos syndrome	Sulfanilamide
Medullary cystic disease	Leigh's encephalopathy
Carbonic anhydrase B defect	Fanconi syndrome
Sjögren's syndrome	Idiopathic
Systemic lupus erythematosus	Hereditary
Hypergammaglobulinemia	Cystinosis
Amphotericin B	Tyrosinemia
Chronic pyelonephritis	Galactosemia
Hydronephrosis	Glycogen storage disease
Secondary to nephrocalcinosis	Hereditary fructose intolerance
Idiopathic	Lowe's syndrome
Hyperthyroidism	Wilson's disease
Hyperparathyroidism	Outdated tetracycline
Vitamin D intoxication	Heavy metal poisoning
Hereditary fructose intolerance	Multiple myeloma
Wilson's disease	Renal transplantation
Fabry's disease	Vitamin D deficiency
Medullary sponge kidney	Cytochrome c oxidase deficiency
	Metachromatic leukodystrophy

or can occur sporadically. It may also occur in association with autoimmune diseases such as Sjö-gren's syndrome and systemic lupus erythematosus, or with interstitital renal diseases, such as occurs with medullary sponge kidney, hydronephrosis, and pyelonephritis. Nephrocalcinosis from idiopathic hypercalciuria, hyperparathyroidism, vitamin D intoxication, and hyperthyroidism can also give rise to distal RTA. Conversely, nephrocalcinosis itself can be a sequela of chronic un-treated distal RTA from hypercalciuria and decreased urinary citrate. Amphotericin B, an antifungal agent, causes a reversible distal RTA probably by increasing the permeability of the distal nephron membrane to cations, allowing secreted H^+ to "leak back" into the distal tubule cell.

The other major form of RTA is proximal, or type II, and is the result of a defect in the reabsorption of bicarbonate in the proximal nephron. Because of this reabsorptive defect, large amounts of unabsorbed bicarbonate flood the distal nephron, where the low bicarbonate reabsorptive capacity of the distal nephron is overwhelmed, leading to the excretion of a bicarbonate-rich urine. This results in a fall in plasma bicarbonate and extracellular volume contraction. The volume con-traction then leads to a stimulation of proximal bicarbonate reabsorption. A new balance is achieved at which the now reduced filtered bicarbonate load (from the reduced plasma bicarbonate concentra-tion) can be handled by the defective proximal tubule under the stimulus for bicarbonate reabsorp-tion of extracellular volume concentration. At this point, the plasma bicarbonate no longer falls and an acid urine can be elaborated.

Causes of proximal RTA are listed in Table 3–5. Idiopathic proximal RTA, like idiopathic distal RTA, can be sporadic or familial. Drugs that inhibit carbonic anhydrase, such as acetazol-amide and sulfanilamide, can cause proximal RTA, since both membrane and cytosolic carbonic anhydrase are important for proximal bicarbonate reabsorption, as seen in Figure 3–1. Proximal RTA often occurs in association with a generalized proximal tubule dysfunction, the Fanconi syn-drome (see Chapter 23). In childhood, the Fanconi syndrome is often associated with inborn errors of metabolism, such as galactosemia, hereditary fructose intolerance, tyrosinemia, cystinosis, Wil-son's disease, and a rare type of glycogen storage disease.* In several of these diseases—galactosemia, hereditary fructose intolerance, tyrosinemia, and Wilson's disease—abstinence from the offending sugar or amino acid or treatment by chelation of excess copper will ameliorate the proximal tubule dysfunction. Hyperparathyroidism, both primary and secondary, can cause a mild defect in bicarbonate reabsorption in association with phosphaturia and aminoaciduria. Toxins, such as outdated tetracycline, streptozotocin, and heavy metals, can cause proximal RTA in association with the Fanconi syndrome. Other causes of the Fanconi syndrome are multiple myeloma, tubulointerstitial nephritis, nephrotic syndrome, amyloidosis, and renal transplantation.

Metabolic Alkalosis

Metabolic alkalosis occurs when there is a net gain of alkali or loss of acid. This leads to a rise in the serum bicarbonate concentration and pH. In metabolic alkalosis, as in metabolic acidosis, there is a measure of respiratory compensation in response to the change in pH. This is accom-plished by alveolar hypoventilation, but this response is limited, owing to the overriding need to maintain an adequate pO_2. Usually the pCO_2 will not rise above 50 to 55 Torr in spite of severe alkalosis.

Metabolic alkalosis can be divided into two major categories based on the urinary chloride concentration. In the first category, the urine Cl^- is less than 10 mEq/l, and the metabolic alkalosis is responsive to volume expansion with a saline infusion. The classic example of this type is pyloric

---

*The enzymatic defect in patients with glycogen storage disease who develop the Fanconi syndrome has not been identified. These rare cases do not belong to the known types of glycogen storage disease, especially not to type I (glucose-6-phosphatase deficiency). Such patients are characterized by a severe glycosuria in addition to a massive hyperaminoaciduria with phosphaturia and bicarbonaturia. "Renal glucose-losing" syndrome has been applied to these patients by Brodehl et al. (The Fanconi syndrome in hepato-renal glycogen storage disease. *In* Peters, G., and Roch-Ramel, F. (eds.): Progress in Nephrology. Springer, Berlin, 1969, p. 241).

Table 3–6 CAUSES OF
SALINE-RESPONSIVE
METABOLIC ALKALOSIS

Pyloric stenosis
Vomiting
Upper GI suction
Congenital chloride diarrhea
Laxative abuse
Diuretic abuse
Cystic fibrosis
Chloride-deficient formulas in infants
Posthypercapnea syndrome
Poorly reabsorbable anion administration
Post-treatment of organic acidemias

stenosis, in which persistent vomiting with loss of HCl and fluid generates a rise in plasma HCO_3^- and extracellular volume contraction. This extracellular volume contraction stimulates proximal bicarbonate reabsorption, maintaining the raised plasma bicarbonate concentration despite the increased filtered load. Hypokalemia develops as an increased exchange of Na^+ for K^+ occurs in the distal nephron under the influence of increased aldosterone secretion in response to volume contraction. The development of hypokalemia exacerbates the alkalosis by inducing an exchange of intracellular K^+ for extracellular H^+ and an increased H^+ for Na^+ exchange in the distal nephron. This gives rise to the "paradoxical aciduria" in the face of systemic alkalosis. Treatment of this form of metabolic alkalosis is aimed at correcting the volume contraction with the infusion of saline, which will allow the excretion of the excess bicarbonate, normalizing the plasma pH.

Other causes of saline-responsive metabolic alkalosis are listed in Table 3–6. Besides gastric fluid loss, excessive diuretic use will lead to metabolic alkalosis through the development of volume contraction from NaCl losses and hypokalemia from KCl losses. The urine chloride in this situation will be high while the diuretic is present and then will fall when the drug is stopped. The alkalosis will persist in spite of stopping the diuretic until the extracellular volume and potassium losses are restored.

Other causes of saline-responsive metabolic alkalosis are administration of poorly reabsorbable anions, posthypercapnea, and post-treatment of organic acidemias. Poorly reabsorbable anions in large quantities, such as carbenicillin, penicillin, and sulfate, can cause metabolic alkalosis by increasing the luminal negativity of the distal tubule, facilitating urinary acidification and potassium excretion, especially in the dehydrated patient. Rapid correction of chronic respiratory acidosis, i.e., placing a patient on a ventilator, will lead to metabolic alkalosis, since the serum bicarbonate concentration is high as a consequence of renal compensation. Further, these patients are often volume contracted and potassium depleted, especially if they have received diuretics. Primary treatment of certain organic acidemias, such as diabetic ketoacidosis, can result in an "overshoot" alkalosis. Administration of insulin in ketoacidosis will lead to catabolism of the ketone bodies to HCO_3^- which can cause an alkalosis, especially when exogenous bicarbonate has been given.

Three forms of saline-responsive, low urinary chloride metabolic alkalosis that are unique to pediatrics are found in cystic fibrosis, in the feeding of a chloride-deficient formula, and in congenital chloride diarrhea. Sweat from children with cystic fibrosis contains a concentration of NaCl that approaches normal saline. With sweating, large electrolyte and significant volume contraction can occur, leading to enhanced proximal tubule bicarbonate reabsorption. From this increased proximal bicarbonate reabsorption, metabolic alkalosis ensues, which is responsive to saline replacement.

Recently, some infant formula manufacturers have reduced the sodium chloride content of their formulas because of concern over giving more salt than necessary to young infants. This has resulted in very low chloride concentrations in some of these formulas. In conjunction with this change in manufacturing, several infants have developed a significant metabolic alkalosis with very low urine chloride concentrations. The causative factor in these infants appears to be this chloride-deficient formula, although in some, vomiting may have also played a role.

Congenital chloride diarrhea is a rare syndrome, and its hallmark is a watery, acid diarrhea from birth. The diarrhea appears to stem from a defect in the normal absorption of chloride from the ileal lumen in exchange for bicarbonate. Sodium exchange for hydrogen ion proceeds normally, generating an alkalosis. Chronic chloride losses lead to volume contraction, maintaining the raised serum bicarbonate concentration.

The second type of metabolic alkalosis is unresponsive to saline and is associated with a high urine chloride and hypertension. In most of the causes in this form of metabolic alkalosis mineralocorticoid excess plays a central role in the generation of the acid-base disturbances. Primary aldosteronism is the classic example, in which persistently elevated secretion leads to increased NaCl reabsorption and volume expansion. Nonetheless, this volume expansion does not increase unrelentingly. Soon, other mechanisms, such as "third factor" (naturetic factor), lead to proximal sodium rejection, which floods the distal tubule with sodium salts. Here, the exchange of luminal Na^+ for intracellular K^+ and H^+, under the influence of the elevated aldosterone levels, generates an alkalosis. This especially occurs when potassium intake is limited. The resulting hypokalemia enhances proximal $NaHCO_3$ reabsorption, maintaining the alkalosis.

Most of the saline-unresponsive forms of metabolic alkalosis are quite uncommon in pediatrics, except that caused by the exogenous administration of steroids, and are listed in Table 3–7. Heritable defects in steroid synthesis, 17α-hydroxylase and 11-β-hydroxylase deficiencies, can result in metabolic alkalosis from the excessive deoxycorticosterone production. The 17α-hydroxylase block also leads to deficient production of both androgens and estrogens, which manifests as failure of secondary sexual development and primary amenorrhea in the female and ambiguous genitalia to female genitalia in the male. Liddle's syndrome presents in infancy with hypokalemic metabolic alkalosis and hypertension and low levels of plasma renin and aldosterone. An unidentified mineralocorticoid is presumed responsible for this heritable syndrome. Licorice has mineralocorticoid activity and can lead to metabolic alkalosis and hypertension. Finally, severe hypokalemia will convert saline-responsive forms of metabolic alkalosis to saline-resistant ones, requiring replacement of the potassium deficit for correction.

An interesting cause of metabolic alkalosis presenting in childhood is Bartter's syndrome. These children are characterized by failure to thrive, metabolic alkalosis, resistance to the hypertensive effects of an angiotensin II infusion, polyuria, and profound hypokalemia. The urinary chloride in this illness is quite high, as is the plasma renin and aldosterone. However, these children are usually in a state of volume contraction in contrast to the volume-expanded state found with the other causes of metabolic alkalosis with a high urinary chloride. Bartter's syndrome is probably the result of a primary disturbance in sodium or chloride transport leading to volume contraction and increased aldosterone secretion. This, in turn, results in hypokalemia and alkalosis in the manner

Table 3–7 CAUSES OF SALINE-RESISTANT METABOLIC ALKALOSIS

Primary hyperaldosteronism
Cushing's syndrome
Hyper-reninemic hypertension
Renal artery stenosis
Heritable block in steroid hormone synthesis
  17α-OH deficiency
  11β-OH deficiency
Licorice
Liddle's syndrome
Bartter's syndrome
Severe potassium deficiency

previously described for primary aldosteronism Also, of note in these patients is the marked urinary prostaglandin excretion, which has led to the use of prostaglandin synthetase inhibitors, such as aspirin and indomethacin, with good results in some but not all patients.

Respiratory Acidosis and Alkalosis

Respiratory acidosis occurs whenever there is an interference with the pulmonary clearance of CO_2. This can occur because of CNS disturbances, disorders of the phrenic nerves and those supplying the intercostal muscles, disturbances of the intercostal and diaphragmatic muscles, primary lung disease, and, finally, obstruction anywhere along the airway. This retention of CO_2 leads to an increase in H_2CO_3 and H^+ that is represented by a fall in blood pH. This fall in pH is reduced to some extent by intracellular proteins buffering some of the increased H^+. In addition, intracellular HCO_3^- is exchanged for extracellular Cl^- by the erythrocyte raising the plasma bicarbonate concentration slightly. These acute mechanisms raise the plasma bicarbonate concentration by only 3 to 4 mEq/l. The major mechanisms of compensation for respiratory acidosis are increased HCO_3^- reabsorption and increased H^+ excretion by the kidney under the influence of the raised pCO_2. Renal compensation for respiratory acidosis, however, takes several days to achieve maximal effect, unlike the respiratory compensation for metabolic acidosis in which maximal effect occurs within hours.

Respiratory alkalosis occurs whenever there is an increase in the pulmonary clearance of CO_2 leading to a decrease in H_2CO_3 and H^+. As in respiratory acidosis, erythrocytes and intracellular proteins act to buffer the change in pH acutely. This occurs through the release of hydrogen ions from intracellular stores in exchange for extracellular Na^+ or K^+. The erythrocyte also exchanges intracellular Cl^- for extracellular HCO_3^-. In addition, lactic acid is released from cells and dissociates into H^+ and lactate, buffering some of the rise in pH. These mechanisms will lower the plasma bicarbonate by only 2 to 3 mEq/l. However, the major organ for compensation is the kidney, just as it is in respiratory acidosis. Under the influence of the lowered pCO_2 levels, bicarbonate reabsorption by the kidney is diminished. This diminished reabsorption leads to a fall in plasma bicarbonate over several days and is the major compensation for respiratory alkalosis. Major causes of respiratory alkalosis are listed in Table 3–8.

Mixed Disturbances

In the real world of clinical medicine, one often encounters several disease processes occurring together in a single patient. Each of these disease processes may have a different effect on the acid-base status of the patient, with the measured pH reflecting the dominant disturbance. It is even possible to have a normal pH due to significant but counterbalancing influences on blood pH. Obviously, it would still be important to identify and treat each disease process.

The ability to identify each disease process depends first on a careful history and physical examination as well as several pieces of laboratory data. The major aid in identifying the various influences on the acid-base status of a patient is, as in so many other aspects of medicine, a careful history. A history can furnish facts, such as that an episode of severe vomiting or diarrhea had occurred; or that a child had received a large amount of aspirin or was found playing near an open container of methanol; or that the patient had been taking diuretics. Such information may be crucial in interpreting the laboratory data from a particular patient. In the same context, a careful physical examination is also necessary in assessing whether an acid-base disturbance may be present and in interpreting the clinical data. The state of hydration, the depth and rate of respiration, stigmata of poisonings, and the presence of the "olive" of pyloric stenosis are but a few of the clues that can be garnered from a careful physical examination and that would be helpful in understanding the acid-base disturbance in a particular patient.

Besides a careful history and physical examination, there are certain guides that are helpful in

Table 3–8 CAUSES OF
RESPIRATORY ALKALOSIS

CNS lesions
  Trauma
  Cerebral hemorrhage
  Infection
  Anxiety
Pulmonary Disorders
  Pneumonia
  Pulmonary embolus
  Asthma
  Mild pulmonary edema
  Restrictive lung disease
Systemic Disorders
  Hyperthyroidism
  Endotoxemia
  Anemia (severe)
  Fever
  Pregnancy
Hyperammonemia
  Hepatic failure
  Reye's syndrome
  Lysinuric protein intolerance
  Urea cycle disorders
    Carbamylphosphate synthetase deficiency
    Ornithine transcarbamylase deficiency
    Citrullinemia
    Argininosuccinic aciduria
    Arginase deficiency
Pharmacologic Agents
  Salicylate intoxication
  Paraldehyde intoxication
  Epinephrine
  Progestational agents
  Amphetamines
Mechanical Overventilation

determining whether an acid-base disturbance is a simple or complex one. These guides have been generated by determining the usual range of values for pCO_2 and HCO_3^- for a given change in pH for a particular type of acid-base disturbance. Again, as stated earlier, the direction of the change in pH, whether toward the acidotic or alkalotic side, determines the predominant disturbance. One of these guides was worked out by Winters and his colleagues for metabolic acidosis. They noted that the usual fall in pCO_2 in response to metabolic acidosis could be determined from the following equation:

$$pCO_2 = 1.5\ [HCO_3^-] + 8 \pm 2$$

Finding a pCO_2 much above or below this value indicates that there is a respiratory disturbance in addition to metabolic acidosis. Also, the last two digits of the pH nearly equal the pCO_2 in fully compensated metabolic acidosis. For determining the expected pCO_2 in metabolic alkalosis, van Ypersele de Strihan and Frans have described the following equation:

$$pCO_2 = 0.9\ [HCO_3^-] + 15.6$$

Again, finding a pCO_2 significantly different from that determined by this equation suggests an additional respiratory disturbance.

    For respiratory disturbances, expected ranges for serum HCO_3^- concentration have been developed. In acute respiratory acidosis the serum HCO_3^- concentration will increase by only 3 to 4

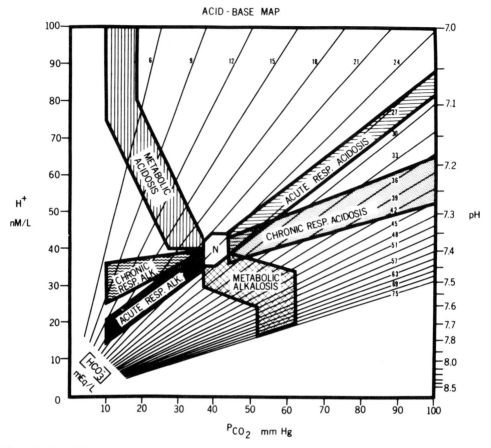

Figure 3-5 Acid-base map. Area of normal values is labeled N. Numbered lines represent isopleths for bicarbonate in milliequivalents per liter. (From Goldberg, M., Green, S.B., Moss, M.L., et al.: Computer-based instruction and diagnosis of acid-base disorders: A systematic approach. JAMA 223:269, 1973. Copyright 1973, American Medical Association.)

mEq/l. With chronic respiratory acidosis, the serum HCO_3^- concentration should increase by 0.3 mEq/l for each 1 Torr rise in pCO_2. Similarly, the serum HCO_3^- concentration in acute respiratory alkalosis will fall by only 2 to 3 mEq/l, while in chronic respiratory alkalosis the serum HCO_3^- concentration will fall by 0.5 mEq/l for each 1 Torr fall in pCO_2.

Because of the difficulty in determining whether a mixed disturbance exists, Goldberg et al. (1973) have developed a map of the confidence bands for pH, pCO_2 and HCO_3^- concentration for the various acid-base disturbances (Fig. 3-5). Points lying outside these bands suggest that a mixed disturbance is present. Points falling within these bands suggest that a single disturbance exists. However, having a point fall within a confidence band does not completely exclude a mixed disturbance. Information gleaned from the history and physical examination is very helpful in deciding whether a single or mixed disturbance exists.

REFERENCES

Body Buffers

Masoro, E.J., and Siegel, P.D.: Acid-Base Regulation. 2nd ed. W.B. Saunders Co., Philadelphia, 1977, pp. 12-61, Chapters 2, 3, and 4.
Meeroff, J.C., Pennock, B.E., and Llach, F.: Rapid conversion of pH to. [H⁺]. Hosp. Prac. *16:*17, 1981.

Buffer Capacity

Swan, R.C., and Pitts, R.F.: Neutralization of infused acid by nephrectomized dogs. J. Clin. Invest. 34:205, 1955.
Swan, R.C., Axelrod, D.R., Seys, M., and Pitts, R.F.: Distribution of sodium bicarbonate infused into nephrectomized dogs. J. Clin. Invest. 34:1795, 1955.

Renal Regulation of Acid-Base Balance

Harrington, J.T., and Lemann, J., Jr.: The metabolic production and disposal of acid and alkali. Med. Clin. North Am. 54:1543, 1970.
Kildeberg, P., Engel, K., and Winters, R.W.: Balance of net acid in growing infants. Acta Pediatr. Scand. 58:321, 1969.
Rector, F.C., Jr.: Renal acidification and ammonia production; Chemistry of weak acids and bases; Buffer mechanisms. *In* Brenner, B.M., and Rector, F.C., Jr. (eds.): The Kidney. W.B. Saunders Co., Philadelphia, 1981, pp. 318–343.

Other Factors in Renal Acidification

DeSousa, R.C., Harrington, J.T., Ricanti, E.S., et al.: Renal regulation of acid-base equilibrium during chronic administration of mineral acid. J. Clin. Invest. 53:465, 1974.
Pitts, R.F., Jr.: Physiology of the Kidney and Body Fluids. 3rd ed. Year Book Medical Publishers, Inc. Chicago, 1974, pp. 198–241, Chapter 11.
Schwartz, W.B., and Cohen, J.J.: The nature of the renal response to chronic disorders of acid-base equilibrium. Am. J. Med. 64:417, 1978.
Simpson, D.P.: Pathways of glutamine metabolism in renal cortex in chronic metabolic acidosis. J. Clin. Invest. 51:1969, 1972.

Metabolic Acidosis

Emmett, M., and Narins, R.G.: Clinical use of the anion gap. Medicine 56:38, 1977.
Narins, R.G., and Goldberg, M.: Renal tubular acidosis: pathophysiology, diagnosis and treatment. Disease-A-Month, March, 1977.

Mixed Disturbances

Goldberg, M., Green, S.B., Moss, M.L., et al.: Computer-based instruction and diagnosis of acid-base disorders. JAMA 223:269, 1973.
Narins, R.G., and Emmett, M.: Simple and mixed acid-base disorders: a practical approach. Medicine 59:161, 1980.
van Ypersele de Strihou, C., and Frans, A.: The respiratory response to metabolic alkalosis and acidosis in disease. Clin. Sci. Mol. Med. 45:439, 1973.

4

Bilirubin Metabolism

Bilirubin is a tetrapyrrole molecule derived from heme-containing molecules, in a degradative process carried out by the reticuloendothelial system. The inherent differences between adult and newborn production and handling of bilirubin have taught us a great deal about biological control mechanisms. Therefore, a review of the development of bilirubin metabolism is in keeping with a major theme of this book and will be presented here.

PRODUCTION (Table 4–1)

Heme serves as the prosthetic group of hemoglobin as well as other hemoproteins, including myoglobin (the oxygen storage protein), the cytochromes b_5 and P_{450}, and catalase (Table 4–2). Since no biological molecule can persist unchanged throughout the life of the organism (for reasons elaborated in Part I), it is reasonable to assume that hemoglobin in the red blood cell and other hemoproteins have a finite life span. The erythrocyte of the normal adult persists an average of 120 days in the circulation, while this period is somewhat shorter in the fetus. The precise mechanism by which the reticuloendothelial cells select out senescent red cells is not known, but it is clear

Table 4–1 BILIRUBIN METABOLISM

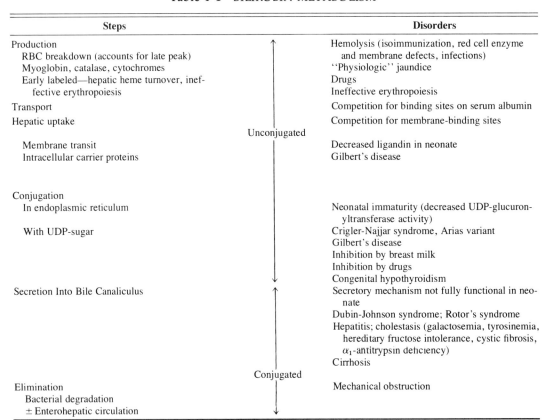

Steps	Disorders
Production	Hemolysis (isoimmunization, red cell enzyme
RBC breakdown (accounts for late peak)	and membrane defects, infections)
Myoglobin, catalase, cytochromes	"Physiologic" jaundice
Early labeled—hepatic heme turnover, ineffective erythropoiesis	Drugs
	Ineffective erythropoiesis
Transport	Competition for binding sites on serum albumin
Hepatic uptake	Competition for membrane-binding sites
Membrane transit	Decreased ligandin in neonate
Intracellular carrier proteins	Gilbert's disease
Conjugation	
In endoplasmic reticulum	Neonatal immaturity (decreased UDP-glucuronyltransferase activity)
With UDP-sugar	Crigler-Najjar syndrome, Arias variant
	Gilbert's disease
	Inhibition by breast milk
	Inhibition by drugs
	Congenital hypothyroidism
Secretion Into Bile Canaliculus	Secretory mechanism not fully functional in neonate
	Dubin-Johnson syndrome; Rotor's syndrome
	Hepatitis; cholestasis (galactosemia, tyrosinemia, hereditary fructose intolerance, cystic fibrosis, α_1-antitrypsin deficiency)
	Cirrhosis
Elimination	Mechanical obstruction
Bacterial degradation	
± Enterohepatic circulation	

Unconjugated

Conjugated

66

Table 4–2 SOURCES OF BILIRUBIN

Heme Proteins	Adult Body Content	Sources
Hemoglobin	500–700 g	70 percent circulating RBC's 10 percent erythroid precursors (early labeled peak)
Myoglobin	35–200 g	muscle
Other Catalase Some peroxidases Cytochromes b_5, P_{450}		20 percent hepatic hemes and bone marrow erythroid production (early labeled peak)

that the hemoglobin from such cells is the major source of bilirubin in both the fetus and the adult. Catabolism of 1 g of hemoglobin results in production of 34 mg of bilirubin.

The initial step in the production of bilirubin from heme is removal of iron from the molecule and oxidation of a methylene bridge to form the tetrapyrrole structure known as biliverdin (Fig. 4–1). This reaction is carried out by the enzyme heme oxygenase, which is found predominantly in spleen, liver, and bone marrow. In fetal rats, hepatic heme oxygenase is present at 100 to 150 per cent of adult levels by the beginning of the third and final week of gestation. Intrauterine hemolysis induced experimentally can stimulate hepatic heme oxygenase activity to still higher levels. It is, therefore, possible that the relative instability of the fetal hemoglobin molecule and shorter half-life of fetal erythrocytes are the stimuli for these higher heme oxygenase levels. Subsequent conversion of biliverdin to bilirubin occurs briskly via the reaction catalyzed by biliverdin reductase, which is present in excess even in fetal rat tissues.

Heme oxygenase shows activity only with porphyrins containing iron, accounting for the fact that in the porphyrias the free porphyrins are excreted intact (see Chapter 35). This enzyme appears to be unique in that it is the heme group from the substrate, acting in concert with the enzyme, which carries out the oxidation. The mechanism is similar to the microsomal hydroxylation carried out by the cytochrome P-450 system. However, whereas with the cytochromes the heme is part of the enzyme, in the case of heme oxygenase, the heme must be provided by the substrate.

Paradoxically, the conversion from biliverdin to bilirubin appears to decrease aqueous solubility, thus rendering the final product more difficult to excrete. In the fetal state this apparent liability is resolved simply: bilirubin traverses the placental barrier readily without the need for further fetal

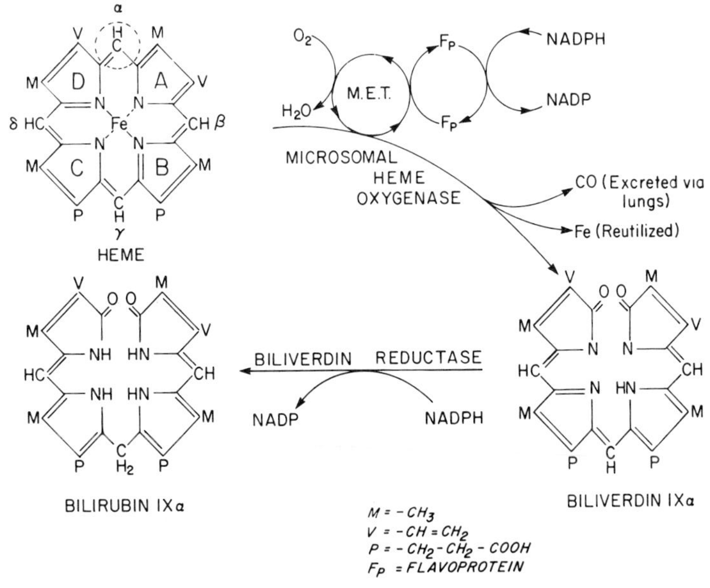

Figure 4–1 Conversion of heme to bilirubin. Removal of the iron and oxidation of a methylene bridge between rings A and D are carried out by heme oxygenase. (Modified from Tenhunen, R. et al.: Trans. Assoc. Am. Phys. 82:363–371, 1969.)

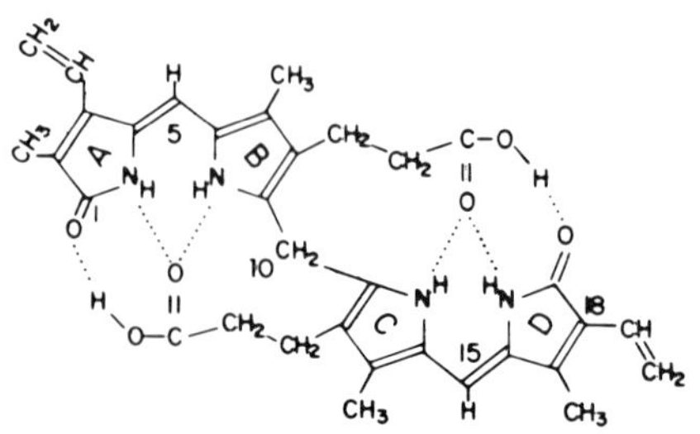

Figure 4–2 Structure of the bilirubin molecule. Rings A and D have polar keto groups, while rings B and C have propionic acid side chains. Intramolecular H-bonding involving these polar groups superimposes a rigid conformation to bilirubin and diminishes aqueous solubility. (From Berk, P.D.: Disorders of Bilirubin Metabolism. *In* Bondy, P.K., and Rosenberg, L.E.: Metabolic Control and Disease. Philadelphia, W.B. Saunders Co., 1980.)

processing of the molecule as occurs after birth. The biological economy of this situation is reflected in the low fetal and neonatal levels of hepatic UDP-glucuronyltransferase, the conjugating enzyme whose action confers aqueous solubility on the bilirubin molecule.

As shown in Figure 4–2 bilirubin IXα contains polar propionic acid side-chains and keto groups on the pyrrole rings. This should make the compound water soluble because of the potential for hydrogen bonding of these polar groups with water. However, this potential is not realized. Instead, X-ray crystallographic studies reveal that these groups engage in intramolecular hydrogen bonding, which results in a rigid folded configuration; such bilirubin is insoluble in aqueous media. It is not entirely hydrophobic (lipid soluble) either. Indeed, studies by Brodersen (1979) suggest that it can interact with polar phospholipid residues in cell membranes. Such interactions could well be the basis for the neurotoxicity of unconjugated bilirubin.

What then is accomplished by conjugating bilirubin with glucuronic acid? As discussed below (Conjugation), it prevents the intramolecular hydrogen bonding, thereby opening up the molecule and apparently facilitating transport into the bile canaliculus.

In summary then, the mature fetus has a capacity to produce bilirubin in quantities equal to or greater than an adult. However, the solubility properties of the unconjugated bilirubin make it dependent upon the placenta for removal from the circulation, rendering the fetal conjugating ability relatively inadequate. This discrepancy between production and conjugation may mirror the developmental difference between two cell types; development of productive capacity occurs earlier in the reticuloendothelial system than does conjugation capacity in the hepatocytes.

As noted above, while the bulk of bilirubin arises from hemoglobin of senescent erythrocytes, approximately 10 to 20 per cent is derived from heme of red cell precursors and red cells with a very short life span, as well as myoglobin and other hemoproteins. In the normal adult, daily bilirubin production is in the range of 3.6 to 4 mg/kg. Bilirubin released from tissues possessing heme oxygenase is transported in plasma bound tightly to albumin. Unconjugated bilirubin is also found in liver.

TRANSPORT

The mechanism for release of unconjugated bilirubin from reticuloendothelial cells of the spleen, bone marrow, and hepatic sinusoids is not well known. Whatever the means of release, unconjugated bilirubin is tightly bound by plasma albumin. Although each molecule of albumin is able to bind two of bilirubin, there is evidence to suggest that one of the binding sites is normally occupied by an organic anion competing with bilirubin, such as a fatty acid. Other anions that may compete for the albumin binding sites are sulfonamides, certain antibiotics, and bile acids.

It is important to understand that the binding of bilirubin to albumin is nonspecific, unlike that of a substrate to its enzyme. This is clear from the fact that most tissues in the body also have some degree of binding affinity for bilirubin, so that the balance between the tissue protein and serum albumin affinities for bilirubin plays a large role in its distribution in vivo. A major determinant of the relative binding capacity of serum albumin is pH, the affinity for bilirubin dropping off sharply with decreasing pH. This factor will also, therefore, affect bilirubin distribution in the body tissues and blood. What is unclear is the means by which bilirubin detaches from albumin and traverses the hepatocytic membrane, probably by an active transport mechanism, for further metabolism. Although a definite answer is not possible yet, it is at least plausible to suggest that the relatively low pH and high fatty acid content of hepatic sinusoidal blood may contribute significantly to release of free, unconjugated bilirubin. This unbound bilirubin may then enter the hepatocyte unhindered.

CONJUGATION

Either within the hepatocyte membrane or at its cytosolic surface, unconjugated bilirubin is bound to a so-called "Y-protein," or ligandin, thought to be identical with the enzyme glutathione S-transferase. Ligandin appears to mediate intracellular translocation of the bound, unconjugated bilirubin to the microsomal membrane, a process whose secrets are as yet unrevealed. Nonetheless, this translocation is essential, since only through conjugation with glucuronic acid by microsomally bound UDP-glucuronyltransferase can free bilirubin be converted to a water-soluble glucuronide.

As we have already mentioned (see Production), activity of UDP-glucuronyltransferase is very low in the fetus and neonate, reflecting the effective action of the placenta in the clearance of unconjugated bilirubin from the fetal circulation. The enzyme catalyzes the transfer of glucuronic acid from uridine diphosphoglucuronic acid (the cofactor for the reaction) to the propionic acid side-chain of free bilirubin, thus forming bilirubin glucuronide. Since the bilirubin molecule possesses two such propionic acid substituents, two glucuronides may be found in bile, the monoglucuronide and diglucuronide in a ratio of about 30:70 per cent. Acknowledging the role of intramolecular hydrogen bonds in freezing the configuration of bilirubin, it seems likely that conjugation by disrupting these hydrogen bonds facilitates the interaction of bilirubin with its membrane carrier. Hence, transfer out of the hepatocyte would be enhanced by this change in the geometry of the molecule.

EXCRETION

Of all the steps in the complex catabolic pathway of heme that we have so far examined the process of removal of conjugated bilirubin from hepatocyte to bile canaliculus is the least well-understood. It is certain that this transfer occurs across a lipid barrier and against a high concentration gradient, factors that strongly suggest an energy-requiring active transport system. However, evidence supporting this is lacking.

The glucuronide esters of bilirubin comprise the bulk of the so-called "bile pigments," and intestinal excretion is their major route thereafter. Conjugated bilirubin is not significantly recirculated via the enterohepatic circulation, and there is further metabolism by bacteria to urobilin in the large intestine. Some urobilin is reabsorbed and finally cleared by the kidney.

Since unconjugated bilirubin is bound tightly to albumin, it does not undergo renal excretion. Some conjugated bilirubin is removed by the kidney. Hence, bilirubin in the urine denotes a component of conjugated hyperbilirubinemia. When bilirubin excretion into the bile canaliculi is impaired, conjugated hyperbilirubinemia results. The mechanism is unclear but probably involves disruption of both the structure and vectorial transport function of cells forming the bile canaliculus. Thus, under normal circumstances no bilirubin and very little urobilin can be detected in urine.

Developmental Aspects of Bilirubin Metabolism

We have already seen that fetal and newborn liver have greater capability than adult for bilirubin production. The advantages derived from this, when fetal red cells are turning over very rapidly, have been discussed. However, many changes occur simultaneously and immediately at birth to which the infant must adapt if he is to survive. It is these circumstances that we wish to consider here.

During fetal life, with a high in utero rate of unconjugated bilirubin production the placenta efficiently clears the blood of this catabolic product. With severance of the umbilical cord and

Table 4–3 FACTORS CONTRIBUTING TO NEONATAL "PHYSIOLOGIC" JAUNDICE

Bilirubin Production (8.5 mg/kg/day in newborn versus 3.8 in adult):
　　Increased numbers of red cells with decreased survival (82 ± 15 days)
　　Increased early labeled bilirubin from ineffective erythropoiesis
　　Increased enterohepatic circulation—phase II (possible reabsorption; less bacterial degradation)
Transport: Bilirubin binding to albumin may be diminished—competition
Hepatic Uptake: Decreased ligandin and competition for sites on ligandin and Z protein by organic
　　anions (phase II)
Conjugation: Decreased UDP-glucuronyltransferase activity
Secretion into Bile Canaliculus: Immaturity of mechanism
Elimination: Diminished bacterial degradation

initiation of spontaneous respirations, several changes occur. Without the placenta, lipid solubility of an end-product like bilirubin becomes a liability rather than an asset; interruption of placental circulation during birth causes hypoxia and consequent acidosis, decreasing albumin-bilirubin–binding interactions; and, fetal hemoglobin synthesis is "switched off" and adult hemoglobin must be made by reutilizing body iron stores. Closely related to the latter is the reduction of packed red cell volume due to the relative oxygen richness of the extrauterine environment. All of these factors impinge upon the rather feeble capability of the newborn to accomplish anything but a high rate of unconjugated bilirubin synthesis.

However, body tissues offer a large potential reservoir for the accumulated unconjugated bilirubin, leading to the situation known as "physiologic" jaundice of the newborn (Table 4–3). Moreover, there is good evidence from animal studies that accumulation of bilirubin triggers an increase in hepatic microsomal UDP-glucuronyltransferase. In rats, UDP-glucuronyltransferase levels reach those of adult animals by the third postnatal day and exceed the latter by 15 to 20 per cent on the fifth day. Correspondingly, fetal and newborn mammalian livers have a decreased amount of ligandin, which also rises during the immediate postnatal period. Thus, the hepatocyte adapts rapidly to accommodate the large capacity for bilirubin production and meet the need for conversion to bilirubin conjugates.

In addition, the newborn gut is rapidly colonized by saprophytic organisms. This aids in conversion of bilirubin to urobilin, which, in turn, is less potentially toxic and can be excreted via the kidney following reabsorption. It is the coincidence of all of these mechanisms that leads to the typical clinically observed pattern of increasing hyperbilirubinemia in the first three days of life and a rapid return to normal by the fifth day.

Finally, the discerning reader may already have asked himself: Why, if nature is so thrifty, is it necessary to catabolize the heme portion of the hemoglobin molecule rather than recycle it? This is a fascinating question and it has no ready answer. The protein globin corresponds roughly to the apoprotein portion of an enzyme molecule. As such, it is subject to the conformational alterations that all proteins undergo (see Chapter 2). However, heme functions as a cofactor in the hemoglobin molecule and one wonders why it should turn over completely. The only answer that can be given at present is purely speculative: it may be that heme itself is a significant biological toxin. If this is true, then evolution has provided a relatively straightforward detoxification system beautifully adapted to the needs of the organism. Indeed, since heme is the obligatory cofactor for the enzyme (heme oxygenase) that converts it to biliverdin, it would appear that its elimination from the body is essential and readily accomplished.

REFERENCES

Bonnett, R., Davies, J.E., and Hursthouse, M.B.: Structure of bilirubin. Nature 262:326, 1976.
Brodersen, R.: Bilirubin—solubility and interaction with albumin and phospholipid. J. Biol. Chem. 254:2364, 1979.
Eriksen, E.F., Danielsen, H., and Brodersen, R.: Bilirubin-liposome interaction. J. Biol. Chem. 256:4269, 1981.

Ezhuthacan, S.G., and Gartner, L.M.: Physiology of bilirubin metabolism. *In* Lifshitz, F. (ed.): Clinical Disorders in Pediatric Gastroenterology and Nutrition. Marcel Dekker, New York, 1980, p. 3.

Karp, W.B.: Biochemical alterations in neonatal hyperbilirubinemia and bilirubin encephalopathy: a review. Pediatrics 64:361, 1979.

Jew, J.Y., and Sandquist, D.: CNS changes in hyperbilirubinemia. Arch. Neurol. 36:149, 1979.

McDonagh, A.F., Palma, L.A., and Lightner, D.A.: Blue light and bilirubin excretion. Science 208:145, 1980.

Schmid, R.: Bilirubin metabolism: State of the art. Gastroenterology 74:1307, 1978.

Schmid, R., and McDonagh, A.F.: Formation and metabolism of bile pigments in vivo. *In* Dolphin, D. (ed.): The Porphyrins. Vol. VI. Academic Press, New York, 1979, p. 257.

Swartz, H.M., Sarna, T., and Varma, R.R.: On the nature and excretion of the hepatic pigment in the Dubin-Johnson syndrome. Gastroenterology 76:958, 1979.

Turkel, S.B., Miller, C.A., Guttenberg, M.E., et al.: A clinical pathologic reappraisal of kernicterus. Pediatrics 69:267, 1982.

Valaes, T.: Bilirubin metabolism. Review and discussion of inborn errors. Clin. Perinatol. 3:177, 1976.

5

Calcium and Phosphorus: Bone Disease

ROLE OF CALCIUM AND PHOSPHORUS IN CELLULAR FUNCTION

Calcium and phosphorus serve in a number of pivotal biochemical functions in the body (Table 5–1); hence, derangements in their homeostasis can have far-reaching effects on the well-being of the individual. Despite the obvious role of the skeleton in support and locomotion, this role is often subordinated to that of a mineral reserve for calcium and phosphorus. Indeed, the liability of the skeleton to suffer abnormalities in composition or volume in a wide variety of clinical states underscores the tenacity with which normocalcemia is defended.

It is worthwhile to probe into a rationale for this defense, employing an argument based upon biochemical evolution. All evidence for the origin of life points to its emergence in the sea, under conditions in which hydrophobic interactions would direct the formation of lipid micelles, bilayers, and vesicles, the last being the crucial precursor to the cell and its plasma membrane. As these primordial cells were developing, K^+ and Mg^{2+} were abundant constituents of the oceans while Na^+ and Ca^{2+} were minor constituents. This fact explains the preponderance of K^+ and Mg^{2+} as intracellular cations and accounts for the role they play in the action of many enzymes. However, as billions of years elapsed the oceans underwent a change in ionic composition so that Na^+ became the predominant cation. To meet this challenge to the integrity of the internal milieu of cells, transport systems for specific ions evolved. Such systems were able to protect the cell from the constant threat of Na^+ entry down its concentration gradient, and thus conferred upon these cells enhanced survival value in their new environment.

The consequences of this evolutionary strategy deserve special emphasis. Not only was the intracellular environment thus protected from the potential ravages of heightened sodium concentration and swelling but this transmembrane gradient of K^+ and Na^+ was utilized to develop excitable membranes (see Chapter 8). Transmembrane potential differences are a prerequisite for a nervous system and hence for the development of a complex, multicellular organism.

As noted in Table 5–1 calcium serves a critical role in membrane electrophysiology. Although the molecular events accompanying the action potential flowing down a neuron are still not clear, there is evidence that an exchange of ions in the membrane may bring about a change in the conformation of macromolecules. Such a change in their configuration may engender the enhanced sodium and potassium flux across the membranes. Hence, all three ions are intimately involved in the creation of the action potential, the currency of communication of the neurons.

Because of this and other functions served by calcium and phosphorus (Table 5–1), it is clear that means had to be "found" to ensure their ready availability to the body. The large multicellular organism's need for support and locomotion demands a scaffolding in the form of either an exoskeleton or an endoskeleton. The dual needs of a calcium-phosphorus mineral bank and support for

Table 5–1 FUNCTIONS SERVED BY CALCIUM AND PHOSPHORUS

Functions Served by Calcium

Extracellular ionized Ca controls membrane excitation, neural excitability, and muscle contraction

Coupling of excitation to secretion; neurotransmitter release

Activation of enzymes in clotting (glycogenolysis, gluconeogenesis, amylase, lipases, trypsinogen, ATPase)

Cell-cell interactions
Decreased extracellular calcium associated with decreased cell adhesion

Biological messenger
Information molecule for many processes

Functions Served by Phosphorus

Formation and metabolism of the following constituents of the cell depend upon availability of adequate phosphate:
Nucleic acids
High-energy organic phosphate compounds for group-transfer reactions and coupling ATP
Phospholipids (membrane components)
Phosphorylated intermediates in metabolism (predominantly carbohydrate)

Phosphorylation of key serine and threonine residues in certain proteins is a major factor in covalent regulation of metabolism
Signal molecules—cAMP, 2,3-DPG
Urinary buffer system (titratable acid)

the organism were met by the development of the hydroxyapatite-based endoskeleton. Remembering that the role of calcium and phosphorus in cell biochemistry antedated their skeletal role by billions of years, it follows that their biochemical functions would be protected at the expense of their skeletal functions. Hence, bone disease often occurs in a setting in which perturbations in calcium and phosphorus homeostasis are buffered by bone.

Of these two ions, calcium appears to be under more stringent regulation than phosphorus, but since much of what impinges on calcium ultimately affects phosphorus, they are loosely coupled. Moreover, of the three hormones affecting calcium and bone, i.e., parathormone, vitamin D, and calcitonin, the first two have direct effects on phosphorus homeostasis as well. Considering the importance of these ions, multiple controlling factors would be expected. Indeed, divalent ion homeostasis is a complicated affair. Control of bone mass is under the aegis of the remodeling cell system. Plasma calcium is regulated by another system in bone which is responsive to hormonal signals. The kidney, through reabsorption of phosphate and magnesium, exerts the major regulatory influence on these ions and in so doing assures that calcium levels will be maintained without a major contribution from bone.

It is worthwhile to compare the major effects of these three hormones in broad overview (Table 5–2). Parathormone (PTH) is charged with the defense of the extracellular ionized calcium concentration. It buffers decreases in this fraction by augmenting bone resorption and increasing renal tubule reabsorption of calcium. Further, by stimulating the production of the gut-active metabolite of vitamin D (1,25(OH)$_2$D$_3$), it increases gastrointestinal absorption as well. Finally, by causing phosphate loss in the urine it prevents calcification through a decrease in the calcium-phosphorus product.

Vitamin D is a sterol hormone made in the skin that undergoes further activation (processing) in the liver and kidney. The 1,25(OH)$_2$D$_3$ form of this hormone maintains the mass of bone by providing adequate calcium and phosphorus for mineralization of new bone. It does this by increasing intestinal calcium and phosphate absorption and stimulating bone resorption (acting to potentiate the action of PTH). This latter effect provides calcium and phosphorus for new bone from resorbed bone. Additionally, there is inferential evidence for a direct effect of vitamin D on the mineralization process itself.

Calcitonin inhibits bone resorption and appears to have a more important role in lowering serum calcium concentration in the young individual than in the older person. Further discussion of these hormones is found in this chapter under Hormones Affecting Calcium.

Table 5–2 HORMONES AFFECTING MINERAL HOMEOSTASIS AND BONE

Hormone	Chemistry	Functions			Biochemical Mechanism of Action
		Bone	Intestine	Kidney	
Parathyroid Hormore Main determinant of ionized calcium in extracellular fluid—increases plasma Ca and decreases plasma P	Protein Prohormone cleaved to hormone (84 amino acids) Residues 1–34 have biological activity	Regulates activation of bone metabolic units Increases rate of skeletal remodeling and resorption Principal effect is marked increase in number of osteoclasts Short-term effects— ↑ osteolytic activity of osteoclasts and osteocytes and ↓ osteoblastic activity	Increases GI absorption of Ca, secondary to stimulating synthesis of 1,25-Vit. D by kidney ↑P, Mg absorption	Prompt onset of phosphaturia Regulates conversion of 25-Vit. D to 1,25-Vit. D. Believed to ↑ tubular reabsorption of Ca, Mg	Activation of adenylcyclase in target tissues
Calcitonin Hypocalcemic agent— more effect in young than in old individuals	Polypeptide (32 amino acids) synthesized as prohormone	Inhibits osteoclastic activity—decreases brush border, which leads to ↓ bone resorption	Inhibits GI secretion but stimulates intestinal secretion—results in delayed absorption of Ca from gut	Decreases tubular reabsorption of P, Ca, Mg Inhibits conversion of 25-Vit. D to 1,25-Vit. D	Acts through adenylcyclase
"Vitamin D" Enhances mineralization of bone by increasing Ca and P concentration in serum	Sterol—synthesized in skin (UV light) with subsequent processing in liver (25-Vit. D) and kidney (1,25-Vit. D)	Stimulates bone resorption Question of a direct effect of 1,25-Vit. D on mineralization Mobilizes Ca into circulation—used in mineralization	Increases absorption of Ca Increases phosphate absorption by a system that is distinct from the one mediating Ca uptake	Increases proximal tubule reabsorption of Ca and P	Intestine—binding to cytosol receptor, which is transported to nucleus where it activates mRNA transcription

Calcium-Phosphorus Solubility Product (K$_{sp}$)

Since bone crystal is extremely small, has a variable composition, and is bathed by a mixed salt solution, it does not exhibit a fixed K$_{sp}$, or solubility product constant. In calcium phosphate solutions above pH 6.2 the K$_{sp}$ of secondary calcium phosphate (CaHPO$_4$) governs the solubility at equilibrium. This product is 0.89×10^{-7}. As this number represents an approximate or relative relationship rather than a true physical chemical solubility product, it is frequently referred to as a "biological solubility product."

Because the product of calcium and phosphorus is a constant value, there exists a reciprocal relationship between the concentrations of calcium and phosphate in blood. Thus, any procedure or condition that alters the concentration of one ion will result in an opposite change in concentration of the other. It is not surprising then that the K$_{sp}$ remains within the normal range during moderate alterations of parathyroid gland activity. However, it is not uncommon in serious disturbances of calcium-phosphorus metabolism to find serum calcium or phosphate ions or both abnormally depressed or elevated. Factors other than physical principles are involved in the control of the concentration of these ions in blood. It is necessary to distinguish the true chemical solubility product relationships just described from the frequently encountered clinical solubility product used for diagnostic purposes. The product of the total calcium and inorganic phosphorus of serum, expressed in milligrams per cent, is often referred to as the solubility product and is used as an index of degree of calcification in rickets. The value is low in rickets and elevated in young and growing children. The normal value is 30 to 40 for adults and 40 to 55 for children.

It is generally agreed that the extracellular fluids are normally supersaturated with respect to bone material. While the magnitude of the K helps to determine the rate of bone deposition, the amount of calcifiable and partially calcified matrix available determines the net removal of calcium and phosphate from the extracellular fluid, since it is the matrix that will become hardened bone.

BONE AND SKELETAL FUNCTIONS

All tissues in the living organism undergo constant renewal consonant with the need to refurbish denatured membranes and proteins (see Chapter 2). The function of bone as a reservoir for Ca^{++} and phosphorus implies the existence of mechanisms for removal and replacement of bone tissue. What makes this process in bone unique is the focus of this tissue turnover on the secreted products of the cells rather than the cells themselves. The constant resorption of bone, coupled closely with formation, results in a process known as remodeling. The "remodeling units" that carry out this process consist of osteoclasts, mitotically active mesenchymal cells, a capillary loop, mononucleocytes, and osteoblasts, all carrying out independent functions in a concerted fashion (Table 5–3). The control mechanisms responsible for this organized complex of functions are not known, although vitamin D plays a major role.

Bone possesses varying internal architectures to serve different needs; the main types of bone and their properties are compared in Table 5–4. The specific arrangement of compact cancellous bone provides the combination of strength and density essential for support of the vertebrate organism while providing the mobility essential to vertebrate survival. Trabecular (woven) bone, found at the ends of long bone, with its weblike structure is able to withstand shock across a joint. Indeed, bone is remarkably capable of being bent and returning spontaneously to its initial shape once the perturbation is removed.

In addition to serving as a reservoir for calcium and phosphorus, substantial amounts of magnesium and sodium are stored in bone as well. As we have emphasized, the functional properties of a macromolecule or a tissue are a derivative of structural organization. With bone the extracellular components are related as follows: a solid mineral phase exists in close association with a predominantly collagenous organic matrix, admixed with a variety of glycoproteins, and some proteoglycans. The major components of the mineral phase are microcrystals of 3-(Ca$_3$(PO$_4$)$_2$ hydroxyapatite Ca(OH)$_2$ and so-called "amorphous" calcium phosphate. Finally, there are other ions present in the external layers. Deposition of the mineral phase of bone occurs in apposition to the

Table 5–3 CELLULAR ELEMENTS OF BONE

Cell Type	Microscopic Anatomy	E/M Features	Functions	Factors that Influence Function
Osteoblast life span—few days–weeks	Situated on surface of growing bone. Cuboidal to fusiform, 15–20μ	Well-developed E/R, Golgi, mitochondria. High-content alkaline P-ase	Formation of bone matrix—secretes collagen, glycosaminoglycans, glycoproteins. Matrix laid down as osteoid and becomes calcified thereafter, taking about 5–10 days to complete the process. Mineralization (in vesicles) occurs in two steps: nucleation and crystallization.	PTH, CT, estrogen, vitamins A, C, and "D"
Osteocyte ca. 26,000/mm^3 of bone tissue	Entombed osteoblasts that have become included in lacuna and are subsequently buried in the mineralized matrix. Fusiform cell body with many projections	Similar to osteoblast with less elaborate E/R	Short-term regulation of Ca homeostasis—exist as part of elaborate canalicular systems, which in concert with osteolysis feed Ca from bone resorption into the blood	PTH, CT, vitamin A, vitamin D
Osteoclast life span—few hours–days	Large multinucleated cell on surface of bone. Striking feature is brush border (ruffled border) of irregular microvilli in contact with matrix of bone	Numerous lysosomes, vesicles, and phagocytic vacuoles serve in resorption. Little E/R, large numbers of mitochondria	Long-term Ca homeostasis—maintenance of normocalcemia. Bone Resorption. Remodeling of bone. By exocytosis excrete H$^+$ ions, which dissolve bone mineral, and lysosomal hydrolases and collagenases, which degrade bone matrix	PTH stimulates osteoclast formation and therefore resorption (+)PTH, T$_4$, 1,25(OH)$_2$D$_3$, GH, (−)CT, estrogens, glucocorticoids

Table 5–4 COMPARISON OF SPONGY AND COMPACT BONE

	Spongy	Compact
Synonyms	Woven, trabecular	Cortical, lamellar
Characteristics	Three-dimensional lattice-work of trabeculae that are highly branched and surround vascular marrow	Consists of haversian systems (onion skin-like). Solid calcified matrix
	Osteocytes scattered randomly in the matrix	Osteocytes oriented in relationship to vascular channels
	Bone laid down without directionality (impermanent)	Formed only at an existing surface
	Less responsive to hormonal stimulation than compact	Responsive to hormonal stimulation
Locations	Vertebrae, flat bones, ends of long bones	Shafts of long bones
	Embryonic bone (fetal bone)	Accounts for about 80 percent of skeleton
Functions	Transmits compressive load across a joint	Resistance to bending and torsion
	Serves as a temporary structure en route to more permanent lamellar bone	

collagen fibrils. In fact, there are "holes" within the collagen fibrils, and these are the site of deposition. Such structural organization of mineral and matrix engenders a two-phase material possessing a prodigious mechanical stability. It is very likely that collagen and other macromolecules serve to direct the sites at which the inorganic phase is established (assembled).

Woven bone, endochondral cartilage, and healing callus cartilage (all relatively disorganized structures) serve as temporary expedients on the road to more permanent structures. The highly organized crystals of lamellar bone take time to mature, a delay incompatible with the needs for immediate repair served by the simpler forms of bone. Since hydroxyapatite ($Ca_{10}[PO_4]_6[OH]_2$) contains 18 ions, it seems necessary for there to be simpler calcium phosphate compounds, such as dicalcium phosphate dehydrate, to act as precursors to the hydroxyapatite crystal.

Mesenchymal cells first secrete the organic matrix, which thereafter is mineralized (primary mineralization), but the entire process requires several weeks for completion (secondary mineralization). In the course of mineralization the osteoblast is entombed, being transformed into an osteocyte, with the canalicular system serving as the life line with its blood supply (Fig. 5-1).

Formation of bone involves deposition of mineral into a previously elaborated organic matrix. Calcium and phosphorus constitute the predominant elements of the mineral phase, and the extracellular concentrations are important factors in determining the kinetics of mineralization. Collagen serves as the nidus for nucleation of the mineral phase, so that mineralization occurs within a collagen matrix.

Calcification is a complex process that appears to involve a unique cell product (at least in endochondral bone)—the extracellular matrix vesicle. These vesicles are believed to form by budding off of the plasma membrane of bone or cartilage cells. They contain a high concentration of lipids, alkaline phosphatase, and pyrophosphatase. They do not possess lysosomal or mitochondrial

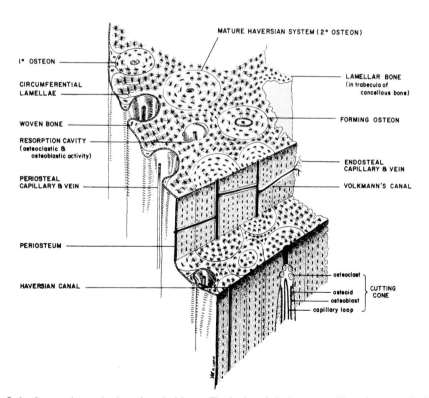

Figure 5-1 Structural organization of cortical bone. The basic unit is the osteon (Haversian system); the entombed osteoblast is nourished through the Haversian canal system, linked to the vascular system of the periosteum. (From Kelley, W.N., Harris, E.D., Jr., Ruddy, S., and Sledge, C.B.: Textbook of Rheumatology. Philadelphia, W.B. Saunders Co., 1981.)

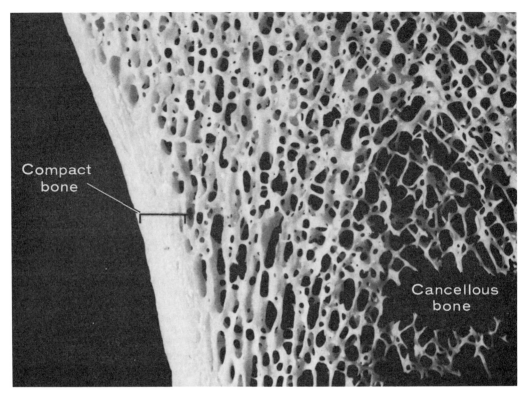

Figure 5–2 The relationship of cortical and trabecular bone in the tibia. (From Bloom, W., and Fawcett, D.W.: A Textbook of Histology. Philadelphia, W.B. Saunders Co., 1975.)

enzymes or a protein-synthesizing apparatus. The importance of these vesicles in intramembranous bone formation is less well established, but they do seem, at least, to play a role in initiation of calcification.

Once situated in the extracellular space these vesicles proceed to accumulate calcium and phosphorus previously stored in mitochondria. Calcium uptake probably involves binding to acidic phospholipids and proteoglycans, while phosphorus accumulates through the action of phosphatases on pyrophosphates and other phosphate esters. Thereafter, amorphous calcium phosphate begins to form within the vesicle, subsequently undergoing modification into hydroxyapatite. Once this compound is formed in the vesicle the stage is set for continued growth of these crystals outside the matrix vesicle in the extracellular space by vesicle rupture.

The role of the phospholipids in this process deserves a brief comment: there is evidence that they have a pivotal role in forming a complex that serves as a nidus for proliferation of hydroxyapatite. Attraction between calcium and lipids is well known to any one who has attempted to make a lather with soap in hard water.

At this point the reader may be wondering why calcification does not occur everywhere collagen is present and the solubility product of calcium and phosphorus is exceeded, a common set of circumstances indeed. The answer appears to reside in the properties of inorganic pyrophosphate, which exerts a potent inhibitory influence on mineralization. Hence, alkaline phosphatase, mediating hydrolysis of pyrophosphate, would exercise a regulatory role in calcification.

Mineralization of the skeleton of the fetus commences around the eighth week of gestation. Fetal bone is of the woven type, with coarse fiber bundles and a relatively high ratio of cells to matrix. As gestation continues, lamellar bone begins to fill in this latticework in the cortical areas, alongside the trabecular (Fig. 5–2). Endosteal resorption accounts for the formation of the marrow. In both the embryo and growing child there are two types of bone formation: intramembranous formation without a cartilaginous framework and endochondral bone formation in a cartilaginous matrix. After birth the marrow cavity begins to grow at the expense of the cortex, which becomes quite thin as replacement with new lamellae (secondary osteons) commences. By two years of age all of the fetal bone has undergone remodeling.

During childhood, growth in length of bone occurs at the epiphysial plates, with proliferation of cartilage cells the prime determinant of the rate of growth. Prior to the adolescent growth spurt linear growth slows but gives way to an accelerated pace at puberty followed by epiphysial closure and termination of linear growth. Growth in width occurs by periosteal surface deposition at a rate that exceeds endosteal surface resorption.

Resorption

During the process of resorption calcium and phosphorus ions are released into the extracellular fluid, with subsequent hydrolysis of the organic matrix. While this is probably a life-long process, it is likely to achieve greatest import during growth and development when bones assume their normal contours. Since this process is mediated by intracellular enzymes released into the matrix, it follows that the process begins in proximity to osteoclasts and osteocytes. Collagenases accomplish degradation of collagen, while lysosomal hydrolases degrade the mucopolysaccharides and proteoglycans (see Chapter 27).

Resorption involves the action of mononuclear cells as well as multi-nucleated osteoclasts. These latter cells possess a brush border at which resorption is carried out. It is likely that mineral is resorbed before the matrix is degraded. While osteocytic resorption occurs as well, it is probably more involved in calcium homeostasis than bone remodeling per se.

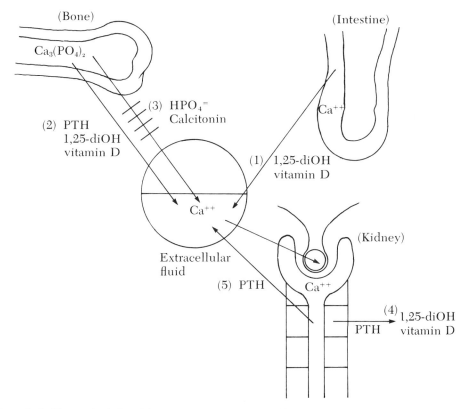

Figure 5–3 Hormonal role in calcium homeostasis. Intestinal Ca^{++} transport (*1*) requires 1,25-dihydroxy vitamin D; bone resorption (*2*) requires parathyroid hormone and 1,25-diOH vitamin D; process (*2*) is blocked by $HPO_4^=$ and calcitonin (*3*); hydroxylation of 25-OH vitamin D requires parathyroid hormone (*4*); Ca^{++} reabsorption in the renal tubule is enhanced by parathyroid hormone (*5*). (From Harrison, H.E., and Harrison, H.C.: Disorders of Calcium and Phosphate Metabolism in Childhood and Adolescence. Philadelphia, W.B. Saunders Co., 1979.)

Table 5–5 FUNCTIONS SERVED BY SKELETON (BONE)

Mineral Reservoir
  Ca and phosphorus are so essential to the biochemistry of the body that this function takes precedence over structural functions of bone
Support Body and Protect Internal Organs
  Bone marrow and hematopoiesis enjoy protected status
Acidosis Defense
  After physicochemical (immediate) buffering by lungs and kidney, bone serves as a defense against acidosis in chronic states
Acts as a trap for blood-borne ions
  Pb can exchange with Ca in lead intoxication

CALCIUM

Calcium Homeostasis (Fig. 5–3)

Calcium levels in the extracellular fluid are monitored and maintained closely and depend predominantly upon intestinal absorption (vitamin D-mediated) and the balance between incorporation of calcium into bone mineral and blood-bone exchange whereby calcium departs from bone. As regards extracellular phosphate homeostasis, concentrations fluctuate more widely than calcium levels, since in addition to bone accretion and resorption, intracellular uptake for metabolic processes is more a factor in the phosphate economy than it is with calcium. Nonetheless, renal excretion of phosphate is the major single factor in setting the serum phosphate level.

In accord with the function of the skeleton as a mineral bank and as a structural support (Table 5–5) approximately 98 per cent of the 1 to 2 kg of calcium in the body is located in the skeleton. We have noted previously the critical role of extracellular ionized calcium in neuromuscular irritability. The normal range consistent with these biochemical requirements is fairly narrow (Table 5–6), with the calcium being found in several forms (free ions, protein-bound, and diffusible complexes with bicarbonate, lactate, phosphate, citrate, or sulfate). While serum albumin concentration is important in determining total calcium levels, that fraction bound to protein does not play a role in the multiple cellular processes requiring calcium.

Most Americans consume dairy products and other foodstuffs that provide between 500 and 1000 mg of calcium daily. While less than 50 per cent of the available calcium is absorbed in adults, that absorbed during the growth spurt and during pregnancy and lactation is a considerably greater percentage. Vitamin D availability is an important factor in determining the magnitude of absorption. Although the duodenum is most efficient in calcium absorption, the bulk of ingested calcium gains entrance into the blood from the ileum. Active transport processes are more important in the proximal segments, while passive diffusion-limited processes predominate in the jejunum. Adequate levels of $1,25(OH)_2D_3$ are essential to the integrity of gastrointestinal absorption.

Table 5–6 DISTRIBUTION OF CALCIUM, PHOSPHORUS, AND MAGNESIUM SPECIES

	Ca (mg/100 ml)	P	Mg
Serum Concentration			
Total	10.0 (100) *	3.5 (100)	1.9 (100)
Ionized	4.7 (46.9)	1.9 (53)	1.1 (55)
Complexed	1.3 (13.6)	1.2 (35)	0.2 (13)
Protein-bound	4.0 (39.5)	0.4 (12)	0.6 (32)
Intracellular Concentration			
Total	4 mg%	140	30–40
	(2 mEq/l)	mEq/l	mEq/l
Ionized	0.4 mg%		
	(0.2 mEq/l)		

*(per cent of total).

On the debit side calcium is found in gut secretions with a daily loss of about 760 mg/24 hr in the adult. Another 100 to 300 mg/day exists in the urine; restriction of calcium intake to less than 200 mg/day will decrease excretion to less than 100 mg.

Role of Kidney in Calcium Homeostasis

As anticipated, the kidney is charged with retention or excretion of calcium, modulating its response depending upon availability of calcium in the extracellular fluid. Usually the daily glomerular filtrate contains approximately 10,000 mg of calcium; the urine, ultimately elaborated, contains only 100 mg of calcium per day. It is noteworthy that the prodigious ability of the kidney to conserve calcium is not complemented by an equal ability to rid the body of excess calcium in hypercalcemia. This apparently depends upon the relationship between calcium and phosphorus homeostasis. Phosphorus is both reabsorbed and excreted by the kidney tubule (see Chapter 14). Apparently the primary role of the kidney in augmenting phosphorus excretion imposes a ceiling on its ability to simultaneously excrete calcium, owing to the clear and present danger of precipitation of calcium phosphate in the tubules (see the section Calcium-Phosphorus Solubility Product [K_{sp}]). While this may be an oversimplified view of these complex inter-relationships, the reader can nonetheless readily appreciate why the kidney's ability to excrete calcium may have to be limited because of the relatively enormous amounts of phosphorus it excretes.

In summary, the ability of the kidney to conserve calcium in hypocalcemic states is far greater than its ability to excrete calcium in hypercalcemia. The avidity of calcium conservation in hypocalcemic states assures adequate calcium for its variegated informational functions. Beyond that lower limit, it would seem reasonable for the kidney to have the same flexibility in ridding the body of too much calcium. But in that case the possibility of precipitation of Ca-P salts in the kidney is so likely that increase in calcium excretion has been avoided. Consequently, the body has no immediate defense against hypercalcemia.

Calcium Binding and Receptor Proteins

In Part I of this book, we discussed the role of proteins as the functional constituents of the living system. There we also emphasized that enzymes possess, in addition to the active (catalytic) site, additional sites that allow the binding of other small molecules serving an informational role in the metabolic economy. Here we wish to consider the interaction of calcium with a group of calcium-binding proteins. These proteins are present in different cells within the body and in each instance serve a distinct and unique informational role.

Inquiring into the suitability of calcium for these specific biochemical roles leads inevitably to the question as to why other divalent cations, in particular magnesium, cannot serve the same function. Undoubtedly the answer must reside in the trial and error aspect of evolution, a viewpoint that directs our attention to the evolutionary forces that must have been at work. Proteins that possess a specific affinity for calcium are able to concentrate a number of oxygen atoms (each possessing a partial or full negative charge) in stereochemical position to generate a cavity capable of interacting with a positively charged ion with a radius of 0.99 Å. This size requirement excludes magnesium, which has a radius of 0.65 Å. Although magnesium can undoubtedly enter the specific cavity possessed by calcium-binding proteins, because of its smaller size (as well as other factors) it is unlikely to serve as well. In other words, it is unable to engage in the specific interactions with the calcium-binding proteins that generate the necessary conformational changes in the protein structure. This is yet another example of the way in which conformational adaptability transmits information to a macromolecule.

The unsuitability of transition metals such as zinc, cadmium, and manganese for the role subserved by calcium is probably a consequence of their inability to saturate these binding sites owing to their vanishingly small cytosolic concentration. This is accentuated by the enormous and readily available body stores of calcium. It is worth noting that magnesium and several of the transition metals often act in an antagonistic fashion to calcium both in vitro and in vivo, an observation that is most easily understood by reasoning that magnesium, while being able to fit the calcium-protein lock, is unable to turn the key to elicit the biochemical response.

Calcium and the Transmission of Information Within the Cell

At a physiologic level the many roles of calcium as coupling agent for excitation-transmission in the central nervous system, excitation-contraction in muscle, stimulation-secretion in glands, as well as in blood coagulation have been known for many years (see Table 5–1). Additionally, calcium has now been shown to serve a role in a number of metabolic pathways, including glycogenolysis and gluconeogenesis. Its actions in such a wide variety of physiological responses suggest general and specific features shared by all these systems that provide for the appropriate response to calcium when the stimulus is applied.

Normal plasma calcium concentration is approximately 2.5 mM or 10 mg/dl, with about 1 mM of the total being ionized; the intracellular total calcium concentration is 2 mM (2×10^{-3} molar). In muscle and nerve, for which the most accurate data exist, the free concentration varies between 10^{-8} molar and 10^{-6} molar. Hence, intracellularly bound calcium predominates, probably most of it as phosphate complexes within mitochondria and microsomes, with the rest bound to protein and organic ions. The current view is that the bound calcium exists in a nonionized state within the cell; this awaits experimental verification.

It is remarkable that the calcium that serves as an informational cation does so in the range of 10^{-8} molar during nonstimulated states and approximately 10^{-6} molar during stimulated states. This is in the face of an external concentration of ionized calcium that is 1 mM (10^{-3} molar). This decided concentration gradient has been shown to depend upon a calcium "pump" that requires ATP as its energy source. The sequestration of calcium in mitochondria and microsomes is also maintained by calcium pumps situated in the membranes of those organelles. The exceptionally narrow dynamic range of calcium concentration utilized to signal the onset of a biochemical response (between 10^{-8} and 10^{-6} molar) is dependent upon the ability of a specific protein to bind calcium preferentially. Further clarification of the role of calcium comes from the discovery of a monomeric protein (M.W. 17,000) termed calmodulin that is widely distributed throughout the animal and plant world. It is the intracellular calcium receptor, and the calmodulin-calcium complex regulates calcium-dependent biochemical processes. In this manner a small molecule, such as calcium, may act as a biochemical lever inducing a conformational change in a macromolecule, which can then initiate a series of events at a biochemical level. When millions of cells respond simultaneously to the applied stimulus, the event is expressed at a macroscopic or physiological level. Indeed, as noted before, this theme of small molecules affecting the activity of macromolecules is at the center of the life process.

HORMONES AFFECTING CALCIUM

Parathyroid Hormone

In the evolutionary scheme the parathyroids appeared when animals left the sea (amphibians). No longer able to avail themselves of that calcium-rich bath for constant replenishment, the need to maintain normocalcemia had to be met.

Parathyroid hormones act on several organs (bone, kidney, and gut) to maintain the ionized calcium concentration of extracellular fluid (see Table 5–2). Feedback regulation of parathyroid production is predominantly under the control of the serum ionized calcium concentration. It is not clear whether the sensing mechanism responds to rate of change of calcium as well as to absolute level. When serum calcium falls, as in starvation, parathyroid hormone secretion increases, stimulating bone resorption, with the result that calcium enters the blood. Further, it increases renal tubule reabsorption of calcium and by stimulation of $1,25(OH)_2D_3$ production augments absorption as well. Normally 7 to 10 g of calcium is filtered per day; urinary excretion is in the range of 100 to 300 mg. When serum concentrations fall to 7.5 mg/dl, urinary loss is almost totally abated.

Proteolytic cleavage is a well-defined mode of activation of enzymes, as occurs with intestinal zymogens and enzymes in the coagulation sequence. Such a processing sequence characterizes the steps in the biosynthesis of PTH, which begins as a pre-prohormone with 115 amino acids and is further modified to the prohormone with 90 amino acids. This enzymatic cleavage occurs immediately after synthesis of the pre-proPTH. Conversion to the hormone occurs in the Golgi apparatus and requires another hydrolytic cleavage, which produces the active hormone with 84 amino acid residues. It is likely that the sequences of amino acids present in pre-proPTH and pro-PTH serve as recognition signals or attachment sites during transport of the precursor to the site of modification.

Mode of Action

The key to the action of PTH on both kidney and bone appears to be stimulation of plasma membrane adenylate cyclase, with a consequent rise in intracellular cAMP. Phosphaturia is the first observable result of this cAMP production.

An additional action of PTH, believed to be important in eliciting its biological effects, is enhancement of Ca influx into the cell. There calcium can also act as a signal to regulate enzymatic reactions, as discussed earlier.

Vitamin D

In actuality, vitamin D is a hormone. The Industrial Revolution, with its deleterious effects on the atmosphere, prevented easy access to sunlight, which effects the conversion of 7-dehydrocholesterol by skin into cholecalciferol (vitamin D). Thus was a normal biochemical reaction blocked by a change in the environment, rendering the hormone a vitamin. It follows that adequate exposure to sunlight provides adequate "D". Nonetheless, it is found in fish liver oils and irradiated yeast and is now added to certain staples, among which are milk, milk products, and some cereals.

The last 15 years have witnessed an explosion of information regarding vitamin D, the essence of which is that it must undergo modifying reactions (hydroxylation) to be transformed into active metabolites (Fig. 5–4). This requires a two-step process, beginning in the liver with conversion to $25(OH)D_3$ and followed by a second step in the kidney that produces $1,25(OH)_2D_3$.

We have remarked earlier regarding the body's ability to increase the efficiency of calcium absorption during growth, pregnancy, or lactation or when calcium in the diet is in short supply. Such flexibility in absorptive capacity depends upon $1,25(OH)_2D_3$ and its action on intestine.

Mechanism of Action

Experimental data support the view that $1,25(OH)_2D_3$ acts, as do other steroid hormones, through a specific cytosol receptor that is transported to the chromatin, activating the transcription process. While a specific calcium-binding protein is one of the products of this stimulation, unfortunately its role in the enhancement of calcium absorption is not as neatly defined as one might like. A similar lack of clarity shrouds the calcium-dependent ATPase, whose synthesis is also stimulated by $1,25(OH)_2D_3$. Exactly how vitamin D increases calcium absorption is unclear; however, the stimulation of Ca^{++} uptake is perhaps its most obvious and important action.

While vitamin D potentiates the resorptive action of PTH on bone, it is believed that this is part of an overall effect to provide calcium for mineralization of new bone. Enhancing gastrointestinal absorptive action, vitamin D acts to provide adequate calcium and phosphorus for calcification. An additional, direct effect of vitamin D on bone mineralization is a frequently postulated action for which there is tantalizing inferential evidence. Some investigators believe that a direct action of some D metabolite will eventually be demonstrated in an appropriate system. Such a direct effect may involve the matrix structure or transport (as in the intestine), to pose two possibilities.

These combined effects of vitamin D point to a primary role in controlling skeletal growth rather than in controlling serum calcium levels. High doses of vitamin D can act like PTH, stimu-

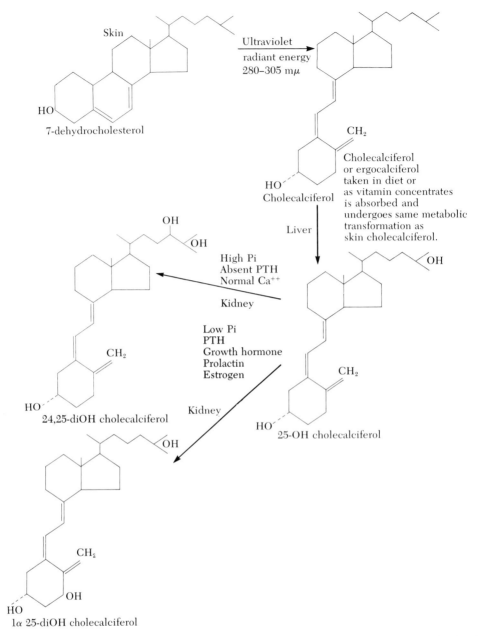

Figure 5–4 Metabolic cycle of vitamin D that leads to formation of active vitamin D hormone, 1,25-diOH vitamin D, and also of 24,25-diOH vitamin, which may have physiologic activity but is on the pathway to inactivation and elimination of vitamin D. (From Harrison, H.E., and Harrison, H.C.: Disorders of Calcium and Phosphate Metabolism in Childhood and Adolescence. Philadelphia, W.B. Saunders Co., 1979.)

lating bone resorption and thereby raising serum calcium and phosphorus for the calcification process. Indeed, in hypoparathyroidism, pharmacologic doses of vitamin D can maintain normocalcemia. This is not surprising, since one of the consequences of decreased PTH is diminished production of $1,25(OH)_2D_3$.

Calcitonin

Calcitonin (CT) has actions antagonistic to those of PTH, decreasing bone resorption and increasing calcium excretion by the kidney. Response of the thyroid to changes in serum calcium levels is prompt and direct, i.e., increase in calcium leads to increase in calcitonin and vice versa. Despite this clear-cut relationship, it does not appear that this is its major physiological role.

Calcitonin has been found to inhibit secretion of gastric acid and pepsin while stimulating secretion by the small intestine. Although it apparently does not influence mineral absorption directly, its differential effects on mobility and secretion result in diminished absorption of calcium from a meal. However, these gastrointestinal effects are demonstrable only at pharmacological levels of the hormone, casting doubt on their physiological relevance.

Mode of Action

Calcitonin acts through cAMP formation, of necessity at membrane sites distinct from those that bind PTH. Calcium appears to have a modulating role in the action of calcitonin. This raises a dilemma, however, since both PTH and CT increase calcium entry into osteoclasts. One way around this problem has been to propose that it is the level of intracellular calcium (as in muscle contraction-relaxation cycle) that is key. At moderate concentrations resorption is stimulated, but when calcium rises to higher levels resorption ceases. This makes sense; it remains to be seen whether plausibility presages reality.

Physiological Role

As the matter now stands, despite the antagonism to the action of PTH, the predominate action of CT appears to be resistance to hypercalcemia after eating. The effect on bone would also blunt a tendency to increased serum calcium.

Disorders of Calcium

Hypocalcemia

Any chemical definition of hypocalcemia must be somewhat arbitrary, particularly in light of interlaboratory variability in arriving at norms. Nonetheless, it seems prudent to consider hypocalcemia when total calcium is less than 8 mg/dl and ionized calcium is below 2.6 mg/dl. It is essential to realize that, as with anemia, hypocalcemia can be multicausal and so a search for its basis is necessary. Etiologies are considered from the vantage point of the different age groups liable to develop hypocalcemia, such a consideration emphasizing as well the varying manifestations with age. Hypoalbuminemia decreases serum total calcium roughly 0.8 mg/dl calcium for each mg/dl depression of albumin.

Hypocalcemia During the Neonatal Period. It is appropriate to distinguish early neonatal hypocalcemia from a later-onset variety (Table 5–7). All infants experience a transient decrease in serum calcium at birth as maternal supplies are cut off. Decrease below 8 mg/dl is an accentuation of this characteristic phenomenon, found predominantly in low birth weight infants (during the last trimester the bulk of maternal-fetal calcium transport occurs) or in infants experiencing significant prenatal or perinatal stresses (toxemia, abruptio placentae, hyaline membrane disease, asphyxia, or central nervous system damage).

In addition to abrupt cessation of calcium supply from the mother at birth, there is a transient decrease in PTH levels (secondary to the in utero augmentation of calcium transfer to the fetus) that occurs during the final trimester. Further complicating the PTH picture are data that point to a blunted responsiveness of target organs to PTH in the neonate. Finally, elevation of adrenal steroids in the stressed infant may also contribute to the transient hypocalcemia. Acting in concert these factors (and perhaps others yet to be defined) render calcium homeostasis, tenuous in the normal newborn, precarious in the overtaxed infant.

One additional factor contributing to the hypocalcemia of the stressed neonate may be cleavage of intracellular organic phosphate (ATP, creatine phosphate) with release of inorganic phosphate into the blood. Complexation with serum Ca would then lower the Ca^{++} concentration. Inability to

Table 5–7   CAUSES OF HYPOCALCEMIA

Early Onset (up to 72 hours)
  Accentuation of normal neonatal hypocalcemia
    Limited calcium stores
      Premature or small for gestational age
      Maternal deficiency of calcium intake or vitamin D intake (sunlight)
  Stressed infant
    Infant of diabetic mother
    Toxemia
    Cerebral injury
    Sepsis
    Respiratory distress syndrome
Late Onset (usually after 5 days)
  Hyperphosphatemia (cow's milk)
  Magnesium deficiency
  Hypoparathyroidism
    Transient Idiopathic
    Inherited
  End-organ resistance to PTH
    Pseudo- and pseudo-pseudohypoparathyroidism
  Vitamin D deficiency
    Chronic renal insufficiency

normalize the Ca concentration points as well to insufficient response of the parathyroids in these infants, which is further compounded by excessive calcitonin secretion for the level of PTH output. How does this imbalance in calcitonin and PTH levels come about? Since growth is so rapid in utero, it seems reasonable that calcitonin facilitates growth by putting a brake on bone resorption. As part of this growth process the mother is being drained of calcium (particularly during the last trimester), which would increase her parathyroid activity, secondarily depressing parathyroid activity in the growing fetus.

Hypocalcemia involving free calcium ions leads to heightened neuromuscular irritability and the syndrome of tetany (Table 5–8). In infants, hypocalcemia may be manifested only by irritability or lethargy, symptoms that are sufficiently nonspecific that hypocalcemia may not be diagnosed unless it is considered in the differential diagnosis. The full-blown tetanic syndrome, including carpopedal spasm, paresthesias, anxiety, seizures, Chvostek's and Trousseau's signs and laryngospasm, will be expressed at different levels of calcium ions in different individuals and at different ages.

Late-onset neonatal hypocalcemia (see Table 5–7) does not appear until the infant has been given a high phosphate load for several days (usually cow's milk) with consequent hyperphosphatemia, as the infant kidney is unable to excrete the excessive phosphorus. Hypocalcemia is probably

Table 5–8   SIGNS AND SYMPTOMS OF
            HYPOCALCEMIA

Neuromuscular
  Tetany, irritability, memory loss, confusion, seizures
    (Chvostek and Trousseau's signs)
  Difficulty breathing (inspiratory stridor)
Eye
  Cataracts
  Corneal deposition calcium
Neonatal Hypocalcemia
  Requires high level of suspicion because of relatively
    nonspecific symptoms and signs
  Fine tremors of chin and fingers
  Rapid shallow respirations with intercostal retractions
  Tachypnea alternating with apnea
  Vomiting
  Generalized seizures
  Laryngeal signs uncommon

brought about through enhanced deposition of calcium phosphate in bone and diminished PTH effect on bone. During this period the inhibitory effect on bone resorption characteristic of CT may also play a role in the generation of the hypocalcemia.

Magnesium homeostasis is closely tied to that of calcium. Hypomagnesemia occurs either as a result of an inherited defect in intestinal absorption or as a consequence of malabsorption or malnutrition. Under such circumstances hypocalcemia may supervene because of decreased release of PTH, blunted end-organ responsiveness to PTH, diminished gastrointestinal uptake of calcium, and depressed release of calcium from bone secondary to lessened calcium-for-magnesium exchange at bone surfaces. By definition neonatal tetany is self-limited, usually disappearing by 21 days of age. When hypocalcemia persists beyond this period, persistent causes must be investigated (see Table 5–7).

One such cause is transient congenital idiopathic hypoparathyroidism with hypocalcemia and hyperphosphatemia. It is believed that this condition may reflect prolonged physiological hypoparathyroidism, since the mother has normal parathyroid hormone levels. Only minimal supplementation with vitamin D is necessary to maintain normocalcemia. Although it is considered a transient condition, treatment may be required for up to a year.

Better known and more serious than the transient form of hypoparathyroidism are inherited forms, including isolated hypoparathyroidism (X-linked) and DiGeorge syndrome (agenesis of the parathyroids and thymus and defects of the aortic arch).

Other late-onset causes of hypocalcemia include either acquired disorders of the parathyroid or pseudohypoparathyroidism. While there are phenotypic similarities between pseudohypoparathyroidism and pseudo-pseudohypoparathyroidism, in the latter condition serum calcium and phosphate levels are normal. Cataracts are a common physical finding in the hypocalcemia associated with hypoparathyroidism. In an as yet undefined manner, hypocalcemia in this condition impedes active transport processes, with resultant abnormalities of hydration of proteins of the lens.

Hypercalcemia

Hypercalcemia is arbitrarily defined as a total serum level of greater than 11 mg/dl and may be the result of augmented gastrointestinal absorption or an increased rate of bone resorption. When serum albumin levels are increased, total calcium will usually be increased as well; this, however, does not pose a threat as this is nonionized calcium. A list of causes of hypercalcemia is provided in Table 5–9.

Table 5–9 CAUSES OF HYPERCALCEMIA

Agents That Elevate Calcium
  Directly
    Oral or parenteral calcium
    Calcium exchange resins
  Indirectly, by acting on bone
    Hypervitaminosis D or A
Hyperparathyroidism—hypercalcemia mainly due to changes in the blood-bone equilibrium and in renal tubular reabsorption of Ca
  Primary
  Secondary to renal insufficiency
Other Endocrine Causes
  Hyper- or hypothyroidism
  Adrenal insufficiency
Idiopathic Hypercalcemia of Infancy
Other
  Malignant Bone Disease
  Sarcoidosis
  Thiazides
  Prolonged immobilization
  Hypophosphaturia
  Subcutaneous fat necrosis

Table 5–10 SIGNS AND SYMPTOMS OF
HYPERCALCEMIA

Neuromuscular
  Irritability, weakness, confusion, headache, seizures

Renal
  Polyuria, polydipsia (decreased concentrating ability)
  Colic, hematuria
  Hypertension

Other
  Red eyes
  Subcutaneous calcification

Primary hyperparathyroidism, unusual in adults, is a rare disease indeed in childhood. Symptoms are the nonspecific ones of hypercalcemia and are listed in Table 5–10. In addition to symptoms referable to the central nervous system, interference with renal concentrating ability may overshadow the other facets of the clinical picture.

Familial hyperparathyroidism can be part of the spectrum of multiple endocrine adenomatosis, being associated with pituitary and/or pancreatic abnormalities and peptic ulceration in Type I and medullary carcinoma of the thyroid with neural tumors in Type II. Both forms are inherited in an autosomal dominant manner.

Short-lived increases in calcium are also associated with findings in which neurological manifestations predominate (see Table 5–10). When hypercalcemia is of longer duration, renal function, especially concentrating ability, is likely to be diminished. Moreover, when coupled with normal or even modestly elevated serum phosphate, metastatic calcification in a variety of sites, including blood vessels, renal parenchyma, cornea, joint spaces, and gastric mucosa, is not infrequent, with consequent disordered function.

Administration of vitamin D in supraphysiologic amounts can cause hypercalcemia. In such doses considerable tissue stores accumulate (especially in adipose tissue), with abrupt onset of toxicity without warning. Hence careful monitoring of serum calcium and alkaline phosphatase is essential to prevent persistent hypercalcemia, the result of accentuated gut uptake of calcium. As a consequence, dehydrotachysterol is preferred by many because of its rapid onset and decay of action. Hypervitaminosis A can also cause hypercalcemia by increasing bone resorption through a mechanism that remains undefined.

A fracture severe enough to require immobilization, especially in adolescence, will set up a disequilibrium between bone deposition, which decreases abruptly, and bone resorption, which proceeds unabated. The result is unopposed calcium mobilization and hypercalcemia if the kidney cannot excrete the additional load.

Idiopathic hypercalcemia of infancy appears to emanate from a heightened responsiveness of the infants to minimal increments in vitamin D above the daily requirement. These infants are described as having elfinlike facies. In addition to characteristic findings of hypercalcemia, failure to thrive may be the most outstanding clinical finding in these infants. Often it is this that causes them to come to medical attention. They may suffer from transient and relatively benign to life-threatening hypercalcemia. Mental retardation is a part of the clinical picture and does not improve when the hypercalcemia remits, often spontaneously. One can anticipate as well that persistent hypercalcemia would lead to metastatic calcification involving the kidney, lungs, and heart.

In adults hypercalcemia associated with neoplasm is very common; in children, less so. Hypercalcemia is probably due to osseous destruction with synthesis of humoral compounds by the tumor; bone resorptive action may be another factor. Candidates for such a role include peptides with PTH-like activity, sterols with vitamin D-like action, and prostaglandin E, which fosters bone resorption.

PHOSPHORUS

As indicated at the outset of the chapter (see Table 5–1), phosphate compounds have been selected by evolution to mediate the conservation and transfer of energy essential to life's processes. By conserving the energy derived from oxidation in high-energy phosphate bonds of ATP and its relatives, this vital energy is not all lost as heat. Moreover, by storing energy in these stable organic phosphate compounds, energy derived from oxidation can be employed in a temporally unrelated biosynthetic reaction.

Lipmann (1941) and others have emphasized that the uniqueness of these compounds is not their high energy (high group-transfer potential). Rather it is their resistance to reaction in the aqueous environment of all cells. The energy of these compounds can be unleashed only in the presence of suitable enzymes. This situation contrasts sharply with derivatives of carboxylic acids (e.g., acetic anhydride) and hydrochloric and sulfuric acid, which have a fleeting existence in water.

As a component of nucleic acids phosphorus is involved as well in the informational activities of the cells. It also serves in structural functions both at the level of the cell membrane (phospholipids) and at the level of the skeleton. Like calcium, the bulk of the body's phosphorus (100 g) is found in the skeleton (85 per cent), which serves as a reservoir for this mineral.

In contrast to calcium, serum phosphate concentrations are not maintained within the same narrow confines. This presumably reflects the central role of phosphorus in intracellular processes (intracellular concentration is 140 mEq/l) as opposed to calcium's role in regulating Na and K conductance during excitation.

It turns out that extracellular phosphate plays an important role in providing adequate intracellular phosphate for oxidative phosphorylation ($ADP + Pi \rightarrow ATP$) and phospholipid synthesis. Nucleotide degradation in the cell is also affected by intracellular phosphate levels. From what has been said one would expect cellular organic phosphorus concentrations (200 to 300 mg/dl) to exceed inorganic phosphorus levels (3 to 4 mg/dl). Because of this large difference in how phosphorus is sequestered intracellularly, administering glucose (provided insulin is available) can increase the organic phosphate pool at the expense of the inorganic reservoir. This promotes extracellular phosphate entry into cells to replenish intracellular inorganic phosphate levels. Indeed, 100 to 200 g of carbohydrate can decrease serum phosphate by 1 to 1.5 mg/dl within 2 to 2½ hours of ingestion.

Serum phosphorus levels display variability during periods of growth: bone turnover is associated with transient elevation in phosphorus. Indeed, the range of normal values in childhood is age-dependent, reflecting the briskness of the bone turnover, which is the foundation upon which growth is carried out. Hence, serum phosphorus levels are higher in children than they are in adults, there being a rough correspondence between growth rate and phosphorus levels. Normal values and distribution of phosphate species are listed in Table 5–11. An additional point of distinction be-

Table 5–11 PLASMA
PHOSPHORUS*

Organic Phosphorus	
Lipid phosphorus	2.58
Other organic phosphorus	0.19
Total	2.77
Inorganic Phosphorus	
Diffusible phosphorus	0.86
HPO_4^{2-}	0.44
$NaHPO_4^-$	0.26
$H_2PO_4^-$	0.10
$CaHPO_4$	0.04
$MgHPO_4$	0.02
Protein bound	0.22
Total inorganic	1.08
Total plasma	3.85

*In mmol/l.

Table 5–12 CAUSES OF HYPERPHOSPHATEMIA

Shift of Phosphorus Out of Bone Into Blood
  Rapid bone growth
    Healing fracture
    Bone neoplasm
    Pituitary gigantism
  Hemolytic states and leukemia
  Hyperthyroidism
Abnormal Renal Retention of Phosphorus
  Renal failure
  Parathyroid deficiency
    Hypoparathyroidism
    Pseudohypoparathyroidism
    Maternal hyperparathyroidism
Enhanced Gastrointestinal Absorption
  Vitamin D intoxication
  Phosphate enemas
  Acute intestinal obstruction

tween phosphorus and calcium is the relatively minor (approximately 12 per cent) binding of phosphorus to plasma protein. As can be seen from Table 5–11, the multiplicity of different phosphorus-containing species requires a simplifying mode of expressing phosphorus. This is accomplished by reporting elemental phosphorus as mg/dl.

Persistent elevation of serum phosphorus (Table 5–12) serves as a stimulus for ectopic deposition of calcium phosphate. While acute decreases in serum phosphorus may not be associated with any clinical manifestations, chronic depression of serum phosphorus is accompanied by anorexia, dizziness, and proximal muscle weakness. In addition, as a consequence of the phosphopenic state, bone pain and the waddling gait of osteomalacia occur.

Growth retardation is a regular consequence of phosphate depletion (Table 5–13). One reason for this is the decreased erythrocyte, 2,3-DPG level, which diminishes the amount of oxygen delivered to cells. Diminished red cell ATP levels contribute to the increased propensity to develop a hemolytic anemia because of abnormalities in membrane plasticity.

Phosphorus absorption from the intestine is far more efficient than calcium uptake. On limited intakes (less than 2 mg/kg/day) almost 90 per cent is absorbed, while on usual diets (10 mg/kg/day) about 70 per cent is absorbed. Because of the avidity with which phosphorus is taken up by the gut, control of plasma phosphorus resides with the kidney. Usually 90 per cent of phosphorus in the glomerular filtrate is reabsorbed in the proximal tubule. Percentage reabsorption increases with a decrease in phosphorus filtered and decreases with increased loads. Reabsorption of phosphorus

Table 5–13 CAUSES OF HYPOPHOSPHATEMIA

Uptake of Phosphate by Cells
  Phosphorylation of glucose or fructose
  Insulin administration; recovery phase of diabetic ketoacidosis
  Nutritional recovery syndrome
Abnormal Renal Loss of Phosphorus
  Renal tubular defect
    Cystinosis
    Proximal RTA
    Vitamin D-resistant rickets
    Potassium depletion (interferes with renal phosphate reabsorption)
  Primary or secondary hyperparathyroidism
Dietary Inadequacy or Defective Gastrointestinal Absorption
  Malnutrition
  Vitamin D deficiency (malabsorption, liver disease, anticonvulsants)
  Phosphate binding gels in renal failure

depends upon simultaneous sodium reabsorption. These two cations differ in their handling in the distal tubule in that sodium may also experience distal reabsorption whereas phosphorus does not. Hence, in general, drugs or volume expansion augmenting sodium excretion through a proximal tubule action have a similar effect on phosphorus as well.

REFERENCES

Austin, L.A., and Heath, H.: Calcitonin. New Engl. J. Med. 304:269, 1981.

Avioli, L., and Krane, S. (ed.): Metabolic Bone Disease. Academic Press, New York, 1978.

Bordier, P., Rasmussen, H., Marie, P., et al.: Vitamin D metabolites and bone mineralization in man. J. Clin. Endocrinol. Metab. 46:284, 1978.

Cheung, W.Y.: Calmodulin plays a pivotal role in cellular regulation. Science 207:19, 1980.

Cheung, W.Y.: Calmodulin and the adenylate cyclase-phosphodiesterase system. Cell Calcium 2:263, 1981.

DeLuca, H.F.: Recent advances in the metabolism of vitamin D. Ann. Rev. Physiol. 43:199, 1981.

Habener, J.F.: Regulation of parathyroid hormone secretion and biosynthesis. Ann. Rev. Physiol. 43:211, 1981.

Harrison, H.E., and Harrison, H.C.: Disorders of Calcium and Phosphate Metabolism in Childhood and Adolescence. W.B. Saunders, Philadelphia, 1979.

Kreisberg, R.A.: Phosphorus deficiency and hypophosphatemia. Hosp. Pract. (March) 121, 1977.

Lipmann, F.: Metabolic generation and utilization of phosphate bond energy. Adv. Enzymol. 1:99, 1941.

Marcus, R.: The relationship of dietary calcium to the maintenance of skeletal integrity in man—An interface of endocrinology and nutrition. Metabolism 31:93, 1982.

Massry, S.G., and Fleisch, H. (eds.): Renal Handling of Phosphate. Plenum Press, New York, 1980.

Means, A.R., Tash, J.S., and Chafouleas, J.G.: Physiological implications of the presence, distribution and regulation of calmodulin in eukaryotic cells. Physiol. Rev. 62:1, 1982.

Price, P.A., Parthemore, J.G., Deftos, L.J., and Nishimoto, S.K.: New biochemical marker for bone metabolism. J. Clin. Invest. 66:878, 1980.

Raisz, L.G., and Kream, B.E.: Hormonal control of skeletal growth. Ann. Rev. Physiol. 43:225, 1981.

Rasmussen, H., Goodman, D.B.P., Friedmann, N., et al.: Ionic control of metabolism. In Greep, R.O., and Astwood, E.B. (eds.): Handbook of Physiology-Endocrinology. Vol. VII Parathyroid. American Physiology Society, 1976, p. 225.

Stern, P.H.: The D vitamins and bone. Pharmacol. Rev. 32:47, 1980.

Stewart, A.F., and Broadus, A.E.: The regulation of renal calcium excretion: An approach to hypercalciuria. Ann. Rev. Med. 32:457, 1981.

Talmage, R.V., and Cooper, C.W.: Physiology and mode of action of calcitonin. In DeGroot, L., Cahill, G.F., Jr., Martini, L., et al. (eds.): Endocrinology. Grune & Stratton, New York, 1979, p. 647.

Urry, D.W.: Basic aspects of calcium chemistry and membrane interaction: on the messenger role of calcium. Ann. N. Y. Acad. Sci. 307:3, 1978.

6

Cardiovascular Pathophysiology

In this section we will not attempt to discuss individual cardiovascular congenital abnormalities, all of which are well described in any textbook on cardiac disease, but we will outline their consequences for cellular biochemistry and hence physiology of cardiovascular abnormalities. Simply stated, the effect of all cardiovascular disorders is to deprive all or part of the cells of the body of sufficient nutrient and oxygen supply for normal metabolism.

STRUCTURE AND FUNCTION OF THE MYOCARDIUM

The myocardium of the ventricles is composed of interconnecting fibers whose lengths vary from 30 to 60 microns and whose diameters vary from 10 to 20 microns. Thus while cardiac fibers are similar functionally to skeletal fibers, they are smaller than the latter. Cardiac and skeletal muscle fibers are composed of a few thousand cross-banded strands or bundles, termed myofibrils, that traverse the entire length of the fibers. The myofibrils are in turn composed of thousands of sarcomeres that are themselves composed of contractile proteins (actin and myosin) arranged as myofilaments (Fig. 6–1). In cardiac muscle the sarcomeres occupy only about 50 per cent of the mass of the cardiac cell (in contrast to approximately 90 per cent of skeletal muscle) and are aligned end to end, giving the entire fiber a banded or striated appearance. The molecular mechanisms involved in muscle contraction are discussed in Chapter 16.

Considering the role played by the heart, it is not surprising that the energy requirements for the cardiac cell are quite high. Indeed mitochondria constitute 25 to 30 per cent of the entire mass of the cell. They appear to be located in close proximity to the contractile filaments, which may facilitate the transfer of ATP from its site of production in the mitochondria to its site of utilization during contraction.

Membranes Involved in Contraction

The sarcolemma is the surface membrane that invests individual myocardial fibers. Functions served by the sarcolemma include (1) maintenance of the intracellular environment, (2) depolarization, and (3) propagation of electrical depolarization from one fiber to the next, producing gener-

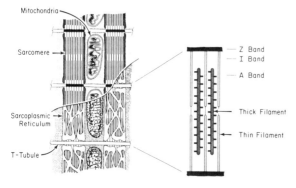

Mitochondria

Sarcomere

Z Band
I Band
A Band

Sarcoplasmic
Reticulum

Thick Filament

Thin Filament

T-Tubule

Figure 6–1 Structure of the myocardial cell. On the left, sarcomeres are shown, aligned end-to-end, thus giving the myofibril its banded appearance. The relative volume occupied by the sarcomeres and the mitochondria appear approximately equal. On the right is shown the relative arrangement of the thick (myosin) and thin (actin) filaments, which are the basic subunits of the sarcomere. (Reprinted, by permission of The New England Journal of Medicine, 290:445, 1974.)

Table 6–1 METABOLIC CAUSES OF HEART FAILURE

Beriberi
Familial systemic carnitine deficiency
Friedreich's ataxia
Hurler's syndrome
Muscular dystrophy
Pompe's disease
Hyperadrenalism
Thyrotoxicosis

alized activation. Hence muscle is an "excitable" tissue. For a discussion of depolarization the reader is referred to Chapter 17, where nervous tissue excitability is considered.

Actin and myosin are the contractile proteins, while troponin and tropomyosin are regulatory proteins. These latter proteins constitute approximately 10 per cent of the myofibrillar protein and are associated with the thin filament. The contraction-relaxation cycle of cardiac muscle is regulated by an absolute dependence upon the intracellular calcium concentration, which in turn is controlled by the sarcoplasmic reticulum and the surface membrane. Inborn errors affecting the contractility of the heart are listed in Table 6–1.

HEMOGLOBIN AND THE RED CELL

Any discussion of cardiovascular physiology must include a description of the interaction between hemoglobin and oxygen, since cyanosis depends upon this specific relationship. It had been known for many years that hemoglobin, deprived entirely of oxygen, had a bluish-violet color and that when fully saturated with oxygen, turned a bright red. Further, it was known that oxygen saturation levels below 80 per cent in vivo usually resulted in cyanosis. However, it was not until Bohr studied the nature of the interaction between various factors such as pH and hemoglobin-oxygen saturation that any clinical relationship between the more subtle factors involved in heart disease and cellular metabolism was recognized.

Bohr, in his now classic experiments, described the relationship between hemoglobin-oxygen saturation and the partial pressure of oxygen in the environment. When these data were plotted on standard graph paper, a sigmoid-shaped curve was obtained (Fig. 6–2). With such a graph, the partial pressure at which hemoglobin is found to be 50 per cent saturated with oxygen is known as the P_{50}. In subsequent experiments, Bohr tested the effect of pH changes on the sigmoid-shaped curve and discovered that as the pH was decreased, the P_{50} was greatly diminished. In other words, as the system becomes more acid, the ability to bind oxygen is decreased. Conversely, with increased pH the binding affinity of hemoglobin for oxygen is increased. This relationship is known as the "Bohr effect." One important physiologic consequence of the Bohr effect is that under conditions in which cellular metabolism might be slowed as a result of metabolic acidosis, hemoglobin is more easily able to give up the oxygen it carries and therefore to augment the delivery of oxygen for continued cell metabolism. Thus, impaired oxygenation of blood in the lungs with an attendant fall in arterial PO_2 leads to a decrease in oxygen saturation, observed clinically as cyanosis (Table 6–2). The metabolic acidosis due to peripheral tissue hypoxia accentuates the problem further.

Here we should call attention to the differences in the structure and function of hemoglobin in an infant as compared with an adult. Hemoglobin is a tetrameric molecule, consisting of two types of protein chains. In adult hemoglobin, known as hemoglobin A, the two types of protein chains are known as alpha and beta chains. In fetal hemoglobin (HbF), the preponderant type found in a newborn infant, they are alpha and gamma chains. As a result of Perutz' classic X-ray defraction studies, we now know that it is the interaction of the two types of chains which determines the ability of hemoglobin to bind oxygen. Substitution of gamma for beta chains in the molecule pro-

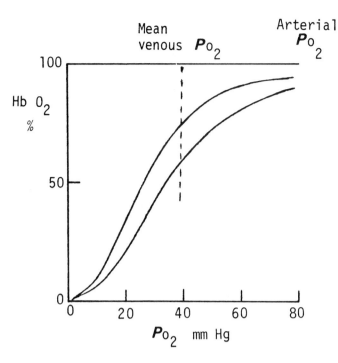

Figure 6-2 Plot of hemoglobin O_2 saturation versus partial pressures of O_2. The two separate sigmoid shaped curves represent adult human hemoglobins with different O_2 affinities. At ambient pO_2 (40 mm Hg) the P_{50} of the two hemoglobins are significantly different. (From Huehns, E.R.: Disorders of carbohydrate metabolism in the red blood corpuscle. Clin. Endocrinol. Metab. 5:657, 1976.)

duces significant differences in oxygen binding of the hemoglobin molecule. Hemoglobin F has a far greater affinity for oxygen at a given pH than hemoglobin A. Physiologically, this greater affinity of hemoglobin F for oxygen may well represent a survival advantage to the fetus, which exists in utero under relatively hypoxic conditions. The normal neonate, however, is exposed to unrestricted oxygen supply in the ambient air, and one would expect that a high concentration of hemoglobin F in the newborn's red cells might actually constitute a risk factor in terms of oxygen supply to the peripheral tissues. Fortunately, replacement of fetal hemoglobin by hemoglobin A begins after birth, thus suiting the newborn better for extrauterine life. The mechanism responsible for this switchover is not presently known.

Since hemoglobin does not exist free in the circulation but is rather contained within the erythrocyte cytosol, it is necessary to note that alterations in the nature of the membrane itself as well as factors in red cell metabolism may affect oxygen binding of hemoglobin. Alteration in the shape of the red cell membrane, brought about by changes in the nature of the membrane composition, may drastically affect the ability of oxygen to diffuse through the membrane and then bind to hemoglobin. It is well-known that the normal shape of the red cell permits maximum rates of diffusion of oxygen into the cell because the greatest amount of surface area is exposed. An example of alterations in red cell membrane that are detrimental to the ability of oxygen to diffuse is

Table 6-2 CAUSES OF CYANOSIS

Apneic (Cyanotic) Attacks in Newborn	Persistent
Aspiration	Congenital cardiac defect
Infection	Respiratory causes
Intracranial bleeding	Pneumothorax
Choanal atresia	Diaphragmatic hernia
Tracheo-esophageal fistula	Unilateral pulmonary agenesis
Metabolic	*Metabolic*
Hypoglycemia	Methemoglobinemia
Hypocalcemia	Sulfhemoglobinemia
Hypernatremia	
Adrenal insufficiency	

Table 6–3 Inborn Errors of the Red Blood Cell

Enzyme	Mode of Inheritance
Hexokinase	Autosomal recessive
Glucose phosphate isomerase	Autosomal recessive
Phosphofructokinase	Autosomal recessive, sex-linked?
Glyceraldehyde-3-phosphate dehydrogenase	Autosomal recessive?
Triosephosphate isomerase	Autosomal recessive
2,3-Diphosphoglycerate mutase	Autosomal recessive, Autosomal dominant?
Phosphoglycerate kinase	Sex-linked, uncertain
Pyruvate kinase	Autosomal recessive
Glucose-6-phosphate dehydrogenase	Sex-linked
6-Phosphogluconate dehydrogenase	Autosomal recessive
Glutathione reductase	Uncertain
Glutathione peroxidase	Autosomal recessive
Glutathione synthetase	Autosomal recessive
γ-Glutamyl-cysteine synthetase	Autosomal recessive

hereditary spherocytosis, in which the membrane composition is altered, imposing a spherical rather than the normal biconcave configuration, thus reducing the surface area of exposure.

The erythrocyte is also unique in respect to its metabolism. The mature red cell possesses no nucleus or mitochondria. The predominant metabolic pathways present in the mature red cells are the Embden-Meyerhof (glycolytic) pathway and the pentose phosphate shunt. Inborn metabolic errors in both of these pathways have led to a better understanding of the relationship between cellular metabolism and oxygen transport (Table 6–3). One of the major factors involved in this relationship is the glycolytic intermediate 2,3-diphosphoglycerate (2,3-DPG). This compound regulates the affinity of hemoglobin for oxygen by two separate mechanisms. First, 2,3-DPG preferentially binds to deoxyhemoglobin, thus altering the equilibrium between oxygen and hemoglobin. The preferential binding of 2,3-DPG to deoxyhemoglobin appears to be due to differences in the molecular structure of deoxy- and oxyhemoglobins. The net effect of this mechanism is to increase the rate of

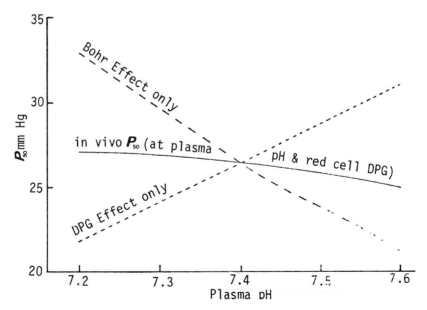

Figure 6–3 Effects of plasma pH and 2,3-DPG on the P_{50} of hemoglobin. The P_{50} is increased linearly with increasing 2,3-DPG concentration at pH 7.4 (- - - - - -). Note the reciprocal relationship of the Bohr effect on P_{50} with variation in pH (– – – –). When physiologic amounts of 2,3-DPG are present, variation in pH produces little change in the P_{50} (———). (From Huehns, E.R.: Disorders of carbohydrate metabolism in the red blood corpuscle. Clin. Endocrinol. Metab. 5:658, 1976.)

dissociation between oxygen and hemoglobin, thus shifting the curve to the right (Fig. 6–3). The second mechanism by which this compound regulates oxygen affinity of hemoglobin is by alterations in the intra-erythrocytic pH relative to plasma pH. With an increased rate of synthesis of 2,3-DPG, the erythrocytic pH drops and thus one obtains a direct effect of changes in pH mediated through 2,3-DPG upon oxygen affinity. Both mechanisms have been shown to occur in the intact erythrocyte.

Since a certain amount of time is required for significant changes to occur in levels of 2,3-DPG in the erythrocyte, there are two distinct mechanisms applicable to the change in oxygen affinity of hemoglobin in vivo. In acid-base changes of relatively acute type, oxygen affinity is regulated by the Bohr effect, while in more chronic states of acid-base change, alterations in the 2,3-DPG levels tend to counteract the pH effect on hemoglobin. Consequently, within reasonable limits oxygen affinity will be kept within a relatively narrow dynamic range.

The regulation of intracellular levels of 2,3-DPG appears to be inversely related to the oxygenation level of the hemoglobin in venous blood. As a consequence, cardiac abnormalities resulting either in low cardiac output without cyanosis or in cyanotic heart disease of a widely assorted variety result in increased erythrocytic 2,3-DPG levels.

OTHER CELLULAR EFFECTS

Infants and children with severe heart disease of either cyanotic or acyanotic type may have decreased oral intake, with concomitant decrease in calories for energetic needs. There is also a shift toward glycolysis in the cell secondary to a lack of oxygen, as discussed earlier with respect to 2,3-DPG. Both of these factors may contribute significantly to a clinical picture of hypoglycemia (see Chapter 12). Another clinically significant consequence of the increase in the rate of anaerobic glycolysis is a concomitant increase in the rate of lactic acid production. The consequences of systemic lactic acidosis are discussed elsewhere in this text (see Chapter 29). However, it should be kept in mind that lactic acidosis cannot be treated by bicarbonate replacement unless the underlying cause is remedied. Thus, in a patient who has congestive heart failure with lactic acidosis the cardiac failure may not be the terminal event but rather a consequence of the lactic acidosis.

Finally, the problem of failure to thrive in clinically significant cyanotic and acyanotic congenital heart disease must be addressed. There is at this time no satisfactory answer to the question as to why such children show, in some instances, such a dramatic picture of poor nutrition and growth. Some investigators have maintained that the energy consumed in breathing and by the overloaded heart can claim the majority of the caloric intake of the child, which is usually marginal in any case. However, in isolation this explanation is difficult to accept. Another mechanism proposed has been edema of the bowel wall secondary to venous congestion, which results in decreased absorption of ingested nutrients. This appears to be more feasible but again is not in itself a totally satisfactory explanation. Another possible explanation is the drastically reduced oral intake of the children, who are usually laboring to breathe and have little energy to expend in eating. The difficulties with all of the explanations are that satisfactory means for measurement of distribution of calories in vivo are not available and that the patients who have been studied have not been separated according to their cardiac lesions, thus providing no experimental discrimination of data.

Growth can be a significant problem, however, when one is faced with the situation of allowing a child to grow somewhat before definitive cardiac surgery and total repair of his lesion can be performed. Often these children become more ill with time and fail to achieve an ideal weight and size for surgery, forcing the physicians involved to deal with a less than optimally prepared patient. At present there are no definitive answers to the problem of growth failure in children with severe congenital heart disease.

One other point ought to be emphasized: a number of well-described congenital cardiac lesions have a high association of extracardiac anomalies. In one recent study, common lesions such as ventricular septal defect and patent ductus arteriosus were associated with a 40 per cent incidence of extracardiac anomalies. Therefore, the physician will do well to search for other less obvious defects in any child who is found to have congenital heart disease. The physiological effects of the extracardiac anomaly may be such that they precipitate heart failure in these tenuously balanced patients, as in some reported cases of inherited enzymatic deficiencies in the presence of congenital heart disease.

HYPERTENSION

The simplest manner in which to approach the problem of hypertension is to define the factors that determine blood pressure with the following equation:

$$BP = \text{cardiac output (CO)} \times \text{peripheral vascular resistance (PR)}$$

Factors Affecting Cardiac Output

Increases in cardiac output that are associated with hypertension occur in two primary ways. There may be increased sympathetic stimulation to the cardiac musculature, such as one sees in anxiety states. This type of increased cardiac output should not result in significant increases in blood pressure for prolonged periods. The other mechanism is presystolic ventricular load increases, such as those caused by increased blood volume due to excessive salt intake or decreased water excretion in renal failure. It is important to note that the increased blood volume of congestive heart failure ordinarily does not result in hypertension because the cardiac output is reduced. In fact it is the reduction of cardiac output in congestive heart failure that defines the state of heart failure.

Increased Peripheral Vascular Resistance

The most straightforward example of this type of hypertension is the anatomic malformation known as coarctation of the aorta. In this condition the thoracic or abdominal aorta is narrowed in such a way as to cause significant obstruction to flow in the more proximal portion of the vessel. Thus hypertension arises in all parts of the body perfused by vessels originating from the portion of the aorta proximal to the narrowing. Starting from this simple example, it should be evident that any condition contributing to a narrowing of the systemic vasculature will result in some degree of increased peripheral vascular resistance and, in the absence of compensation by decreased cardiac output, in increased blood pressure. The factors causing such increased peripheral vascular resistance are numerous and therefore no attempt to classify them will be undertaken here. Many of these factors relate to the kidney and are mediated by the renin-angiotensin system, a complex of enzymes and substrates that has only been worked out in the past 30 years. The details of this system are beyond the scope of this discussion. For more information the interested reader is referred to the works listed at the end of this chapter.

Generally speaking, the renal causes for hypertension may be conceptualized as being due to response by the juxtaglomerular apparatus to poor perfusion pressure of the kidney. It should be recognized immediately, however, that this statement is not proved necessarily in all cases but represents only a convenient way in which to understand the pathophysiology of hypertension in renal disease. When perfusion pressure of the kidney drops significantly, the juxtaglomerular apparatus is activated to release renin, which acts upon the renin substrates circulating in the plasma to produce various effects on peripheral resistance and sodium retention. The major known renal causes of hypertension are listed in Table 6–4. Perhaps the most reasonable example of the relationship between juxtaglomerular perfusion and hypertension is in the situation of complete renal artery thrombosis. In this condition, the perfusion of the glomerular tufts is almost completely interrupted, and the mechanism for renin-angiotensin interactions is set into motion, resulting in marked hypertension.

In summary, it would be well to consider that hypertension is more a symptom of an underlying condition than it is a disease itself, at least so far as it occurs in infants and children. The

Table 6–4 BLOOD PRESSURE ABNORMALITIES

Low Blood Pressure	High Blood Pressure
Adrenal insufficiency	Cardiovascular
Hypokalemia	Riley-Day syndrome (familial dysautonomia)
	Hyperadrenalism
	Hyperthyroidism
	Neural crest tumor (pheochromocytoma)
	Renal failure; nephritis
	Lead encephalopathy (other heavy metals as well)
	Porphyria (other neurologic including Guillain-Barré syndrome)
	Vitamin D intoxication
	Idiopathic hypercalcemia of infancy
	Aldosteronism
	Hypernatremia
	Pseudoxanthoma elasticum

vast majority of etiologies for childhood hypertension (Table 6–4) are amenable to definitive curative measures, making it all the more important to identify the underlying cause. It should also be remembered that the long-term consequence of hypertension from any etiology will be effects upon the renal vascular musculature, resulting in chronically reduced glomerular perfusion with an activation, on a chronic basis, of the renin-angiotensin mechanism and probably a variety of other biochemical mechanisms, the nature of which have not yet been defined. The overall effect of this will be to create a chronic hypertensive picture that will persist beyond removal of the inciting abnormality. Thus, all infants and children deserve the benefit of longitudinal blood pressures at least as much as a measurement of their growth and development as a part of normal well baby care. In the case of adolescents, it is clear that the major cause of hypertension is essential hypertension, again underscoring the utility of routinely obtained blood pressures, in as nonthreatening a manner as possible. Indeed, spacing repeat measurements several weeks apart will by the third visit discriminate those individuals (about 1 to 2 per cent of a normal clinical practice) who require further work-up. This contrasts with the approximate 10 per cent who may manifest hypertension on the first office visit.

REFERENCES

Alpert, N.R., Hamrell, B.B., and Mulieri, L.A.: Heart muscle mechanics. Ann. Rev. Physiol. 41:521, 1979.
Brady, A.J.: Mechanical properties of cardiac fibers. In Berne, R.M., and Sperelakis, N. (eds.): Handbook of Physiology. Sec. 2. Vol. I. Williams and Wilkins, Baltimore, 1979, p. 461.
Cowley, A.W.: The concept of autoregulation of total blood flow and its role in hypertension. Am. J. Med. 68:906, 1980.
Fabiato, A., and Fabiato, F.: Calcium and cardiac excitation-contraction coupling. Ann. Rev. Physiol. 41:473, 1979.
Greenwood, R.D., Rosenthal, A., Parisi, L., et al.: Extracardiac abnormalities in infants with congenital heart disease. Pediatrics 55:485, 1975.
Guyton, A.C.: Arterial Pressure and Hypertension. W.B. Saunders Co., Philadelphia, 1980.
Inagami, T., and Murakami, K.: Prorenin. Biomed. Res. 1:456, 1980.
Johansson, B.: Vascular smooth muscle reactivity. Ann. Rev. Physiol. 43:359, 1981.
Miller, E.D.: The role of the renin-angiotensin-aldosterone system in circulatory control and hypertension. Br. J. Anesth. 53:711, 1981.
Nathan, D.G., and Oski, F.A.: Hematology of Infancy and Childhood. W.B. Saunders Co., Philadelphia, 1981.
Nora, J.J., and Nora, A.H.: Genetic and environmental factors in the etiology of congenital heart diseases. South. Med. J. 69:919, 1976.
Peach, M.J.: Molecular actions of angiotensin. Biochem. Pharmacol. 30:2745, 1981.
Perutz, M.F.: Regulation of oxygen affinity of hemoglobin: Influence of structure of the globin of the heme iron. Ann. Rev. Biochem. 48:327, 1979.
Perutz, M.F.: Hemoglobin structure and respiratory transport. Sci. Am. 239(6):92, 1978.
Reid, I.A., Morris, B.J., and Ganong, W.F.: The renin-angiotensin system. Ann. Rev. Physiol. 40:377, 1978.
Vary, T.C., Reibel, D.K., and Neely, J.R.: Control of energy metabolism of heart muscle. Ann. Rev. Physiol. 43:419, 1981.

7

Ophthalmological Findings in Metabolic Diseases

The eye is the most specialized of the sensory organs and is therefore often implicated in biochemical disorders that affect the senses. It is also a highly specialized neurological organ and thus tends to reflect accurately those diseases that affect the central nervous system. In addition, the complexity of the mechanisms involved in relocation of the lateral embryonic eye to its final anterior position makes the eye liable to many congenital morphological disorders. Because the eye is such a complex organ, one or more of its structural or functional components may be affected by a single disease. Diseases affecting the various structures of the eye are listed in Tables 7–1 to 7–7.

EYELIDS

Because of the recent developments in our understanding of DNA biochemistry, xeroderma pigmentosum is of particular interest in the context of this book. Patients with xeroderma pigmentosum show an unusual sensitivity to ultraviolet light, in particular in the skin, eyelids, and peri-

Table 7–1 DISEASES AFFECTING THE EYELIDS

Metabolic	Chromosomal/Genetic
Ehlers-Danlos syndrome (3)*	Amyloidosis, hereditary
Fabry's disease (3)	Carpenter's syndrome (1)
Familial dysautonomia (3)	Cornelia DeLange syndrome
Farber's disease	Cri du chat syndrome (1–3)
Hypoparathyroidism (1)	Cryptophthalmos (3)
Leigh's syndrome (1–3)	Dyskeratosis congenita syndrome
Mannosidosis (1)	Ectodermal hypohidrotic dysplasia
Porphyria, acute intermittent (3)	Familial blepharophimosis (3)
Porphyria, cutanea tarda	Fanconi syndrome with pancytopenia (1)
Xeroderma pigmentosum	Franceschetti's syndrome
	Freeman-Sheldon syndrome
	Ichthyosis, congenital
	Muscular dystrophy with external ophthalmoplegia
	Myotonia congenita (1)
	Neurofibromatosis (1–3)
	Rubinstein-Taybi syndrome (1)
	Schwartz's syndrome
	Smith-Lemli-Opitz syndrome (1)
	Trisomy 18 (1,3)
	Trisomy 21 (1,3)
	Turner's syndrome (1)
	Waardenburg's syndrome
	Zellweger's syndrome (1,3)

* Associated findings: 1—mental retardation; 2—seizures; 3—neurological other than mental retardation.

ocular regions. Even limited exposure may cause carcinomatous changes resulting in basal cell or squamous cell carcinoma in the skin of the eyelid. The underlying disorder appears to be the absence of an endonuclease that is responsible for part of the repair process of damaged DNA molecules. When cells from normal individuals are exposed to UV light, a certain amount of damage to the DNA segments of the cell nucleus occurs. This damage can be repaired, however, by the initiation of degradation of the damaged DNA portion by the endonuclease, and subsequent repair by a specific DNA polymerase enzyme. Hereditary absence of the DNA endonuclease results in an inability to degrade the damaged portion of the DNA molecule, with resultant mis-sense or no-sense coding for protein synthesis (see Part I). Other disorders affecting the eyelids are shown in Table 7–1.

CORNEA

Diseases that affect the cornea are numerous and often fatal. The three components of corneal tissue (epithelium, stroma, and Descemet's membrane) may be involved separately or simultaneously, depending upon the disease. Disorders involving the cornea are listed in Table 7–2.

One inborn error of metabolism that may be characteristically diagnosed by the findings in the eye is Wilson's disease, or hepatolenticular degeneration (see Chapter 15). The Kayser-Fleischer ring is a pathognomonic finding of Wilson's disease; its absence can only be totally excluded by a slit-lamp examination. Recent chemical studies have shown unequivocally that copper is deposited in Descemet's membrane in affected patients and is responsible for the characteristic appearance of the Kayser-Fleischer ring. Deposition of copper in the tissues of the body in Wilson's disease is now thought to be attributable to increased tissue binding of copper.

CONJUNCTIVA AND SCLERA

The natural history of the disorder known as alcaptonuria, Garrod's prototypic "inborn error of metabolism," is the development of ochronosis. The latter is a characteristic bluish-gray or black pigmentation of cartilaginous and fibrous tissues of the body, often accompanied by a unique kind of osteoarthritis. In this disease, homogentisic acid, the normal catabolic product of tyrosine metabolism, is not converted further as a consequence of a deficiency of homogentisic acid oxidase. Through an alternate pathway, benzoquinoneacetic acid is formed which, in turn, becomes bound to connective tissue macromolecules and is oxidized to form a ochronotic-like pigment. The sclera is often one of the earliest tissues affected by pigmentation, perhaps because of its high degree of vascularization.

Table 7–2 DISEASES AFFECTING THE CORNEA

Metabolic	Chromosomal/Genetic
Cystinosis (crystalline deposits)	Amyloidosis, hereditary (3)
Ehlers-Danlos syndrome (keratoconus) (3)*	Ichthyosis, congenital
Fabry's disease (opacities) (3)	Incontinentia pigmenti (1)
Familial dysautonomia (ulcers and scars) (3)	Meckel's syndrome
β-Glucuronidase deficiency (clouding) (1)	Norrie's disease (1,3)
Hurler's syndrome (clouding) (1,3)	Peter's syndrome (1,3)
Hyperlipoproteinemia, Type II (arcus cornea)	Rieger's syndrome (1,3)
Maroteaux-Lamy syndrome (clouding)	Rothmund's syndrome
Scheie's syndrome (clouding)	Schwartz's syndrome (3)
Tangier disease (opacities) (3)	Trisomy 13 (1,3)
Wilson's disease (Kayser-Fleischer ring) (3)	Trisomy 18 (1,3)
	Trisomy 21 (1,3)

* Associated findings: 1—mental retardation; 2—seizures; 3—neurological other than mental retardation.

Table 7–3 DISEASES AFFECTING THE CONJUNCTIVA
AND SCLERA

Metabolic	Chromosomal/Genetic
Alcaptonuria	Amyloidosis, hereditary
Ataxia-telangiectasia	Hallerman-Streiff syndrome (blue sclerae)
Cystinosis	Sturge-Weber syndrome
Ehlers-Danlos syndrome (blue sclerae) (3)*	
Fabry's disease (3)	
Fucosidosis (3)	
Gaucher's disease (pigmentation and pinguecula) (3)	
Hemophilia A	
Hyperphosphatasia (blue sclerae)	
Hypophosphatasia	
Osteogenesis imperfecta (blue sclerae)	
Porphyria cutanea tarda	
Sickle cell (HbS) disease	
Xeroderma pigmentosum	

*Associated findings: 1—mental retardation; 2—seizures; 3—neurological other than mental retardation.

Conjunctival and scleral involvement in the various forms of porphyria (see Chapter 35) resemble each other and consist of necrosis and scarring. These are a consequence of the bulbous eruptions that occur as a result of extreme photosensitivity in these patients. Other disorders affecting the conjunctiva and sclera are listed in Table 7–3.

LENS

Cataract

Chief among the disorders that affect lenticular metabolism and result in cataract formation are the two forms of abnormal galactose metabolism known as galactokinase deficiency and galactose-1-phosphate uridyl transferase deficiency (see Chapter 26). As a consequence of the enzyme deficiencies in both forms of galactosemia, there is an accumulation of galactose in body tissues, including the lens. The manner in which the lens handles the excess galactose present is to reduce the aldehyde sugar group to an alcohol, thus forming the corresponding sugar alcohol known as dulcitol or galactitol. The enzyme that has been shown to be present in the lens and responsible for carrying out this reduction is known as aldose reductase. Thus, it is not galactose per se that is the cause of cataract formation in galactosemia. Rather it is galactitol, which accumulates within the lens because of the relative impermeability of the lens membrane and the inability of lenticular metabolism to further degrade the sugar alcohol. Owing to the lack of permeability of galactitol, there is a shift of water into the lens with ultimate disruption of the lenticular structure. It is worthy of note that there are several variant forms of the uridyl transferase deficiency, some of which are asymptomatic.

In a fashion very similar to that just described for the development of cataracts in the two forms of galactosemia, there can be cataract formation in severe cases of juvenile diabetes mellitus. It is presumed that the mechanism prevailing in the development of cataracts in this disorder is a conversion of excess glucose present in the lens to the corresponding sugar alcohol, sorbitol. Once again, the osmotic properties of sorbitol result in swelling and structural disruption of the lens.

Another disorder in which cataract formation is typical is the oculocerebrorenal syndrome of Lowe. It is an X-linked recessive disorder, and affected males typically have cataracts and hydrophthalmus, frequently together with glaucoma at birth or shortly thereafter. The underlying biochemical etiology for the development of these abnormalities of the eye in Lowe's syndrome is not known at the present time. Other causes of lenticular cataracts are listed in Table 7–4.

Table 7–4 DISEASES CAUSING CATARACTS OF THE LENS

Metabolic	Chromosomal/Genetic
Diabetes mellitus (juvenile onset)	Acrocephalosyndactyly (Apert's syndrome)
Fabry's disease (3)*	Alport's syndrome (3)
Galactokinase deficiency	Alström's disease (3)
Galactose-1-P uridyl transferase deficiency (1)	Aniridia (3)
Hypoparathyroidism (1)	Cockayne's syndrome (1)
Lowe's syndrome (1)	Congenital alopecia (3)
Mannosidosis (1)	Conradi's disease
Myotonic dystrophy (2,3)	Crouzon's disease (1)
Osteogenesis imperfecta	Ectodermal dysplasia
Refsum's disease (3)	Flynn-Aird syndrome (1–3)
Wilson's disease (3)	Hallermann-Streiff syndrome
	Ichthyosis, congenital
	Incontinentia pigmenti (1)
	Marinesco-Sjögren syndrome (1,3)
	Meckel's syndrome
	Norrie's disease (1,3)
	Oxycephaly (1,2)
	Pachyonychia congenita
	Peter's syndrome (1,3)
	Rubinstein-Taybi syndrome (1)
	Rothmund's syndrome
	Siemen's syndrome
	Sjögren's syndrome (1)
	Pseudo-Turner's syndrome
	Trisomy 13 (1,3)
	Trisomy 21 (1,3)
	Turner's syndrome (1)
	Usher's syndrome (1–3)
	Zellweger's syndrome (1,3)

*Associated findings: 1—mental retardation; 2—seizures; 3—neurological other than mental retardation.

Dislocation

One of the most dramatic ocular consequences of inborn errors of metabolism is dislocation of the lens. Initial consideration of the etiology of dislocated lenses should always include both homocystinuria (see Chapter 22) and Marfan's syndrome (see Chapter 27). So important a diagnostic feature is dislocated lens in these disorders that every patient who is seen for this problem should have a metabolic screen performed on the urine. The older clinical descriptions of both homocystinuria and Marfan's syndrome have included mental retardation as an invariable feature: however, this has turned out to be a grossly exaggerated feature of both diseases. The probable mechanism for lenticular dislocation in each of these two diseases is increasing laxity of collagenous fibers in the zonule of Zinn. The enzyme defect in homocystinuria is known to be cystathionine synthase, the protein that catalyzes the synthesis of cystathionine from homocysteine and serine. The underlying biochemical etiology of Marfan's syndrome is just becoming clear (see Chapter 27). Additional causes for ectopia lentis are listed in Table 7–5.

Table 7–5 DISEASES CAUSING DISLOCATION OF THE LENS

Metabolic	Chromosomal/Genetic
Ehlers-Danlos syndrome (3)*	Weil-Marchesani syndrome
Homocystinuria (1–3)	
Hyperlysinemia, persistent (1,2)	
Marfan's syndrome	
Sulfite-oxidase deficiency (1,3)	

*Associated findings: 1—mental retardation; 2—seizures; 3—neurological other than mental retardation.

RETINA

Macula

Macula involvement in the disorders listed in Table 7–6 generally results from the deposition in the optic nerve of the specific compounds that are stored in other tissues of the body. Individual discussions of macula involvement in each of these diseases is beyond the scope of this book, and the biochemistry of the storage diseases is dealt with in detail in the appropriate chapters of this book.

Vasculature

Involvement of the retinal vasculature in the diseases listed in Table 7–6 is generally a consequence of the secondary effects on the vasculature of the underlying disorders as seen in other portions of the body. The ocular abnormalities seen in the various hemoglobinopathies are illustrative of this point and include retinal vascular changes and proliferation with fibrovascular lesions and angioid streaks. These are a consequence of multiple mini-infarctions throughout the retinal vasculature.

Pigment Epithelium

Among the disorders that might reasonably be expected to affect pigment epithelium of the retina are the various forms of albinism. Clearly, in the absence of normal ability to synthesize

Table 7–6   DISEASES AFFECTING THE RETINA

Metabolic	Chromosomal/Genetic
Macula	
Farber's disease (cherry-red spot)	Aniridia (3)
Gangliosidoses (1–3)*	Jeune's syndrome
GM$_1$	
GM$_2$ (cherry-red spot)	
Metachromatic leukodystrophy (1,3)	
Mucolipidosis I (cherry-red spot) (1–3)	
Neuraminidase deficiency (cherry-red spot with myoclonus) (2,3)	
Niemann-Pick disease (1–3)	
Pseudoxanthoma elasticum	
Vasculature	
Albinism	Renal-retinal dystrophy
Cystic fibrosis	Retinitis pigmentosa (1)
Diabetes mellitus	Sturge-Weber syndrome (1,2)
Fabry's disease (3)	von Hippel-Lindau syndrome
Hemoglobin SC disease	
Porphyria, acute intermittent (3)	
Pseudoxanthoma elasticum	
Sickle-cell (HbS) disease	
Pigment Epithelium	
Abetalipoproteinemia	Aicardi syndrome (1–3)
Albinism	Alström's disease (3)
Chédiak-Higashi syndrome	Cockayne's syndrome (1)
Cystinosis	Flynn-Aird syndrome (1–3)
Farber's disease	Incontinentia pigmenti (1)
Hunter's syndrome (1,3)	Laurence-Moon-Biedl syndrome (1)
Hurler's syndrome (1,3)	Renal-retinal dystrophy
Myotonic dystrophy (1,3)	Retinitis pigmentosa (1)
Refsum's disease (3)	Retinitis punctata albescens (1,3)
von Gierke's disease	Sjögren-Larsson syndrome (1,3)
	Usher's syndrome (1–3)

* Associated findings: 1—mental retardation; 2—seizures; 3—neurological other than mental retardation.

Table 7-7   DISEASES AFFECTING THE OPTIC NERVE

Metabolic	Chromosomal/Genetic
Canavan's disease (1–3)*	Acrocephalosyndactyly (Apert's syndrome)
Charcot-Marie-Tooth disease (3)	Albright's disease
Chédiak-Higashi syndrome	Behr's syndrome (1,3)
Gangliosidosis GM$_2$ (1–3)	Cockayne's syndrome (1)
Hyperphosphatasia (juvenile Paget's disease)	Conradi's disease
Krabbe's disease (1–3)	Cornelia deLange syndrome
Leigh's syndrome (1–3)	Crouzon's disease (1)
Menke's syndrome (1,3)	Incontinentia pigmenti (1)
Metachromatic leukodystrophy (1,3)	Laurence-Moon-Biedl syndrome (1)
Osteopetrosis (3)	Leber's hereditary optic atrophy
Pelizaeus-Merzbacher disease (1–3)	Meckel's syndrome
Porphyria, acute intermittent (3)	Oxycephaly (1,2)
	Renal-retinal dystrophy
	Retinitis pigmentosa (1)
	Trisomy 13 (1,3)

* Associated findings: 1—mental retardation; 2—seizures; 3—neurological other than mental retardation.

pigment as implied by the presence of albinism, the pigment epithelium of the retina would also be expected to manifest a total or partial deficiency of melanin content.

In general, the pigment retinopathies associated with other disorders listed in Table 7–6 are due to storage of the specific compounds found in other tissues. The eye findings in each of these disorders has been noted in the sections of this text dealing specifically with each disease. One entity, however, that does not fit this pattern is cystinosis. In the infantile form of cystinosis there is a retinopathy consisting of hypopigmented patchy areas irregularly alternating with clumped, hyperpigmented regions. The pigmentary changes precede those found in the cornea or conjunctiva and therefore permit diagnosis at still earlier an age.

OPTIC NERVE

The optic atrophy and cortical blindness that occur early in the course of Krabbe's disease (see Chapter 30) are a direct consequence of the severe loss of myelin and oligodendroglia, which are characteristic of this disorder. Optic atrophy may also be seen in hyperphosphatasia (juvenile Paget's disease), but in this disease it is a result of papilledema, with subsequent optic atrophy as a consequence of craniostenosis. The biochemistry of all these disorders is dealt with in other chapters of this book. Optic nerve involvement in other diseases is listed in Table 7–7.

REFERENCES

Cleaver, J.E.: Xeroderma pigmentosum. In Stanbury, J.B., Wyngaarden, J.B., Fredrickson, D.S., et al. (eds.): The Metabolic Basis of Inherited Diseases. 5th ed. McGraw-Hill, New York, 1983, p. 1227.
Goldberg, M.F. (ed.): Genetic and Metabolic Eye Disease. Little, Brown and Co., Boston, 1974.
Harley, R.D. (ed.): Pediatric Ophthalmology. W. B. Saunders Co., Philadelphia, 1975.

8

Fluid and Electrolyte Metabolism

In the first part of this book, we underscored the axial role of proteins in the life process, emphasizing the importance of their three-dimensional structure to their functions. There we discussed the interactions between protein molecules and their aqueous environment in determining this structure. Therefore, it is reasonable to assume that since the synthesis of protein is an essential consequence of the presence of a living organism, the need for an aqueous environment is a prerequisite for life. Crucial as aqueous-protein interactions are, the functions of water in living systems extend beyond this phenomenon. Because of its high dielectric constant, water serves as an efficient solvent for small ionic molecules. Water also serves as an efficient transfer mechanism for the heat produced during metabolism. In complex, multicellular organisms, extracellular water serves as a medium (blood) by which cells within the organism communicate with each other.

Most hypotheses regarding the origin of life agree that it first emerged in a marine environment. Although such origins depended upon the creation of biological molecules like amino acids, the major delimiting feature of the organism from its environment is the cell membrane, with its high lipid content stabilized by hydrophobic interactions. Thus it is possible that the first living organism may have consisted simply of a cell membrane surrounding an internal milieu, the chemical nature of which was only very slightly different from that of the sea water that surrounded it. However, the delineation of the organism by virtue of its membrane gave rise to a fundamental separation of two compartments: the extracellular fluid compartment (ECF) and the intracellular fluid compartment (ICF). No doubt, with the changes in the composition of the sea, the organism had to cope with the altered environment, in which sodium came to preponderate over potassium. In order to survive, the organism had to evolve some means for selecting among the ions and compounds that traversed the delineating cell membrane. At the point at which such selectivity evolved a dynamically maintained difference became established between the ECF and ICF. This, in turn, was the initial evolutionary step towards the escape of life from its marine environment. Phylogenetic studies have demonstrated the concomitant, progressive evolutionary changes in compositional differences between ECF and ICF and a trend toward terrestrial existence. The mammalian species, as we know them today, are composed of organisms that are able to sustain an independent existence by maintaining fluid and electrolyte homeostasis in the absence of a marine environment. It is, therefore, worthwhile to examine more closely the nature of the biological order imposed by virtue of a cell membrane.

THE CELL MEMBRANE

Current thinking conceives of the cell membrane as a bilipid layer structure with impregnated protein molecules throughout (Fig. 8–1); hence, it is stabilized predominantly by hydrophobic interactions. Such a barrier necessitates the existence of limitations on materials traversing the structure in either direction—if only to confine the intracellular contents. For example, if the structure were merely porous, lacking more discriminative selectivity, the major limitation for traversing the barrier would be the molecular radii of the solutes present on either side of the membrane. This, of course, neglects the hydrophobic nature of the cell membrane. Such hydrophobicity further implies

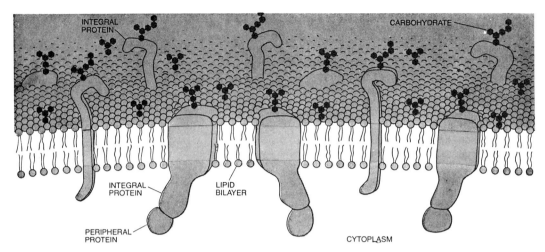

Figure 8–1 The cell membrane. The basic element of the structure is the lipid bilayer, with the hydrophilic portions of these molecules projected toward the surfaces. Proteins are glycoproteins (contain carbohydrate) and are of two types: integral protein, which protrudes beyond the membrane surfaces; and peripheral protein, which is attached to the membrane surface but does not penetrate. (From Lodish, H.F., and Rothman, J.E.: The assembly of cell membranes. Sci. Am. 240(1), 48–63, 1979. © 1979 by Scientific American, Inc.)

that unless pores are, in fact, present in the overall structure, water will be very slow to cross. Even if such pores are present, the speed with which small ions such as Na^+ will penetrate the membrane will depend upon the charge radius of the ion as well as the rate at which water penetrates the membrane. We must also not neglect the solubilization of gases, such as oxygen, which are necessary to metabolic processes. Both oxygen and carbon dioxide are highly lipophilic and are known to traverse biological membranes very rapidly.

Imposition of a cell membrane with creation of ECF and ICF compartments also leads to the need to consider two additional matters. The content of small ions such as sodium and chloride in biological suspending mediums forces us to consider the relative concentrations of such small ions on both sides of the membrane. Such a distribution must obey the absolute need for electrochemical neutrality. Thus while the aqueous environment enclosed by the membrane may contain higher concentrations of an ion such as potassium than is seen in the ECF, the total number of cations must be equivalent on both sides. This implies that another cation such as sodium will have to be higher in concentration in the ECF than in the ICF. This is indeed a well-known biological phenomenon.

The second concern introduced as a consequence of the existence of cell membranes is the principle of osmotic pressure. For our purposes, osmotic pressure can be thought of as a measure of the resistance that a membrane exerts on the unidirectional flow of a given solute molecule; as a result, solvent molecules move in the direction of the solute. Thus, a large molecule such as a protein in the ECF cannot easily pass across the cell membrane barrier. Because of the need to maintain this protein molecule in solution, there is a tendency for the water to flow outward from the cell towards the protein molecule. This tendency is measured in units known as milliosmoles and is related to the molecular weight of the substance and its concentration in the bathing medium. It is, however, important to understand that in situations in which small ions pass with relative ease through membranes the simple relationship that holds for proteins does not exist. Since the number of particles (colligative properties) determines osmotic pressure, substances that ionize affect osmotic pressure according to the degree of dissociation. For example, sodium chloride dissociates into sodium and chloride in such fashion that at 0.154 molar concentration (that of body fluid) there are about 1.85 particles for each original molecule and these exert a pressure of 286 milliosmoles rather than the theoretical 308 milliosmoles.

With such large forces present even with small differences in osmolality and the fact that cell membranes with very limited exceptions (such as the distal nephron of the kidney) are quite freely permeable to water, osmolality must be nearly if not exactly equal within cells and their surrounding extracellular fluids. Such is almost certainly the case despite substantial differences in individual ion content and protein concentration between cells and ECF. In order to permit such ionic discrepancies to exist, other forces must be at work and energy must be expended. The Gibbs-Donnan equilibrium rule provides that under equilibrium conditions, the product of concentrations of any pair of diffusible cations and anions on one side of the membrane will equal the product of the same pair of ions on the other side of the membrane. When a nondiffusible ion is present on one side of a membrane, the situation is altered, so that while the products of the concentration of the pairs of diffusible ions are equal, the concentrations on the two sides are unequal and remain so. Within cells, organic phosphates and protein are nondiffusible and hold an excess of the cations potassium and magnesium. These forces are balanced by the remarkable ability of living cells to keep sodium out of the cell by continuous pumping. This counterosmotic gradient, together with the probability that not all the ions and protein molecules are active (some being bound in large protein aggregates), provides the best current explanation of the ability of the body cell mass to maintain the transmembrane differences that are essential to life. Hence, the major determining factor of osmotic pressure in the plasma is the concentration of plasma protein, but the major determining factor of fluid volume is the concentration of the small ions.

FLUID BALANCE

It is not our intent to restate here what has already been dealt with in exquisite detail elsewhere (see References). Rather, we prefer to deal with some general concepts underlying what is commonly termed fluid balance.

Man requires free water to maintain water balance. Even with maximum concentration of urine solutes, the water contained in the food of a normal diet and the water produced by oxidation of food are inadequate to provide for urinary excretion of the end-products of metabolism and for losses of water through the bowel, the respiratory tract, and the skin. The water content of an ordinary diet can be estimated as 40 to 50 ml/100 kcal. In addition, approximately 10 ml of water are produced by metabolism of the same 100 kcal. Thus, the maximum amount of water that can be produced from an average diet is equal to 60 ml/100 kcal. This figure is a bare approximation of the 40 to 50 ml/100 kcal lost through respiration and perspiration alone and falls far short of the 100 ml/kcal lost by an individual who is not excreting a concentrated (>600 mOsm) urine.

In a normal individual, thirst is the inciting mechanism for ingestion of additional water to maintain a fluid balance. A 350 to 700 ml change in total body water is sufficient to stimulate the CNS thirst centers. The centers for control of thirst are located in the ventromedial and anterior hypothalamus and are in close relationship to or overlap the centers of the neurohypophysis, which regulate antidiuretic hormone (ADH). As thirst is the regulator of the intake of water in man, so ADH has a fundamental role in the regulation of water balance and in the control of water excretion. By altering the permeability to water of the cells of distal renal tubules and collecting ducts, ADH controls the amount of water reabsorbed and the volume of water excreted.

The role of water as a solvent for biologically essential molecules should not be overlooked in this control. As has already been stated, the concentrations of ions, proteins, and other organic molecules affect the osmolarity of body fluids. Hence, these concentrations are important in determining the response of the body to fluid gains or losses. Obviously, ingestion of a large volume of deionized, distilled water will dilute all solubilized molecules, thus reducing their osmolar effect. Such a reduction will evoke two primary off-setting responses: there will be inhibition of ADH secretion to maximize renal free water excretion, and adrenal mineralocorticoid (aldosterone) secretion will be increased to prompt sodium conservation by the distal tubule in an effort to increase the Na^+ concentration. Reversal of these responses would occur with ingestion of hypertonic saline, for example. Thus, we see that the kidney is the major factor in defense and regulation of both fluid and electrolyte balance.

However, electrolytes are not the only osmotically active components of body fluids introduced by diet. The oxidation of carbohydrate and fat generally results in CO_2 and H_2O, which can be simply excreted through the lungs. Oxidation of amino acids, on the other hand, results in production of ammonia and urea. If all the nitrogen in one kilogram of meat is converted to urea, the yield is approximately 1600 mOsm of urea. In the discussion of urea cycle disorders (Chapter 22), the issue of ammonia toxicity is dealt with at length. Conversion of NH_3 to urea provides the human organism with a mechanism for detoxification, but it also transforms a volatile compound, potentially removable via the lungs, into a nonvolatile one that must be excreted by the kidney. Thus, protein ingestion and the ultimate conversion of protein to urea impose an absolute requirement for fluid loss through the kidney. This factor may be especially important in the nutrition of premature infants and patients with chronic end-stage renal disease.

OSMOSIS, DIFFUSION, AND REABSORPTION IN TISSUE NUTRITION

The major exchanges of water, electrolytes, nutrient substances, oxygen, carbon dioxide, and other end-products of metabolism occur by diffusion. Water and plasma electrolytes, which are very small ions, diffuse rapidly back and forth across capillary membranes. Capillary water exchanges with interstitial water several times a second. Sodium, chloride, glucose, and urea diffuse at different speeds, exchanging at rates of twice a second to 40 times a minute. Net transfer by diffusion depends on diffusion down a gradient, with glucose and oxygen moving towards cells and carbon dioxide, organic acids, and solvent water towards the capillary. Because of their lipid solubility, oxygen and carbon dioxide are free to diffuse across all of the capillary membrane, while water and electrolytes are believed to pass through minute pores in the endothelial membrane.

The distribution of fluid volume between plasma and the interstitial fluid compartments is controlled by a balance of hydrostatic forces. Capillary hydrostatic pressure, including both blood pressure and gravity, and high capillary flow rates result in net flow from capillaries to the interstitial fluid. Colloid osmotic pressure of plasma protein, tissue elasticity, and slow capillary flow rates result in a net return flow into capillary. Anything that alters capillary permeability, such as injury due to heat, toxins, or prolonged hypoxia with acidosis, results in varying degrees of loss of plasma protein into the interstitial fluid. Loss of colloid osmotic pressure reduces return flow to the capillary, with resulting local expansion of the intracellular fluid space. Edema becomes clinically evident when the interstitial fluid volume has increased by an increment of 5 percent.

Regulation of cell volume and concentration of ions within cells are energy-requiring processes involving active transport of sodium and potassium across cell membranes. The source of the energy for the active transport system, as for practically every kind of energy expenditure by cells, is the metabolism of ATP (Fig. 8–2). The ubiquitous enzyme sodium-potassium-ATPase enables cells to pump sodium and potassium. This enzyme has an absolute requirement for magnesium but also requires that both sodium and potassium be present together for maximal activity. It has one site with a high affinity for potassium and another quite separate site for sodium.

One of the effects of differing concentrations of potassium and other ions on opposite sides of the cell membrane is the development of an electrical potential across the membrane. A potential of −90 mv exists within muscle cells when compared with the ECF surrounding them. This negative potential may help to explain the rejection of chloride ions by most cells not involved in chloride transport; it is also the proximate cause of neuromuscular excitability (see Chapter 17).

As much as one third of the total resting energy of skeletal muscle cells may be directed to the sodium pump. When hypoxia or any other metabolic inhibitor interferes with the metabolism of cells, cells swell. The mechanism appears to be the entrance of sodium and chloride ions into the cell, producing increased intracellular osmolality, which results in increased water content as water follows solute. At the same time, potassium is lost but not equivalently to sodium, so that the result is a net gain in water.

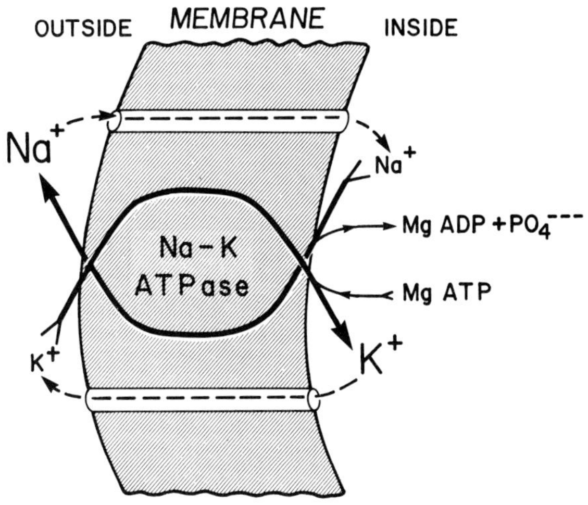

Figure 8–2 The sodium-potassium pump. One molecule each of Na$^+$ and K$^+$ are exchanged at the expense of one molecule of ATP; Mg^{++} is essential to this process. (From Guyton, A.C.: Textbook of Medical Physiology. 6th ed. Philadelphia, W.B. Saunders Co., 1981.)

ELECTROLYTE HOMEOSTASIS

The importance of electrolyte homeostasis in clinical medicine cannot be overstated, but it is essential to recognize that there are many more electrolytes in serum than the sodium, potassium, chloride, and bicarbonate usually examined by most hospital laboratories. Electrolytes comprise a wide variety of compounds, from simple inorganic salts of sodium, potassium, and magnesium to complex organic molecules often synthesized by and unique to the individual. Electrolytes share with water the phenomenon of dissociating into positively and negatively charged ions and have the additional property of variably affecting the concentration of hydrogen ions in a solution: this effect depends both on the individual ion characteristics and on interaction with other completely and partially ionized substances in the solution. Major differences in specific ion characteristics exist between cell fluid and extracellular fluid; these differences are maintained by a substantial expenditure of energy by cells and are critical to cell metabolism and survival.

The hydrogen ion concentrations of intracellular fluid and extracellular fluid differ. Both are held within very narrow ranges by a complex series of reactions within the organism and by the ability of the kidney to excrete acid or base loads selectively (see Acid-Base Balance). Diets vary in the effective amount of acid and base they contain. Metabolic processes of the body create an additional acid load that must be excreted to maintain optimum pH. It should be apparent, therefore, that any discussion of electrolyte homeostasis must take these complex relationships into account. Without undue complexity we will discuss the normal homeostatic mechanisms for the common electrolytes, sodium and potassium, and the various derangements of these processes often seen in patients with inborn errors of metabolism.

Sodium Balance

With an adequate intake of sodium, regulation of the sodium concentration of body fluids and of sodium balance is primarily renal. However, sodium balance is not merely a matter of glomerular filtration and the secretion of sufficient aldosterone to control distal renal tubular reabsorption of sodium. Sodium salts are the primary determinant of the volume and composition of extra-cellular fluid and indirectly determine the osmolality and composition of cells as well. Extra-renal factors are important in renal regulation of sodium balance.

In a normal adult of average size, approximately 125 ml of plasma is filtered through glomerular membranes each minute. This filtrate contains not only the electrolytes of plasma in their normal concentration in plasma water but also glucose, urea, uric acid, amino acids, and creatinine. From the daily total of 180 liters of glomerular filtrate, more than 8 times the total body sodium content and 250 times the average daily intake are reabsorbed. In order to maintain balance, about

99.5 percent of the filtered sodium and chloride, virtually all of the bicarbonate, and 92 percent of the potassium must be reabsorbed along with all of the glucose, most of the amino acids, and a substantial portion of urea and uric acid.

Intrarenal Factors Controlling Sodium Balance

Glomerular Filtration Rate. Since 99.5 percent of filtered sodium is usually reabsorbed, a small change in filtration rate represents a substantial reduction in the filtered load of sodium. With a rise in glomerular filtration rate (GFR) there is relatively little increase in sodium excreted, while a fall in GFR results in a disproportionate decrease in sodium excretion. These observations cannot be explained on the basis of what is known about the functions of the glomerulus in forming a plasma ultrafiltrate. The function of the tubule in sodium reclamation, combined with the above, led to the concept known as *glomerulotubular balance*. This balance provides a buffering device that enables the kidney to defend against large solute losses or gains attendant upon fluctuations in GFR. Thus, if GFR increased by as little as 2 ml/min over a 24-hour period, without the adjustments due to glomerulotubular balance the sodium excretion would increase by more than 20 grams in the same period, almost double the average daily sodium intake. However, this protective mechanism does not play a major role in the relatively fine adjustments needed to maintain sodium homeostasis in the absence of prolonged changes in GFR. For extensive discussions of this fundamental concept of modern nephrology, the interested reader is referred to the sources listed at the end of this chapter.

Tubular Reabsorption. The proximal renal tubule is probably responsible for many of the changes in tubular sodium reabsorption that follow promptly upon changes in GFR. The nature of the control of this system is uncertain at present. Various mechanisms have been proposed, including linkage of sodium to bicarbonate reabsorption and increased ATP consumption with concomitant increases in Na^+, K^+-ATPase activity and sodium pumping. Aldosterone controls distal tubular sodium reabsorption and potassium secretion. Changes in dietary sodium intake induce reciprocal levels of aldosterone secretion by the adrenals, and by this mechanism balance is maintained under normal conditions. Hence, aldosterone secretion results in Na^+ retention. Renin is the stimulus to aldosterone secretion, the former being controlled by the effective blood volume. In essence then blood volume is the major factor regulating Na^+ retention.

Extrarenal Factors Controlling Sodium Balance

Volume Receptors. A decrease in left atrial pressure results in increased renal sodium retention, as does a decrease in blood volume. Conversely, an increase in left atrial pressure results in increased sodium output, as does isotonic volume loading, unless cardiac output is decreased. It is currently felt by most investigators that these responses result from "stretch receptors" present in the left atrial wall that influence secretion of vasopressin and, in turn, renal free water clearance. The precise relationship between the "stretch receptors" and the neurohumoral response is unclear at the present time.

Thirst. Increased osmolality of the ECF, whether due to decreased fluid volume or excessive sodium intake, will result in a sensation of thirst originating in the hypothalamus. Consumption of free water will reduce ECF osmolarity and end hypothalamic stimulation.

Hormonal Factors. Concomitant with the arousal of a thirst sensation, increased ECF osmolality stimulates hypothalamic osmoreceptors, which elicit release of antidiuretic hormone (ADH) from specialized nerve endings into the posterior pituitary and thence into the blood stream. ADH induces increased permeability of the distal tubule and collecting duct to water. In addition, a number of factors such as sodium depletion and hyperkalemia elicit secretion of aldosterone, an adrenal mineralocorticoid. This hormone acts upon the distal tubule to enhance a potassium secretion and sodium reabsorption through an exchange mechanism.

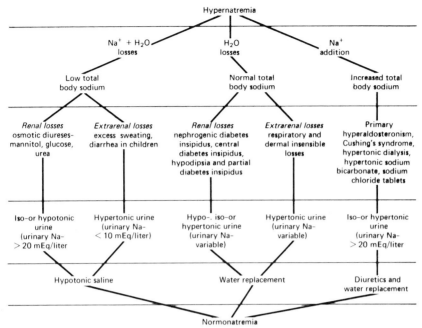

Figure 8–3 Clinical approach to the patient with hypernatremia. (Reprinted from Berl, T. et al.: Clinical disorders of water metabolism. Kidney Int. 10:117–132, 1976.)

Disorders of Sodium Homeostasis

Hypernatremia (Fig. 8–3). In general, excessive levels of Na^+ in the body fluids, predominantly the ECF, are secondary to fluid loss. Perhaps in part because of the vomiting induced by hypertonic saline ingestion, it is exceedingly rare to encounter a primary hypernatremia. The conditions leading to fluid loss may be attributable to one of two basic states: inadequate replacement of obligatory losses or pathological degrees of loss.

In the first instance, the reader will recall that the functioning kidney requires a certain minimal volume of water in which to excrete solutes, this volume varying with the ability of the kidney to concentrate the urine (see Chapter 14). In addition, there is a substantial loss of volume via the skin and lungs, consisting almost entirely of free water. If this net volume is not replaced by ingestion, it will be derived from a shift of water from the ICF to the ECF. With continuing loss in the absence of free water replacement there is increasing intracellular dehydration and extracellular solute concentration, although the total body sodium may actually be decreased.

In the case of pathological losses, this is often due to disruption of the sensorineural pathways for osmotic regulation. Whatever the specific etiology, it is clear that failure to secrete appropriate and timely amounts of ADH will result in massive free water loss at the distal tubular level. This, in addition to insensible free water loss, will cause rapid concentration of sodium in the extracellular compartment and intracellular dehydration.

The most important factor in understanding clinical states involving hypernatremia is the awareness that such a state usually does not imply increased *amounts* of total body sodium but rather increased concentration. Thus, increases in plasma sodium concentration may be seen in spite of sodium depletion. This understanding is vital to a rational therapeutic approach. In keeping with this principle, management of a hypernatremic state should be based upon provision of free water in excess, but not to the exclusion of sodium. An appropriate solution might consist, for example, of 5 percent dextrose in 0.45 percent saline; removal of the glucose by the organs will leave free water in amounts adequate to reduce ECF osmolarity, while the saline will permit repletion of total body sodium. Further details of therapy may be found in the references at the end of this section.

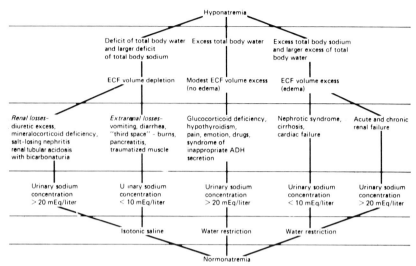

Figure 8–4 Clinical approach to the patient with hyponatremia. (Reprinted from Berl, T. et al.: Clinical disorders of water metabolism. Kidney Int. 10:117–132, 1976.)

Hyponatremia (Fig. 8–4). Clinically, hyponatremic states are far more common than those manifesting hypernatremia. This is particularly true in infancy when, as a consequence of vomiting and dehydration (gastroenteritis), the baby is given hypotonic fluids by mouth inadequate to supply replacement solute following large losses.

The relatively complete exclusion of sodium from the internal milieu of the cell and its role as the predominant extracellular cation make sodium particularly vulnerable to depletion in states in which extrarenal fluid loss is occurring. Alternatively, low serum concentration may be a consequence of an abnormally high free water intake; in such circumstances the hyponatremia is not a reflection of decreased total body sodium.

In addition to the above, hyponatremia is a cardinal feature of a condition known as the syndrome of inappropriate ADH secretion (SIADH). This disorder, usually attributable to CNS disease of diverse etiologies, is due to the water retention by the kidneys in response to ADH secreted inappropriately in the face of markedly diminished serum osmolality. Excretion of a urine higher in osmolality than plasma when the latter is itself slightly lower than normal is a major diagnostic feature of SIADH.

Choice of an appropriate therapeutic regimen in the patient with hyponatremia requires that a

Table 8–1 CONSEQUENCES OF DISTURBANCES IN
POTASSIUM HOMEOSTASIS

Organ System	Hyperkalemia	Hypokalemia
Neuromuscular and Psychiatric	Ascending paralysis Flaccid paralysis Dysarthria Weakness	Weakness Myalgia Flaccid paralysis Depressive reaction Disorientation, confusion
Cardiovascular	Hypotension Arrhythmias Cardiac arrest	Arrhythmias Hypotension Potentiation of digitalis effect
Renal	Oliguria Uremic syndrome	Polyuria Sodium retention Paradoxical aciduria Edema
Gastrointestinal	Paralytic ileus Nausea, vomiting Abdominal pain	Paralytic ileus Decreased gastric acidity Growth retardation

painstaking medical history be obtained. Only in this fashion can the total body sodium be estimated on the basis of a probable etiology. Further details of treatment can be obtained from the references cited at the conclusion of this chapter.

Disorders of Potassium Homeostasis

Since potassium is the predominant intracellular cation of the body, it is predictable that fluctuations of serum potassium outside the normal range will usually represent large shifts in total body potassium. In addition, such fluctuations are usually accompanied by more drastic clinical findings than those seen in disruptions of sodium homeostasis (Table 8–1).

Hyperkalemia. Potassium is filtered by the glomerulus and probably completely reabsorbed in the proximal tubule (see Chapter 14). Urinary potassium excretion is the consequence of K^+ secretion at the distal tubular level, occurring by a $Na^+–K^+$ exchange mechanism. This mechanism is regulated by aldosterone, which promotes conservation of sodium and excretion of potassium.

In general, any factor impinging upon the ability of the cell to maintain membrane or metabolic integrity will cause a loss of intracellular K^+ and a corresponding increase in serum potassium. Such entities include crush injury, in which cell membrane integrity is altered or destroyed, intravascular hemolysis, and acidosis. Clinically, any one of these disorders may be accompanied by acute renal failure, in which loss of the body's compensatory ability to excrete potassium may have an additive effect on serum potassium levels.

Acute renal failure itself is a common cause of hyperkalemia. The anuric phase totally deprives the body of the major excretory route for potassium and causes hyperkalemia; the oliguric phase may perpetuate this finding. Proximal tubular damage may subsequently result in excessive losses with hypokalemia. Chronic renal failure, however, does not generally cause hyperkalemia except in the end stage when GFR falls and tissue catabolism increases.

The differential diagnosis of hyperkalemia, including elevation due to improper handling of specimen or laboratory errors, can be found in Table 8–2. This condition may be defined as a serum potassium greater than 5.5 mEq/l. It is worthwhile to point out that glycogen breakdown may result in elevation of serum potassium. This situation can be rapidly reversed by insulin, a frequently overlooked factor resulting in hypokalemia during treatment of diabetic ketoacidosis. Physical findings of hyperkalemia are the result of abnormal neuromuscular function (see Chapter 17). Hyperkalemia is not consistently associated with EKG abnormalities, but any laboratory value suggesting hyperkalemia requires that an EKG be obtained. If hyponatremia, hypocalcemia, or acidosis alone or in combination is also present, cardiac toxicity may be manifested at lower levels of serum potassium. The evolution of changes in the EKG are as follows: tall, peaked, T-wave; decreased T-T interval; increasing P-R interval; heart block; and cardiac standstill. Therapy in this disorder should be judiciously administered; details can be found in the references given at the end of this chapter.

Table 8–2 CAUSES OF HYPERKALEMIA

Decreased Potassium Excretion by Kidney
  Oliguric acute and chronic renal failure
  Use of potassium-sparing diuretics
  Mineralocorticoid deficiency (Addison's disease, congenital adrenal hyperplasia)
Excessive Potassium Intake
  Salt substitutes; oral KCl supplementation
  Intravenous potassium administration
    Rapid infusion during fluid replacement therapy
    Outdated blood
Shift of Intracellular Potassium to Extracellular Space
  Metabolic acidosis or acute respiratory acidosis
  Massive trauma or infection with widespread tissue damage
  Cytotoxic agents (e.g., antimetabolites)
  Fresh water drowning
  Hyperkalemic periodic paralysis
Artifactual Elevation
  Specimen improperly obtained or mishandled in laboratory resulting in hemolysis

Table 8–3   CAUSES OF HYPOKALEMIA

Increased Potassium Excretion by Kidney
  Renal disease
    Diuretic phase of acute renal failure, relief of urinary tract obstruction
    Distal renal tubular acidosis
    Fanconi syndrome (proximal RTA)
    Bartter's syndrome
    Interstitial nephritis
    Pyelonephritis
  Extrinsic renal causes
    Diabetes mellitus
    Diuretics (non-K sparing)
    Hyperosmolar solutions (e.g., mannitol, hypertonic glucose, urea)
    Loading with hypertonic saline
  Abnormalities of endocrine regulation
    Cushing's disease
    Primary aldosteronism
    Secondary aldosteronism (hypertension, nephritis, etc.)
  Drug-induced
    Diuretics
    Nonreabsorbable anion loads (penicillin)
    Aspirin
  Hypomagnesemia or hypercalcemia
Gastrointestinal Losses
  Vomiting and diarrhea (severe)
  Fistula or prolonged G.I. suctioning
  Chronic laxative abuse
  Frequent use of ion exchange resins
Malnutrition (<30 mEq/K^+/m^2/day)
  Protein-caloric malnutrition
  Prolonged I.V. alimentation with K^+-free fluids
Extracellular K^+ Shifts into Cells
  Total parenteral nutrition
  Alkalosis
  Drugs
Familial Hypokalemia

Hypokalemia.   This condition, represented by a serum potassium of less than 3.5 mEq/1, is most commonly associated with excessive urinary or gastrointestinal losses of potassium (Table 8–3). A low serum value may reflect depletion of total body potassium, but in acute situations hypokalemia may indicate only a shift into the cells. Such a shift occurs in alkalosis and in insulin therapy, for example.

The most common cause of hypokalemia is probably excessive losses through the gastrointestinal tract with vomiting and diarrhea. In general, secretions of the gastrointestinal tract contain large quantities of potassium as well as other electrolytes (see Chapter 9), which are normally reabsorbed. Failure of the reabsorptive process will cause rapid depletion of total body potassium. In addition, the volume depletion attendant upon these losses will elicit aldosterone secretion, the result being an acceleration of renal potassium secretion in favor of sodium reabsorption.

The renal causes of hypokalemia are legion and include a variety of renal tubular syndromes (see Chapter 14), pyelonephritis, and the diuretic phase of acute renal failure (Table 8–3). The general principle underlying all of these is a failure of normal tubular K^+ reabsorption. In addition, the osmotic diuresis of diabetic or iatrogenic glucosuria will accelerate tubular urine flow and diminish potassium reabsorption. Details of diagnosis and therapy of these disorders are beyond the scope of this discussion and may be found in the references.

Chloride, Bicarbonate, and the Anion Gap

The details of anion-gap metabolic acidosis have been dealt with elsewhere (see Chapter 3). It is the purpose of this section to summarize briefly the relationship to acid-base homeostasis.

In any normal individual there is a difference between serum Na^+ (the major extracellular cation) and the sum of serum Cl^- and HCO_3^- (the major extracellular anions). This difference is partially due to the presence of organic acids, the end-products of metabolism, which contribute hydrogen ions and organic anions to the serum. Another portion of this difference (gap) is attributable to phosphate salts, a contribution we will put aside for purposes of our present discussion. Since HCO_3^- is a major source of buffering anions in blood, addition of organic acids results in a fall in HCO_3^-, with replacement of the HCO_3^- by unmeasured organic anion. Thus, the sum of the measured anions diminishes and the gap between this sum and the serum sodium concentration increases.

In contradistinction to the above is the situation known as hyperchloremic acidosis, in which addition of strong acid (HCl) to serum also results in a drop in serum HCO_3^-. This change, however, is offset by the increase in Cl^-, with no net change in the sum of serum anions. Thus, there is no increase in the anion gap. Hyperchloremic acidosis is characteristic of renal tubular acidosis and is much more common in pediatric practice than the anion-gap type.

REFERENCES

Chan, J.C.M.: Bartter's syndrome. Nephron 26:155, 1980.

Feig, P.U., and McCurdy, D.K.: The hypertonic state. New Engl. J. Med. 297:1444, 1977.

Fineberg, L., Kravath, R.E., and Fleischman, A.R.: Water and Electrolytes in Pediatrics: Physiology, Pathophysiology and Treatment. W.B. Saunders Co., Philadelphia, 1982.

Maxwell, M.H., and Kleeman, C.R. (eds.): Clinical Disorders of Fluid and Electrolyte Metabolism. 3rd ed. McGraw-Hill, New York, 1980.

Narins, R.G., Jones, E.R., Stom, M.C., et al.: Diagnostic strategies in disorders of fluid, electrolyte and acid-base homeostasis. Am. J. Med. 72:496, 1982.

Skorecki, K.L., and Brenner, B.M.: Body fluid homeostasis in man. A contemporary overview. Am. J. Med. 70:77, 1981.

Stanton, B., and Giebisch, G.: Mechanism of urinary potassium excretion. Mineral Electrolyte Metab. 5:100, 1981.

Streeten, D.H.P.: Idiopathic edema: Pathogenesis, clinical features, and treatment. Metabolism 27:353, 1981.

Symposium on Body Fluid and Electrolyte Disorders. Med. Clin. North Am. 65:251, 1981.

Weil, W.B. Jr., and Bailie, M.D.: Fluid and Electrolyte Metabolism in Infants and Children: A Unified Approach. Grune & Stratton, New York, 1977.

9

Gastrointestinal Pathophysiology

GASTROINTESTINAL FUNCTIONS

At a gross level, the gastrointestinal tract is little more than a conduit with one opening for input and at the opposite end, an opening for output. Between those two points, however, a multiplicity of processes take place that involve hydrolyses and absorption and eventuate in the complicated process called nutrition. At a clinical level, attention is usually drawn to the gastrointestinal system's involvement in a disease state by virtue of alterations in nature and/or frequency of input, output, or both. Unfortunately, all too often therapy of such disorders is usually directed at altering these abnormal states without consideration of underlying pathophysiology. To go beyond a plumber's view of the gastrointestinal tract demands knowledge of the intricate processes that take place in the digestive tract and of factors that can alter these processes.

Embryologically the gut develops in intimate association with the development of the liver and the pancreas. Subsequent to complete development the gut retains contact, via the bile duct and the pancreatic duct, with its embryologic partners; these connections remain patent in the normal individual throughout life.

In addition to the input from the liver and the pancreas, the gut has enzymatic and transport properties that are quite complex. Indeed, such functions are found only in one other organ of the body—the kidney—whose complex functions are now being elucidated. The gut is lined by mucosa, the nature of which changes depending on its location along the tube. The cells lining the small intestine tend to be tall columnar epithelial cells. Fine structural analysis shows them to have, in addition, a brush border, i.e., a superimposed microvillar structure on the luminal surface. In this chapter we will attempt to analyze the intrinsic properties of these epithelial cells, which, taken in toto, subserve processing and absorption of foodstuffs.

Digestive Functions

The secretions of the embryological derivatives of the gut, the pancreas, and the liver play an important role in digestion. The ducts of the pancreas and the gallbladder open into the duodenum at a point just distal to the pylorus. The highly basic pancreatic and gallbladder secretions neutralize the acid of the chymous material passing from the stomach into the duodenum and change the pH of the material slightly to the alkaline side. The switch to alkalinity is necessary for the optimal activity of the intestinal enzymes, which play a major role in the digestion of food stuffs. The alkaline juice, also rich in mucus, is elaborated by Brunner's glands, the distinctive histological feature of the duodenum. At this point in the digestive tract there are extremely complex interrelationships between the hormones elaborated by Brunner's and Lieberkühn's glands, the liver, gallbladder, and the pancreas.

The introduction of hydrochloric acid, fats, proteins, carbohydrates, and partially digested foodstuffs into the first part of the duodenum from the stomach results in the secretion of at least five separate hormones produced by the glands of the duodenum and upper part of the jejunum (Table 9–1). These hormones are carried via the portal blood to the pancreas, liver, and gallbladder. The proportions of these hormones that are secreted by the intestine will vary with the proportion

116

Table 9–1 GASTROINTESTINAL HORMONES

Hormone	Locus of Action	Functions
Stomach		
Gastrin	Stomach	Stimulates acid secretion
Small Intestine		
Secretin	Pancreas	Bicarbonate secretion and fluid release
Cholecystokinin	Gall bladder, pancreas	Contraction of gall bladder
		Stimulates pancreatic enzyme secretion
		Potentiates actions of secretin
Gastric inhibitory peptide	Pancreas	May play a role in stimulating postprandial insulin release
Motilin	Stomach, intestine	Inhibits pyloric sphincter
		May play a role in normal G.I. motility
Enteroglucagon	Small intestine	Released after feeding—may have a role in G.I. motility—linked to "dumping syndrome"
Vasoactive intestinal peptide	Stomach, intestine	Inhibits gastric acid secretion
		Stimulates insulin release
		Stimulates production of fluid by pancreas and intestine
Somatostatin	Stomach, intestine, and hypothalamus	Inhibits gastrin release and pancreatic enzyme and bicarbonate secretion
		Inhibits release of growth hormone, TSH, insulin, glucagon, motilin, GIP, secretin, enteroglucagon

of the constituents of the chyle introduced into the intestine. The specific details of hormonal control of the gut can be found in the references listed. The *succus entericus,* elaborated by the intestinal wall itself, contains a variety of digestive enzymes (Table 9–2). Hence, it is apparent that the intestine has evolved into an organ eminently able to deal with a wide variety of foodstuffs. The diversity of the enzymes present in intestinal juices and the presence of the obligatory co-reactant water (for hydrolysis) enables the intestine to degrade almost any sort of biological material to its monomeric components for absorption.

Table 9–2 ENZYMES OF THE GASTROINTESTINAL TRACT

Origin	Enzyme	Substrate	Product
Intestine			
("Succus Entericus")	Sucrase	Sucrose	Fructose + Glucose
	Maltase	Maltose	2 Glucose
	Lactase	Lactose	Glucose + Galactose
	Phosphatase	Organic phosphates	Organic molecule + P_i
	Polynucleotidase	Nucleic acids	Nucleotides
	Nucleosidase	Nucleosides	Adenine or Guanine + Ribose
	Lecithinase	Lecithin	Glycerol, fatty acids, phosphoric acid, choline
	Enterokinase	Trypsinogen	Trypsin
Pancreas			
	Trypsinogen*	Proteins	Polypeptides
	Chymotrypsinogen*		
	Peptidases		
	Carboxypeptidase	Terminal peptide bond at carboxyl end of chain	Peptide + Amino Acid
	Aminopeptidase	Terminal peptide bond at amino end of chain	Peptide + Amino Acid
	Dipeptidase	Dipeptides	2 Amino acids
	Amylase	Starch	Maltose
	Lipase	Fat	Fatty acids, glycerol, monoglycerides, diglycerides
		Cholesterol	Cholesterol esters
	Cholesterol esterase	Cholesterol esters	Cholesterol
	Ribonuclease	RNA	Pyrimidine-containing nucleoside-3'-phosphate
			Oligonucleotides ending with pyrimidine nucleotide
	Deoxyribonuclease	DNA	Oligonucleotides ending with nucleotide
			Oligonucleotides ending with 3'-phosphate

* Activated by trypsin.

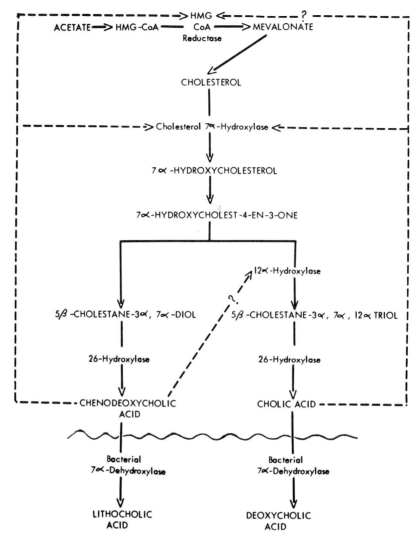

Figure 9–1 Pathway for the de novo synthesis of cholesterol and bile acids. Acetate, which can be supplied from any of the three major catabolic pathways (carbohydrate, lipid, amino acid), is the basic unit utilized for cholesterol synthesis. The point at which mevalonate formation occurs (HMG-CoA reductase) is the rate-limiting step of cholesterol synthesis. The broken lines represent feedback mechanisms, known and postulated. (From Vlahcevic, Z.R. et al.: Disturbances of bile acid metabolism in parenchymal liver cell disease. Clin. Gastroenterol. 6(1):25–43, 1977.)

The secretions of the pancreatic exocrine glands contain enzymes (Table 9–2), which supplement those of the succus entericus, to enable the digestive tract to completely break down any substance likely to be ingested. Pancreatic juice includes a variety of inorganic substances, mainly sodium, potassium, bicarbonate, and chloride. Calcium and zinc are present in small amounts, and the pH is distinctly alkaline (in the range of 7.5 to 8).

In addition to all of these digestive factors present in the intestinal lumen, we should underscore the presence of bile acids and bile salts. Bile is synthesized by the liver and stored in the gallbladder. One of the major functions of the gallbladder is to concentrate the bile by removal of some of the water content. The release of bile from the gallbladder during digestion is stimulated by the hormone cholecystokinin. This hormone, as already mentioned, is secreted by the upper intestine in response to the presence of various foodstuffs. Another hormone already mentioned, hepatocrinin, also secreted in response to the presence of food stuffs by the upper intestine, is a stimulant for the production of bile by the liver. The biochemical mechanisms for the formation of

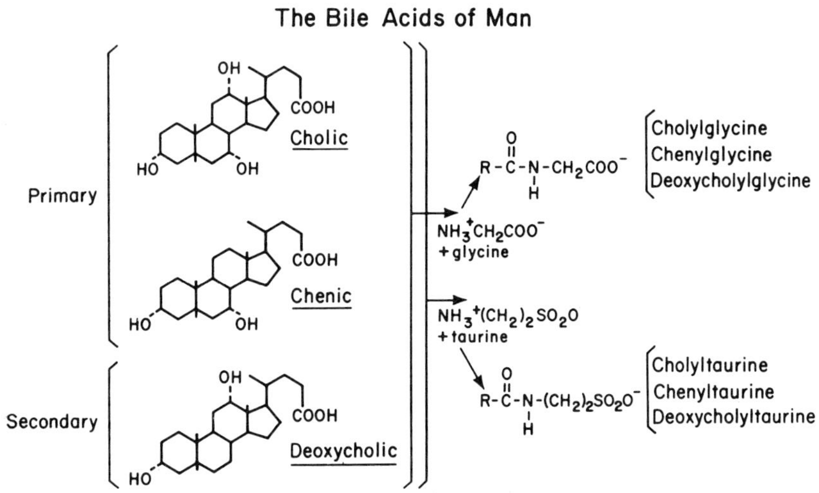

The Bile Acids of Man

Figure 9–2 Synthesis of major bile salts. Taurine conjugates predominate in the neonate (60 to 70 per cent), while glycine conjugates are the major components (60 to 70 per cent) at about 4 months of age. (From Hofmann, A.F.: The enterohepatic circulation of bile acids in man. Clin. Gastroenterol. 6(1):3–24, 1977.)

the bile acids from cholesterol is illustrated in Figure 9–1. These acids are important end-products in the metabolism of cholesterol, which is removed from the blood by the liver for the synthetic process (see chapter 15). However, it should be noted that cholesterol itself is also present in the bile. These bile acids are not excreted into the intestinal lumen in the free form but are conjugated by the liver with glycine or taurine to form glycocholic or taurocholic acids (Fig. 9–2). This conjugation increases the water solubility of the bile acids. Because the bile is of such alkaline nature, the conjugated bile acids may be, and usually are, significantly neutralized by reaction with sodium or potassium. These compounds are the "bile salts," and they exert powerful surface tension and emulsifying effects on the intestinal contents, thus aiding in the digestion of fats, probably through micelle formation. In addition to this, the presence of bile, perhaps due to its alkaline nature and effect on the pH of intestinal contents, activates a number of the pancreatic enzymes.

Absorption of Nutrients from the Gastrointestinal Tract

As with most other biological functions, the means by which the intestine transfers foodstuff elements from the intestinal lumen to the portal blood is quite efficient. As a consequence, the nutritional value of the material reaching the cecum, or the first part of the large intestine, is rather low. If one assumes that material is transferred from one side of the intestinal wall to the other merely by a simple means of diffusion, it is clear that the organism would have to consume an enormous amount of food merely to maintain the body's status quo let alone show the net synthesis so necessary for normal growth. One of the major benefits derived from research being done in gastrointestinal physiology is the demonstration of the role of active transport in intestinal luminal cells. We recall that active transport is a means of transferring a molecule from one side of a membrane to another against a concentration gradient, therefore requiring an expenditure of energy. By this means, a tremendous quantity of material can be transferred in a relatively short time. This makes possible maximum absorption of simple molecules from the intestinal lumen to the greatest benefit of the organism. The recognition of specific transport mechanisms has, in many cases, come about through a pathological state resulting from the absence of one or more of these transport mechanisms.

An excellent example of such a case is the disorder known as *glucose-galactose malabsorption syndrome,* in which the intestinal cell membrane carrier for glucose and galactose has actually been shown to be deficient. In this syndrome, because of a lack of normal caloric intake as well as a superimposed hyperosmolar diarrhea, the individual shows severe malnutrition and failure to thrive.

The simplest means of therapy for this very severe clinical disorder is removal of glucose and galactose from the diet and substitution with fructose. Such a maneuver has been shown to result in normal growth and development. Inborn errors in the intestinal handling of amino acids have also been demonstrated. Hartnup's disease and cystinuria represent prominent examples of such disorders (see Chapter 23).

Other pathological states of intestinal digestive processes may result from absence of one or more of the intestinal disaccharidases. Absence of these enzymes will result in a failure to break down disaccharides into their component monosaccharide units, thus preventing the intestine from carrying out normal sugar absorption. The immediate consequence of this is to increase the osmolar state of the intestinal contents, thus preventing water absorption and, indeed, causing a reversal of the normal water reabsorption processes. The result of all this is to cause a massive diarrhea. One well-known example of such a disorder is *congenital lactase deficiency*. This condition can appear in an acquired form as well as in a congenital form.

In general, then, it should be clear that the presence and normal function of the intestinal brushborder microvilli is critical to digestion and nutrition. As a result of causing varying degrees of damage to any or all of the microvillus mechanisms for absorption, several disease states may result in mimicry of inborn errors. Inasmuch as any severe disruption in the absorptive function of the intestine will result in malnutrition and most often failure to thrive, most of the diseases associated with such dysfunction are discussed in Chapter 10.

Other disorders that affect primarily hepatic or pancreatic exocrine function may manifest themselves in a similar manner. An outstanding example of such a disease is *cystic fibrosis,* in which the pancreatic exocrine function is essentially deficient. Such patients are unable to metabolize dietary fat and protein in a normal fashion, resulting in chronic steatorrhea and marked failure to thrive as a consequence of inability to absorb partially digested foodstuffs. Deficiencies of production or secretion of bile salts in a normal fashion for a variety of reasons may result in a similar picture.

As the food bolus travels down the approximately 25 feet of small intestine about 90 percent of the digested material is absorbed. Water is absorbed at the same time. Absorption of carbohydrates and amino acids is now known to be active, with the bulk of this material transported across the luminal surface of the microvillus by carrier mechanisms. Precisely what processes these materials undergo within the cells of the mucosal surface is not well understood, but the vast majority of the material that crosses the luminal side of the mucosa eventually arrives at the site of the portal veins and is carried from there to the liver. Digestion of fats, however, appears not to be such a simple feat for the intestine to accomplish.

Fat Digestion

The complete hydrolysis of triglycerides produces glycerol and fatty acids. However, hydrolysis of the first, second, and third fatty acids from glycerol occurs with increasing difficulty, removal of the third fatty acid requiring special conditions. It is thought that the actual digestive process commences with removal of a terminal fatty acid to result in alpha-beta-diglyceride, with subsequent removal of the alpha-fatty acid, resulting in a beta-monoglyceride. A very slow isomerization of the secondary ester linkage thus resulting occurs, so that the absorbed glycerides are in the form of alpha- or beta-monoglycerides in addition to the free fatty acids. Within the intestinal wall, alpha-monoglycerides are further hydrolyzed to produce free glycerol and fatty acids, while beta-monoglycerides are reconverted to triglycerides (Fig. 9–3). This latter process requires "activation," involving a reaction of ATP and magnesium ion and the enzyme *phosphokinase*. Normally, plasma free fatty acids are not primarily derived from dietary fat but result from hydrolysis of stored triglycerides within the fat depots. Rather, dietary free fatty acids are reincorporated into triglycerides within the intestinal mucosa. These triglycerides are transported in the form of chylomicrons, which are produced in the lymphatic vessels of the wall of the intestine. Via the lymphatics, these chylomicrons are transported ultimately into the systemic blood. Despite the complexity of this process, normally the feces contain only a very small fraction of the ingested dietary fat.

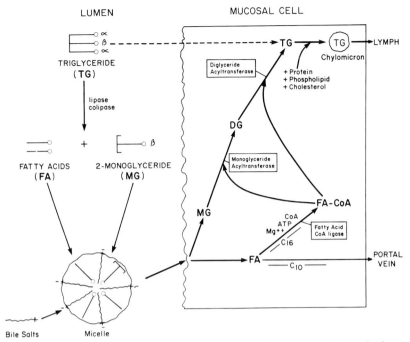

Figure 9–3 Absorptive routes for fatty acids (FA) and triglycerides (TG). Note the hydrolytic cleavage of triglycerides to diglycerides (DG) or monoglycerides (MG) prior to entry into the mucosal cell. (From Gray, M.: Mechanisms of Digestion and Absorption of Food. *In* Sleisenger, M.H., and Fordtran, J.S. (eds.): Gastrointestinal Diseases: Pathophysiology, Diagnosis, and Management. Philadelphia, W.B. Saunders Co., 1978.)

Functions of More Distal Segments of the Gastrointestinal Tract

With passage of the material down the small intestine from jejunum to ileum, the pH gradually increases, so that at the terminal ileal site the pH is approximately 8. Structurally, the histological features of the villi and microvilli of the small intestine change as the foodstuffs progress distally, corresponding to the decreased nutritional content of the luminal material. The villi and microvilli become sparser until both disappear just above the ileocecal valve.

From this point in the intestinal tract to the rectal segment, the major function is reabsorption of electrolytes and water. The reabsorption of sodium by active transport processes appears to be the major factor in fluid and ion shifts in the large intestine. The ratio of sodium to potassium in ileal water is reported to range from 12:1 up to 20:1, while the ratio in stool water is less than 1:3. The colon of the normal adult absorbs approximately half a liter of water per day, while the figure for the normal infant is probably proportionally higher. Thus, the semiliquid ileal contents gradually become more solid with passage through the colon.

The composition of feces on a relatively normal dietary intake will be fairly constant. The relative composition is as follows: water, 65 per cent and solid material, 35 per cent (made up of ash, 15 per cent; ether-soluble substances, 15 per cent; and nitrogen, 5 per cent). The major constituent of the solid material is desquamated epithelial cells from the intestinal mucosa as well as bacteria, most of which are dead. In the final analysis, on a fat intake of 100 grams daily not more than 5 to 7 per cent is normally lost in the feces, while on a protein intake of 100 grams per day, the fecal nitrogen content will not exceed 10 per cent of the intake. Thus, we can see that the digestive and absorptive processes of the gastrointestinal tract are quite efficient and operate to increase the survival advantage of the organism.

One final factor in digestion that needs to be considered in more detail is the intestinal putrefaction and fermentation process. During this process considerable bacterial activity occurs, resulting in the production of various gases, such as CO_2, methane, hydrogen, nitrogen, and hydrogen sulfide. Many amino acids undergo decarboxylation as a result of the action of intestinal bacteria, resulting in toxic amines. Thus, cadaverine is produced from lysine, tyramine from tyrosine, putresine from ornithine, and histamine from histidine. The amino acid tryptophan undergoes a series of reactions to form indole and methylindole, two substances that contribute to the characteristic odor of feces. Large quantities of ammonia are also produced by bacterial activity in the large intestine. This compound is absorbed into the portal circulation, but under normal conditions, it is rapidly removed from the blood by the liver, which converts it to urea (see Chapter 11).

Finally, lest the reader consider intestinal bacterial action to be potentially detrimental in all cases, it is necessary to point out that bacterial action is required for the biological synthesis of vitamin K and possibly certain members of the vitamin B complex. These vitamins are essential to normal metabolism and are made available to the body by bacterial action. Therefore, purposeful or inadvertent manipulation of the intestinal bacterial flora may be detrimental to the total organism in many cases and should be considered as a significant effect of therapy.

CLINICAL DISTURBANCES OF THE GASTROINTESTINAL TRACT

There are five major clinical disturbances of the gastrointestinal tract that now need brief consideration—pain, distention, diarrhea, malabsorption, and vomiting. Despite the enormous frequency with which these disorders are present in clinical practice, very little is known of the molecular mechanisms underlying their development.

Abdominal Distention

Distention of the abdomen can be acute or chronic, mechanical or biochemical in etiology. The most common cause of distention in infancy is excessive intragastric air. Most of the other common mechanical causes (Table 9–3) are due to accumulations of peritoneal fluid (ascites), conditions accompanied by severe pain with secondary paralytic ileus, or poor nutritional status with loss of abdominal muscle tone.

On the other hand, most of the biochemical causes of distention (Table 9–3) are mediated through effects of acidosis and electrolyte imbalance on gastrointestinal motility (see Vomiting). The exceptions to this are the storage diseases, which result in visceromegaly.

Table 9–3 CAUSES OF ABDOMINAL DISTENSION

Acutely Ill	Chronically Ill
Acute surgical abdomen	Liver-cirrhosis with ascites
Peritonitis	Tumor (adrenal, kidney)
Renal colic	Nephritis, nephrotic syndrome
Acute pancreatitis	Uremia
Pneumonia	Pancreatic pseudocyst
Renal vein thrombosis	Starvation (nutritional edema)
Infections—G.I. or G.U.	Malabsorption (carbohydrate and fat)— celiac, cystic fibrosis
Metabolic	
Adrenal insufficiency	Cystic fibrosis
Galactosemia	Celiac disease
Hereditary fructose intolerance	α-Antitrypsin deficiency
Tyrosinemia	Glycogen storage diseases
	Galactosemia
	Hereditary fructose intolerance
	Tyrosinemia
	Mucopolysaccharidoses
	Lipid storage disease
	Cretinism
	Rickets
	Hirschsprung's disease
	Ileus from hypokalemia
	Ectopic kidney

Table 9–4 CAUSES OF ABDOMINAL PAIN

Gastrointestinal	Infectious	Metabolic
Surgical Abdomen	Pneumonia and pleural effusion	Acidosis from any cause including
Appendicitis, Obstruction	Parasitic infestation	organic acidemias (Chapter 3, 34)
Perforation, Cholelithiasis	Urinary tract infection	Diabetes mellitus in relapse
Mesenteric lymphadenitis		Porphyria
Ovarian cyst, Hydronephrosis		Hypoglycemia
Medical Causes		Hyperlipidemia (I, III, IV, V)
Hepatitis, pancreatitis, cholecysti-		Celiac disease
tis, ileitis, colitis, gastroenteritis		Sickle cell anemia
Ulcer		Cystic fibrosis
Collagen vascular disease		Lactose intolerance
Rheumatic fever		Renal calculi
Henoch-Schönlein purpura		Hemophilia
Renal colic		***Intoxications***
Muscle pain (black widow spider)		Lead poisoning
Acute nephritis		Irritant poisons—salicylates
Abdominal seizures		
Psychological		

Abdominal Pain

Pain in the abdomen can be of three basic types: visceral, peritoneal, and referred. In general, the abdominal viscera are poorly innervated by sensory pain fibres, and visceral pain is not therefore usually well-defined and localized. Pain sensation from viscera are usually the result of distention of the hollow viscus, and such distention must take place rather rapidly. Peritoneal pain is often the result of inflammation, such as that seen in acute appendicitis. Referred pain is the result of sensory nerve stimuli in one of multiple rami of a nerve trunk that are felt in one or more of the areas of distribution of the other rami.

The molecular cause for the abdominal pain of acidosis is unknown, although ischemia is thought to increase tissue metabolite concentrations around sensory nerve endings, thus inducing pain. The mechanism for the abdominal pain of diabetic ketoacidosis and other biochemical disorders resulting in acidosis may be analogous. The numerous diseases that are accompanied by abdominal pain are listed in Table 9–4.

Diarrhea

Staggering numbers of individuals throughout the world are afflicted with diarrhea each year, the vast majority of the cases being secondary to infectious etiologies. The intestine is primarily an absorptive and transport organ facilitating transfer of substances from an extracorporeal space (the gut is continuous with the external milieu) to intracorporeal sites. In light of this fact, most etiologies of diarrhea may be traced to one of four basic mechanisms: (1) presence in the gut lumen of unusual amounts of poorly absorbable, osmotically active substances, (2) absence or interference

Table 9–5 DIARRHEAL MECHANISMS

Osmotic: excess of poorly absorbable or unabsorbable solute in gut
  Disaccharidase deficiency
  Malabsorptive states
  Cathartics
  Immune deficiency states
Abnormalities of Active Transport Processes: chloride losing diarrhea; glucose galactose malabsorption
Secretory: increased secretory activity of gut—persists despite cessation of oral feeds
  Enteric infections (invasive and toxin producing)
  Accumulation of secretogogues—bile salts, hydroxy fatty acids
Motility Abnormalities: hypocalcemia, hyperthyroidism, adrenal insufficiency, carcinoid syndrome; cholinergic drugs

Table 9–6   CAUSES OF FAT MALABSORPTION

Pancreas	Liver and Biliary Tract	Intestine
Cystic fibrosis (1,2)*	Cirrhosis (1)	Blind loop syndrome (1)
Schwachman's	Biliary atresia or	Chronic infection (1)
syndrome (1,2)	obstruction (1)	Short bowel syndrome (1,2)
Lipase deficiency (1)	Bile acid abnormalities (1)	Immune deficiency (2)
		Celiac disease (2)
		Enterokinase deficiency (1)
		Abetalipoproteinemia (3)
		Acrodermatitis enteropathica (2)
		Severe malnutrition (1–3)
		Intestinal lymphangiectasia with protein-losing enteropathy (4)
		Wolman's disease (4)
		Parasites (1,2)
		Radiation damage (2)

*Stage of process deranged: 1—hydrolysis of lipids or micelle formation impaired; 2—absorption of products of hydrolysis impaired; 3—chylomicron formation impaired; 4—lymphatic drainage impaired.

with a normal active absorptive process, (3) augmented intestinal secretion (some involve cAMP effect on gut), and (4) deranged intestinal motility. Examples of these general classes are shown in Table 9–5. Notwithstanding this classification, many diarrheal states are caused by factors from more than one of the categories.

Fat Malabsorption (Steatorrhea)

Digestion, absorption, and transport of lipid is a highly complex process that is still incompletely understood (see Chapter 31). Since lipid supplies about 50 per cent of the daily caloric

Table 9–7   CAUSES OF VOMITING

Amino Acid Disorders
   Nonketotic hyperglycinemia (1,3,4)*
   Hypervalinemia (4)
   Phenylketonuria (2–4)
   Lysinuric protein intolerance (3,4)
   Tyrosinemia (1,2)
Organic Acidemias
   Maple syrup urine (1–4)
   Methylmalonic aciduria (1,3,4)
   Propionic acidemia (1,3,4)
   Isovaleric acidemia (1–4)
   Lactic acidosis (1,3)
Urea Cycle Defects
   Argininosuccinic aciduria (1,3,4)
   Carbamylphosphate synthetase deficiency (1,3,4)
   Ornithine transcarbamylase deficiency (1,3,4)
   Citrullinemia (1,3,4)
   Hyperornithinemia (1,3,4)
Other
   Galactosemia (1,4)
   Adrenogenital syndrome (1,3)
   Hereditary fructose intolerance
   Metabolic acidosis—all causes including diabetes mellitus
   Uremia (3)
   Cystic fibrosis
   Renal tubular acidosis
   Porphyria
   Leigh's syndrome (1,3,4)

*Other diagnostic clues: 1—catastrophic neonatal disease; 2—odor; 3—seizures; 4—mental retardation.

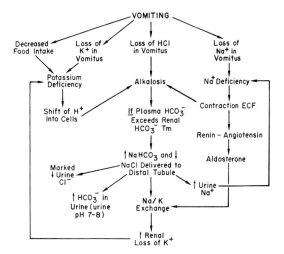

Figure 9–4 Metabolic consequences of vomiting. (From Feldman, M.: Vomiting. *In* Sleisenger, M.H., and Fordtran, J.S. (eds.): Gastrointestinal Diseases: Pathophysiology, Diagnosis, and Management. Philadelphia, W.B. Saunders Co., 1978.)

requirements, the percentage varying but slightly with age, failure of these processes can have significant consequences on growth and general well-being. The young infant is particularly vulnerable in this respect, since the total bile acid pool and the jejunal microvilli are smaller than in the adult. Taken together, these two features cause impaired micellar formation and decreased absorptive capacity.

Essential to proper lipid absorption are the actions of pancreatic lipase and cholesterol esterase, both of which reduce dietary lipid to its component parts. Impairment in production or secretion of these enzymes will result in presentation of unabsorbable lipid to the microvilli and excessive fat excretion in stool. This is the probable mechanism of steatorrhea in cystic fibrosis. Other conditions in which steatorrhea is a part are listed in Table 9–6.

Vomiting

From the biochemical point of view, the metabolic consequences of vomiting are of far greater significance than the act itself, which is relatively nondiagnostic. The results, shown in Figure 9–4, consist of dehydration, alkalosis, hypokalemia, and hyponatremia. The biochemical ramifications of each of these separate disorders are discussed in detail in appropriate sections throughout this book. Many of the inherited diseases of which vomiting is a part of the clinical presentation are shown in Table 9–7.

REFERENCES

Duttie, H.L., and Wormsley, K.G. (eds.): Scientific Basis of Gastroenterology. Churchill Livingstone, Edinburgh, 1979.

Fitzgerald, J.F., and Clark, J.H.: Chronic diarrhea. Pediatr. Clin. North Am. 29:221, 1982.

Lebenthal, E. (ed.): Textbook of Gastroenterology and Nutrition in Infancy. Raven Press, New York, 1981.

Lifshitz, F. (ed.): Clinical Disorders in Pediatric Gastroenterology and Nutrition. M. Dekker, New York, 1980.

Olsen, W.A.: A pathophysiologic approach to diagnosis of malabsorption. Am. J. Med. 67:1007, 1979.

Rehfeld, J.F.: Four basic characteristics of the gastrin-cholecystokinin system. Am. J. Physiol. 240:G255, 1981.

Riley, J.W., and Glickman, R.M.: Fat malabsorption—Advances in our understanding. Am. J. Med. 67:980, 1979.

Schulz, I., and Stolze, H.H.: The exocrine pancreas: The role of secretagogues, cyclic nucleotides and calcium in enzyme secretion. Ann. Rev. Physiol. 42:127, 1980.

Shiau, Y-F.: Mechanisms of intestinal fat absorption. Am. J. Physiol. 240:G1, 1981.

Sleisinger, M.H., and Fordtran, J.S. (eds.): Gastrointestinal Disease. 2nd ed. W.B. Saunders Co., Philadelphia, 1978.

Weems, W.A.: The intestine as a fluid propelling system. Ann. Rev. Physiol. 43:9, 1981.

10

Growth and Development

THE GROWTH PROCESS

Even to the casual observer the growth of the human infant is a cause for wonder. However, any discussion of the phenomenon of growth begs the question, Why does growth occur? One might speculate that if the fertilized ovum contains a full genetic complement and is truly totipotential, then this single cell should be capable of carrying out simultaneously all of the coupled biochemical and physiologic functions manifested by the human adult organism. This is ludicrous, but why? There are three aspects to the answer: first, the limits set by the extracellular milieu upon the stupendous metabolic fuel requirements of this imaginary unicellular organism and, of course, the diffusional limits of oxygen at ambient (20 per cent) concentration in such a huge cell; second, the intrinsic replicative ability of the fertilized ovum; and third, the reality that functional differentiation can only be achieved with a critical mass of cells acting in concert.

The cell surface area varies as the square of its radius, while volume varies as the cube of the radius. Hence, the slightest increase in cell diameter affects the diffusion space out of proportion to the diffusion surface. There is, therefore, an inherent limitation in the size a cell may achieve and still survive. The concept of a totipotential cell implies total expression of the genetic potential for protein (including enzyme) synthesis. This, too, is inherently restricted by the solubility of all of these proteins and the enormous volume of cell water required to prevent precipitation and denaturation (see Chapter 2). Thus, biochemical expression of the entire genotype requires both cell division and specialization, with various portions of the genotype repressed in different cells. Such a strategy permits development of the complex multicellular organism whose functions are shared by the different organs comprising the individual.

Differentiation in multicellular organisms demands permanent repression of selected information contained in the genome of the fertilized egg. Hence, cell types of a particular organ express certain characteristic phenotypic biochemical and physiological capabilities. Such a view follows from the fact that two organs, brain and liver, while sharing certain general biochemical capabilities (e.g., protein synthesis and glycolysis) have distinctively different biochemical phenotypes. It is inevitable that fertilization of the ovum will produce a number of cells whose cumulative size and mass will be larger than the single parent cell, thus clearly defining growth.

How many cells are enough? To restate this, we might ask why growth, as defined by increased cell number and total mass, does not proceed throughout life. Again, we can turn to physical limitations for at least a partial answer. From the fertilized ovum, which weighs approximately 5 μg to the term neonate weighing 3.25 kg, there has been a weight increase of 650 million times! If the growth rate over the first month of gestation persisted unchanged until the age of 20 years, the body mass would equal that of the known universe in size. This makes clear the need for inherent size limitations, although it does little to clarify the mechanisms creating the limits. The change from intra- to extra-uterine environment cannot be the sole limiting factor, for if the growth rate evidenced from birth to one year were to continue until the age of 20 years, the individual would be more than 1100 feet in height and weigh tens of millions of pounds! Such dimensions are food for fairy tales and science fiction but cannot apply to humans as we know them. While it is relatively easy to accept the fact that inadequate nutrition and chronic disease can adversely affect normal growth, it is difficult to understand the more subtle factors that alter and moderate the rapidly enlarging infant to prevent the ultimate emergence of a colossus.

Since the information for all of the proteins (both functional and structural) is contained in the genome and since it is clear that many external factors can alter growth, it is likely that growth itself depends upon the interaction of multiple genetic factors (determined by the information in the individual's DNA pool) with the ever-changing environment. Such environmental factors include adequate supplies of water, oxygen, and substrates as well as specific regulators and inhibitors. Consequently, it is unlikely that growth, involving a highly complex group of both simultaneous and sequential events, is the expression of one gene or the action of one signal molecule (hormone).

Like all life processes the conduct of the action begins at the level of the cell, the smallest entity envincing those properties characteristic of living things. Limitation of the raw materials for accretion of cellular protoplasm will limit the ability to carry out certain specific functions as well as to grow, even in the presence of the appropriate stimulus. As noted above, the ability to grow appears to be one of the inherent attributes of living organisms. What it is that limits the size of birds and mammals (poikilotherms manifest less intrinsic growth limitation) is a matter of speculation and investigation. Presently it seems that there is an innate tendency in the presence of adequate raw materials for organs and tissues and the whole organism to grow—presumably at the direction of growth-promoting substances. Such chemicals must include certain hormones (Table 10–1) but are certainly not limited to them. However, it has been documented repeatedly that maternal growth hormone does not cross the placenta in significant quantities. Although fetal growth hormone, may, indeed, support late gestational growth, prior to development of the pituitary at about 15 weeks this is highly unlikely. This provides further evidence of the intrinsic genetic growth potential of the fertilized ovum.

As growth and biochemical development of organs proceed, a complex negative feedback process (the nature of which is almost entirely unknown) ensues and limits the ultimate size of the organs and the organism. Such a process appears to involve secretion of organ-specific inhibitors, termed chalones, which inhibit the mitotic process. Such agents are secreted by the organ itself, so that negative feedback involves an informational loop within the organ in question. It seems reasonable to assume that such responses are integrated with the biochemical processes occurring in the organism. In other words, if a functional demand for muscle hypertrophy were placed upon the

Table 10–1 HORMONAL EFFECTS ON GROWTH

Growth Hormone
Increase in cell size mediated through stimulation of production of somatomedins. Probably has separate roles stimulating:
  maturation of epiphyseal cartilage
  proliferation of cartilage
Somatomedins may be under control of other factors besides GH—perhaps insulin (in obesity) and (?prolactin)
Thyroid
Important for maturation of brain and skeletal muscle
Regulates basal metabolic rate
Affects cell size—i.e., has an effect on protein synthesis
In absence of GH, thyroid may promote some degree of maturation but not growth
Insulin
Prime storage hormone of protein, fat, and carbohydrate
Promotes addition of protein within the cell and therefore affects cell size
Stimulates amino acid transport and affects carbohydrate metabolism
Glucocorticoids
Pharmacologic doses inhibit growth—perhaps through inhibition of production of somatomedin as well as direct inhibitory effects on growing cartilage
Androgens
Stimulate both hyperplasia and hypertrophy in responsive organs
Estrogens
Stimulate growth in muscle cell size but inhibit multiplication

organism, then growth might continue because of the new environmental conditions. Hence growth, which normally would continue until the size is "just right," can under certain circumstances be augmented further.

The opposite situation, inability to fulfill this inherent growth potential, can come about through a number of clinical situations that impair substrate supply or utilization, limit the energy supply for the cell's needs, or interfere with the production of or response to signal molecules that modulate the growth process. Evidence is accumulating for a role of the cell surface in growth, both on the basis of specific surface antigens as well as through reception of informational molecules. Such molecules would not be limited to hormones but would include neurotransmitters, prostaglandins, and tissue-specific signals such as the particular growth factors for nerve, epidermis, and fibroblast.

GROWTH AND DEVELOPMENT

While the stimuli for growth may be both general and tissue specific, here we want to focus both on what these signals accomplish and on the integrated or orchestrated quality of the growth process. Growth involves an increase in size of a part or all of the body. In utero, cell proliferation (i.e., an increase in cell number) predominates over an increase in cell size and intercellular matrix in a process that involves the integration of DNA and RNA proliferation, protein synthesis, and cell division. This phase is characterized by hyperplasia, indicating mitosis as the preponderant mode of growth. While cell division continues after birth, increase in cell size begins to predominate as the mode of growth and eventually becomes the main component of growth.

Because at base it is the interaction of enzymes with their environment that mediates growth, it should be clear that adverse changes in hydrogen ion concentration, availability of intracellular trace metals, and energy-yielding substrates can all have profoundly negative effects on growth (see Tables 10–2 and 10–3). An adequate supply of essential amino acids (or their keto analogues) must be furnished to permit growth of tissue, which is always based on a protein matrix of structural and functional molecules.

Growth is closely coupled to an even more remarkable process, i.e., differentiation. This latter process, whose control must reside in some complex interaction of the changing internal environment of the cell with the genome, results in the formation of the different tissues and organs of the

Table 10–2 PATTERNS OF FAILURE TO THRIVE

Characterization	Parameters	Growth Rate	Differential Diagnosis
I. Abnormal genetic potential or IUGR (constitutional)	HA < BA; BA = CA* (i.e., short patient with normal skeletal age)	Normal Potential for growth is limited but is achieved	Genetic short stature, osteochondrodystrophies, chromosomal disorders, intrauterine growth retardation (including maternal drugs), storage diseases, pseudohypoparathyroidism
II. Normal genetic potential with superimposed familial variant or systemic disease of limited duration ("delayed growth")	HA = BA; BA < CA Despite retarded BA, child grows at normal rate	Normal	Normal variant (constitutional delay) familial trait, mild malnutrition, metabolic or other chronic illness, hypoxia, hypophosphatemia (rickets)
III. Normal genetic potential with superimposed chronic disease ("arrested growth")	BA < HA and CA	Subnormal but inherent potential for growth is normal	Marked: Hypothyroidism Moderate: Hypopituitarism, malnutrition (trace metals), pH disturbances, chronic organ or multisystem disease, glucocorticoid excess

*HA = height age; BA = bone age; CA = chronologic age.

Table 10–3 CAUSES OF FAILURE TO THRIVE

Deficiency of Calories or Oxygen—impaired intake, digestion, or absorption (transport)
  Appetite diminished in chronic disease—congenital heart disease, renal failure, advanced brain disease
  Malabsorption states—cystic fibrosis, celiac disease, lactase deficiency, chronic diarrhea, megacolon, inflammatory bowel
    disease, hepatic insufficiency, abetalipoproteinemia
  Nutritional deficiency—calories, protein, vitamins, minerals—obtain careful 1-day feeding history
  Impaired oxygen transport—hemoglobinopathies, cyanotic congenital heart disease
  Increased expenditure (accentuated catabolism—see below, Abnormalities of Intermediary Metabolism)
    Chronic disease—infection, chronic renal failure, acidosis, lung, liver, heart, GI, immune deficiency, spasticity, neo-
      plasm, hyperthyroidism
Abnormalities of Fluid and Electrolyte Homeostasis
  Chronic renal disease, chronic diarrheal states
Abnormalities of Intermediary Metabolism (may involve inability to utilize ingested calories)
  Amino acid disorders causing acidosis or accumulation of toxic materials
    Urea cycle
    Organic acidemias
    Tyrosinemia
  Carbohydrate disorders
    Diabetes
    Galactosemia, hereditary fructose intolerance
    Glycogen storage disease
  Storage diseases that cause CNS dysfunction and impair metabolism
    Glycosphingolipidoses
    Mucopolysaccharidoses
  CNS disease
    Subdural, diencephalic syndrome (brain tumors)
Endocrine Disorders
  Hypothyroidism, growth hormone
  Adrenal disorders
  Emotional deprivation syndrome
Failure of Bone or Cartilage to Respond to Growth Stimulators
  Pseudohypoparathyroidism
  Hypophosphatasia—unable to calcify osteoid
  Intrauterine growth retardation (hypoplasia—smaller than normal complement of cells)—infection, placental insufficiency—
    as a group these infants are hypermetabolic).
  Chromosomal and Genetic Syndromes
    Down's syndrome
    Turner's syndrome
    Trisomy D syndrome
    Trisomy E syndrome
    Cri du chat syndrome
    Cornelia de Lange's syndrome
    Seckel's syndrome
    Silver's syndrome
    Achondroplasia
  Lysosomal storage— decreased ability to respond to growth regulators

multi-cellular organism over the course of time. Unequivocal delineation of specific organs and their functions occurs fairly early in the first trimester, and with differentiation begun, growth in size and emergence of biochemical capabilities unfold. It is this latter process, through which various organs develop the biochemical apparatus to carry out their physiological functions, that many designate as development. In the fully developed individual the highly organized and specialized organ factories spoken of earlier interact to orchestrate the functions of the total organism (see Chapter 2).

There are some distinctive differences between the fetus and the infant. Most obviously and profoundly the fetus is a "captive" audience in utero, dependent upon the integrity of the placenta and uterus as well as maternal health and nutrition. The mother must supply the fetus with adequate glucose, lactate, and amino acids for energy needs while providing the raw materials for accretion of new tissue. Less obviously, growth in utero is governed by the information contained in the genome and maternal hormones (placental lactogen and prolactin), which appear to have growth-promoting properties. This is in sharp contrast with the infant, in whom thyroxine and growth hormone have important growth-stimulating roles (see Table 10–1). Part of the lack of hormonal effect of thyroid and pituitary hormones on intrauterine growth is due to the late onset of hormonal secretion in utero mentioned above. It has been suggested that part of the action of placental lactogen may be to shift maternal energy supply to a fat economy, thereby diverting much needed glucose and amino acids away from the mother to the developing fetus.

Morphogenesis

In Chapter 2 we emphasized the central role of control mechanisms in the life process to protect the integrity of the organism against internal and external perturbations. Perhaps nowhere is this more essential than in the growth process, for there are countless ways in which it can be disturbed. After all, if the enzymes of a metabolic pathway must interact in a faultless manner, how much more important is such correlated and integrated functioning in a process as complicated as growth.

It should be clear that orchestration in life presupposes that no cell, tissue, or organ in the normal organism is ever permitted to "do its own thing." It follows, then, that a malfunctioning organ may be unable to do its part for the organism, so that certain higher order functions (e.g., growth, differentiation, morphogenesis, and thought) are impaired temporarily or permanently, depending upon the timing and duration of the abnormality. These higher order functions are by their very nature *critical mass functions;* they depend upon a minimal number of supercellular structural and functional elements acting in an integrated fashion in both space and time. Such a situation obtains in the symphony orchestra, which provides a simple analogy to such involved processes in life. Just as the sound qualities, harmonies, and amplification achieved by the symphony orchestra cannot be produced by single instruments, so it is clear that certain life processes require the simultaneous and amplified performance possible only when millions to billions of cells act in concert in the presence of adequate raw materials and appropriate stimuli (e.g., hormones).

Lest these general remarks suggest that growth or morphogenesis is well understood we hasten to emphasize that the means by which the organs of the fetus take form and acquire the sophisticated and specific biochemical functions that distinguish them as differentiated are still an enigma. Indeed many current models rely upon the role of nonequilibrium thermodynamics and generation of oscillations in the developing mass of cells of an organ. References discussing these models are listed at the end of this section.

Growth in utero proceeds at the fastest pace during the early part of pregnancy, achieving a peak at about 5 months. Thereafter, the rate slows somewhat, this relative decrease in growth rate persisting until 3 years of age, when growth achieves a steady pace. This variable pattern of growth velocity, which begins in utero, is characteristic of growth throughout the whole of childhood. At the onset of puberty growth rate accelerates until full adult stature is achieved.

POSTNATAL GROWTH

While growth in length proceeds most rapidly in infancy, it begins a decline in rate during this period. This overall pattern must be linked to the concept of individual variations in growth. Although we have stressed the over-riding importance of the genome in regulating growth rate and potential, we must resist the temptation to think simplistically. The random assortment of genes, which occurs during meiosis, ensures that the union of two germ cells will produce a genetically unique fertilized ovum. This fact, combined with the multigenic and enormously complex process of differentiation can account for individual relative rates of growth and development of the various organs and the child as a whole. Thus, the period of time necessary for "tuning the orchestra" will vary from individual to individual. Only after the biochemical capacity of all of the organs can support the genetically endowed growth potential can the overall growth pattern of the child emerge. Consequently, major shifts in linear growth percentile rank are the norm in early infancy, but by 2 years of age a stable linear growth course, which the individual will continue to follow until puberty, is usually firmly fixed. Linear growth up until puberty is the result of a predictable rate of bone growth, itself the result of endochondral bone formation.

Much evidence supports the view that an organism grows so as to achieve a genetically predetermined size. Generally, between age two and the onset of puberty, normal children maintain growth along a particular centile, with little tendency to stray from that growth curve. This has been termed channelization, and careful measurements reveal that healthy children often have short-term fluctuations in height in order to remain on their predetermined centile for height. It is likely that minor intercurrent illnesses may be the cause of a slowdown in growth velocity, which then engenders a compensatory acceleration when the illness has passed. More profound delay in growth is common in chronic illness, but even here compensatory changes can occur when successful therapy is achieved. At present, we must assume that the factors maintaining channelization of growth inhere in the genetic program of the organism itself. Indeed, by two years of age one can predict the individual's height on the basis of parental height. Moreover, individuals with two Y chromosomes are taller than siblings, suggesting that some factors for bone growth may reside on that chromosome.

Since boys experience their onset of adolescence later than girls, on average, and since they achieve a greater adult height, it seems that the longer period of pre-pubertal growth in boys accounts for this discrepancy. In conditions that accelerate closure of the epiphyses this pattern is reversed, furnishing further evidence for the importance of pre-pubertal growth.

Studies by Hommes (1980) indicate that, as a rough estimate, approximately 2 per cent of calories ingested are involved in growth, i.e., generation of ATP to be used in protein synthesis. Others place the figure closer to 13 per cent. Such bookkeeping exercises can only define general boundaries for the age-dependent caloric requirement for the growth process.

Patterns of growth impairment are shown in Table 10–2, which also presents a differential diagnosis of disorders evincing each pattern. Any classification of failure to thrive (FTT) must depend upon arbitrary separations that may not apply to the actual patient. Our classification emphasizes the crucial role that timing (during vulnerable periods of growth) and severity of the perturbation have on fulfillment of the child's genetic potential for growth. As a consequence certain disease categories shown in the differential diagnosis column in Table 10–2 appear in both categories II and III but are differentiated on the basis of their duration and severity. Most importantly, many of the disorders are amenable to palliation and some can be cured. Accordingly, a search for the underlying cause must be undertaken with vigor.

GROWTH DISORDERS

Disorders of Intrauterine Growth

Intrauterine growth retardation (IUGR) signifies an infant whose birth size is less than expected for gestational age; usually this means an infant below the tenth percentile on the Lubchenco graphs. Such infants may be retarded either because of a primary retardation of linear growth or impairment of fetal nutrition. In the former group are conditions involving a decrease in cell number in various organs—e.g., hypoxia, some primordial dwarfs, congenital rubella, and various congenital heart defects. Limited growth in these conditions suggests that bone, as well as other tissues, has suffered a decrease in its normal complement of cells. Experimental studies of fetal malnutrition show a deleterious effect on both cell number and cell size, although these effects will depend upon the innate vulnerability of different tissues to the insult at different times. Since the fetus is dependent on nutrition and oxygen supply from the mother, maternal disease or inadequacy of placental functions can be the cause of fetal malnutrition. Maternal factors include malnutrition, vascular disease, drug addiction, chronic disease, and alcoholism. There is evidence that cell number can increase later on despite adverse effects during vulnerable periods; this may explain the catch-up growth seen in some of these infants.

Primordial (Congenital) Dwarfs Presenting with IUGR

Disorders of fetal linear growth may result from myriad causes, including genetic, chromosomal, and infectious causes, and drugs. Dysmorphic features may be the first clue to a disorder that affects linear growth as well. Bone dysplasia usually presents with abnormal skeletal proportions and will result in permanent dwarfism. Examples include the osteochondrodystrophies, of which achondroplasia is the most common variant. Hypophosphatasia is another less frequent cause.

Disorders of Postnatal Growth

Linear growth may be adversely affected by disorders affecting either bone growth or the factors that determine bone development. In the latter category such insults may persist or may have occurred at a particular vulnerable time in bone growth. Reference to Table 10–2, which relates bone age, height age, and chronologic age to the differential diagnosis for growth delay, should help in the diagnostic exploration.

Individuals who are intrinsically short cannot grow to normal height because their inherent growth potential is limited; nonetheless, their growth rate is normal. In contrast, individuals suffering from severe acquired or inherited disorders have a markedly depressed rate of growth (bone age is less than chronological and height ages) despite inherently normal growth potential. Such patients often show normal growth until the onset of the perturbation that affects growth so adversely, with a dramatic fall off on the growth chart.

Between these two extremes is a category of children whose bone age is delayed but who grow at a normal rate. This is a heterogeneous group whose growth delay is either on a familial (constitutional) basis or the result of acquired or inherited disease. Certain milder forms of disorders that cause arrested (impaired) growth may be responsible for this growth pattern as well. When there is a family history of such delay in growth wih delayed puberty but eventual normal development, one can be more hopeful regarding the outcome. Nonetheless certain screening tests are desirable. In this pattern, the growth charts reveal a curve below but parallel to the third percentile for height, with a normal advance in bone age after about two years of age.

Intrinsic Shortness

The inability of bone to respond to signals for growth is usually a congenital defect, although evidence of such a problem may not become manifest until after the perinatal period. Often the cause is a chromosomal abnormality, and severe mental retardation of a static rather than progressive nature is very common.

Delayed Growth

Patients evincing this growth pattern usually have a normal genetic potential for growth but are delayed in achieving that either because of a familial pattern of delay or because of a superimposed systemic illness of limited duration. So-called constitutional or familial delay is by far the most common cause of such a pattern. Nonetheless, it is a diagnosis of exclusion, and systemic illness must be sought as a potential treatable cause of delay (careful history and physical and laboratory examinations for systemic disorders). Particularly helpful in making this diagnosis is a history of a parent or close relative of normal height who suffered from constitutional delay, most commonly manifest as delayed puberty.

Arrested Growth

Strikingly abnormal growth, usually well below the third percentile, is almost always a consequence of severe systemic, endocrine, or metabolic disease (Tables 10–2 and 10–3).

Generalized metabolic disturbances, especially those affecting pH (see Chapter 3), impair

Table 10–4 FACTORS
IMPLICATED IN GROWTH
FAILURE FROM RENAL
DISEASE

Anorexia
Protein restriction
Acidosis
Hyperparathyroidism
Decreased production of 1,25 Vit. D
Somatomedin deficiency

growth. Such disorders include inborn errors, leading to accumulation of acid, as well as chronic renal disease. The latter is complicated by a host of secondary perturbations, which are listed in Table 10–4. Severe malnutrition or deficiency of an essential amino acid diminishes growth velocity (see Chapter 37).

DIAGNOSTIC APPROACH TO DISORDERS OF GROWTH

Routinely maintained growth charts based upon carefully and accurately measured height and weight values are the bulwark of the physician's early warning growth delay recognition system.

Table 10–5 ASSESSMENT OF THE "SMALL" CHILD

1. **How Small?**
   a. Length—normal is <2.5 standard deviations below norm for age
   b. Weight—determine relationship to length; caloric deprivation results first in poor weight gain
   c. Head circumference—small head size suggests either severe primary malnutrition (reflected in length and weight) or defective brain or skull growth secondary to genetic or congenital etiology
2. **What were Birth Length, Weight, and Head Circumference?**
   a. Proportional low parameters—suggest either congenital dwarfism or miscalculated EDC with early delivery
   b. Normal length and head circumference, low weight—suggests late placental insufficiency or postmaturity
3. **Accuracy of Current Measurements**
   a. Length is especially subject to error
   b. Serial measurements are essential to avoid misdiagnosis
4. **Pattern of Growth Disturbance**
   a. Must be based upon serial measurements
   b. Distinguish between cessation of growth (e.g., severe acute illness) and abrupt decrease in growth velocity (e.g., chronic illness)
5. **Parental Stature and Early Growth Patterns**
   a. Generally, large parents have large children
   b. Lean body mass at birth can be correlated with lean body mass of the mother
   c. Timing of growth spurts tends to be familial, as does onset of puberty
6. **Is Nutrition Adequate for Normal Growth?**
   a. Dietary history is important, particularly with respect to adverse reactions to specific types of foods (e.g., hereditary fructose intolerance)
   b. Common, borderline malnutrition often distinguishable by isolated poor weight gain and normal motor development
7. **Emotional Stability of Home Situation**
   a. Multiple caretakers may result in overall poor nutrition
   b. Maternal neglect may cause severe malnutrition
   c. Maternal emotional withdrawal may cause "emotional deprivation syndrome" manifested by stunted growth
8. **Physical Evidence of Chronic Disease**
   a. Dysmorphic features suggest syndromes that often interfere with growth
   b. Congenital heart disease or cystic fibrosis
   c. Neurological and/or developmental difficulties
      1. MPS or lipidosis syndromes
      2. Aminoacidopathies
      3. Organic acidemias
      4. Galactosemia
   d. Amenorrhea (primary or secondary)
      1. Anorexia nervosa
      2. Hypophyseal tumor

Precious time can be lost when such critical diagnostic information is unavailable. Statistically, approximately a third of children who are outside the 95 per cent confidence limits of normal manifest only a variation of normal, but one cannot assume this is so without sequential measurements.

It is useful to observe the pattern of growth as manifested by the growth chart. Deviation from the previously traversed centile curve, so that the child crosses several lines and follows a curve well below any of the standard curves, is strong evidence for a cause of growth delay that must be investigated. When the curve manifesting persistent deviation from the norm begins at an early age, a congenital condition should be suspected. Acquired conditions do not announce their presence until later; thus the curve will be normal up to a point, whereupon deviation will become manifest. Finally, individuals with constitutional delay or familial short stature, while growing below the norms, will continue to parallel the standard curves, thus growing at normal rates as they fulfill their limited growth potential.

Bone age is the best predictor of growth, being superior to height or weight and chronological age. For example, when a short child has a bone age and chronological age that are equivalent, his potential for ultimate height is not as great as another child whose bone age is delayed relative to chronological age. While X-ray determination of bone age lacks specificity in terms of diagnostic categories—it is delayed both in endocrine disorders causing short stature as well as in constitutional growth delay, while it tends to be normal in familial short stature—it does provide an objective way to begin an evaluation. Hence, if the bone age is normal and the child is short, he has familial short stature with limited growth potential. When growth delay is on a nutritional basis, the height age is usually closer to the norm than is the weight age. As a general approach, when the physician has evidence for delay in growth or development, one must consider the categories listed in Table 10–2 and 10–3. Table 10–5 presents an outline to the assessment of a child with suspected failure to thrive.

REFERENCES

Battaglia, F.C., and Meschia, G.: Principal substrates of fetal metabolism. Physiol. Rev. 58:499, 1978.
Cheek, D.B.: Human Growth: Body Composition, Cell Growth, Energy, and Intelligence. Lea & Febiger, Philadelphia, 1968.
Garrod, D.R., and Nicol, A.: Cell behaviour and molecular mechanisms of cell-cell adhesion. Biol. Rev. 56:199, 1981.
Goldbloom, R.B.: Failure to thrive. Pediatr. Clin. North Am. 29:151, 1982.
Gospodarowicz, D.: Epidermal and nerve growth factors in mammalian development. Ann. Rev. Physiol. 43:251, 1981.
Hakamori, S.: Glycosphingolipids in cellular interaction, differentiation and oncogenesis. Ann. Rev. Biochem. 40:733, 1981.
Heby, O.: Role of polyamines in the control of cell proliferation and differentiation. Differentiation 19:1, 1981.
Hommes, F.A.: The energy requirement for growth. A re-evaluation. Nutrition and Metabolism. 24:110, 1980.
Kauffman, S.A., Shymuko, R.M., and Trubert, K.: Control of sequential compartment formation in Drosophilia. Science 199:259, 1978.
Krogman, W.M.: Child Growth. The University of Michigan, Ann Arbor, 1972.
Lacalli, T.C., and Harrison, L.G.: Turing's conditions and the analysis of morphogenetic models. J. Theor. Biol. 76:419, 1979.
Lowrey, G.H.: Growth and Development of Children. Year Book Medical Publishers, Chicago, 1978.
Lubchenco, L.O.: Assessment of gestational age and birth. Pediatr. Clin. North Am. 17:125, 1970.
Mehls, O., Ritz, E., Gilli, G., and Kreusser, W.: Growth in renal failure. Nephron 21:237, 1978.
Rosenfield, R. L.: Somatic growth and maturation. *In* DeGroot, L., Cahill, G. F., Jr., Martini, L., et al (eds.): Endocrinology. Grune and Stratton, New York, 1979, p. 1805.

11

Hyperammonemia

Marc Yudkoff

NITROGEN ECONOMY

Hyperammonemia represents a failure by the liver to dispose of excess ammonia, a neurotoxic agent derived from catabolism of nitrogen-containing compounds that normally is converted to urea in the liver and is excreted as such in the urine. Hyperammonemia therefore represents a disorder of abnormal nitrogen retention, and to understand the pathogenesis of hyperammonemia a basic review of body nitrogen economy is necessary.

The preponderance of body nitrogen is contained in protein, which constitutes 20 percent of adult dry body weight. This protein, both structural and enzymatic, must be constantly replenished if nitrogen balance is to be maintained. Table 11-1 shows the amount of nitrogen lost in the stool, sweat, and urine, as well as the nitrogen needed for continued growth. The body's need for protein is, for all practical purposes, a constant need; we do not store any appreciable amount. This is a very different situation from the body's ability to store excess dietary carbohydrates and fat as glycogen, cholesterol, and triglycerides. The reason for this discrepancy in our ability to store dietary components can be found in an examination of biological specificity. In Chapter 2 we discussed the fact that the wide diversity and specific structure and function of protein molecules derive from DNA coding and weak-bonding forces. The latter result in molecules that are relatively labile, thus requiring constant degradation and resynthesis. The inability to store excess dietary protein as body protein accounts for the presence of ammonia in body fluids, since the pre-eminent fate of dietary nitrogen in excess of the nitrogen requirement is the oxidation of the constituent amino acids.

Ammonia is one product of the oxidation of amino acids, as is seen in Figure 11-1. This figure outlines the major routes of utilization of all amino acids. The first is, of course, the synthesis of proteins. A small fraction is used for synthesis of certain specialized compounds like thyroxine and catecholamines. Those amino acids in excess of minimal requirements are oxidized. The first step in this oxidation pathway is the removal of the amino group in a deamination reaction, which forms the keto analogue of the amino acid and ammonia. Further oxidation of the keto acids allows the end-product to enter the citric acid cycle, where it is catabolized to carbon dioxide and water.

It is noteworthy that the total plasma amino acid concentration equals about 50 mg/dl. The blood ammonia concentration, however, is dramatically lower—only about one-thousandth the con-

Table 11-1 NORMAL NITROGEN BALANCE

1. Must replace: Nitrogen lost + nitrogen needed for growth
2. 1st year: Losses = 60 to 150 mg/kg/day (urine, stool, sweat)
   Growth = 100 mg/kg
   Total = 160 to 250 mg/kg/day

3. In terms of protein this amounts to:
   1st year requirement: 1.5 g protein/kg/day
   2nd year requirement: 1.0 g protein/kg/day
   or
   6 to 7 per cent total calories

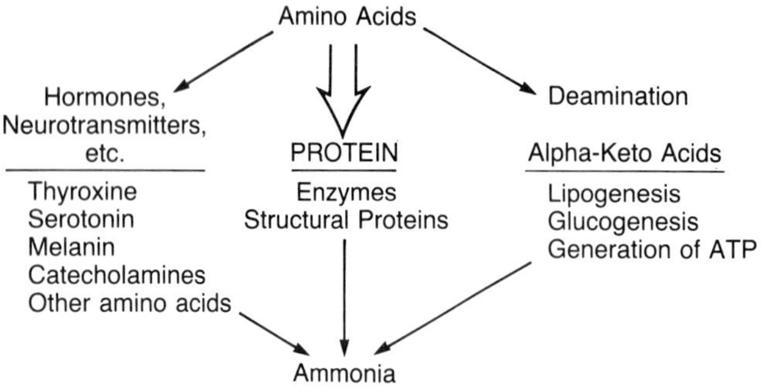

Amino Acids

Hormones, Neurotransmitters, etc.

Deamination

PROTEIN

Alpha-Keto Acids

Thyroxine
Serotonin
Melanin
Catecholamines
Other amino acids

Enzymes
Structural Proteins

Lipogenesis
Glucogenesis
Generation of ATP

Ammonia

Figure 11–1 Metabolic disposition of amino acids.

Plasma alpha-amino nitrogen = 4 to 8 mg/dl
Total plasma amino acids = 35 to 65 mg/dl
Plasma ammonia = 50 to 100 µg/dl

Deamination
Reaction:
$$R-\underset{\underset{NH_2}{|}}{C}H-COOH \xrightarrow[H_2O]{NAD} R-\underset{\underset{O}{\|}}{C}-COOH + NH_3$$

centration of the amino acids from which ammonia is derived. This discrepancy is undoubtedly the result of the need to protect against the toxicity of high concentrations of ammonia to living tissues. The biochemical basis of this toxicity is not yet well understood, although a deleterious effect on the generation of ATP appears to be at least one factor (see below). Thus, the survival of the organism requires that ammonia levels be maintained at a relatively low level. While some fish accomplish this simply by permitting ammonia to diffuse into the surrounding sea, terrestrial existence necessitated the evolutionary trial and error search for an alternative mechanism for the disposal of ammonia. This mechanism is the urea cycle, shown in Figure 11–2.

Urea Synthesis

By this mitochondrial process, glutamate serves as the source of the two amino groups in urea, one through deamination and the other by transamination. This catalytic cycle employs the carbon

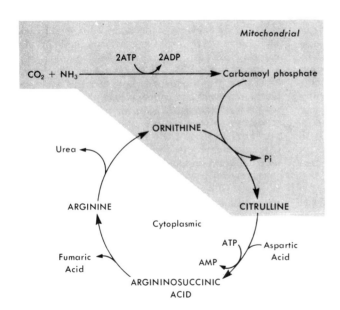

Figure 11–2 Urea cycle. (From Sodeman, W.A., Jr., and Sodeman, T.M.: Pathologic Physiology: Mechanisms of Disease. 6th ed. Philadelphia, W.B. Saunders Co., 1979.)

skeleton of ornithine to form arginine (ornithine plus a guanidine group), with the subsequent splitting of arginine to form ornithine and urea (from the guanidinium group of arginine). Certain intermediates of this cycle, such as citrulline and argininosuccinic acid, may accumulate when a child is born with a congenital deficiency of a urea cycle enzyme. Urea contains two amino groups, one derived from ammonia and the other from aspartate. The first group is formed by deamination of glutamate in a reaction mediated by glutamate dehydrogenase. This NH_3 combines enzymatically with HCO_3 to form carbamoyl phosphate, which subsequently transfers the carbamoyl group to ornithine to form citrulline. The second amino group derives from transamination to OAA by glutamate with the formation of aspartate. The enzyme responsible for catalyzing this reaction—glutamate-oxaloacetate transaminase—is the SGOT that is employed for the diagnosis of hepatic and cardiac disease. Its importance in terms of the urea cycle is that it provides a vehicle by which the amino group of almost any amino acid is able to enter the cycle and be transformed into urea. This is because glutamic acid itself is formed from the reaction between any amino acid and alpha-ketoglutarate, an intermediate of the tricarboxylic acid cycle:

$$\text{alpha-ketoglutarate} + \text{amino acid} \rightleftarrows \text{glutamic acid} + \text{alpha-ketoacid}$$

Reaction of aspartate and citrulline yields argininosuccinate, which then undergoes an elimination reaction with formation of fumarate and arginine. In the final step arginine is hydrolyzed to urea with simultaneous regeneration of ornithine.

Further Means to Dispose of Ammonia

It is worthwhile to note that the body possesses other means of ammonia detoxification in addition to the urea cycle mechanism (Fig. 11–3). Reversal of the glutamate dehydrogenase reaction can be carried out to form glutamate from alpha-ketoglutarate and free NH_3. This process can proceed one step further with the synthesis of glutamine from glutamate and free NH_3:

$$\text{glutamate} + NH_3 + ATP \xrightarrow{Mg^{++}} \text{glutamine} + ADP + P_i$$

This reaction is facilitated by the enzyme glutamine synthetase and permits the use of glutamine by the body as a temporary repository for NH_3. Release of the ammonia occurs via glutaminase, which is widely distributed in body tissues. Further, as pointed out above, the process of

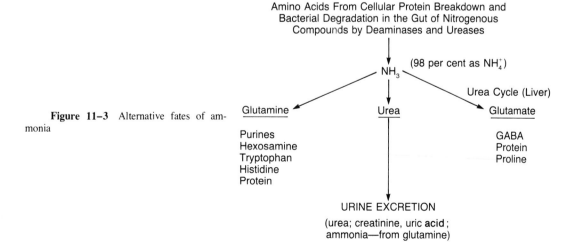

Figure 11–3 Alternative fates of ammonia

Amino Acids From Cellular Protein Breakdown and
Bacterial Degradation in the Gut of Nitrogenous
Compounds by Deaminases and Ureases

NH_3 (98 per cent as NH_4^+)

Urea Cycle (Liver)

Glutamine — Urea — Glutamate

Purines
Hexosamine
Tryptophan
Histidine
Protein

GABA
Protein
Proline

URINE EXCRETION
(urea; creatinine, uric acid;
ammonia—from glutamine)

transamination can be utilized to pass the amino group from glutamate to other amino acids whose carbon skeletons are derived from glucose, i.e., alanine.

Causes of Hyperammonemia

This overview of normal nitrogen metabolism forms the basis for our understanding of the hyperammonemic syndromes. Hyperammonemia may occur as a primary event, as in the congenital urea cycle defects, or as a secondary phenomenon, as in Reye's syndrome or cirrhosis of the liver. Focusing for the moment on inborn errors of the urea cycle, we must emphasize the diversity of clinical expressions of these syndromes. Not only may the signs and symptoms of the urea cycle defects differ markedly from syndrome to syndrome, they may even be quite varied in patients with the same enzyme deficiency. Clearly, then, the phenocopy of these disorders results from the interplay between a defective genetic endowment and environmental factors. Most prominent among the latter are ingestion of excess protein and exposure to infectious agents, which accentuate protein catabolism (see Chapter 37).

Defects of Urea Synthesis

There are at least ten inborn errors of metabolism that may cause hyperammonemia of varying degree. To focus on shared aspects of these disorders, we will review the clinical manifestations of the urea cycle defects as a group. Table 11–2 outlines the clinical manifestations.

The first type of presentation (fortunately not the most common) is that of the newborn infant who becomes catastrophically ill with hypotonia, coma, and lethargy during the first few days of life. In most cases, the first clinical impression will be sepsis neonatorum, although all cultures subsequently are negative. The arterial blood gas analysis often reflects a mild metabolic acidosis or alkalosis depending on efficiency of renal NH_3 excretion relative to its production rate. Respiratory alkalosis is distinctly unusual, especially in neonates, and should always alert the clinician to the possibility of a urea cycle defect. Often the liver is enlarged because of ammonia toxicity, and the liver function tests may show elevation of the serum transaminases. The blood ammonia elevations are extraordinary: concentrations above 2000 micrograms/dl are common. Treatment of such extremely ill babies is difficult, although hemodialysis, exchange transfusions, peritoneal dialysis, and administration of glycine and arginine have been described and are discussed in the section on the urea cycle defects.

The second mode of presentation is that of an older infant who fails to attain developmental milestones on schedule. A history of postprandial vomiting is very common. Most patients have been evaluated for some form of intestinal obstruction—often pyloric stenosis—before the diagnosis of a urea cycle defect has been made. A careful history may reveal a relationship of the onset of

Table 11–2 MODES OF PRESENTATION OF UREA
CYCLE DEFECTS

1. Neonatal catastrophe—masquerading as sepsis neonatorum
   a. Seizures, hypertonicity, vomiting, coma, death
   b. Extreme elevations of NH_3: over 1000 μg/dl
2. Subacute presentation in infancy
   a. Recurrent vomiting and growth failure
   b. Intermittent ataxia
   c. Seizures, mental retardation, developmental regression
3. Presentation later in childhood
   a. Psychomotor retardation
   b. Intermittent ataxia
   c. Vomiting, protein intolerance—history of poor feeding during infancy
   d. Overt symptoms after mild illness
4. Asymptomatic variant
   a. Usually shows amino acid abnormality without hyperammonemia

symptoms to initiation of feedings with cow's milk, which has a much higher protein concentration than human milk or regular infant formula.

The degree of metabolic compensation may be tenuous. Sometimes the relatively trivial catabolic stress of the first DPT immunization or upper respiratory infection precipitates the full-blown syndrome. Blood dyscrasias may occur during the period of ammonia intoxication. This is true also of the neonate with hyperammonemia secondary to an organic acidemia. Pulmonary hemorrhage is a common cause of death. The response to dietary protein restriction is usually favorable in the child presenting in later infancy.

A third group of patients present after infancy. These youngsters, who generally manifest some degree of mental retardation, usually have intermittent ataxia and vomiting once they are exposed to unduly high levels of protein, either because of dietary indiscretion or the catabolic stress of an acute infection. Often careful questioning of the parents will reveal that the child was a poor feeder during infancy and that the formula had to be changed frequently. Measurement of fasting blood ammonia levels may be normal, but after an oral protein load, this level will rise above 200 micrograms/dl. We should note, however, that occasionally hyperammonemia may be absent even though the amino acid abnormality may be detected in blood. This is especially true of citrullinemia.

AMMONIA TOXICITY

The common denominator of all of these variant forms of clinical expression is the fact that ammonia in high concentrations is toxic to living tissue. The organ that is most exquisitely sensitive to ammonia poisoning is the brain. Despite this sensitivity to NH_3, brain tissue constantly produces ammonia as a consequence of its metabolic processes. Indeed, in adult animals it is known that brain ammonia concentrations are 60 to 100 percent greater than those in blood. However, toxic effects are normally avoided by diffusion of NH_3 into blood and the fixation of ammonia into glutamate and especially glutamine, as discussed above. When blood ammonia levels increase, as in hepatic failure, for example, there is a slowing of ammonia transfer out of the brain and a progressive deterioration of brain function in response to ammonia toxicity. This progressive toxicity, reflected in CNS function, can be divided into early effects that correlate with reversible functional changes (e.g., stupor) and late effects that result in more severe functional changes (e.g., coma) and probably structural alterations as well.

Several factors undoubtedly play a role in these symptoms. Most attention has been focused on altered cerebral energy metabolism. We know, for example, that cerebral oxygen uptake is diminished by half during hepatic coma and that the same response is observed in animals who are injected with large amounts of ammonium chloride.

A rather plausible theory for how NH_3 interferes with energy production by the brain has recently been advanced by Hindfeldt et al. (1977) based upon animal experiments. These workers were able to show, by acute ammonium acetate infusion into rats with portacaval shunts, that functional disturbances in the brain preceded changes in high-energy phosphate intermediates (ATP, ATP/ADP). However, the functional disturbances were paralleled by alterations in cytosolic and mitochondrial $NADH/NAD^+$ ratios and by decreased asparate and glutamate with rises in pyruvate and alanine. Since reducing equivalents are shuttled from cytosol to mitochondrion via the aspartate-malate shunt, rather than by direct transfer to NADH, the data were interpreted to mean that the primary disturbance of hyperammonemia was related to decreased shunting and diminished neuroexcitatory compounds (aspartate and glutamate). Eventually, a decrease in glutamate is reflected in diminished supplies of α-ketoglutarate, a slowing of the Krebs cycle, and a decrease in ATP and ATP/ADP. These observations are consistent with the known fall in cerebral oxygen consumption that occurs with hyperammonemia and deserve further investigations.

EVALUATION OF A PATIENT WITH HYPERAMMONEMIA

The evaluation of a patient with a suspected urea cycle defect is shown in Table 11–3.

As is so true of most clinical problems, the most important feature is the history. In many

Table 11–3 EVALUATION OF
SUSPECTED UREA
CYCLE DEFECT

History
   a. Family history
   b. Food intolerance
   c. Response to infection
   d. Intermittent, static, progressive
Physical Examination
   a. Neurological
   b. Hepatomegaly
   c. Growth failure
   d. Microcephaly
   e. Hair
Laboratory Data
   a. Blood NH_3—precautions to be taken
   b. Blood and urine amino acids
   c. Liver function testing
   d. BUN
   e. Urinary sediment
   f. Arterial PO_2, PCO_2, pH
   g. Enzyme analysis
      —fibroblasts
      —WBC's
      —liver
      —post-mortem

instances, there will be a history of prior neonatal deaths or stillborn infants. The relationship between feeding or acute infection and the appearance of symptoms usually is rather obvious, although some exceptions do occur. Occasionally the mother herself gives a history of aversion to protein.

The physical findings are not pathognomonic for a urea cycle defect. The findings listed here will occur, of course, in any number of other kinds of diseases. For this reason consideration of a hyperammonemic syndrome seems warranted in any patient with unexplained neurological findings, particularly if the history suggests such a disorder.

The sine qua non of the diagnosis, of course, is a measurement of the blood ammonia. However, it is vital to recognize the fact that the degree of hyperammonemia is often highly variable. Indeed, patients without blood ammonia elevations have been reported. A few words of caution about blood ammonia measurement are in order. Plasma (heparinized) is required and should be placed on ice immediately after collection. The plasma must be separated as quickly as possible. Delay in actual assay of the blood ammonia must be minimized, as the blood level will rise if the plasma is permitted to stand for any appreciable length of time. Factitious elevation of ammonia occurs when either oxalate or citrate is employed as the anticoagulant.

In several of these disorders, for example, argininosuccinic aciduria or citrullinemia, there will be characteristic plasma and urinary amino acid profiles. In ornithine transcarbamylase deficiency or carbamoyl phosphate synthase deficiency, however, there is no pathognomonic amino acid pattern, but elevations of blood glutamine, alanine, and lysine are frequent.

Liver function testing commonly reveals a mild hypertransaminasemia. Usually it is not difficult to distinguish a primary hyperammonemia syndrome from one that is secondary to liver disease, since hyperammonemia of extreme magnitude will occur only very late in the course of liver disease.

The definitive diagnosis of a urea cycle defect depends upon the demonstration of a specific enzyme defect in the patient's tissues. Unfortunately, the enzymes mediating the first two steps of urea synthesis are rather labile (unstable). For this reason, it is critical that the enzyme assays be performed either on fresh, biopsied tissue or on liver tissue obtained shortly after death. This means that the post-mortem examination ought to be done as quickly as possible and that the tissues ought to be kept frozen, preferably at -80 degrees, until the assay can be performed. Some of the enzymes, although not all, are contained in skin fibroblasts, and therefore a culture of skin obtained by biopsy may prove quite useful. As discussed in Chapter 22 several of these diseases can be diagnosed by assaying the suspected enzyme in leukocytes.

REFERENCES

Grisolia, S., Báguena, R., and Mayor, F. (eds.): The Urea Cycle. J. Wiley and Sons, New York, 1976.

Hindfelt, B., Plum, F., and Duffy, T.E.: Effect of acute ammonia intoxication on cerebral metabolism in rats with portacaval shunts. J. Clin. Invest. 59:386, 1977.

Lockwood, A.H., McDonald, J.M., Reiman, R.E., et al.: The dynamics of ammonia metabolism in man. J. Clin. Invest. 63:449, 1979.

Onstad, G.R., and Zieve, L.: What determines blood ammonia? Gastroenterology 77:803, 1979.

Stewart, P.M., and Walser, J.: Failure of the normal ureagenic response to amino acids in organic acid-loaded rats. J. Clin. Invest. 66:484, 1980.

Visek, W.J.: Ammonia metabolism, urea cycle capacity and their biochemical assessment. Nutr. Rev. 37:273, 1979.

12

Hypoglycemia

Hypoglycemia represents a medical emergency because of the almost complete reliance of the brain on glucose as substrate for its inexorable energy requirements. In contrast most tissues (save for brain, red cell, testis, kidney, and adrenal medulla) can employ one of a number of substrates to supply their energy needs, depending on their availability at any moment. Except for the situation in prolonged starvation, in which ketones may supply much of the brain's energetic requirements (see below), the brain does not manifest this type of flexibility. Indeed, diminution of blood glucose to below 40 mg/dl or a precipitous fall from elevated levels to normal but momentarily insufficient levels can bring about symptoms of cerebral dysfunction, while calling forth secretion of epinephrine to counteract the fall in glucose. It is the epinephrinemia that produces the symptoms associated with hypoglycemia i.e., sweating, trembling, hunger, and tachycardia. Central nervous system manifestations include repeated yawning, headache, blurred vision, and confusion, which may progress to coma and seizures. In the pediatric age group repeated or prolonged hypoglycemic episodes may profoundly alter brain function permanently.

ENERGY SOURCES FOR THE BODY

Maintenance of Plasma Glucose

Since man spends relatively little of his time eating, it follows that plasma glucose must be maintained by glucose generated from within the body from stored materials rather than from exogenously ingested fuels. Of course, these stored materials were originally supplied by ingestion; the excess over that required for maintenance of blood glucose is converted to glycogen, fat, and protein to serve the myriad needs of the body. Recalling that protein serves either a structural or an enzymatic function, maintenance of the plasma glucose concentration at the expense of body protein would be a costly (indeed, intolerable) solution to a common biochemical need. Here we want to review the modalities available to the organism to support the relative constancy of the blood glucose given the enormous energy requirements of the brain.

Hepatic Glycogenesis and Triglyceride Synthesis

After a meal, much of the glucose metabolized by the liver undergoes conversion to glycogen to serve as a ready source of glucose in time of need. The total liver glycogen in an average man is meager, however (approximately 70 g) and obviously cannot supply the glucose needs of the organism for more than 8 to 12 hours. At the end of a full-term pregnancy hepatic glycogen concentration may reach 10 per cent of liver weight—about twice the amount in the adult. Since the liver itself metabolizes fatty acids for most its energy needs, what then is the function of the glycolytic pathway in that organ? It seems to be generation of glycerol for the formation of triglycerides. The latter are then transported in the blood as very low-density protein (VLDL) to be stored in adipose tissue as a relatively inexhaustible source of substrates for tissues able to metabolize fat.

Hepatic Glycogenolysis and Glucogenesis

In the postabsorptive state (4 to 12 hours) the glucose supply of the various body tissues is maintained by liberation of free glucose from liver glycogen through a series of degradative steps involving principally the enzyme glycogen phosphorylase (see Chapter 28).

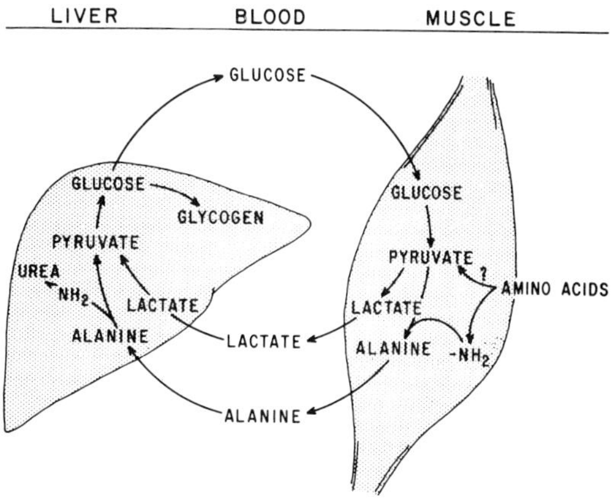

Figure 12–1 The Cori cycle and its relationship to the alanine cycle. (From Felig, P.: Disorders of carbohydrate metabolism. *In* Bondy, P.K., and Rosenberg, L.E. (eds.): Metabolic Control and Disease. 8th ed. Philadelphia, W.B. Saunders Co., 1980.)

Beyond the postabsorptive phase, synthesis of new glucose by the liver assumes a pivotal role in the energy economy of certain systems—especially the central nervous system, erythrocytes, renal medulla, and testes. Sources of smaller precursors for the 6-carbon glucose skeleton are lactate, pyruvate, glycerol, and amino acids. Lactate, the product of glycolysis in red cells and the renal medulla, enters the blood and then is carried to the liver (and kidney) to undergo resynthesis of glucose (Cori cycle).

Glycerol released by lipolysis of triglycerides in adipose tissue stores can also serve as a source for glucose synthesis. The fatty acids released can provide for the energy needs of tissues that possess the facultative ability to utilize whatever substrate is in abundance and thereby cut down on glucose consumption by the body. As we shall see, some of these fatty acids are converted to ketone bodies, an adaptive response of major import in the whole process of coping with prolonged starvation.

Amino acids (alanine and glutamine) represent the third major source of carbon skeletons for gluconeogenesis. A great deal of controversy surrounds the ultimate source of these carbon skeletons. Some believe that the carbon skeleton appearing in alanine is formed as a consequence of muscle proteolysis, with the sources being the branched-chain amino acids. Others have presented data that ingested glucose rather than endogenous amino acids supplies the carbon skeleton used in muscle to form alanine for the so-called glucose-alanine cycle. These latter studies indicate that the action of branched-chain amino acids in gluconeogenesis is the inhibition of oxidation of glucose-derived pyruvate as well as provision of the amino group for transamination with pyruvate. Regardless of the source, the glucose-alanine cycle (Fig. 12–1) represents an important source of glucose as muscle and liver interact to maintain the blood sugar. We will consider the gluconeogenic process after concluding our overview of energy sources for the body.

Ketogenesis

As fasting continues for several days in the adult, a key adaptation in the fuel economy takes place: lipolysis produces fatty acids, which undergo oxidation to ketone bodies. These substrates, β-hydroxybutyrate and acetoacetate, now assume increasing importance in serving the energy needs of the brain, thus diminishing the need for gluconeogenesis to continue at the normal rate of about 160 g/24 hr. In obese adults, by 3 weeks of fasting ketone bodies provide for over half of the brain's needs, and gluconeogenesis (by now carried out by kidney as well as liver) accounts for about 80 g/24 hr. By this time, however, the bulk of the carbon skeletons for glucose come from lactate and glycerol, with amino acids now representing a meager source. The ketone bodies function, in an as yet undefined manner, to diminish alanine release from muscle, thereby conserving protein.

Gluconeogenic Pathway

The combustion of glucose within the cell begins with the process termed "glycolysis," in which glucose is anaerobically converted through a number of enzyme-mediated steps into pyruvate or lactate, with the generation of ATP in this anaerobic process. Further, complete combustion of glucose requires oxygen, generates additional ATP, and requires the integration of several mitochondrial systems: the pyruvate dehydrogenase multienzyme complex, the citric acid cycle, and the electron transport chain (Fig. 12–2).

Lactate itself cannot be further metabolized; either it can be converted back to pyruvate and then enter the citric acid cycle or it can serve as a precursor for gluconeogenesis. The former pathway occurs readily in heart, brain, and red muscle (mitochondria-rich) fibers, while the latter is limited to liver and kidney.

Here, we are concerned with the gluconeogenic sequence. Since ATP is generated during glycolysis, it would not serve the needs of the cell if all of that ATP could be broken down to ADP and inorganic phosphate merely by reversing the pathway of glycolysis. Hence, there are three enzyme-mediated steps in the glycolytic sequence that are for all intents and purposes irreversible *

---

*This irreversible or nonequilibrium state of the glycolytic sequence mirrors at a microscopic level the nonequilibrium state of living organisms. In the context of a specific metabolic pathway, if the overall pathway is to be kept removed from equilibrium, some heat must be lost irretrievably; of course, some of the energy evolved in the chemical reactions must be captured as ATP (or a suitable equivalent) if the combustion is to serve the energy needs of the cell. As we have noted in Part I, when a system reaches equilibrium, no work can be performed by that system. In the case of a living system this means the death of the organism.

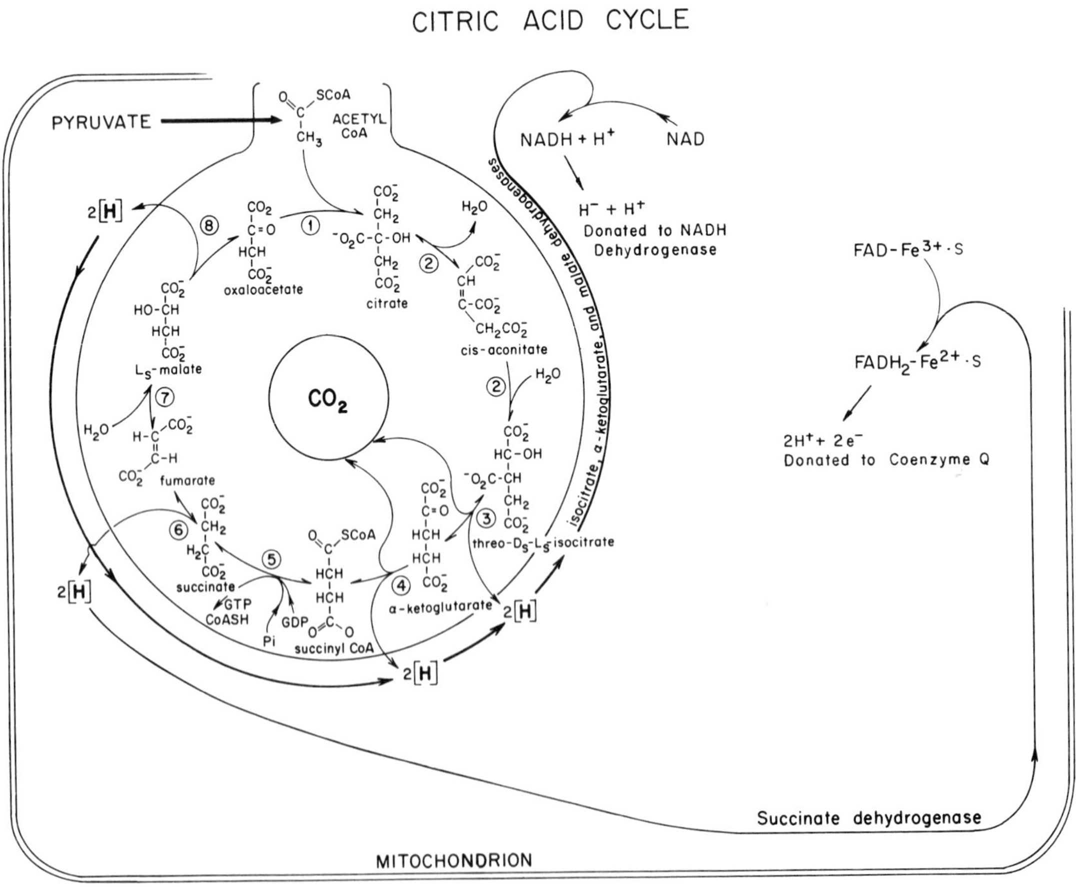

Figure 12–2 The complete oxidation of pyruvate to CO_2 and generation of ATP by the electron transport chain. (From Coleman, J.E.: Metabolic interrelationships between carbohydrates, lipids and proteins. *In* Bondy, P.K., and Rosenberg, L.E. (eds.): Metabolic Control and Disease. 8th ed. Philadelphia, W.B. Saunders Co., 1980.)

Anaplerosis and Gluconeogenesis

Figure 12–3 Initial steps of gluconeogenesis. (From Coleman, J.E.: Metabolic interrelationships between carbohydrates, lipids and proteins. *In* Bondy, P.K., and Rosenberg, L.E. (eds.): Metabolic Control and Disease. 8th ed. Philadelphia, W.B. Saunders Co., 1980.)

CYTOSOL

reversal of glycolysis

PEP

PEP carboxykinase

GDP PEP

GTP $\rightarrow CO_2$

ADP

pyruvate kinase

ATP

activators F-1,6-diP

inhibitors alanine ↑ATP

Amino Acids

OXALOACETATE $\diagdown$ NADH $\diagdown C_{ox}$

malate — NAD$^+$ $\diagdown C_{red}$

$PYRUVATE$

MITOCHONDRION

malate $\rightarrow$ NAD$^+$ $\diagdown C_{red}$

NADH $\diagdown C_{ox}$

pyruvate carboxylase

$PYRUVATE$

OXALOACETATE

ATP + CO$_2$ + Biotin

activator

ACETYL CoA $\leftarrow$ — FAT oxidation

pyruvate dehydrogenase complex

Citric Acid Cycle

(hexokinase, phosphofructokinase, and pyruvate kinase) and that must be replaced by other enzymes if the glycolytic sequence is to be "turned around," permitting the resynthesis of glucose from simpler precursors.

Gluconeogenesis requires the regeneration of phosphoenolpyruvate, a process that involves several steps, all directed to circumventing the irreversible pyruvate kinase step of glycolysis. Pyruvate carboxylase, a mitochondrial enzyme, converts pyruvate to oxaloacetate. Since the mitochondrial inner membrane is impermeable to oxaloacetate, it must be converted to either malate or aspartate, which then gains entrance into the cytosol. There, reconversion to oxaloacetate occurs, and the enzyme phosphoenolpyruvate carboxykinase mediates formation of phosphoenolpyruvate from oxaloacetate (Fig. 12–3). Thereafter, the glycolytic pathway may be traversed in reverse until fructose-1,6-diphosphatase circumvents the phosphofructokinase reaction and glucose-6-phosphatase does the same for the hexokinase step.

Inborn errors of each of these gluconeogenic enzymes have been described; as expected, hypoglycemia and lactic acidosis are prominent findings in these disorders.

Role of Insulin in Fuel Homeostasis (Fig. 12–4)

Insulin is best thought of as an anabolic or storage hormone that facilitates uptake, metabolism, and storage of glucose, fat, and protein. As regards glucose homeostasis it stimulates glycogen

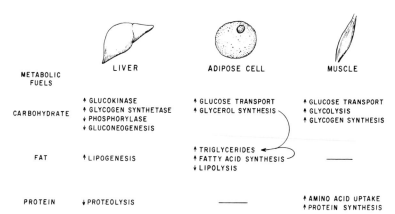

METABOLIC FUELS	LIVER	ADIPOSE CELL	MUSCLE
CARBOHYDRATE	↑ GLUCOKINASE ↑ GLYCOGEN SYNTHETASE ↓ PHOSPHORYLASE ↓ GLUCONEOGENESIS	↑ GLUCOSE TRANSPORT ↑ GLYCEROL SYNTHESIS	↑ GLUCOSE TRANSPORT ↑ GLYCOLYSIS ↑ GLYCOGEN SYNTHESIS
FAT	↑ LIPOGENESIS	↑ TRIGLYCERIDES ↑ FATTY ACID SYNTHESIS ↓ LIPOLYSIS	—
PROTEIN	↓ PROTEOLYSIS	—	↑ AMINO ACID UPTAKE ↑ PROTEIN SYNTHESIS

Figure 12–4 Sites of action of insulin. (From Felig, P.: Disorders of carbohydrate metabolism. *In* Bondy, P.K., and Rosenberg, L.E. (eds.): Metabolic Control and Disease. 8th ed. Philadelphia, W.B. Saunders Co., 1980.)

synthesis while diminishing gluconeogenesis. It stimulates fat synthesis in liver and adipose tissue and decreases proteolysis in liver while stimulating protein synthesis in muscle.

Since insulin increases glucose uptake by liver while concomitantly decreasing gluconeogenesis, abnormally high levels of insulin output by the pancreas that are not in tune with the blood sugar level can profoundly lower the blood sugar concentration.

Glucagon has antagonistic effects to those of insulin, so that during a fast, concomitant with decline in insulin secretion there will be an augmentation of glucagon output by the pancreatic alpha cells. Glucagon stimulates glycogenolysis and, with diminished insulin, probably contributes to augmented lipolysis, which provides alternate fuels for facultative organs. Indeed, ketone body formation is stimulated under these physiological circumstances—a hint of the gross overproduction of ketones that attends diabetic ketoacidosis, in which glucagon is unopposed by insulin.

HYPOGLYCEMIA

Clinical Considerations

Although there are a number of etiologies for hypoglycemia at all ages, those primarily concerned with the care of children will find it convenient to divide the syndrome of hypoglycemia according to the age group in which it occurs. Accordingly, we can look at hypoglycemia in the perinatal, neonatal, infancy, and childhood periods. The underlying reason for this system of classification derives from the biochemical changes that occur throughout the process of maturation.

Clearly, the immediate neonatal period is one of enormous change in the method of support blood glucose levels. Prior to delivery the infant has had a constant and relatively unlimited supply of glucose via the placental circulation from the mother. From the moment of birth, the infant is forced to find ways in which to support the blood level on his own. However, the mechanisms for gluconeogenesis are not well developed in the immediate perinatal period, nor are the enzymes for ketogenesis completely developed. Thus, the neonate is at a serious disadvantage in that there is a severely restricted supply of glucose from a variety of carbon sources in addition to a relative deficiency of ketone bodies. Support of the blood sugar in this period is thought to depend upon glycogenolysis. Therefore, an infant born premature or dysmature may be compromised as a result of diminished quantities of prestored hepatic glycogen.

Following the immediate perinatal period relatively efficient gluconeogenesis and ketogenesis develop, so that factors governing the development of hypoglycemia are more likely to be a result of either endogenous or exogenous toxicity than in the perinatal period. It is in this age group that we see many of the inherited metabolic disorders present initially with hypoglycemia.

Beyond the perinatal and neonatal periods the infant and child manifest a virtually unlimited range of possibilities in the development of hypoglycemia. Within this age group we may see etiologies ranging from inborn errors of metabolism through the hormonal and nutritional etiologies all the way to drugs and such poorly understood causes as "idiopathic" and Reye's syndrome. It is, therefore, best to deal with each age group as a separate entity.

Clinically hypoglycemia is rare when the blood glucose exceeds 40 mg/dl. Statistical arguments notwithstanding, we believe that level should serve as the lower limit for the true blood sugar regardless of age or maturity. Hypoglycemia most profoundly affects brain function, and in the adult the symptom complex is highly suggestive, if not diagnostic. Symptoms include irritability, confusion, headaches, unusual behavior, hypothermia, seizures, and coma. Certain of the symptoms reflect the effects of adrenaline output: increased heart rate, pallor, sweating, and nervousness. However, the neonate appears to respond to hypoglycemia in a much more nonspecific manner, manifesting poor feeding, high-pitched cry, cyanosis, lethargy, and irritability. The reader may already have taken note of the fact that all of these findings suggest not only hypoglycemia but infection and a host of inborn errors of metabolism as well. Hence, the multiplicity of diagnostic studies required in this age group should always include a blood sugar. The differential diagnosis of hypoglycemia in different pediatric age groups is shown in Table 12–1.

Table 12–1 DIFFERENTIAL DIAGNOSIS OF
HYPOGLYCEMIA

Neonatal

Stressed Infant
   Asphyxia
   Hypothermia
   Sepsis, meningitis
   Hyaline membrane disease
   Adrenal hemorrhage
   Intrauterine undernutrition (limited fuel stores)
     Placental abnormalities
     Prematurity
     Multiple pregnancies
   Intracranial injury
Hyperinsulinism (most common cause under 1 year of age)
   Islet cell adenoma, hyperplasia
   Maternal diabetes mellitus
   Erythroblastosis fetalis
   Beckwith-Wiedemann syndrome
   Sudden discontinuance glucose infusion
Inborn Errors
   Defects in gluconeogenesis
   Defects in glycogenolysis
   Branched-chain amino acid disorders
   Congenital adrenal hyperplasia

Infancy and Childhood

Ketosis—? limitation of gluconeogenic precursors
Hyperinsulinism
Disorders of gluconeogenesis—gluconeogenic enzymes, organic acidemias
Disorders of glycogenolysis
Deficiency of insulin antagonistic hormone: thyroid, adrenal, pituitary
Other
   Reye's syndrome (liver failure)
   Severe malnutrition (kwashiorkor)
   Salicylate toxicity

Perinatal Causes of Hypoglycemia

In general the causes of hypoglycemia in the perinatal period derive either from maladaptation to intrauterine life, often resulting in prematurity or dysmaturity, or from agents exogenous to the fetus that were ingested by the mother during pregnancy. Among the maladaptive causes are maternal diabetes, intrauterine growth retardation, and maternal toxemia. Fetal alcohol syndrome and maternal oral hypoglycemic agents are common causes of exogenous toxicity. It is thought that the effect of maternal diabetes is to expose the fetus throughout gestation to excessively high levels of blood glucose, engendering islet cell hyperplasia in the fetal pancreas. Clearly, so long as this excessively high blood glucose level persists in intrauterine life, excessive insulin secretion by the hyperplastic islet cells will not affect glucose homeostasis in the fetus. However, at the moment the umbilical circulation is cut the infant must himself maintain the blood glucose. Thus, the legacy of hyperinsulinism secondary to intrauterine exposure to high glucose is a persistent and antagonistic influence on the normal physiological adaptation to extrauterine life.

Inadequate glycogen stores underlie the development of hypoglycemia in infants who are small for gestational age. In infants with placental insufficiency, consumption of prestored glycogen is necessary to maintain fetal blood sugar in the face of decreased supply from the mother. Finally, among other causes for endogenously generated hypoglycemia in the infant is erythroblastosis fetalis. The precise mechanism by which hypoglycemia occurs in this disease is unclear, but the final common denominator appears to be islet cell hyperplasia and hyperinsulinism.

The mechanism by which hypoglycemia occurs in infants of alcoholic mothers is poorly understood. The hypoglycemia seen in infants of diabetic mothers who have been treated with oral hypoglycemic agents is known to be due to the placental transfer of these drugs, which in turn will cause excess insulin secretion in the baby. Salicylates may also be incriminated in the hypoglycemic perinatal infant, probably owing to uncoupling of oxidative phosphorylation in the cells, which in turn leads to decreased energy production from consumption of substrate.

Neonatal Causes of Hypoglycemia

As has already been stated, there are multiple causes for hypoglycemia after the first 24 hours of life. Chief among the preventable causes are delayed feeding practices, hypothermic stress, hypoglycemia due to exchange transfusion of blood containing little or no glucose. Inherited metabolic disorders that may result in hypoglycemia (usually late in the first week of life) include maple syrup urine disease, methylmalonic aciduria, propionic acidemia, and isovaleric acidemia (see Organic Acidemias). Although galactosemia has classically been included among inherited causes for hypoglycemia of the newborn, it has been our experience as well as that of others that galactosemia rarely if ever can be indicted in this regard.

Other physiological stresses that overwhelm the adaptative mechanisms of the newborn include such disorders as polycythemia, sepsis, hemorrhage, respiratory distress syndrome, and, it is worth emphasizing again, delayed feeding practices. A variety of causes for hyperinsulinism can be seen in this age group, including nesidioblastosis and Beckwith's syndrome.

Infancy and Childhood Causes of Hypoglycemia

In this age group the two most significant general causes of hypoglycemia are endocrine and hepatic gluconeogenic enzyme deficiencies. So-called ketotic hypoglycemia is also commonly seen. This variant of hypoglycemia appears to be an exaggerated expression of the normal response to fasting. One of the puzzles about this variant is why the elevated ketones are not used by the brain to ameliorate the symptoms. In any event the ultimate prognosis is good, since these episodes disappear by the end of the first decade. Provision of a bedtime snack and a prompt breakfast on awakening may be all that is necessary to eliminate these troublesome attacks.

Among the enzymatic deficiencies responsible for causing hypoglycemia are the defects in either glycogen storage or glycogen breakdown. These disorders are discussed elsewhere in this book. Once again, we may see defects in metabolism of protein responsible for hypoglycemia in this age group embraced under the general rubric of organic acidemias. In addition to the gluconeogenic defects noted above there are a number of poorly characterized inherited disorders of lactate metabolism that also manifest lactic acidosis and hypoglycemia. These are considered in more detail in Chapter 29, Lactic Acidosis.

Other causes for hypoglycemia in infancy and childhood include nutritional deficiencies (such as Kwashiorkor) and hyperinsulinism resulting from disorders such as islet cell adenoma, Reye's syndrome, neuroblastoma, and hepatoma. In addition, exogenous toxicity can be an important cause of hypoglycemia in this age group. Chief among the agents causing hypoglycemia are salicylates. The mechanism for generation of hypoglycemia in salicylate toxicity is thought to be an uncoupling of oxidative phosphorylation. The result is an increased utilization of glucose with significantly lowered energy yield and diminished gluconeogenesis. All of these etiologies are summarized in Table 12–1.

Diagnosis

In the absence of persuasive data to the contrary several authorities recommend that a true glucose level of 40 mg/dl should be accepted as the minimum normal level at all ages. Clearly, initial diagnosis of hypoglycemia is dependent upon an index of clinical suspicion. Despite the wide use of Dextrostix in the approximation of true blood glucose, particularly in the neonate, these glucose-oxidase-impregnated paper strips should not and, indeed cannot, be used as a substitute for a blood glucose determination by chemical means. In fact, dependence upon the Dextrostix for determination of blood glucose and the need for therapy can result in disaster. Accordingly, any patient with a combination of the findings outlined earlier in this section should be suspected of having hypoglycemia and given the benefit of a "stat" true blood glucose determination by chemical methods.

Following the demonstration of blood glucose levels below 40 mg/dl, the approach to etiological diagnosis should be done in a physiological manner, always taking care to defend the blood sugar level, in the event of decline below that level. Since the body's homeostatic mechanisms are geared toward maintenance of normal blood glucose, stressing these homeostatic mechanisms to determine which of them may be at fault can be very helpful. This can be done by means of a very carefully monitored fasting study on a metabolic ward. In our unit, this study is carried out by insertion of a heparin lock line, to allow both blood sampling and immediate glucose therapy if it becomes necessary during the study. Baseline blood glucose, ketone body, triglyceride, lactate, pyruvate, amino acid, and insulin levels are drawn. During the first 6 to 8 hours of the fast, these studies should be obtained at least every 2 hours, and the urines should be saved for later measurement of amino acids, glucose, and ketone bodies. As the study progresses beyond 8 hours, the child should be closely observed for signs of hypoglycemia, and the blood glucose sample should be obtained hourly. In this context, it is important to understand that the blood glucose should be determined promptly, preferably by means of a glucose oxidase glucose analyzer. In this fashion the physiological response of the blood glucose level to starvation can be estimated fairly accurately. At such time as the blood glucose level falls below 40 mg/dl, the study may be terminated by administration of glucagon in order to determine the patient's ability to carry out glycogenolysis. If there is no response to glucagon, intravenous glucose may be given through the heparin lock. This sort of study is exceedingly complex and should be carried out under very close observation in a clinical research center.

The advantage of performing such an intricate fasting study is the enormous yield of information. Most normal infants are able to tolerate at least a 16-hour fast with no fall in blood glucose below 40 mg/dl. Most normal children can tolerate such a fast for 24 hours, and some may be able to tolerate as much as 36 hours of starvation. Measurement of the various parameters indicated above is important, in order that one may assess the adequacy of the different physiological responses to starvation. Interpretation of the data obtained from this study is complex and is complicated by the obvious factors such as age of the child, hormonal interrelationships with carbohydrate metabolism, and so on. However, certain physiological principles can be outlined. The normal response to deprivation of carbohydrate is a decrease in the serum insulin level, with a concomitant increase in lipolysis. Thus, a study that demonstrated a constant fall in blood glucose without a rise in plasma free fatty acids might suggest excess circulating levels of plasma insulin. To take this situation one step further, if such a study demonstrated falling blood glucose levels, rising plasma free fatty acid levels, and no significant change in levels of ketone bodies, one might be concerned that there was a difficulty in metabolism of free fatty acids through beta oxidation to produce such ketone bodies. Alternatively, a variation on the same theme might be appropriate rises in plasma free fatty acids and ketone bodies, with disproportionate increases in either plasma lactate, pyruvate, or both. These observations might indicate a defect in gluconeogenesis. It is the intent of these examples to point out what is perhaps by now obvious: a fasting study cannot demonstrate a specific enzymatic defect in a given patient. Nonetheless, it is extremely useful when performed properly in localizing a defect within a particular area of carbohydrate metabolism (Table 12–2).

In an otherwise normal study, excepting of course a fall in blood glucose, termination of the study with glucagon should produce a rapid rise in blood glucose. If such a rise does not occur, it indicates the possibility of a glycogen storage disease in which glycogen breakdown cannot occur in response to glucagon. In this situation, if there is also an inordinately high plasma lactate, it is very likely that the diagnosis is glycogen storage disease type I. Nonetheless, despite the deficiencies of a fasting study in pointing out a specific diagnosis, it is exceedingly useful to perform such a study in order to determine the approximate nature of the underlying defect. Once having done so, it is appropriate to refer such a patient to a well-equipped modern academic center for specific enzymatic diagnosis.

Table 12–2 24-HOUR FASTING STUDIES IN VARIOUS CAUSES OF HYPOGLYCEMIA

	Glucose	FFA	Ketones	Lactate	Pyruvate	Alanine	Insulin	Other
Normal	↓	↑	↑	Slightly ↓	Slightly ↓	Slightly ↓	↓	
Normal newborn (<12 hours)				Slightly ↑	Slightly ↑	Slightly ↑	N	Maturational delay in both gluconeogenesis and ketogenesis
Hyperinsulinism	↓¹	↓	↓	N	N	N	±↑	Large birth weight infant; Glucagon will ↑ glucose—overcome inappropriate conservation of liver glycogen
Ketotic hypoglycemia	↓²	↑	↑³	Slightly ↓	Slightly ↓	Slightly ↓	↓	Exaggeration of normal response
Defect gluconeogenesis (G-6-Pase deficiency)	↓¹	↑	±↑	↑	↑	↑	↓	Perinatal problems; cataracts rarely; growth retarded; ↓ adipose tissue; Hepatomegaly (see Chapter 15)
Defect glycogenolysis (debrancher)	↓¹	↑	↑	N	N	N	↓	Hepatomegaly (see Chapter 15)
Growth hormone deficiency	↓²	↑	↑	N	N	N	N	GH ↓
Panhypopituitarism	↓¹	↑(↓)	↑(↓)	N	N	N	N	(↓ lipolysis sometimes in early infancy)
Cortisol deficiency	↓²	↑	↑	N	N	↓	N	Glucocorticoids ↓
SGA infant (pattern suggests delay in onset gluconeogenesis)	↓	↓	↓	↑	↑	↑	N	
Defect in hepatic fatty acid oxidation	↓²	↑	↓	?	?	?	N	Defect in hepatic fatty acid oxidation to form ketones; Examples: Systemic carnitine deficiency; glutaric aciduria type II; HMG CoA lyase deficiency; carnitine palmityl transferase deficiency

N = Normal.
1 = Hypoglycemia develops several hours (3–12) after beginning of fast.
2 = Hypoglycemia develops 12 or more hours after beginning of fast.
3 = Ketonuria precedes ↓ in glucose.

Therapy

Therapy will depend upon the nature of the underlying defect, and discussions of specific disorders should be consulted for the approach to the patient. In patients with islet cell hyperplasia, diazoxide is often of use. Individuals with nesidioblastosis or pancreatic adenoma will often require subtotal pancreatectomy.

The acute treatment of hypoglycemia is always the administration of intra-venous glucose (25 to 50 per cent) at the dosage level of 1 to 2 ml/kg, followed by a continuous glucose infusion as a 10 to 15 per cent glucose solution. In infants this should be provided by a constant infusion pump so as not to elicit an augmented insulin output. It is also important to recognize that such acute therapy may only be supporting blood glucose levels in a patient with an underlying defect of amino acid metabolism whose CNS damage continues to progress. This underscores the necessity for rapid and accurate diagnosis of the underlying etiology of the hypoglycemic episode. Particularly in the perinatal period, no hypoglycemic episode should be shrugged off as "idiopathic" or secondary to nonspecific intra- and post-partum stress. A vigorous search should be made for other etiologies.

REFERENCES

Cornblath, M., and Schwartz, R.: Disorders of Carbohydrate Metabolism in Infancy. 2nd ed. W.B. Saunders, Co., Philadelphia, 1976.

Hanson, R., and Mehlman, M. (eds.): Gluconeogenesis: Its Regulation in Mammalian Species. John Wiley & Sons, New York, 1976.

Hetenyi, G., Jr., and Cowan, J.S.: Glucoregulation in the newborn. Can. J. Physiol. Pharmacol. 58:879, 1980.

Senior, B., and Wolfsdorf, J.I.: Hypoglycemia in Children. Pediatr. Clin. North Am. 26:171, 1979.

Snell, K.: Muscle alanine synthesis and hepatic gluconeogenesis. Biochem. Soc. Trans. 8:205, 1980.

Stanley, C.A., and Baker, L.: Hyperinsulinism in infants and children: diagnosis and therapy. Adv. Pediatr. 23:315, 1976.

13

Ketogenesis

While the role of body fat as an energy source is self-evident, the nature of the linkage between lipid and glucose (which permits lipid to serve as an alternative substrate) is only now being elucidated. For many years, the rise in blood ketone bodies (acetoacetate, acetone, and β-hydroxybutyrate) during starvation or illness was viewed as an indication that lipid was providing increased energy through the β-oxidation pathway. It is now recognized, however, that the ketone bodies themselves are important energy sources and are vital links in the control of both lipid and carbohydrate metabolism.

KETONE BODY PRODUCTION

Placement of a major lipid storage depot in the intestinal mesentery, with venous drainage directly into the hepatic portal vein, creates an ideal anatomical situation for the liver as the major site of ketone body production. Conversely, such an anatomical arrangement also guarantees that a major share of ingested dietary lipid will pass directly to the liver for immediate metabolism and/or storage.

Within the hepatocyte (Fig. 13-1), fatty acids are activated to their fatty acyl CoA analogues by the enzyme fatty acid thiokinase, which is located in microsomes and the outer mitochondrial membrane. Following this step, the fatty acyl CoA compounds can proceed in two directions: (1) reaction with glycerol to form mono-, di- and triglycerides and (2) reaction with carnitine to form acyl carnitine, a step mediated by the enzyme carnitine acyltransferase I (CAT I) located in the outer mitochondrial membrane. This makes possible the transfer of fatty acids across the mitochondrial membrane barrier.

Initially it was thought that the rate of delivery of free fatty acids to the liver was the sole factor determining which of the two metabolic fates predominated. However, it has become clear

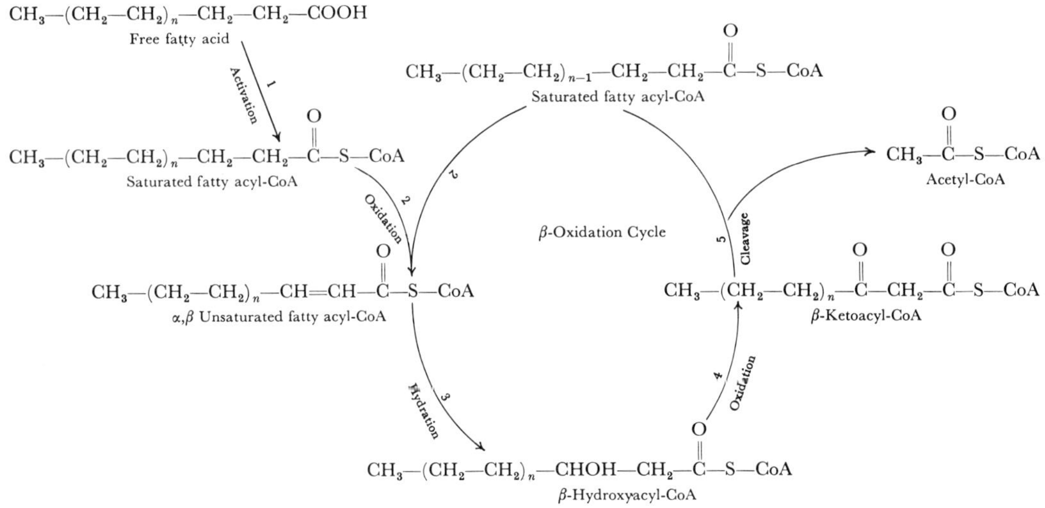

Figure 13–1 Scheme of fatty acid oxidation in the hepatocyte. (From Masoro, E.J.: Lipids in Mammals. Philadelphia, W.B. Saunders Co., 1968.)

Table 13-1 METABOLIC STATES OF THE LIVER

Carbohydrate Replete	Starvation (Ketosis)
Low glucagon:insulin ratio	High glucagon:insulin ratio
Malonyl CoA ↑	Malonyl CoA ↓
Fatty acid synthesis is brisk	Fatty acid synthesis is inhibited
Fatty acid oxidation is inhibited	Fatty acid oxidation is activated
Malonyl CoA inhibitory effect on CAT ensures formation of triglycerides and VLDL	Glucagon acutely stimulates ketogenesis by limiting formation of malonyl CoA

that plasma free fatty acids can be elevated in the absence of ketosis and, conversely, that ketosis can prevail in situations where plasma free fatty acids are not elevated. Thus, in addition to substrate availability, other factors must impinge upon the hepatocyte in regulation of ketone body production. It turns out that ketone body production, like so many other metabolic processes, is regulated at both the cellular and the organ level.

Control of the intramitochondrial β-oxidation of fatty acyl CoA must be linked to carbohydrate metabolism, since each pathway results in production of acetyl CoA units. The frugal nature of biological processes (see Part I) dictates that two energy-yielding substrates not be consumed simultaneously to supply requirements for which one substrate alone would be sufficient. Hence, the description by McGarry and Foster (1980) of the role of malonyl CoA in regulation of fatty acid oxidation provided a key to understanding the metabolic regulation of ketogenesis. Malonyl CoA is the first intermediate formed in biosynthesis of fatty acids, by carboxylation of acetyl CoA formed from glucose. Hepatic levels of malonyl CoA would be expected to fluctuate in parallel with rates of fatty acid synthesis as, in fact, they do (Table 13-1). Thus, under conditions in which glucose is in excess, malonyl CoA will be present in large amounts and net lipid synthesis will occur. Obviously for net synthesis of fatty acids to occur, there must be inhibition of β-oxidation. According to the scheme proposed by McGarry and Foster (Fig. 13-2), the regulatory process leading to slowed β-oxidation results from an interaction of malonyl CoA with CAT I that inhibits entry of

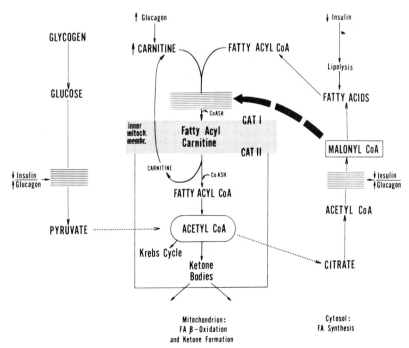

Figure 13-2 Factors controlling ketogenesis. CAT I and II, carnitine acyltransferase enzymes I and II. (From Baruh, S. et al.: Diabetic ketoacidosis and coma. Med. Clin. North Am. 65(1):117–132, 1981. Modified from McGarry, J.D.: New perspectives in the regulation of ketogenesis. Diabetes 28:517–523, 1979, by permission of the American Diabetes Association, Inc.)

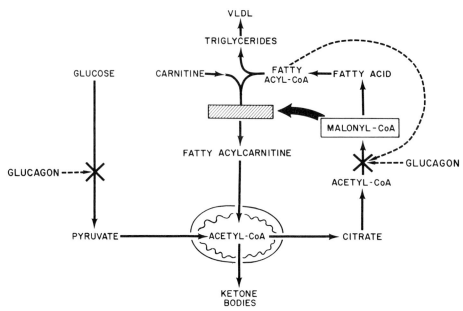

Figure 13–3 Sites of regulation of ketogenesis by glucagon and malonyl CoA. (Reproduced, with permission, from the Annual Review of Biochemistry, Volume 49. © 1980 by Annual Reviews Inc.)

fatty acyl CoA into the mitochondria. The mechanism of this inhibition is presently unknown, but it appears to be relatively specific for malonyl CoA among many CoA esters tested.

Thus, intracellular regulation of fatty acid metabolism occurs at the level of the mitochondrial membrane. With a large carbon flux through glycolysis, intracellular levels of acetyl CoA in excess of that required for TCA cycle operation result in malonyl CoA accumulation in the cytosol, with consequent inhibition of fatty acyl CoA entry into the mitochondrion. Therefore, metabolic disposition of fatty acyl CoA compounds must occur via conversion to glycerides, the only pathway remaining open to them. Conversely, depletion of acetyl CoA deriving from glucose leads to a drop in malonyl CoA levels, in turn permitting facilitation of the CAT I–CAT II system transfer of fatty acyl CoA into mitochondria for β-oxidation to acetyl CoA.

At the outset we noted that body fat stores represent an alternative energy source to glucose, thus implying a need for integration and regulation of their use by the body. Initially, it was thought that insulin's suppressive effect on lipolysis was the body's sole mediator of ketogenesis. This, however, could not explain a number of disparate facts, among them the observation that ketogenesis can proceed briskly in the absence of an insulin-deficient state. A further observation that glucagon promoted ketogenesis in isolated liver preparations and the knowledge that plasma glucagon concentration increases as insulin levels fall helped provide the key to the problem. Currently it is believed that glucagon exerts its inhibitory effect on fatty acid synthesis at two levels (Fig. 13–3): (1) inhibition of glycolysis, which leads to a decrease in glucose-derived carbon flux into acetyl CoA and hence, decreased levels of malonyl CoA, and (2) inhibition of a more distal step in the cellular pathways, probably at the level of acetyl CoA carboxylase. The role of insulin in expediting entry of glucose into the cell and in its subsequent degradation should not be neglected, however. Thus, it is probably the plasma glucagon:insulin ratio rather than the absolute concentration of either hormone that is paramount in overall metabolic control of ketogenesis.

Biochemical and Physiological Correlates of the Regulatory Mechanisms

The liver occupies a central position in the economy of ketone bodies, being the major contributor to plasma ketone body production. As might be expected by its central role in production it is unable to consume ketones for its energy needs. The reason for this is that further metabolism

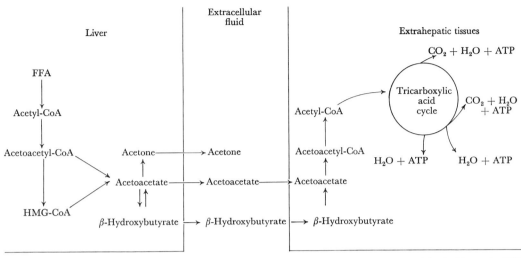

Figure 13–4 Pathways of ketogenesis and ketone body utilization. (From Masoro, E.J.: Lipids in Mammals. Philadelphia, W.B. Saunders Co., 1968.)

of ketone bodies requires acylation to the corresponding thioester, acetoacetyl CoA; 3-oxoacid transferase, the enzyme responsible for this conversion, is absent in liver but present in peripheral tissues.

Cleavage of the thioester bond occurs via a rather complex pathway (Fig. 13–4). Direct deacylation by *deacylase* occurs, but this is considered to be a minor path. Alternatively, acetoacetyl CoA and acetyl CoA are combined (HMG CoA synthase), and subsequently the HMG CoA is cleaved (HMG CoA lyase) to yield acetyl CoA and free acetoacetate. In its characteristically economical fashion, by the latter process the cell manages to conserve part of the energy required to cleave a C—C bond of HMG by converting a hydroxyl to a keto-group on the β-carbon of acetoacetate.

Acetoacetate and β-hydroxybutyrate are readily interconvertible in liver and from the liver enter the blood to supply needs of other tissues. It should be appreciated that the ketone bodies are not intermediates of fatty acid β-oxidation. In contrast to intermediates of fatty acid degradation, which are the "activated" coenzyme A derivatives, the ketone bodies exist free. Moreover, free β-hydroxybutyrate has the D-configuration as opposed to the L-configuration of the intermediate form from long-chain fatty acid oxidation.

With continued research into the metabolic role of the ketone bodies their pivotal role in the energy economy of the body has become obvious. In particular the integrated use of glucose and lipid in supplying energetic needs of tissues is such that when plasma glucose is low, as with carbohydrate restriction (starvation) or in diabetes mellitus (when it cannot be utilized), plasma free fatty acids increase. Concomitantly plasma ketone bodies also increase, providing yet another alternative fuel to glucose when it is unavailable for body needs. This adaptation has been termed physiological ketosis and should be viewed as a normal switching mechanism. Indeed because the increased ketone body production is met by increased utilization, the rise in plasma levels is negligible.

It seems curious that the body should provide fat as a fuel in two different forms. Free fatty acids are less soluble in aqueous media than ketone bodies and they have been shown to uncouple oxidative phosphorylation. Perhaps for those and other undefined reasons ketone bodies fulfill a biological need.

PATHOLOGICAL KETOSIS

For ketosis to develop, adipose tissue must provide augmented supplies of free fatty acids and the liver must divert these lipids from triglyceride synthesis (esterification) to β-oxidation and ketogenesis. The signals that bring about mobilization of lipid from adipose tissue stores include the hormones epinephrine and glucagon and the adrenal steroids. They bring about (1) hydrolysis of triglycerides within the adipocyte; (2) transport of free fatty acids out of the adipocyte, facilitated greatly by albumin in plasma; and (3) distribution in the circulation to various organs of the body. It should also be recalled that as plasma glucagon levels rise, insulin levels fall, with the net effect of a facilitation of fatty acid mobilization coupled with decreased glucose utilization.

As we have already seen, increase in the glucagon:insulin ratio also facilitates fatty acid oxidation in the hepatocyte by depressing glycolysis and inhibiting acetyl CoA carboxylase (through a phosphorylation-dephosphorylation mechanism), causing a drop in malonyl CoA levels and increasing transport of fatty acyl CoA into the mitochondria for β-oxidation. How the increased rate of acetoacetyl CoA production consequent to this process is integrated with the HMG CoA pathway to release increased amounts of free acetoacetate into the blood is not well defined. In any case, when the above adaptations result in accelerated ketone body production and release beyond what peripheral tissues are capable of utilizing, total ketone body (acetoacetate and β-hydroxybutyrate) levels in blood begin to rise above the usual 0.1 mM.

A working definition of ketosis has been proposed as a total blood ketone body level above 0.2 mM. With this level, it is important to distinguish between "physiological ketosis," "pathological ketosis," and "ketoacidosis." Elevations in total ketone bodies above the 0.2 mM level may be the result of a stimulus and response that are normal. For example, in fasting, late pregnancy, and vigorous exercise (all normal states), blood ketones may reach 2 mM. Such states are considered to represent *"physiological ketosis."* It should, therefore, be clear that the term *"pathological ketosis"* denotes a state that involves an underlying metabolic abnormality resulting in disruption of the complex inter-relationships of the various pathways culminating in formation of acetyl CoA. Implicit in such a definition is imbalance between rates of production and utilization, with overproduction prevailing. As ketone bodies are strong acids, their accumulation in the blood to the point at which blood buffers can no longer maintain a normal pH represents the state known as *"ketoacidosis."*

Starvation Ketosis

The discussion of carbohydrate metabolism (Chapter 12) emphasized that total body glycogen stores are inadequate to meet energy demands for a period longer than about 6 hours. Depletion of hepatic glycogen during fasting sets the stage for ketone body production from lipids by reducing the supply of acetyl CoA from glycolysis, hence reducing the malonyl CoA levels that have been depressing the transfer of lipid into mitochondria. In addition, the ketogenic liver is characterized by an elevated carnitine content. The means by which hepatic carnitine is increased, however, remains obscure. Within the first 12 to 24 hours of fasting, this increase in β-oxidation is reflected in an increase of total blood ketone body concentration from less than 0.2 mM to about 0.3 mM. While this appears to be a minimal change, it must be remembered that this increase occurs in the face of the increased demand for alternate energy sources by peripheral tissues. Fasting, prolonged for 48 to 72 hours, results in blood ketones of up to 3 mM. This tenfold increase in an alternate energy substrate despite accelerated peripheral consumption of ketones points up the tremendous ketogenic capacity of the liver.

Clearly, this process must have some regulation brought to bear upon it, since ketone body production at a rate in excess of consumption would result in ketoacidosis and total metabolic disarray. In fact, starvation for longer than 72 hours does not result in a further rise in blood ketones, and in prolonged fasting blood ketones tend to fall to lower levels. The primary control mechanism accounting for these observations appears to be a direct ability of ketone bodies to elicit a release of insulin from the pancreatic islets, causing suppression of lipolysis. There is also some evidence that ketone bodies exert a direct antilipolytic effect on adipose tissue. Thus, despite the enormous potential of the liver to produce ketone bodies during starvation, this ability is kept in check by indirect feedback mechanisms. The system is, in fact, self-limited by product inhibition, a process examined in more abstract terms in Chapter 2.

Diabetic Ketoacidosis

A basic regulatory factor in controlling the massive ketogenic ability of the liver is restriction of lipid availability by stimulation of pancreatic insulin release by ketone bodies. Failure of this feedback loop due to insulin deficiency in diabetes mellitus results in unfettered ketone body production by the liver because of unrestricted availability of free fatty acids. Because of the rise of free fatty acids to extremely high values (2.5 to 3.5 mM), the liver (in this insulinopenic state) is driven to produce ketone bodies far in excess of the ability of extrahepatic tissues to utilize them. Consequently, blood ketone body concentration approaches 20 mM, generating a life-threatening metabolic acidosis. Hepatic fatty acid oxidation capacity and ketogenesis are maximal, owing to the increased glucagon:insulin ratio and consequent massive adipose tissue breakdown.

Acetoacetate and β-hydroxybutyrate, both strong organic acids, are completely dissociated at body pH (pK = 3.8), each producing 1 mEq of hydrogen ion and keto acid anion. However, uncontrolled ketone body production soon leads to acidosis, which ensues when body buffer base is consumed and respiratory compensation is no longer able to maintain a normal pH. Under normal circumstances when ketones are oxidized by brain and skeletal muscle, bicarbonate (consumed by acid buffering) is replenished by metabolism of ketones.

There is evidence that the hyperketonemia of starvation and diabetic ketoacidosis is partially attributable to a concomitant impairment of utilization in the periphery as well as to overproduction. Insulin-deficient dogs utilize ketones at a slower rate than do normal dogs; the rate picks up with insulin administration. The mechanism of this reversal remains obscure, but in the case of diabetic ketoacidosis, impairment of ketone body utilization can be a major contributing factor to the severity of the disease.

REFERENCES

Baruh, S., Sherman, L., and Markowitz, S.: Diabetic ketoacidosis and coma. Med. Clin. North Am. 65:117, 1981.

Felig, P., and Koivisto, V.: Recent advances in body fuel metabolism. *In* Freinkel, N. (ed.): Contemporary Metabolism. Vol. 1. Plenum Press, New York, 1979, p. 359.

McGarry, J.D., and Foster, D.W.: Regulation of hepatic fatty acid oxidation and ketone body production. Ann. Rev. Biochem. 49:395, 1980.

Robinson, A.M., and Williamson, D.H.: Physiological roles of ketone bodies as substrates and signals in mammalian tissues. Physiol. Rev. 60:143, 1980.

Sokoloff, L.: Metabolism of ketone bodies by the brain. Ann. Rev. Med. 24:271, 1973.

Unger, R.H., and Orci, L.: Glucagon and the A cell: Physiology and pathophysiology. New Engl. J. Med. 304:1518, 1575, 1981.

Zammit, V.A.: Intrahepatic regulation of ketogenesis. Trends in Biochemical Sciences Feb. 1981, p. 46.

14

Kidney Function
and Malfunction

The kidney is charged with maintaining the composition of the extracellular fluid of the body, and in so doing it regulates the environment in which all cells reside, an environment that reflects the origin of life in the primeval oceans. Obviously the fluid medium of the human body, in which widely diversified cells carry out life processes, must provide a wide range of substances basic to these processes. It is the kidney that maintains the composition of this complex nutritional medium, termed the ''milieu interieur'' by Claude Bernard, in the face of a variable range of ingestion of solutes and water. Since there is a continuous flux of water and solutes across all cell membranes, the kidney indirectly regulates the volume and tonicity of intracellular fluid as well.

In the normally functioning kidney maintenance of fluid homeostasis is a composite of four processes: (1) filtration of the plasma by the glomerular unit, (2) selective reabsorption by the tubule of materials required to maintain the internal environment, (3) secretion by the tubule of certain substances from the blood into the tubular lumen for excretion in the urine, and (4) secretion of hydrogen ion and production of ammonia. Since there is secretion from the blood into the lumen of a variety of waste substances and a secretion of hydrogen ions in defense of blood pH, it follows that a certain degree of net fluid loss to maintain solubility of excreted solutes is obligatory. Hence, it should be clear that cessation of this net fluid loss through the urinary tract constitutes a serious disruption of function, irrespective of the underlying cause. Energy requirements for these secretory and reabsorptive processes amount to approximately 10 per cent of basal oxygen consumption (Table 14–1). Following the theme of the suitability of structure to serve biological function, we expect that the multiplicity of functions carried out by the kidney is reflected by a wide diversity of specialized cell types. This is indeed so, with the mesenchyme serving as progenitor of the renal secretory system, which includes glomeruli, proximal tubules, and loops of Henle. In contrast, the portions of the kidney whose functions are relatively simple arise from the coelomic epithelium, or entoderm, in intimate relationship with the developing gonadal system.

At the end of a full-term gestation each kidney contains between 850 thousand and 1 million nephrons. As this constitutes the full complement of nephron units present in the mature kidney, further development of the organ consists of differentiation of the cell types into mature forms rather

Table 14–1 RENAL METABOLISM

Structure	Constituents	Metabolic Characteristics
Cortex and outer medulla	70 percent of total kidney weight	Aerobic environment
	Straight limb proximal tubule	Many mitochondria
	Thick ascending limp Loop of Henle	Citric acid cycle
	Distal tubules	Fatty acids major fuel; others are glutamine and citrate
	Collecting tubules	Gluconeogenesis (linked to acid-base status, i.e., ↓ intracellular pH → ↑ gluconeogenesis)
Inner medulla and papilla	Thin limb loops of Henle	Relatively oxygen poor
	Collecting ducts	Few mitochondria
	Early regions of thick ascending limb	Glycolysis (high levels of hexokinase and pyruvate kinase)
		Glucose major fuel

than formation of new units beyond 36 weeks. It is well known that renal function in the normal neonate is not mature in comparison with that of the older child, because of immaturity of nephron units. It follows that prenatal influences that impair normal differentiation of the kidney will be reflected in clinical states in the newborn that are relatively permanent, since no mechanism exists for later differentiation of nephron units. It is also apparent that the complexity of organogenesis and the clear delineation of development of cell types before 36 weeks results in a multiplicity of renal abnormalities attributable to congenital influences.

GLOMERULAR FILTRATION

For descriptive purposes, the process of glomerular filtration has been thought of as the forcing of water and small molecules through a sieve, the driving force being supplied by the arterial blood pressure in the efferent capillary. Actually this is a gross oversimplification of what appears to be a very complex process. Nonetheless, the end result of these contributing factors is a passive process dependent upon hydrostatic pressure. To appreciate fully what is presently known about the mechanisms of glomerular filtration, let us imagine the primitive nephron unit as a cylinder with one blind end. As development of the nephron proceeds, the efferent and afferent arteriolar complex pushes progressively further into the blind end of the nephron. As a result the capillary tuft is eventually surrounded by a double-walled structure with a space enclosed between the double walls which is continuous with the lumen of the tubule. The inner layer of epithelial surface of this indentation is applied directly to the glomerular tuft and separated from it only by its basal membrane. This inner layer is known as the visceral glomerular epithelium, while the outer layer left by the indentation (which is continuous with the inner layer) is known as the parietal or capsular epithelium. With continued development of the glomerulus, the outer or capsular epithelium remains a typical squamous layer of flat polygonal cells, but the layer of visceral epithelium becomes more extensively modified so that it is barely recognizable as epithelium in the typical sense. The mature epithelial cell of the visceral layer is known as a podocyte.

The podocytes possess processes that radiate in a stellate manner, giving rise to a number of secondary processes called pedicles or foot processes. Interdigitation of foot processes from adjacent podocytes generates a complex system of intracellular openings known as slit pores. In the electron micrograph the relationship of the foot processes to the subjacent glomerular capillary reveals that the foot processes are arranged along the outer surface of a continuous basal lamina, which is their only separation from the endothelium of the underlying glomerular capillary (Fig. 14–1). Collagen and glycoprotein represent two major components of the basal lamina. Adjacent processes are not in actual contact but are separated by very narrow slits. These intracellular gaps are bridged by a thin dense line, which is a slit membrane. It extends between the outer portions of the plasma membranes of adjacent foot processes of the visceral surface of the basal lamina. The opposite surface of the basal lumina, the endothelial lining of the glomerular capillary, is also thin and thought to be penetrated by circular pores 700 to 900 Å in diameter.

As yet there is no entirely coherent view of the structural-functional inter-relationships that account for the remarkable permeability of the glomerulus. Two viewpoints, which are not necessarily mutually exclusive, have been championed by the pore theory and basement membrane gel theory. The former holds that the diameter of membrane pores sets limits to the nature of proteins that will be able to traverse the glomerulus, while the latter views the charge of the basement membrane to be the crucial factor in determining permeability characteristics. This latter view is supported by the presence of trace amounts of large proteins in the urine. Additionally, the evidence for pores is inferential. The basal lamina, which is the only continuous layer in the entire structure, serves a key role in filtration of large molecules. Controversy surrounds the ability of the adjacent podocytes to control the size of the epithelial slit pores. In any case, the basal lamina is now known to be replenished, on a continuing basis, by the podocytes. Thus, we see from the foregoing that in addition to physiological influences accounting for the filtration of blood by the capillary, morphological features of the capillary contribute as well.

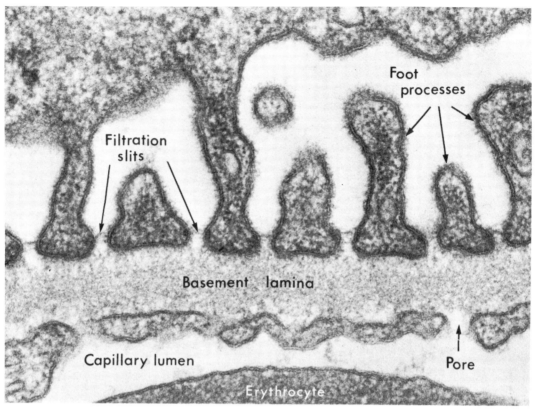

Figure 14–1 Relationship of the visceral epithelial cell (podocyte) to the capillary. The foot processes of the podocytes are applied to the visceral surface of the basement lamina, which is continuous and which separates them from the capillary endothelium. (From Bloom, W., and Fawcett, D.W.: A Textbook of Histology. 10th ed. Philadelphia, W.B. Saunders Co., 1975. Courtesy of Daniel Friend, M.D.)

Because of the presence of glycoproteins in various layers of the glomerular capillary wall it is to be anticipated that electrostatic forces would also play a role in the selectivity of the glomerulus to passage of plasma proteins. Indeed, the anionic glycoproteins retard the passage of albumin, which also behaves as an anion. Damage to the glycoprotein constituents is then one factor in albuminuria.

The process of filtration implies a driving force to enable the filtrate to traverse the capsular barrier. In the case of the glomerulus, the force driving the filtration process is the hydrostatic pressure of the blood. Approximately 20 to 25 per cent of the cardiac output at rest passes through the kidney each minute. Therefore, within 5 minutes a volume of blood equivalent to the total body blood volume has passed through the renal circulation. This is possible because of the tremendously complicated and extensive circulatory system with which the kidney is endowed. The normal pressure in the efferent glomerular capillary is currently a matter of debate. However, this driving force for filtration is counterbalanced by a number of factors: (a) osmotic pressure of nonfilterable plasma components, (b) renal interstitial pressure, and (c) renal intertubular pressure. Thus, the net filtration pressure driving the formation of the actual glomerular filtrate is classically put at 25 mm Hg. More recent measurements, however, indicate that it may be closer to 15 mm Hg. At this net filtration pressure, in the normal adult, approximately 120 ml of glomerular filtrate is formed in Bowman's capsule per minute.

Clearly, many factors can affect this glomerular filtration rate: a significant drop in systemic blood pressure will result in a drop in the driving force of filtration so that the resultant net filtration pressure may be equal to the opposing forces; this same net effect could be created by partial obstruction of the arterial supply to the kidney or to the glomerulus; inflammatory processes may increase the interstitial renal pressure; increased resistance to flow in the tubular portion of the nephron due to obstruction distally may also affect the net filtration pressure; significant decreases in osmotically active components of plasma may increase the amount of filtration occurring at the glomerulus. In addition, the various permeability barriers in the glomerulus may be adversely affected by disease, so that the glomerulus does not function as a filter for the blood. In such cases, blood cells and plasma protein may leak through the damaged glomerular capillary complex and find their way into the urine.

The Proximal Tubule

Reference to Table 14–2, comparing the normal constituents of glomerular filtrate and urine, underscores the marked changes that occur in the luminal fluid from one end of the nephron to the other. We have already examined the filtration properties of the glomerulus, from which it follows that the ultrafiltrate entering the proximal tubule is composed of water and small molecules, such as glucose and electrolytes, in approximately the same concentration as in the plasma. Since the total volume of glomerular filtrate formed in 24 hours is in the neighborhood of 180 liters, it is clear that the individual could not long survive without drastic alterations to this ultrafiltrate. A large number of these changes occur in the proximal tubule, a segment of the nephron approximately 14 mm long that makes up the bulk of the renal cortex. It is composed of a convoluted portion (pars convoluta) and a straight portion (pars recta) (Fig. 14–2).

Contiguous with the parietal epithelial layer of the glomerular capsule is the proximal portion of the proximal tubule. Those cells are cuboidal or columnar epithelium with brushborder microvilli that increase the absorptive capability. Indeed, the lumen of the proximal tubule normally appears rather narrow because of the huge numbers of brushborder microvilli that extend into the lumen. Between the microvilli arise numerous tubular invaginations that extend downward into the apical cytoplasm. These are the *apical canaliculi,* which are probably involved in the reabsorption of protein by the proximal tubule.

In addition to the reabsorption of filtered protein, the proximal tubule accomplishes the bulk of the reabsorption of glucose and amino acids, electrolytes (sodium, bicarbonate, phosphate and potassium), and water (Table 14–3). Furthermore, the proximal tubule also has the capacity for

Table 14–2 CONSTITUENTS OF GLOMERULAR FILTRATE AND URINE

	Glomerular Filtrate (24 hr)	Urine (24 hr)
Metabolites		
Glucose	200 g	<50 mg
Amino Acids	10 g	50–150 mg
Ions		
Sodium	24,000 mEq	50–200 mEq
Potassium	680 mEq	30–100 mEq
Chloride	20,000 mEq	50–200 mEq
Calcium	7–10 g	200 mg—restricted intake
Phosphorus	9000 mg	600–800 mg or 10 mEq
Magnesium	200 mEq	300 mg
Waste		
Urea	40–60 g	25–30 g
Creatinine	1.8–2 g	1–1.5 g
Urate	>95% reabsorbed	250–750 mg
Acidification Products		
H^+	pH 7.35	pH 5–6.5
Titratable acid	0	20–75 mEq
Bicarbonate	5000 mEq	2–5 mEq
Ammonium	<1 mEq	40–75 mEq
Water	180 l	1.5 l

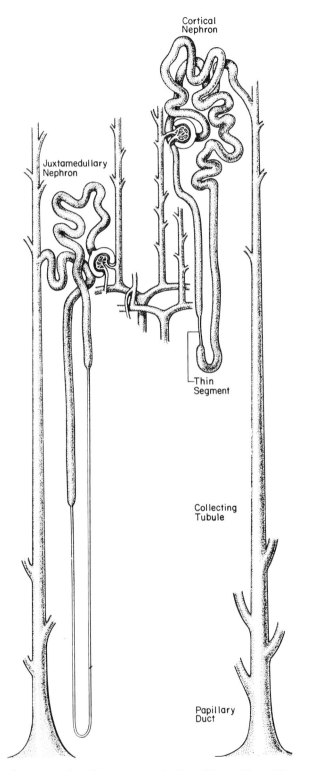

Figure 14–2 Schematic representation of the nephron unit. (From Bloom, W., and Fawcett, D.W.: A Textbook of Histology. 10th ed. Philadelphia, W.B. Saunders Co., 1975.)

active secretion of certain substances into the luminal fluid. From the fact that all these processes occur simultaneously, as well as bi-directionally, one cannot help but be impressed with the tasks accomplished by this simple epithelial tube. Indeed, the fact that vanishingly small amounts of any essential substance found in the blood, such as glucose or amino acids, ultimately appear in the urine is nothing short of awesome.

Furthermore, the rate at which 180 liters of fluid pass through the relatively minute spaces of the nephrons is necessarily quite rapid, demanding that the reabsorptive processes be extremely efficient in order to remove a maximum amount of material from a large volume of fluid in a relatively short time. It is not possible for these functions to be carried out by the simple process of diffusion. In fact, removal of solutes from the glomerular filtrate is carried out, for the most part, by active (energy requiring) reabsorptive processes. In addition, the selectivity of the reabsorptive processes necessitates an ability to recognize certain substances and to reject others. This function is generally ascribed to the presence of a membrane carrier for individual substances. That such specific carrier molecules probably exist is inferred from the fact that humans have been identified who have inabilities to reabsorb certain amino acids but not others. Such disorders are discussed in Chapter 23, Amino Acid Transport Disorders.

The localization of reabsorptive processes to the membrane carrier molecules implies a limit to the capacity to bind all transported molecules. When the concentration of a given transported substance in the glomerular filtrate has exceeded the capacity of the carrier system to remove it from the glomerular fluid, we speak of exceeding the "threshold" for that substance. A substance, such as glucose, is known as a "high" threshold substance. This statement implies that the blood glucose may vary widely in concentration, up to approximately 200 mg/dl, before significant glucose is detectable in the urine. The maximum rate at which a substrate can be reabsorbed is known as the tubular maximum (T_m). In the case of glucose this has been determined to be approximately 350 gm of glucose per minute. Assuming an arterial plasma level of 100 mg of glucose per dl and a glomerular filtration rate of 120 ml per minute, 120 mg of glucose is delivered into the glomerular filtrate each minute. However, normally not more than 1 g of sugar is excreted in the urine per day. This amounts to a total loss of 0.6 per cent of the 173 g of glucose normally filtered through the glomerulus. Amino acids, which are handled in a fashion similar to that of glucose, show the same order of efficient reabsorption from the glomerular filtrate.

At a given plasma concentration of any of the essential dietary components such as glucose or amino acids, it should be apparent that any decrease, however small, in the numbers of membrane carriers or in the efficiency of their operation will be reflected in a decreased ability to reabsorb the small molecules from the enormous quantity of fluid passing through the tubule each day. Such conditions are known as either renal glycosuria or renal aminoacidurias. On the other hand, even in the presence of normal numbers and efficiency of carriers, the plasma levels of these small molecules may be increased under certain conditions beyond the ability of the carrier systems to transport and completely reabsorb. Such conditions are illustrated by the situation in diabetes mellitus. In this disease, at the point at which the blood sugar level has exceeded the threshold for glucose, the glucose is "spilled" by the kidney into the urine. What this means is the glomerulus has filtered, for example, 400 mg/dl of sugar, which is in excess of the 350 mg per minute T_m for glucose. A small amount of this glucose will therefore pass on beyond the proximal tubule, carrying water with it as a result of its osmotic properties. The net result of this will be both glycosuria as well as an osmotic diuresis, or passage of excess water in the urine.

Of the 180 liters of glomerular filtrate formed each day, approximately 150 liters are reabsorbed in the proximal tubules. Although the volume of water in the luminal fluid is drastically decreased during its passage through the proximal tubule, the concentration of sodium does not change, nor does the osmotic pressure of the luminal fluid. There is now little doubt that active reabsorption of sodium ions occurs and is primary with respect to that of water, which follows passively. Under normal conditions approximately 85 per cent of the filtered sodium is actively reabsorbed at the proximal tubule site, and in order to maintain electrochemical neutrality chloride ion is reabsorbed simultaneously.

Table 14–3 FUNCTIONS OF NEPHRON SEGMENTS

	Glomerulus	Proximal Tubule (Convoluted)	Loop of Henle
Histology	Capillary endothelium more permeable than elsewhere in body	Brush border, many mitochondria E/M—lysosomes, Golgi, peroxisomes, lipid droplets	Thin descending and ascending—mi villi rare and short; few mitochonc
Permeability Characteristics	Permeable to spherical particles with M.W. $<40,000$; ready passage of substances with M.W. ~ 5000	Permeable to water, NaCl	Descending: permeable to water; im permeable to NaCl; urea Ascending: reverse of descending
Functions	Ultrafiltration of blood, 50–65 nl/min/nephron	Reabsorbs metabolites and ions essential to cell functions Isotonic, isoelectric reabsorption of 70% water, 70% Na reabsorbed, 90% HCO_3 reabsorbed; H^+ secretion in distal PT. Secretion of drugs that are weak acids and bases Active reabsorption—glucose, amino acids, P_i, lactate (Na linked)	Creates osmotic gradient to adjust o molality of urine Water absorbed into hyperosmotic i stitial fluid that bathes descending limb In ascending limb passive NaCl real sorption occurs with urea secretio Net result is loss of solute with di tion of tubular fluid. In so doing s without water is added to the mec lary interstitium
Special Characteristics	GFR is dependent on renal plasma flow	Glomerulotubular balance (% Na and water reabsorbed unchanged with change in GFR). Reabsorbtion inhibited by volume expansion, carbonic anhydrase inhibitors	Urea exerts osmotic effect on thin [

There is persuasive evidence that sodium reabsorption serves as the driving force for the active transport of glucose and amino acids. Such evidence includes (but is not limited to) demonstration of the dependence upon the presence of sodium ion for in vitro renal tubular transport of a variety of physiological substrates.

Despite the enormous changes in volume and composition of the luminal fluid, the pH of the proximal tubular fluid remains much the same as that of the glomerular filtrate. This is largely due to the reabsorption of filtered bicarbonate. The mechanism for this bicarbonate reabsorption, illustrated in Figure 14–3, is based upon the chemical reaction of water with carbon dioxide to form carbonic acid. The carbonic acid hydrolyzes to form hydrogen ion and bicarbonate ion. The hydrogen ion produced diffuses into the luminal fluid down an electrical gradient, to combine with the filtered bicarbonate. The H_2CO_3 formed in this manner results in a generation of CO_2 and water through hydrolysis. The sodium ion that had been filtered by the glomerulus, in combination with the filtered bicarbonate is actively reabsorbed by the tubular cell and ultimately enters the glomerular afferent capillary as sodium bicarbonate. Thus, the net result of this process is the reabsorption of one sodium ion and one bicarbonate ion in exchange for the loss of one CO_2 molecule, one water molecule, one chloride, and one hydrogen ion.

Both phosphate and potassium reabsorption take place primarily in the proximal tubule. Reabsorption of the filtered phosphate is restricted to the proximal tubule and is incomplete, so that there is some urinary loss under normal circumstances. The filtered load of potassium, however, is completely reabsorbed in the proximal segment. Nevertheless, the urine does contain some potassium. It follows then that this urinary potassium must be derived from secretion in some other segment of the nephron.

Thus, we have seen that the composition of the fluid that is reabsorbed from the lumen of the proximal tubule resembles strongly that of the original glomerular filtrate. The volume, pH, and concentration of glucose, amino acid, sodium, bicarbonate, phosphate, and potassium are essentially equivalent to the glomerular filtrate. There is far less urea and sulfate and no creatine. Hence the proximal tubule constitutes the main defense against excess loss of fluid and solute.

Loop of Henle (Thick Ascending)	Distal Diluting	Distal Convoluted	Collecting Segment
ɔidal, basement membrane ᵻnner than in proximal tub- e	Macula densa—first part of distal tubule	Second part of DT	Extensive basal surface labyrinth
ᵻrmeable to water	Impermeable to water, permeable to NaCl	Impermeable to water and NaCl	Permeable to water and NaCl in presence of ADH
of diluting segment. ᵻ removed without water— y to countercurrent mecha- ᵻm. Cl⁻ actively transported a⁺ and K⁺ passively) cre- s osmotic gradient in inter- ium. Tubule fluid becomes ᵻre dilute	Makes final adjustments in excretion of Na, K, and H Shows transition from Cl⁻ transport to Na⁺ transport	Na^+ actively transported; negative transmembrane potential, ADH affects water permeability Aldosterone ↑ Na^+ reabsorption. Acid-base balance controlled	Active reabsorption Na^+; secretion of K^+ and H^+, impermeable to urea In conjunction with distal tubule modulates final osmolality of urine to be excreted
ve PD*	PD at beginning + 8 mV gradually changes to − 30 mV at end	Negative potential creates an electrochemical gradient for K+ and H+	Both Na^+ transport and voltage show mineralocorticoid dependency

⁼ potential difference.

The Loop of Henle

As the urine passes through the nephron, it abruptly encounters a narrowing of the lumen from a width of about 60 micrometers in the true proximal tubule to a space about 15 micrometers in diameter. There is a concomitant change in the epithelial lining of the lumen from the cuboidal epithelium of the proximal tubule to squamous epithelium. Also disappearing abruptly is the brush-border, which is replaced by very sparse, irregularly oriented microvilli on the luminal surface. These cells rest upon a moderately thick basal lamina, and the cytoplasm contains relatively few organelles. There are cytoplasmic extensions of neighboring cells, which interdigitate with each other somewhat in the fashion of two meshing gears. If one traces the course of the descending loop, one sees fewer and fewer cytoplasmic organelles in the cells until the inner zone of the medulla is reached and the actual loop is encountered.

The decrease in the number of cytoplasmic organelles in this area of the nephron appears to be correlated with the lack of specialized function of this segment (Table 14–3). It is thought that the descending limb of the loop of Henle is freely permeable to sodium and to water, while the ascending limb is believed to be impermeable to water. In contrast to the other segments of the nephron, the voltage orientation across the thick ascending limb is positive (ca. + 7 mV). Since NaCl concentration declines progressively as fluid travels along this segment, it follows that Cl⁻, and not Na^+, is the actively transported ion, with sodium following passively to maintain electroneutrality. The cells of the ascending limb of the loop of Henle are the site of a sodium pump that moves Na^+ from the urine into the interstitial spaces of the medulla, increasing the osmotic concentrations in the latter. Therefore, water leaves the descending limb of the loop of Henle by passive diffusion and the urine becomes increasingly concentrated as it passes deeper into the medulla toward the bottom of the loop. Sodium is pumped out the lumen of the ascending limb into the interstitium, from which it escapes passively either into adjacent blood vessels or into the descending limb of the loop of Henle following a concentration gradient. Therefore, the descending limb of the loop contains fluid that is hypertonic with respect to plasma. As the fluid rounds the bend of

PROXIMAL TUBULE

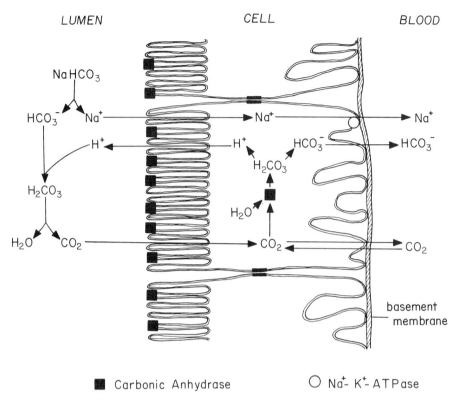

Figure 14–3 Bicarbonate reclamation in the proximal tubule.

the loop, the descending limb and the ascending limb contain fluids that are momentarily isosmotic. The osmotic pressure difference between the loops is abolished, and the subsequent active secretion of sodium from the ascending limb sets up a new osmotic difference, so that the tubular fluid descending to the tip becomes more hypertonic. In the meantime the capillary blood vessels in the medulla, which are arranged in parallel rows, exhibit a simple countercurrent exchange, for sodium is neither secreted nor reabsorbed actively by either limb of the capillary loop and simply follows the concentration gradient.

The net result of the countercurrent system is that both the tubular fluid and also the capillary blood become progressively more concentrated as they reach the tip of the loop, but subsequently they become more dilute as they ascend toward the cortex again. This process results in the delivery of a hypotonic urine to the distal convoluted tubule. Thus, we may summarize the function of the loop of Henle as that of concentration and dilution of the luminal contents, with a net reabsorption of sodium and production of a hypotonic urine.

The Distal Tubule

The cells of the distal convoluted tubule are generally cuboidal in shape and have very small, sparse microvilli projecting into the lumen. As this portion of the nephron approaches the vascular pole of the glomerulus, it becomes attached at the angle between afferent and efferent arterioles. This junction is known as the macula densa, which is believed to play a role in renal hemodynamics in an as yet poorly defined manner.

With the passage of urine thus far into the nephron, the major defense of the integrity of the extracellular fluid compartment has already been accomplished: the bulk of volume and solute excreted into the glomerular filtrate has been reabsorbed, the tonicity of the urine with respect to plasma has been adjusted in the loop of Henle, and the buffer base (bicarbonate) excreted into the glomerular filtrate has been reclaimed. Only one major task remains to be accomplished—the secretion of hydrogen ion for the maintenance of extracellular fluid pH (Table 14–3). This function is the principal one of the distal tubule, the main site of acidification of the urine.

A distinction should be made here with respect to the hydrogen ion secretion that occurs in the proximal tubule in exchange for one sodium and one bicarbonate ion, inasmuch as at that location there is little change in the pH of the urine. Although the mechanism for reabsorption of sodium and secretion of hydrogen ion by the distal tubule is similar to that in the proximal tubule, it is even more straightforward (see Fig. 3–3, p. 52). Carbon dioxide, derived from metabolism of the cell itself, as well as from the blood, is combined with water in the cytosol of the distal tubular cell in the presence of carbonic anhydrase to form H_2CO_3. As in the proximal tubule cell, carbonic acid ionizes to hydrogen ion and bicarbonate ion. In the tubular lumen, however, sodium is now predominantly present as disodium hydrogen phosphate, which ionizes to form one sodium and the anion sodium hydrogen phosphate. The ionized sodium is exchanged at the luminal surface of the distal tubular cell for the hydrogen ion produced intracellularly. The sodium ion thus reabsorbed is secreted into the blood in combination with the bicarbonate ion derived from the carbonic anhydrase reaction. Thus, there is a net reabsorption of one sodium and one bicarbonate, with excretion in the luminal fluid of one molecule of sodium dihydrogen phosphate. The distal tubular cell has at its disposal an additional means for secretion of hydrogen ions—the production of ammonia. These cells have a high concentration of the enzyme glutaminase, which converts glutamine to glutamate, liberating NH_3. This enzyme appears to be activated and regulated by the intracellular pH of the distal tubular cell, its activity increasing with decreased pH. The ammonia thus formed can combine with hydrogen ion, either within the cell or in the tubular lumen, producing the ammonium cation. To preserve electrochemical neutrality, one sodium ion is reabsorbed in exchange for this ammonium cation. This sodium ion can also be combined with the bicarbonate ion produced intracellularly by the action of carbonic anhydrase, thus resulting in net secretion of one hydrogen ion for one ion of sodium reabsorbed with bicarbonate.

One final feature of the role of the distal tubular cell in regulation of pH worthy of note is the linkage of the hydrogen ion secretory mechanisms with potassium ion. These two ions appear to compete for secretion into the tubular lumen, so that when hydrogen ion concentration inside the cell is high, potassium secretion is reduced. Conversely, when there is an increase in intracellular potassium, competition for the secretory mechanism favors potassium and therefore more potassium will be secreted. This exchange is always made for sodium ions. The ion exchange mechanism, which proceeds independently, is also partially regulated by the adrenal mineralocorticoid aldosterone.

The solute exchange that occurs in the distal tubule is the last opportunity for the nephron to alter the solute composition of the urine. Beyond this point in the urinary tract, the only alteration that occurs in urine composition is the alteration in volume and tonicity.

MECHANISM OF URINARY CONCENTRATION

Because water tends to follow solute by the process of simple diffusion, cell membranes that are specialized for the conservation of body water, such as those lining the distal and collecting tubules of the kidney, must regulate the passive diffusion of water by selective permeability to solutes. The membranes of these cells appear to be selective in their ability to transfer sodium and urea, water following passively (Table 14–3). Under normal circumstances, the membranes of these cells are effectively completely impermeable to water and solute. However, in states of dehydration, the membranes appear to alter their permeability characteristics (presumably through conformational changes) to allow solute (salt and urea) to cross the barrier into the blood, taking with them a corresponding quantity of water.

The mechanism by which concentration occurs is dual and is mediated by both baro- and osmoreceptors. Baroreceptive control over fluid reabsorption occurs via the juxtaglomerular apparatus with activation of the renin-angiotensin system.

In a sense, therefore, the kidney is autoregulatory in the matter of fluid reabsorption, the angiotensin II produced by the system set into motion by the baroreceptor, causing increased release of aldosterone from the adrenal gland. The effect of aldosterone is primarily on the distal tubule; the subcellular location is not yet precisely defined, although it may act at the nuclear level. Experimentally, aldosterone causes a rapid increase in RNA synthesis and thus indirectly increases the synthesis of protein and enzyme. However the biochemical effect is mediated, the effect of aldosterone on transport is to increase the retention of sodium, thus accentuating the exchange mechanism by which sodium is transferred to the blood in exchange for potassium at the distal tubular level. Water moves in accordance with the shift toward increased concentration of sodium, therefore increasing the amount of water reabsorbed at this level of the nephron. In addition, the level of serum potassium may have a direct effect upon the adrenal cortex in altering the secretion by that tissue of aldosterone. It should be recalled that while water will follow sodium, it must also be present as a solvent for the nontransported waste materials present in the luminal tubule. This leads to a limitation in water reabsorption, directed by the amount of water necessary to maintain the urinary solutes in solution.

Osmoreceptive control over the urinary concentrating mechanisms is primarily located in the anterior hypothalamus. Contact of these osmoreceptors with blood that is hypo-osmotic results in neural impulses being transmitted to the posterior pituitary gland, which inhibits pituitary secretion of the antidiuretic hormone (ADH). In the absence of ADH secretion the permeability of the wall of the distal and collecting tubules is meager, resulting in diuresis. On the other hand, with deprivation of water the osmoreceptors stimulate secretion from the posterior pituitary, mediating an effect on permeability of the wall of the distal and collecting tubule, with increased water reabsorption as a consequence. That the effect of ADH on the distal and collecting tubular cells is mediated through cyclic AMP is clear. Precisely how the increase in cyclic AMP accomplishes this is not well understood. Whatever the mechanisms at the cellular level the net effect on urinary concentration is impressive. While the luminal fluid entering the distal tubule from the ascending limb of the loop of Henle is approximately one third isosmolar, the urine entering the terminal portion of the papilla may be up to five times isosmolar.

The daily requirement for electrolyte and urea excretion in the urine amounts to 600 mOsm. This osmotic burden can be excreted in maximally concentrated urine (1200 mOsm/500 ml) or maximally dilute urine (60 mOsm/10 l). Usually the actual osmolarity and volume will fall between these two physiological extremes. Obviously an individual with compromised renal function who cannot concentrate beyond 350 mOsm/l must excrete 1700 ml of urine to remove the 600 mOsm per day required.

PATHOLOGICAL STATES OF THE NEPHRON

This section focuses on certain metabolic derangements of kidney function accompanying progressive renal insufficiency and considers certain primary derangements (e.g., mellituria, nephrolithiasis) that have a metabolic cause. Acute renal failure (acute tubular necrosis) is not discussed, since the causes are very rarely the direct result of an inborn error.

Earlier we spoke of the coherence of life's processes. From this point of view it follows that the normal kidney is under the control of biological "signal" molecules that, under normal circumstances, act to control the economy of various solutes regulated by the kidney. When the kidney is damaged, these same signal molecules, elaborated to an increased degree, can still orchestrate the activity of the individual nephrons and maintain the normal concentrations of key solutes, i.e., sodium, potassium, hydrogen ion, calcium, and phosphorus, in the extracellular fluid. Such a view demands an individual "signal" molecule to control the homeostasis of each solute. This is best understood in the case of phosphate and has led Bricker et al. (1978) to formulate the *intact nephron hypothesis,* which emphasizes the role hormones play in maintaining normal function. Of course, augmented function by the nephron in the face of diminishing numbers of functioning units exacts its price—a *"trade-off"* in Bricker's terminology.

Table 14–4 STAGES OF RENAL FAILURE

	Diminished Reserve	Insufficiency (Instability Introduced)	Frank Renal Failure	Uremia
Clinical	Asymptomatic or hypertension	Nocturia. Patient tenuously balanced—perturbations of fluid and electrolytes, infection—may lead to azotemia and acidosis	Polyuria	GI, CNS, cardiorespiratory symptoms as result of renal decompensation, oliguria, bone disease, purpura, pruritus
Pathophysiology	Decreased creatinine clearance, but as a whole excretory and regulatory functions are intact	$Cr_{Cl} < 50$ml/min (adult)	$Cr_{Cl} < 10$–15ml/min	Uremic toxins—middle molecules, endocrinopathy (trade-off)
Laboratory Values	Hyperuricemia. Proteinuria	Mild ↑ BUN, creatinine. Hyposthenuria. Mild anemia	Serum Cr 5.5–11 mg/dl, ↓Ca, ↑P_i, Metabolic acidosis ↓Cl, ↓Na, ↑K^+—occasionally	Pronounced azotemia. Hyperkalemia

Common to all causes of chronic renal failure is a progressive and irreversible loss of nephron function. It is possible to distinguish four separate stages in the evolution of renal failure: diminished reserve, insufficiency, failure, and the uremic syndrome. The biochemical and clinical characteristics are compared in Table 14–4. According to the intact nephron hypothesis, as the number of functioning nephrons decreases with progression of renal failure, the metabolic and transport activity of each nephron rises to meet the challenge of defending the internal milieu. They do so by sensing the level of the particular solute to be regulated and then operating in an oscillating manner, seeking to return the individual solute to its normal range—the so-called null point.

Secondary Hyperparathyroidism and the Trade-Off Hypothesis

Development of hyperparathyroidism during the course of renal failure forms the basis for the trade-off hypothesis, which posits that the stimulus to augment tubular function comes from hormones whose main target is a region of the nephron. This compensation is the price that other organs must pay because of excessive hormone secretion to maintain calcium and phosphorus homeostasis. As the number of functioning nephrons diminishes, phosphate clearance falls, generating an increase in serum phosphate that promotes calcification, consequently lowering the serum calcium concentration. To correct this imbalance PTH secretion increases, augmenting phosphate excretion and defining a new set-point that persists until further nephron death forces repetition of the chains of events. Of course, a point is reached when compensating hyperparathyroidism can no longer affect tubular function, at which point serum calcium and phosphate are persistently abnormal and bone manifests the ravages of PTH stimulation.

As we have pointed out earlier, formation of the active metabolite of vitamin D is accomplished by the kidney. Hence, progressive renal failure is also associated with diminished formation of $1,25(OH)_2D_3$, not only because of damaged renal tissues but also because of elevated inorganic phosphate. With diminished levels of $1,25(OH)_2D_3$, calcium absorption from the gut is severely diminished, acting as another stimulus to compensatory hyperparathyroidism. Skeletal lesions are not limited to the osteitis fibrosa of hyperparathyroidism. Rickets (decreased mineralization of osteoid) as a consequence of lack of $1,25(OH)_2D_3$, osteoporosis (decreased bone volume), osteosclerosis, and, of course, metastatic calcification round out this rather variegated and clinically distressing picture.

Glucose Intolerance

Most patients with uremia show a delay in the rate of fall of blood glucose to an oral or intravenous glucose tolerance test. Insulin resistance, thought to reside at the level of the glucose transport system in the cell or in the intracellular metabolism of glucose, accounts for this diabetic-like picture. The absence of fasting hyperglycemia or ketosis may be helpful in distinguishing this form of glucose intolerance from diabetes mellitus. Plasma insulin levels are elevated in uremia, probably as a result of both impaired sensitivity to insulin by peripheral tissues and diminished degradation by the kidney.

To distinguish between true insulin resistance and a generalized defect in carbohydrate metabolism, studies compared the rate of metabolism of fructose to that of glucose in uremic tissues. Since fructose is phosphorylated by fructokinase, an enzyme that acts independently of insulin, the finding of normal fructose metabolism distinguishes glucose intolerance and its dependence on insulin from a more general defect in hexose catabolism.

Another factor that may play a role in the apparent resistance to insulin in uremia is the elevated levels of blood glucagon in patients with chronic renal failure. Since glucagon is normally degraded by the kidney, decreased functioning renal tissue could result in a longer half-life for the hormone in the circulation. It is also possible that the uremic state, with decreased ionized serum calcium, may be associated with the increased secretion of glucagon. Additionally other insulin antagonists, for example, cortisol and catecholamines, may also be elevated in advanced renal failure.

Triglyceride Metabolism

Metabolism of fat is also affected in the uremic syndrome. Patients usually exhibit hypertriglyceridemia but normal serum cholesterol concentrations. Peripheral insulin resistance is thought to be a contributing factor to the hypertriglyceridemia, which underlies the propensity to premature atherosclerosis in uremia. Furthermore, patients with uremic hyperlipemia also demonstrate elevations of very low-density lipoproteins (VLDL) (prebeta or alpha 2): taken together these are the findings in type 4 hyperlipemia (see Chapter 31). The liver and intestine are the two major sites of synthesis of triglyceride, which is packaged for the circulation as a component of the VLDL. The major site of removal is peripheral adipose tissue. Both increased rate of synthesis and decreased rate of removal are believed to contribute to hyperlipemia. Insulin resistance may augment the synthesis of triglyceride by liver, as lipolysis in adipose tissue augments plasma free fatty acids. In addition, there is evidence that plasma triglycerides are removed more slowly than normal in uremic patients. Adipose tissue lipoprotein lipase activity, an insulin-responsive enzyme, is decreased in uremia. Located in adipose tissue capillaries, it is responsible for removal of fatty acids from triglyceride; diminished activity is then another consequence of insulin resistance. Further evidence for abnormalities in the lipoprotein economy in uremia derives from the finding that both low-density lipoproteins (cholesterol rich) and high-density lipoproteins are decreased in patients with chronic uremia as well as in patients with the inherited defect lipoprotein lipase deficiency.

Protein Metabolism

Since absorption of nitrogenous foodstuffs from the gastrointestinal tract is so efficient, it falls to the kidney to excrete waste products of nitrogen metabolism. This is reflected by the fact that elevated BUN and serum creatinine characterize both acute and chronic renal failure. Although most urea is eliminated by the kidney, approximately a quarter of that produced by the liver re-enters the gastrointestinal tract, where it is hydrolyzed to ammonia by bacterial ureases. The ammonia thus produced diffuses passively into the portal blood in a process that appears to be related to HCO_3^- secretion into the gut. In patients with chronic uremia, there is a decrease in the extrarenal clearance of urea attributable to the action of bacterial ureases, probably as a result of changes in the nature of the colonic mucosa. It may be that one of these changes is decreased HCO_3^- secretion into the gut lumen. Thus, uremia is compounded by the occurrence of decreased extrarenal clearance of urea superimposed on the failing capacity of the nephron to excrete urea.

Several features of the uremic syndrome augment the difficulties with the protein economy. Among these is occult gastrointestinal bleeding, which can be responsible for a significant loss of protein. Digestion of the blood with reabsorption of nitrogen-containing constituents causes augmented urea production and also leads to depletion of hemoglobin and albumin. Gastrointestinal loss of albumin is compounded by albuminuria. Furthermore, both potassium deficiency and hypercalcemia promote degradation of nitrogen-containing body constituents. Underlying these influences is the relative carbohydrate intolerance discussed above. Impairment of normal carbohydrate utilization processes will in turn increase the rate of protein degradation to provide calories normally supplied by glucose.

Uremia and the Identity of Possible Toxins

Classification of various stages of renal insufficiency in Table 14–4 preceded a more detailed consideration of causes of the clinical findings that characterize uremia. These gastrointestinal, neurological, and cardiorespiratory manifestations are ameliorated by dialysis, even while protein continues to be ingested. Moreover, in experimental studies plasma from uremic patients interferes with a number of cell functions, but after dialysis it fails to interfere with these functions. Such findings are tantalizing suggestions to many investigators that "toxic metabolites" are responsible for the uremic syndrome and abnormalities of cell function.

Candidates for uremic toxins include metabolites of nitrogen metabolism, i.e., urea, creatinine, methylguanidine, guanidinosuccinic acid, phenols, and indoles, as well as certain larger molecules, the so-called middle molecules (M.W. 400 to 5000). As yet a cause and effect relationship between the manifestations of the uremic syndrome and any of these molecules remains to be demonstrated. The evidence must be characterized as suggestive at best.

As the logical extension of the trade-off hypothesis and its negative effects on certain organs Bricker has proposed that the abnormalities in uremia are manifestations of endocrine-induced dysfunction. The particular ion implicated is Na^+, whose homeostasis requires increased production of the putative "natriuretic hormone" to elicit the increased Na^+ excretion per surviving nephron. Here the trade off is postulated to be derangement in transmembrane Na^+ transport in other organs, with the global consequences noted above. By interfering with the function of the ubiquitous Na^+, K^+-ATPase, sodium (which would normally be extruded from within the cell) can accumulate, causing the transmembrane potential difference to decrease, with the result that some potassium will exit from the cell. This view of the uremic syndrome is both provocative and heuristic. Indeed the intracellular sodium content of muscle, red cells, and nervous tissue is increased in individuals with uremia. Nonetheless, the cause of the uremic syndrome must still be viewed as an enigma.

Reducing Substances in Urine

The substances included within this category are defined by the Fehling's or Benedict's reaction, which is dependent upon the oxidation of a ketose or aldose by divalent copper ions to produce the corresponding organic acid and cuprous (monovalent) ion. The majority of clinically important compounds that carry out this reaction are monosaccharides, although such compounds as sialic acid and homogentisic acid as well as cephalothin and ampicillin may give false positive reactions (Table 14–5). Primary among the clinically significant monosaccharides included in this group are glucose, galactose, and fructose. Lactose is the only common dietary disaccharide that gives a positive Benedict's reaction.

The presence of a reducing substance in the urine necessitates determining if the cause is an artifact or a clinical disorder. Since a positive Benedict's reaction is nonspecific, further investigation into the nature of the reducing substance is essential. We begin with glucose oxidase sticks, since these are specific for glucose. If that test is positive, it is necessary to quantitate the blood

Table 14–5 REDUCING SUBSTANCES

Glucosuria
  Diabetes mellitus
  Renal glycosuria
  Cystinosis
  Fanconi syndrome (see Defects of Renal Transport)
  Thyrotoxicosis
  Hyperadrenal states
  Pheochromocytoma
Galactosuria
  Galactosemia
  Severe liver damage
Fructosuria
  Hereditary fructose intolerance
  Essential fructosuria
  Severe liver damage
Lactosuria
  Lactose intolerance
  Severe liver damage
  Severe intestinal disease
Positive Benedict's Test Only
  Alcaptonuria (oxidation product of homogentisic acid)
  Essential pentosuria
  Pentosuria ingestion of fruit
  Sialic acid
  Cephalothin
  Ampicillin

sugar level at a time when the urine is positive for reducing substances. Unquestionably, the most common cause of glucose in the urine is diabetes mellitus, as a result of a simple overflow or "spillage" phenomenon. The amount of glucose in the glomerular filtrate exceeds the capacity of the tubule to reabsorb it, resulting in escape of some glucose into the urine. Glycosuria may also be the consequence of failure of the tubule to reabsorb glucose at its normal level. Examples of such disorders are renal glycosuria, glucose-galactose malabsorption, and the Fanconi syndrome. Most individuals with renal glycosuria appear to have a reduced threshold for glucose, so that with normal glomerular filtration the tubule is unable to reabsorb a fraction of it. These patients are generally asymptomatic, and there is no evidence that renal glycosuria leads to later development of diabetes mellitus. In glucose-galactose malabsorption, glycosuria appears to be due to a decreased number of glucose carriers. Because the same defect is present in the intestinal mucosa, it is a troublesome disorder resulting in severe dehydration, diarrhea, and intolerance to all usual dietary carbohydrates except fructose. Failure to thrive is a very prominent finding in this disorder. The cause of the glycosuria in the Fanconi syndrome is enigmatic at present but appears to be due to a metabolic defect in the tubule induced by a variety of different toxins. Metabolic acidosis, aminoaciduria, and failure to thrive are prominent associated findings in the Fanconi syndrome. More complete discussion of these disorders can be found elsewhere in this text in Chapter 23, Transport Disorders.

Further identification of reducing substances that fail to react with glucose oxidase can be carried out in a variety of ways. A dip stick will detect galactose by galactose oxidase reaction. The finding of a positive urine Benedict's reaction with negative glucose oxidase and positive galactose oxidase should be considered presumptive evidence of the disorder known as galactosemia (see Chapter 26). There are two primary forms of galactosemia known as the galactose-1-phosphate transferase deficiency and the galactokinase deficiency. Transferase deficiency, which represents classic galactosemia, is associated with failure to thrive, vomiting, milk intolerance, hepatomegaly, jaundice, cataracts, and mental retardation. Galactokinase deficiency, on the other hand, appears to be a much milder form of the disorder. Definitive diagnosis of transferase deficiency galactosemia requires assay of red cell enzymes.

The presence of a Clinitest-positive substance that is neither glucose nor galactose leaves fructose as the next major possibility. In patients with hereditary fructose intolerance (fructose-1-phosphate aldolase deficiency), the clinical presentation should sensitize the clinician to the possibility of that disorder. This picture consists of vomiting, failure to thrive, severe hypoglycemia, the Fanconi syndrome without rickets, and an aversion to all sweets. When fructose is detected in the urine of a completely asymptomatic patient, essential fructosuria (fructokinase deficiency) is likely. Fructose-diphosphatase deficiency, a disorder of gluconeogenesis, is characterized by lactic acidemia, not fructosuria.

Clinical disorders associated with the presence of lactose in the urine are generally also associated with prominent gastrointestinal symptoms. If the reducing substance has not been identified after employing the above tests, chromatography is in order. It is likely that the carbohydrate is lactose and that will require medical attention. In essential pentosuria, the reducing test is also positive, but this is a biochemical curiosity unassociated with symptoms.

Mellituria, like all other laboratory findings, is to be interpreted in light of the picture the patient presents. Since the liver is the major site of carbohydrate metabolism, there are many primary liver disorders that will result in the appearance of some or all of the reducing sugars in the urine by the same mechanism that glucose appears in the urine in diabetes mellitus. In the case of a patient with "galactosemia," this may significantly complicate the diagnosis, since it may be difficult to distinguish galactosemia with liver disease from liver disease from other causes associated with galactosuria. Since specific enzyme assays on erythrocytes are available for all of these disorders, diagnosis should be a straightforward matter, unless the patient has been transfused recently.

Abnormal Coloration (Table 14–6)

The major determinant of urinary color is the degree of concentration. Normally, urine color varies from pale yellow to amber, but the neonate's urine may be colorless. The chief pigment found in urine is urochrome, but there are also small quantities of urobilin and hematoporphyrin. Any circumstance, such as fever, that leads to increased urinary concentration will also darken urine color.

Table 14–6 ABNORMAL COLORATION OF URINE

Orange
  Bile pigments
  Certain drugs: rhubarb and senna
Red
  Blood pigments
  Porphyrin
  Uro-erythrin
  Pyridinium
  Beetroot
  Blackberries
  Phenolphthalein
  Certain aniline dyes in seeds
  Urates (pinkish or reddish)
Dark Brown or Black
  Methemoglobin (large amounts)
  Phenolic drugs (phenol, cresol)
  Phenylhydrazine
  Oxidation products of homogentisic acid
  β-HPPA in tyrosinemia
Green or Blue
  Biliverdin
  Methylene blue
  Indigocarmine
  Indigo-blue
  Carbolic acid or flavine derivatives

Of course, urinary constituents can affect the color of the urine. Liver disease, in which the bile pigments are excreted in the urine in excessive quantities, may color the urine green, brown, or deep yellow, depending upon the predominant species of bile pigment. Whole blood, hemoglobin, or myoglobin may confer upon the urine a smoky to deep red color. Methemoglobin, the oxidation product of hemoglobin, which will increase in the hemoglobinuric patient after allowing the urine to stand, will turn the urine dark brown. The same is true of homogentisic acid, which may result in dark brown to black urine. A knowledge of the drugs being administered to a patient is an important aspect in evaluation of the urinary color, since many drugs may color the urine. As an example, methylene blue will make the urine green, while cascara and other cathartics may give it a brown color.

In general, the urine is transparent, although alterations in urinary pH will affect solubility of any one of a number of less soluble materials in the urine. Characteristically, strongly acid urine will cause precipitation of uric acid salts, resulting in a pink coloration of the urine. Increased turbidity of the urine may be an important clue to either renal acidification defects or renal transport disorders.

Proteinuria

Urinary excretion of protein normally does not exceed 150 mg per day. About two thirds of this urinary protein originates from plasma, of which approximately 10 per cent is albumin. A large number of other plasma protein components have been identified in the urine, some occurring intact while others are fragments. The majority of nonplasma protein excreted in urine is accounted for as Tamm-Horsfall mucoprotein, which is secreted by the renal tubular epithelial cell.

It is generally accepted that urinary protein normally arises as a result of filtration across the glomerular barrier. Thereafter, as with other substances that gain entrance to the urine at the glomerulus, the ultimate amount excreted will depend upon the amount filtered and the amount reabsorbed in the tubule. The filtration process occurring at the glomerular level is a result of complex interactions involving protein size and shape, driving force for filtration, and pore size and functional integrity of the glomerular barrier. The last is determined to a large extent by the polyanionic components of the endothelium, which represent a electrostatic barrier. Tubular protein reabsorption is a result of energy-dependent selective endocytosis.

There are four fairly well-defined varieties of proteinuria. (1) Overflow proteinuria resembles the spillage type of renal tubular aminoaciduria examined earlier in this chapter. Here there is an abnormal quantity in plasma of low molecular weight plasma proteins, e.g., Bence-Jones protein, which are filtered through the glomerular barrier relatively easily and saturate tubular reabsorptive processes. (2) Proteinuria of tubular origin, characterized by an absence of high molecular weight plasma proteins in the urine, occurs in the presence of normal quantities and types of proteins in the plasma and the glomerular ultrafiltrate. The absence of high molecular weight proteins is due to the fact that they are simply not filtered through the glomerulus, which in this condition remains intact. (3) Specific inflammatory disease may result in the secretion of protein into the urinary tract. This is known as secretory proteinuria and is relatively uncommon. (4) Finally, the most frequent cause of proteinuria is glomerular proteinuria. This is the result of excessive filtration of plasma protein at the glomerular level and is almost always associated with large molecular weight proteinuria, the bulk of which is albumin.

Nephrolithiasis

Despite the recognition throughout antiquity of renal stone disease, the propensity of certain individuals to form stones is poorly understood. Urine is an exceedingly complex fluid containing inorganic ions, organic waste products, proteins, and glycosaminoglycans, among other elements, so that many factors are involved in arriving at an approximation of solubility in this complex fluid. Such considerations are complicated further by fluctuations in osmolarity, solvent capacity, pH, and ionic strength. These multiple factors and their complex inter-relationships are responsible for the lack of a one to one correspondence between the chemical composition of renal stones and an excess of constituents in the urine. Regardless of how the crystal nidus forms, it acts as a matrix upon which further crystal growth and aggregation may occur, resulting in formation of a clinically significant stone.

Factors that have been implicated in stone formation include increased excretion of certain ions and small molecules (calcium, urate, oxalate, cystine, xanthine); changes in the pH, ionic strength, and composition of urine, especially with respect to inhibitors of stone formation (pyrophosphate, magnesium, citrate, GAGs, urea, peptides); and anatomical defects that predispose to stasis.

Cystinuria

Cystine was recognized as a cause of one form of urinary stone at the turn of the 19th century. As the most insoluble amino acid, its presence in excess in the urine presents a clear and present danger with respect to precipitation. Since the maximum solubility of cystine at a urine pH of 4.5 to 7 is 300 mg per liter, the adult homozygote excretes from 600 to 1600 mg per day; eventually precipitation of cystine must occur. Cystine crystals present in urine from an affected homozygous infant probably serve as the nidus for later crystal deposition and renal stone formation. Further discussion of cystinuria can be found in Chapter 23.

The Primary Hyperoxalurias

Although approximately two thirds of the total number of renal stones formed are due to deposition of calcium oxalate, only a very small number of patients with calcium oxalate stones form them as a result of an inborn error of oxalate metabolism. In fact, the most common cause of hyperoxaluria is greatly increased absorption of oxalate from the gut. This occurs in a variety of disorders of the gut (e.g., granulomatous disease, blind loop, pancreatitis) in which it appears that oxalate and fatty acids in the bowel lumen vie for available calcium. In this competition the fatty acids prevail, leaving excess uncomplexed oxalate, which then diffuses across the gut mucosa. The two rare inherited disorders termed primary hyperoxaluria are characterized by excretion of large amounts of oxalate on a prerenal basis, nephrolithiasis, and nephrocalcinosis, with early onset of renal failure.

Oxalic acid is a relatively strong dicarboxylic acid, soluble to the extent of 8.7 g per 100 g of water at 20°C. At neutral or alkaline pH the calcium salt of oxalate is rather insoluble (0.67 mg per 100 g of water pH 7 at 13°C). The precipitation of calcium oxalate is inhibited by a number of compounds normally present in urine, including urea and various ions such as magnesium, citrate, sulfate, and lactate. In patients with primary hyperoxaluria, urinary oxalate excretion averages approximately 240 mg per 24 hours and in some patients exceeds 400 mg per 24 hours. Under such circumstances, despite the presence of inhibitors in urine, nidus formation can commence. In addition to the intrarenal and urinary tract stone formation in these disorders, there is a generalized deposition of calcium oxalate salts throughout the tissues in the body.

It is important to recognize that since the vast majority of patients with renal stones do not suffer from an inborn error, hyperoxaluria may be missed unless the physician's index of suspicion is rather high. Complicating matters still further, primary hyperoxaluria can only be diagnosed by chemical measurement of urinary oxalate excretion. As a rule of thumb, any patient in the pediatric age group with nephrolithiasis and impaired renal function should be given the benefit of such investigation.

Inborn Errors of Uric Acid Metabolism

Uric acid is the end-product of purine metabolism in man, and excluding dietary intake, its excretion reflects the balance between purine ribonucleotide formation and degradation. Except in situations such as leukemia in which large amounts of nucleoprotein are being degraded, the rate of purine ribonucleotide synthesis de novo is the most important factor in determining the size of the uric acid pool. This in turn is regulated by the availability of phosphoribosylpyrophosphate (PRPP), which is a substrate both in the first specific reaction in the de novo pathway of purine ribonucleotide synthesis as well as in the purine salvage reactions.

Complete deficiency of hypoxanthine phosphoribosyl transferase (HPRT) is known as the Lesch-Nyhan syndrome, a sex-linked disorder causing severe hyperuricemia (Chapter 36). With the persistent degree of hyperuricemia present, nephrolithiasis is inevitable. Indeed, despite the terrible severity of the behavioral manifestations of the Lesch-Nyhan syndrome, the mortality in this disease occurs as a result of the injury to the kidney by nephrolithiasis.

Glucose-6-phosphatase deficiency (type 1 glycogen storage disease) is associated with increased purine biosynthesis de novo as well as with uric acid retention produced by the lactic acidosis that occurs in this disorder of gluconeogenesis. At the tubular brush border level there is a competitive inhibition of uric acid excretion by the lactate. In this disorder, the hyperuricemic complications do not usually occur until adolescence or early adult life. Possible causes of the enhanced purine synthesis are discussed under glycogen storage diseases.

2, 8-Dihydroxy Adeninuria

2,8-Dihydroxyl adenine is formed by hepatic xanthine oxidase, which catalyzes the oxidation of adenine. The generation of excess adenine, which leads to the formation of the 2,8-dihydroxyadenine, is the result of a complete deficiency of adenine phosphoribosyl transferase (APRT). This enzyme is the second enzyme in the purine salvage pathway specific for adenine. 2,8-Dihydroxyadenine is far less soluble in urine than uric acid, their solubilities being 1 μg per ml and 150 μg per ml, respectively, at pH 5.0.

Xanthinuria

This disorder is a result of congenital xanthine oxidase deficiency. Stone formation as a result of excess xanthinuria is not frequent in such patients, occurring only in about one third of all reported cases. Indeed, they are usually picked up because of hypouricemia (Table 36–2) on a routine screening profile, which leads to further investigation.

The Orotic Acidurias

Urinary tract obstruction occurs in these two inborn errors of metabolism, primarily as a result of masses of orotic acid crystals rather than stone formation. Orotic acid is an intermediate in the synthesis of pyrimidines. Hence, patients presenting with crystalluria as well as symptoms and signs of urinary tract obstruction should be given the benefit of orotic acid measurements of urine. For absolute confirmation, activities of orotate phosphoribosyl transferase and orotate monophosphate decarboxylase in erythrocytes, leukocytes, or cultured skin fibroblasts are available in some institutions. Onset of clinical manifestations is relatively early, occurring at 3 to 6 months of age with failure to thrive and megaloblastic anemia; development is stunted, the hair is sparse, nail growth is poor, and the spleen is enlarged. Oral replacement therapy with uridine will essentially correct all abnormalities save for the retarded mental development, the recoverability of which is unclear.

REFERENCES

Bergström, J., Furst, P., and Zimmerman, L.: Uremic middle molecules exist and are biologically active. Clin. Nephrol. 11:229, 1979.
Brenner, B.M., and Rector, F.C. (eds.): The Kidney. Vol. II, W. B. Saunders Co., Philadelphia, 1981.
Brenner, B.M., Hostetter, T.H., and Humes, H.D.: Molecular basis of proteinuria of glomerular origin. N. Engl. J. Med. 298:826, 1978.

Bricker, N.S., Fine, L.G., Kaplan, M., et al.: "Magnification phenomenon" in chronic renal disease. N. Engl. J. Med. 299:1287, 1978.

Coe, F.L.: Nephrolithiasis. In Brenner, B.M., and Stein, J.H. (eds.): Contemporary Issues in Nephrology. Vol. 5. Churchill Livingstone, New York, 1980.

Cohn, R.M., Yudkoff, M., and McNamara, P.D.: Servomechanisms and oscillatory phenomena. In Herman, R.H., Cohn, R.M., and McNamara, P.D. (eds.): Principles of Metabolic Control in Mammalian Systems. Plenum Press, New York, 1980, p. 295.

DeFronzo, R.A.: Pathogenesis of glucose intolerance in uremia. Metabolism 27:1866, 1978.

Dennis, V.W., Stead, W.W., and Myers, J.L.: Renal handling of phosphate and calcium. Ann. Rev. Physiol. 41:257, 1979.

Epstein, F.H.: Metabolic requirements for renal function. Hospital Pract. June, 1979, p. 93.

Hollenberg, N.K.: Set point for sodium homeostasis: Surfeit, deficit, and their implications. Kidney Int. 17:423, 1980.

Klein, K.L., and Kurokawa, K.: Metabolic and endocrine alterations in end-stage renal failure. Postgrad. Med. 64:99, 1978.

Knochel, J.P.: Pathogenesis of the uremic syndrome. Postgrad. Med. 64:88, 1978.

Kopple, J.D., Jones, M., Fukuda, S., and Swendseid, M.E.: Amino acid and protein metabolism in renal failure. Am. J. Clin. Nutr. 31:1532, 1978.

Mitch, W.E., and Wilcox, C.S.: Disorders of body fluids, sodium, and potassium in chronic renal failure. Am. J. Med. 72:536, 1982.

Nortman, D.F., and Coburn, J.W.: Renal osteodystrophy in end-stage renal failure. Postgrad. Med. 64:123, 1978.

Robinson, R.R.: Isolated proteinuria in asymptomatic patients. Kidney Int. 18:395, 1980.

Ryall, R.L., Harnett, R.M., and Marshall, V.R.: The effect of urine, pyrophosphate, citrate, magnesium and glycosaminoglycans on the growth and aggregation of calcium oxalate crystals in vitro. Clin. Chim. Acta 112:349, 1981.

Ryan, G.B.: The glomerular sieve and the mechanisms of proteinuria. Aust. N. Z. J. Med. 11:197, 1981.

Silverman, M.: Glucose reabsorption in the kidney. Can. J. Physiol. Pharmacol. 59:209, 1981.

Slatopolsky, E., Martin, K., and Hurska, K.: Parathyroid hormone metabolism and its potential as a uremic toxin. Am. J. Physiol. 239:F1, 1980.

Stoff, J.S., Epstein, F.H., Narins, R., and Relman, A.S.: Recent advance in renal tubular biochemistry. Am. Rev. Physiol. 38:46, 1976.

Suki, W.N., and Rouse, D.: Mechanisms of calcium transport. Mineral Electrolyte Metab. 5:175, 1981.

Symposium on Advances in Nephology. Aust. N. Z. J. Med. Vol. 11, Suppl. 1, 1981, pp. 1–111.

Symposium on Renal Metabolism. Med. Clin. North Am. 59:505–799, 1975.

Thomas, G.H., and Howell, R.R.: Selected Screening Tests for Genetic Metabolic Diseases. Year Book Medical Publishers, Chicago, 1973, p. 43.

Ullrich, K.L.: Sugar, amino acids, and Na^+ cotransport in the proximal tubule. Ann. Rev. Physiol. 41:181, 1979.

Walser, M.: Determinants of ureagenesis, with particular reference to renal failure. Kidney Int. 17:709, 1980.

Wright, F.S., and Briggs, J.P.: Feedback control of glomerular blood flow, pressure and filtration rate. Physiol. Rev. 59:958, 1979.

15

Liver

Situated between the portal circulation on the one hand and the systemic circulation on the other, the liver is in the optimal location to carry out its pivotal metabolic functions. Excepting material transported via the mesenteric lymphatics to the thoracic duct, all ingested materials must pass through the liver before being distributed to the rest of the body. The liver serves both as a warehouse for metabolic substrates as well as a factory for conversion of one metabolic substrate to another. It also carries out detoxification of various exogenous toxins and foreign substances (including drugs) in preparation for excretion either in the bile or via the kidney. While relatively few distinctive cell types compose the liver, its multiple functions are reflected by a complex architecture of cellular arrangements. Figure 15–1 illustrates the relationships of hepatocytes to other structures in the liver. Note particularly the relationships of the bile duct, hepatic artery, portal vein, and central vein. Bile secreted by the hepatocytes flows toward the periphery into the bile ductule; blood from the hepatic artery and portal vein ramifications flow in the opposite direction toward the central vein. In a sense then, the liver acts as a filtration system as it processes the blood before the filtrate enters the central vein. As with all organs, the integrity of the relationship between the individual cells and their blood supply is key to function. With the liver the relationship of the hepatocytes to the liver's vascular supply varies throughout gestational life and is radically altered at the time of birth. Umbilical vessels, which in fetal life supplied the liver with oxygenated blood from the maternal circulation, are obliterated, and less well oxygenated portal venous blood then supplies the liver. Corresponding alterations in metabolism may partly account for the frequent observation of liver dysfunction in the first 1 to 2 weeks of postnatal life.

The neonate's liver assumes functions that include maintenance of glucose homeostasis, particularly in the face of the prodigious requirements of the brain for this substrate, bilirubin conjugation and excretion, and elaboration and secretion of the bile components. Detoxification of drugs and development of the reticuloendothelial elements of the liver to protect against absorption of endotoxins, microorganisms, and proteolytic enzymes through the gut must also now be accomplished by the liver.

Another consequence of postnatal life is a slow change in the pressure-flow relationships through the liver as a result of the alterations in cardiac structure. Within the first few months of postnatal life, right-sided cardiac pressures remain relatively high, partially accounting for the fact that in normal infants the liver is usually palpable 2 to 3 cm below the right costal margin at the midclavicular line.

CARBOHYDRATE METABOLISM

The ability to mobilize carbohydrate stores has been demonstrated in human fetal liver in response to hypoxia. Evaluation of glycogenolytic enzyme levels in fetal livers showed that while many of these enzymes were present in lower levels than in adult liver, the amyloglucosidase responsible for hydrolysis of glycosyl-1,6–linked residues in glycogen to yield glucose approximated levels found in adult liver. It appears, therefore, that the capacity for fetal glucose mobilization from glycogen is potentially rather high. Other studies have demonstrated glucose-6-phosphate dehydrogenase, the first enzyme of the hexosemonophosphate shunt, to be present at adult levels of activity by 24 weeks of gestation. Two roles are probably served by the latter precocious enzyme activity: the first is the synthesis of lipids for brain and membranes derived from the NADPH

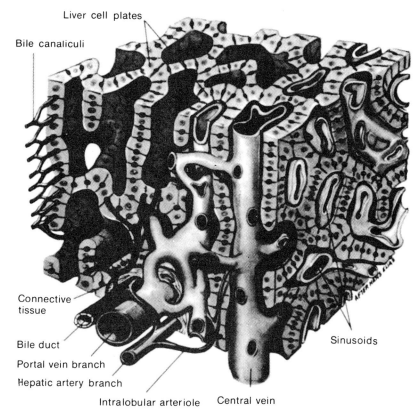

Liver cell plates

Bile canaliculi

Connective tissue

Bile duct

Portal vein branch

Hepatic artery branch

Intralobular arteriole   Central vein

Sinusoids

Figure 15–1   Hepatic lobular architecture. Arterial blood (for oxygenation) and intestinal venous blood (for metabolic processing) are carried to the liver by the hepatic artery and the portal vein, respectively. After passing over the plates of hepatic parenchymal cells, this blood arrives at the central vein and flows into the caval vessels. Bile, produced by the hepatocytes, flows from the bile canaliculi to the cholangiole and then into the bile ducts of the portal canal. Thus, blood flow is in a direction opposite to that of the bile. (From Routh, J.I.: Liver Function. *In* Tietz, N.W.: Fundamentals of Clinical Chemistry. 2nd ed. Philadelphia, W.B. Saunders Co., 1976.)

production from this pathway; the second is provision of ribose units needed for DNA and RNA synthesis.

BILIRUBIN METABOLISM

Kernicterus, a disorder that threatens the integrity of the central nervous system and surely the very survival of the neonate, emphasizes the essential role played by the neonatal liver in conjugation and excretion of bilirubin. The fetal liver does not carry out this process. Indeed, it appears that the placenta is able to clear only unconjugated bilirubin, which is then metabolized by the maternal liver and excreted. Since there is a tremendous positive balance of net bilirubin synthesis in the early neonate and young infant, a drastic augmentation in hepatic mechanisms for handling of bilirubin must occur soon after birth. Measurements of fetal glucuronyl transferase levels in liver indicate that in utero the infant is not capable of high degrees of bilirubin conjugation; furthermore, increased levels of beta-glucuronidase in fetal intestine suggest that the fetus is capable of hydrolyzing any conjugated bilirubin formed, thus permitting rapid clearance by the placenta. The ability of the normal neonate to deal with hyperbilirubinemia within the first 3 to 4 days of life testifies to the rapidity with which the liver achieves the capacity to metabolize bilirubin after birth. Hyperbilirubinemic states are discussed further in Chapter 24.

DRUG METABOLISM

As with bilirubin transport across the placenta, lipid-soluble materials cross this barrier more rapidly than do water-soluble conjugates. It seems reasonable to assume that the immaturity of drug oxidative and conjugating mechanisms that characterizes the fetal liver represents a biological protective mechanism, since conversion of lipid-soluble drugs to hydroxylated derivatives might represent a serious risk to normal fetal development. (Several recent reviews of neonatal pharmacology are noted in the references to this chapter.)

In a broad view of liver function, the development of hepatic metabolic processes promotes survival of the fetus, with specific systems developing in response to environmental exposure through maternal circulation or through intestinal absorption by the neonate. While much remains to be learned about these processes, it is probably fair to say that disruption in the timing of these processes by exposure to undue amounts of an exogenous or endogenous toxin may have serious consequences for the newborn infant. It is clinically useful to examine these consequences and the responsible mechanisms at a cellular level.

HEPATIC DYSFUNCTION

During the first two years of life the liver is easily palpable 2 to 3 cm below the right costal margin at the midclavicular line. Extension greater than 3 cm below the right costal margin with a span of greater than 7 to 8 cm can be considered abnormal. Jaundice, in association with hepatomegaly, is the most common presenting manifestation of liver dysfunction in childhood. Since most metabolic liver disease does not present with jaundice, but rather with either hepatomegaly or hepatosplenomegaly, we will consider only the pathophysiological mechanisms involved in liver enlargement here. (Chapter 24 discusses disorders of bilirubin metabolism.)

Somewhat simplistically the liver may be viewed as a tough, distensible bag full of a limited variety of cell types. Hence, enlargement may be viewed as the result of excess fluid, fatty infiltration, accumulation of glycogen or complex lipid, an increase in the number or size of one or more cell types, or a combination of the foregoing. Since intracellular storage of a variety of compounds and/or an increase in the number of cells present requires a relatively long time, rapid increases in liver size are likely to be attributable to accumulation of fluid within the distensible sinusoidal and vascular spaces. Even in cases in which cellular material accumulates rapidly, as with a hepatic tumor, rapid enlargement of the liver is usually attributable to accumulation of fluid, e.g., bleeding as a result of tumor invasion of a vessel. (It is worthwhile to note parenthetically that most tumors of the liver in infancy and childhood are metastatic rather than primary.)

The in utero characteristics of the cardiovascular system that contribute to maintenance of high right-sided pressures render the neonatal liver an accurate mirror of the right-sided cardiac status. Hence, congestive heart failure of even mild degree may cause a significant increase in liver size, particularly because of the relative distensibility of the neonatal liver capsule. While right-sided heart failure is rather rare in the infant, right-sided pressures are subject to wide variations as a result of events occurring on the systemic side of the circulation. Sudden hepatic enlargement may also be seen rarely in obstruction of the hepatic vein secondary to thrombosis or tumor (Budd-Chiari syndrome). Therefore, any child or infant presenting with a sudden or rapid enlargement of the liver should have a chest X-ray to evaluate cardiac size and shape. Furthermore, any infant with any degree of dysmorphia and hepatic enlargement should first be suspected of having congenital heart disease rather than a storage disease.

Increased Intracellular Material

The diseases that fall into this heterogenous group are known as "storage" diseases, embracing disorders of glycogen, lipid, and mucopolysaccharide metabolism. In general, storage is the result of defective or absent activity of a specific lysosomal hydrolase or catabolic enzyme, which results in an inability to carry out the sequential "piece by piece" degradation of compounds into smaller components. The glycogen storage diseases cannot be sheltered under the umbrella of the foregoing generalization, as we shall see below. Disorders with liver enlargement manifesting hypoglycemia are generally those of either carbohydrate or amino acid metabolism, while those presenting with unusual structural features or central nervous system dysfunction are likely to be disorders of lipid or lipoprotein metabolism.

Glycogen Storage Diseases

Among the carbohydrate disorders in which there is a common association between hepatomegaly and hypoglycemia is type I (glucose-6-phosphatase deficiency) glycogen storage disease. Serving as the fulcrum of glycogenolysis and gluconeogenesis, glucose-6-phosphatase releases free glucose from glucose-6-phosphate derived from glycogen and from gluconeogenesis, thereby maintaining the blood sugar during fasting. In addition to the massive hepatomegaly, the patient manifests lactic acidemia in association with hypoglycemic episodes. Ketosis is conspicuously absent, although transient ketonuria may be seen. In addition, there is also a frequent hyperuricemia observed. Development of lactic acidosis in glycogen storage disease is unique to type I, since glucose-6-phosphate produced from glycogen breakdown cannot be dephosphorylated, preventing its release from the cell. As a result, glucose-6-phosphate can only be metabolized to lactate, which then escapes into the blood.

Type II glycogen storage disease (acid maltase deficiency or Pompe's disease) should be mentioned to note that the enzymatic defect does not result in storage of glycogen within the liver. Rather, when hepatic enlargement occurs, it is a consequence of the severe and persistent cardiac failure characteristic of this lysosomal disorder (see Chapter 28). Indeed, liver function in this disorder is remarkably well preserved.

Type III glycogen storage disease (amylo-1,6-glucosidase deficiency, debrancher) is another form of carbohydrate disorder that presents with massive hepatomegaly and hypoglycemic episodes, often associated with convulsions. The debrancher enzyme mediates the transformation of the glycogen molecule from a complex, branched molecule to a straight glucose monomer chain. Therefore, in an affected patient in response to lowering of the blood sugar, the glycogen can be broken down only to the branching point. In consequence, the liver cell retains a considerable amount of glycogen in a partially degraded form. Since some degradation of glycogen can occur, the normal levels of glucose-6-phosphatase allow release of glucose into the blood, producing an attenuated response to fasting in comparison to that seen in type I disease. While ketosis is a feature of this disorder, lactic acidemia is not, since free glucose can be released from the hepatocyte.

Type VI disease is typified by prominent hepatomegaly but has minimal if any symptoms of hypoglycemia. Liver phosphorylase, the enzyme responsible for cleavage of α-1,4 linkages to yield glucose-1-phosphate is defective in this disorder. As discussed more fully in Chapter 28, phosphorylase is one of a number of regulatory enzymes that exists in active and inactive forms, being interconvertible by covalent modification. The pathophysiology in this disorder is the same as in type III glycogenesis, the defect being partial in relation to glycogen breakdown.

One patient with so-called type IX glycogen storage disease has been reported, the patient being shown to have a deficiency of phosphorylase kinase, which phosphorylates liver phosphorylase, converting it to the fully active form. The clinical findings are virtually indistinguishable from those of patients with type VI glycogenosis. A more detailed consideration of the enzymology and regulation of the glycogen economy as well as the glycogen storage diseases can be found in Chapter 28.

Other Carbohydrate Disorders

Other inborn errors of carbohydrate metabolism that often result in enlarged livers are hereditary fructose intolerance (fructose-1-phosphate aldolase deficiency) and galactosemia (galactose-1-

phosphate uridyl transferase deficiency). Because the major dietary sugar in the newborn is lactose, a galactose-containing disaccharide, signs and symptoms of galactosemia are ordinarily seen earlier than those of hereditary fructose intolerance. At the age at which weaning has begun, with introduction of sucrose-containing foods, the signs and symptoms of hereditary fructose intolerance (HFI) may become evident. Hypoglycemia in galactosemic infants has been reported but is rare. On the other hand, hypoglycemia in HFI is common and is often one of the clinical hallmarks of this disorder. The biochemical mechanism for this frequent hypoglycemia in HFI is not entirely clear, although inhibition of glycogenolysis by elevated intracellular fructose-1-phosphate has been incriminated. Enlargement of the liver in both of these diseases appears to be due to fatty degeneration as a result of a reaction of liver tissue to the presence of excess amounts of toxic intermediates in each of the two pathways. Untreated, cirrhosis may supervene.

Amino Acid Disorders

Of the numerous aminoacidopathies, only a few manifest hepatomegaly. These include cystinosis (in which hepatomegaly is a late manifestation) and familial protein intolerance with dibasic aminoaciduria. The cause of the enlarged liver in late cystinosis is not clear but may involve the severe metabolic derangements occurring in the end-stage renal disease seen in such patients. Familial protein intolerance with dibasic aminoaciduria (lysinuric protein intolerance) is an autosomal recessive defect of diamino acid transport manifest in both kidney and intestine and characterized by renal hyperdiaminoaciduria and hyperammonemia following protein ingestion. Failure to thrive, with diarrhea and vomiting, engendered by protein intake characterizes the disorder in infancy. In older infants and children, there is an aversion to protein-rich foods with severe growth retardation, hepatomegaly, hyperammonemia, and deficient urea production. Although the cause of the liver enlargement is not clear, the hyperammonemia appears to be related to a depletion of total body pools of lysine, ornithine, and arginine, which restrict the availability of substrates for the urea cycle. Since normal operation of the urea cycle involves interconversion of ornithine and arginine, a deficiency of both as a result of the severe intestinal and renal malabsorption of the dibasic amino acids would be expected to cause significant impairment of this reaction sequence. Following this line of reasoning, some patients have been treated with either oral arginine or ornithine. As hoped, urea production was normalized following a normal dietary protein load. Recently it has been proposed that hepatic transport of dibasic amino acids is deranged as well in this disorder. If correct, the hepatomegaly may be related (in a manner yet to be defined) to the deficiency in the hepatocyte of lysine, an essential amino acid. Tyrosinemia is another aminoacidopathy in which hepatomegaly, with drastically impaired liver function, is characteristic. Progression to cirrhosis appears relentless.

Wilson's Disease

Hepatic enlargement in Wilson's disease occurs as a consequence of storage of copper within the hepatocyte. This has been attributed to the presence of an abnormal copper-binding protein. Normally copper enters the hepatocyte to be distributed throughout the cytosol and subcellular organelles, where the metal is stored, incorporated into copper metallo-enzymes, or excreted. The metal-binding protein metallothionein present in the hepatocyte is thought to be a temporary storage protein; in several patients with Wilson's disease it was shown to have a significantly increased affinity for copper. Whether this is generally true is not yet clear, but this increased binding affinity could shift the normal equilibrium of the hepatic copper pool, resulting in both depressed biliary copper excretion and decreased incorporation of copper into ceruloplasmin, the copper transport protein in blood. Eventually, with continuing accumulation and binding of the copper by the abnormal protein, the binding sites become saturated and the excess copper is ingested by the hepatic lysosomes. It should be noted that in untreated Wilson's disease, as in tyrosinemia, there is eventual progression of the liver disease to cirrhosis.

Lipidoses and Lipoprotein Disorders

As a class, the disorders of lipid and sphingolipid metabolism that cause liver enlargement typically announce themselves by means of retardation of development and delayed growth. Clinical description antedated assignment of specific enzyme deficiencies by many years, accounting for the the existence of several alternative names for many of these disorders. Here we will use the most recent diagnostic terms. Type I hyperlipoproteinemia is commonly associated with hepatomegaly; 75 per cent of the reported patients experience hepatomegaly, some developing liver enlargement as early as 8 months of age. Eruptive xanthomas and episodic abdominal pain are also characteristic of this disorder. As dietary fatty acids enter the intestinal mucosal cells, those with chain lengths of C_{12} or greater are reassembled into glycerides that coalesce into particles called chylomicrons, which incorporate a stabilizing layer of phospholipid, cholesterol, and protein into the final aggregate. The chylomicrons are transported in the lymphatic channels, filtered through lymph nodes, and eventually reach the plasma by way of the thoracic duct. In type I hyperlipoproteinemia, the normal process for the removal of chylomicrons from plasma appears to be defective; deficiency of plasma lipoprotein lipase activity accounts for the defect in type I hyperlipoproteinemia. This enzyme is normally active in clearing of triglycerides from blood by hydrolysis with subsequent release of free fatty acids. It is not known whether the chylomicrons in this disorder attach themselves to or are engulfed by reticuloendothelial cells. However, the Kupffer cells in the liver take up the chylomicrons, which are present in such tremendous excess and are transformed thereby into "foam cells."

Types IV and V familial hyperlipoproteinemias are less frequently associated with hepatomegaly (in the range of 20 to 35 per cent of reported patients). Neither of these two types of familial disease are usually diagnosible in the childhood period nor is hepatomegaly likely to supervene before adulthood. The mechanism for the enlargement of the liver in these disorders is unclear.

The sphingolipidoses (see Chapter 30) comprise a group of inherited disorders of lysosomal enzyme functions that are characterized by pathological accumulations of a specific class of membrane lipids in various organs and tissues of affected individuals. Several present with hepatomegaly, often in association with splenomegaly. Moreover, mental retardation is usually seen in association with the organomegaly. In GM_1 (generalized) gangliosidosis hepatomegaly is invariably present by 6 months of age but may be present at birth or soon thereafter. Analysis of the accumulated material isolated from tissues of affected patients reveal storage of a complex glycolipid accompanied by a good bit of mucopolysaccharide.

Activity of lysosomal beta-galactosidase in brain and liver possessing activity with ganglioside GM_1 and certain mucopolysaccharides with β-galactosyl groups as substrates is in the range of 3 to 6 per cent of normal. In the absence of this enzyme, storage of GM_1 ganglioside and of the mucopolysaccharide occurs in the lysosomes of affected tissue. Stored material is accumulated in the lysosomes of hepatocytes and Kupffer cells and/or histiocytes.

Gaucher's disease is probably the most frequently encountered lipid storage disease. Prominent clinical features are splenomegaly, hepatomegaly, erosion of the cortices of the long bones, anemia, and thrombocytopenia. The disease has been divided into three clinical categories (Chapter 30). In this disorder, there is deficiency of a catabolic enzyme required for the hydrolysis of the beta-glucosidic bond of glucocerebroside, a derivative of sphingosine. The type of Gaucher's disease with which a given patient suffers is correlated with both clinical severity and degree of enzyme deficiency; patients with the infantile form of the disease have enzyme activity ranging from 0 to 9 per cent of normal. The major precursors of glucocerebroside that accumulate in the histocytic cells of the reticuloendothelial system in patients with Gaucher's disease appear to be glycolipids of degraded red and white blood cells. The histocytes containing the nondegradable glucocerebroside, known as Gaucher cells, are dispersed throughout the reticuloendothelial system, particularly in the sinusoids of the liver and bone marrow. In contradistinction to the generalized gangliosidosis type storage, the hepatocytes themselves are not involved in the storage products. Therefore, enlargement of the liver results from increased storage within the recticuloendothelial cells alone, perhaps explaining the lesser enlargement in Gaucher's disease in comparison with generalized gangliosidosis.

The combination of cachexia, hepatosplenomegaly, and impaired mental development is always suggestive of the possibility of an inherited lipid storage disease, and these manifestations are especially prominent in the classic infantile form of Niemann-Pick disease. The predominant substance accumulating in tissues of patients with Niemann-Pick disease is sphingomyelin. Elevated serum and urinary levels of sphingomyelin have not been reported, consonant with the fact that this is a lysosomal storage disease. Normally, catabolism of sphingomyelin involves hydrolysis to yield phosphoryl choline and ceramide residues, a reaction catalyzed by the enzyme sphingomyelinase. The highest activity of this enzyme is found in liver tissue. Measurement of sphingomyelinase activity in liver obtained from patients with the classic infantile form of Niemann-Pick show reduction to approximately 7 per cent of that in age-matched control specimens. Sphingomyelin is found in the plasma membrane of all mammalian cells and in various subcellular organelles as well. Parenchymal liver cells as well as Kupffer cells are involved in storage of sphingomyelin, which in the former case may arise from turnover of the hepatocytic membrane itself. As a consequence of the defective catabolism of sphingomyelin, storage of the material increases with age, thus resulting in constantly enlarging viscera.

There are two other rare familial diseases associated with neutral lipid storage: Wolman's disease and cholesteryl ester storage disease. Hepatomegaly is a constant feature of Wolman's disease and has been reported as early as 4 days of age. The significant biochemical feature of Wolman's disease is the accumulation of both cholesteryl esters and triglycerides in various organs. Under neutral and alkaline conditions, homogenates of liver from cases of Wolman's disease have a normal capacity to hydrolyze triglycerides and cholesteryl esters. However, activity has been reported to be undetectable in homogenates of liver or spleen from cases of Wolman's disease when measured under optimum acid conditions (pH 4.4 in phosphate-citrate buffer). The evidence obtained by enzymatic analysis thus suggests that the accumulation of triglycerides and cholesteryl esters occurs in the tissues of these patients as the result of a deficiency of a lysosomal acid esterase that normally acts upon both types of lipids. Both hepatocytes and Kupffer cells are grossly enlarged and vacuolated, presumably because of an accumulation of neutral fat, which is dissolved in the process of fixation. Hepatic damage results in periportal and portal fibrosis, which may progress to cirrhosis.

Two other diseases presenting with hepatomegaly in association with mental retardation are fucosidosis and mannosidosis. The clinical features of both represent a combination of GM_1 gangliosidosis and Hurler's disease. In fucosidosis both hepatocytes and Kupffer cells are filled with unique lamellar structures in the cytoplasm, composed of a complex mixture of complicated polysaccharides, mucopolysaccharides, increased amounts of glycogen, a ceramide tetrasaccharide and a ceramide pentasaccharide (containing the major part of liver fucose), and large amounts of glycolipids. There is a complete absence of lysosomal α-fucosidase activity. Mannosidosis presents a very similar clinical picture, including hepatomegaly and mental retardation. In this disorder, the material stored in liver lysosomes is very rich in mannose. The disorder appears to be due to a deficiency of alpha-mannosidase.

Mucopolysaccharidoses

The mucopolysaccharides are a group of heterogeneous polysaccharide molecules that are components of intercellular ground substance. They are not, however, simple repeating monomer sugar units such as those found in glycogen. Common to all mucopolysaccharide molecules is the presence of an amino sugar, usually D-glucosamine or D-galactosamine. Still greater heterogeneity is conferred upon this group of molecules by the variable presence of either glucuronic or iduronic acids, as well as variable sulfated oxygen or nitrogen residues. The linkages of the uronic acid and hexosaminic acids vary from one type of molecule to another. Further complexity is conferred upon polysaccharide molecules by the nature of their linkage to protein, the form in which mucopolysaccharides are found in tissue.

Table 15–1 HEPATOMEGALY

Abetalipoproteinemia*
Ceroid lipofuscinosis
Cretinism
Diabetes mellitus*
Fructose diphosphatase deficiency*
Galactosemia*
Gaucher's disease*
Glycogen storage disease*
Hepatic cirrhosis
Hereditary fructose intolerance
Hyperlipoproteinemias (types I,V)*
Lactic acidosis*
Lysinuric protein intolerance
Methylmalonic aciduria*
Mucolipidoses
Mucopolysaccharidoses
Multiple sulfatase deficiency
Niemann-Pick disease*
Pipecolic acidemia
Porphyria
Sandhoff's disease*
Tyrosinemia*
Urea cycle defects
Wilson's disease
Wolman's disease*

*Fatty infiltration may account for all or part of the increase in size

Understandably, then, the mucopolysaccharidoses constitute a diffuse and heterogeneous group of diseases (see Chapter 32). In general, the disorders are those of lysosomal degradation processes, resulting in enlargement of the intracellular lysosomes. Hepatomegaly is a common but not invariable symptom in a number of the inherited disorders of mucopolysaccharide metabolism. Because of this variability and the tremendous diversity of the enzymes involved in degradation of mucopolysaccharides, any patient with physical findings attributable to defects in the ground substance, such as hyperelasticity, bony defects, or cardiac defects, probably deserves the benefit of a thorough evaluation for the possibility of a mucopolysaccharide disorder. Enzyme studies necessary for a thorough evaluation are usually available only in major medical centers.

Mental retardation is not an essential part of the diagnosis of mucopolysaccharide disorders, since there are at least three types of these disorders in which intelligence is normal. Furthermore, the presently available screening tests for mucopolysaccharide excretion in urine are not at all reliable. The physician who feels strongly that a patient may have such a disorder should request further investigation.

Various other causes of hepatomegaly due to impaired metabolism of physiological compounds are listed in Table 15–1.

Fatty Liver

Perhaps one of the most remarkable functions carried out by the liver is the assessment of the balance of nutrients arriving via the portal circulation from the gut. When imbalances are striking, the liver usually responds by storing excess substances until necessary material is available for construction of macromolecules for export. Hartoff (1973) has put forward such a point of view to rationalize the numerous situations that result in fatty infiltration of the liver. He has described the liver as the "nutritional guardian of the body." This rationale imputes to the liver an informational function that ensures that energy sources will be utilized when the cofactors and body needs warrant. In Chapter 2 we placed heavy emphasis on the integration and correlation of diverse pathways to orchestrate the metabolic economy. The liver occupies a pivotal position in this scheme, as it appraises the availability of raw material and produces new molecules from the building blocks it receives. Hormonal interactions round out this integrated system.

Accumulation of excess hepatic lipid may take one of four patterns: centrilobular, midzonal, periportal, or diffuse. Factors accounting for one pattern over another have not been fully clarified, but the concept of spatial and temporal organization of hepatocytes occupying different regions of the hepatic acinus (Gumucio and Miller, 1981) points the way toward clarification of this and other enigmas of liver function.

Absorption and Handling of Fat

As described in Chapter 31, exogenous triglycerides are hydrolyzed and resynthesized in the mucosal cell into chylomicrons, the form in which they are absorbed into the lymph. Hepatic lipoprotein lipases located on capillary endothelium remove fatty acids from the triglycerides, forming chylomicron remnants. These remnants are further catabolized within hepatocytes, releasing glycerol and free fatty acids. To this supply of fatty acids are added others deriving from adipose tissue lipolysis and synthesis, which are oxidized to provide ATP or to manufacture triglycerides, phospholipids, and cholesterol esters. The liver releases triglycerides into the blood as lipoproteins (very low-density lipoproteins [VLDL]).

Pathophysiology

Production of lipoproteins by the liver requires the integration of lipid synthesis and protein synthesis as well as the presence of the raw materials for these processes. It is evident that anything interfering with either process or their integration could lead to accumulation of fat within the liver. Hence, fatty liver can result if any of the following abnormalities acts alone or in concert to disrupt lipid metabolism and synthesis by the liver: impaired triglyceride clearance (VLDL secretion), increased hepatic lipogenesis, decreased fatty acid oxidation, and increased lipolysis in adipose tissue (augmentation of precursor pool).

Any perturbation that impairs or diminishes synthesis of the apolipoproteins will curtail lipoprotein elaboration. In consequence the other raw materials of VLDL (lipids) will accumulate in liver. Nutritional deficiency that limits amino acid supply for protein synthesis is the most common cause of such a situation (see Chapter 31).

Similarly, enhanced adipose tissue lipolysis, due to starvation or uncontrolled diabetes mellitus, can disturb the incorporation of lipid and protein precursors for lipoprotein elaboration, leading to engorgement of the liver with fat. Insulin as the main storage hormone has wide reaching effects on the fat economy; the result is diminution of lipolysis. Children who are malnourished usually suffer from deficiency of proteins, vitamins, and calories. Consequently, lipolysis is accelerated and lipoprotein clearance is impaired.

As we emphasized in the sections on ketogenesis and hypoglycemia, fat and carbohydrate metabolism are correlated and inter-related. Defects in glucose availability or its utilization (starvation, diabetes mellitus, glycogenoses, and so on) are associated with diminished insulin activity and enhanced lipolysis. For example, the augmented supply of free fatty acids arriving at the liver for esterification can overwhelm the capacity to incorporate triglycerides into lipoproteins. This disparity of delivery and construction leads to fatty infiltration. A similar disparity can occur when glucose in excess of energetic needs is diverted to lipogenesis.

Abnormalities in vitamin B_{12} and folate may also cause fatty liver. While the cause of steatosis in methylmalonic aciduria is not known, that emanating from folate deficiency appears to relate to impaired formation of choline, a lipotropic (fat-mobilizing) factor. Other vitamin deficiencies associated with steatosis include those of pantothenic acid, pyridoxine, and riboflavin. Pantothenic acid, a component of co-enzyme A, is required for acetylation of choline, as mentioned above. Pyridoxine is a structural component of glycogen phosphorylase, while the flavin coenzymes are involved in the electron transport system.

Table 15–2 CIRRHOSIS

Zone 1
  Blood supply near
  Metabolically most active cells—rich in oxidative enzymes, mitochondria
  Most resistant to destruction by pathological process

Zone 2
  Intermediate in proximity to blood supply and level of metabolic activity and susceptibility to injury

Zone 3
  Furthest from blood supply
  Most vulnerable to injury
  Least able to regenerate
  Rich in anaerobic enzymes—lactate dehydrogenase and enzymes of drug metabolism

Table 15–3 GENETIC CAUSES OF CIRRHOSIS

Galactosemia
Glycogen storage disease (amylopectinosis) [III, IV]
Tyrosinosis
Hereditary fructose intolerance
Alpha-antitrypsin deficiency
Wilson's disease
Iron overload (hemochromatosis)
Cystic fibrosis
Hereditary hemorrhagic telangiectasia
Abetalipoproteinemia
Thalassemia
Lipid storage disease
Mucopolysaccharidoses

Hepatotoxins that interfere with β-oxidation in mitochondria can cause fatty infiltration by decreasing the amount of lipid traversing that sequence of reactions. Exogenous toxins, e.g., hypoglycin A and amanitatoxin, and Reye's syndrome, which produce fatty liver, seem to do so by affecting mitochondrial function. Fatty liver is a frequent concomitant of sepsis, which is attended by hypoxia because of deranged respiratory and cardiac function. Hence, the common denominator leading to fatty infiltration would be hypoxia and interference with energy metabolism. Because of the nexus between carbohydrate, protein, and lipid metabolism, abnormalities in the handling of any one component of energy metabolism impinge upon the handling of the others.

Cirrhosis

It is not our intent, in this section, to review all the salient features of the pathogenesis and pathophysiology of cirrhosis, particularly since the monograph by Galambos (1979) does this so admirably. However, we do wish to present enough background to relate this complex process to its numerous metabolic causations. The key to the integrated function of the hepatic acinus (lobule) is the microcirculatory unit and the anatomical relationship of the acini to their blood supply, bile ductules, and lymphatics. It is useful to divide the lobule into three zones based upon the immediacy of the relationship of the hepatocytes to their nutrient blood supply. These are shown in Table 15–2.

After an insult to the hepatic parenchyma, cells in zone 3, which are least able to withstand injury, are likely to be replaced by cells from the other zones. As regeneration continues the crucial factor is whether or not fibroblast activation occurs, with its elaboration of mucopolysaccharides (glycosaminoglycans), glycoproteins, and collagen. By definition hepatic fibrosis means the increased synthesis of new connective tissue in an abnormal distribution. How this comes about is at present unknown.

Normally, hepatic collagen is attached to the cell surface, so that growth is organized within the context of the normal cell architecture. However, in the fibrotic process the collagen is formed without regard to cell architecture. It is therefore disorganized, and hence the normal anatomical relationships are severely disrupted.

The development of hepatic cirrhosis is related to the nature, extent, and chronicity of the insult to the hepatic parenchyma. The liver has an astonishing capacity for regeneration, illustrated by the fact that if two thirds of the rat liver is removed, the normal bulk of liver can be regenerated in a relatively short space of time. However, in this instance the injury to the organ is of an orderly nature rather than being a diffuse cellular-type injury. On the other hand, in a condition such as

Wilson's disease, in which the hepatic parenchymal cells are continually exposed to high intracellular, nonphysiological concentrations of a substance (i.e., copper), the injury is diffuse throughout the liver as well as chronic. Such chronic injury results in the disorderly regeneration of cirrhosis. The underlying factors that determine this distinctly hepatic response to an insult are as yet not well understood. Nevertheless, as a consequence of cirrhosis the hepatic lobule loses normal architecture and normal function as well. Pathologically the process is characterized by distortion of the hepatic landscape by nodules of fibrous connective tissue and regenerating parenchymal cells. Continued insult to diffuse areas of the liver result in the same process occurring throughout the organ. Eventually, deprivation of normal blood flow through the hepatic lobule will result in further cell death, with more extensive fibrosis and the eventual loss of regenerative ability. The inevitable result is an inability of the remaining hepatic parenchyma to cope with the tremendous metabolic demands placed upon the liver by the rest of the human organism. As the process becomes more and more extensive, there is a shrinking of the organ due to loss of cellular volume. In the initial stages of cell injury and regeneration, however, the early cirrhotic liver is enlarged. Several inherited metabolic disorders are known to result in the picture of hepatic cirrhosis (Table 15–3). These include tyrosinemia, Wilson's disease, galactosemia, hereditary fructose intolerance, and hemosiderosis. The biochemistry of these diseases is discussed more extensively in Part III.

REFERENCES

Andres, J.M., Mathis, R.K., and Walker, W.A.: Liver disease in infants. J. Pediatr. 90:686, 864, 1977.

Boyer, J.L.: New concepts of the mechanisms of hepatocyte bile formation. Physiol. Rev. 60:303, 1980.

Colon, A.R.: Hepatic steatosis in children. Am. J. Gastroenterol. 68:260, 1977.

Galambos, J.: Cirrhosis. Vol. XVII. In Smith, L.H., Jr. (ed.): Major Problems in Internal Medicine. W.B. Saunders Co., Philadelphia, 1979.

Gumucio, J.J., and Miller, D.L.: Functional implications of liver cell heterogeneity. Gastroenterology 80:393, 1981.

Hartroft, W.S.: The liver: Nutritional guardian of the body. In Gall, E., and Mostofi, F., (eds.): The Liver. Williams & Wilkins Co., Baltimore, 1973, p. 113.

Hoyumpa, A.M., Desmond, P.V., Avant, G.R., et al.: Hepatic encephalopathy. Gastroenterology 76:184, 1979.

Javitt, N.B.: Hyperbilirubinemic and cholestatic syndromes. Postgrad. Med. 65:120, 1979.

Jones, A.L., and Schmucker, D.L.: Current concepts of liver structure as related to function. Gastroenterology 73:833, 1977.

Lewan, L., Ynger, T., and Englebrecht, C.: The biochemistry of regenerating liver. Intl. J. Biochem. 8:477, 1977.

Lu, A.Y.H., and Miwa, G.T.: Molecular properties and biological functions of microsomal epoxide hydrase. Ann. Rev. Pharmacol. Toxicol. 20:513, 1980.

Mezey, E.: Liver disease and nutrition. Gastroenterology 74:770, 1978.

Misra, P.: Hepatic encephalopathy. Med. Clin. North Am. 65:209, 1981.

Roberts, R.K., Branch, R.A., and Desmond, P.V., et al.: The influence of liver disease on drug disposition. Clin. Gastroenterol. 8:105, 1979.

Rothschild, M.A., Oratz, M., and Schreiber, S.S.: Albumin synthesis. In Javitt, N.B. (ed.): Liver and Biliary Tract Physiology. Intl. Rev. Physiol. Vol. 21. University Park Press, Baltimore, 1980, p. 249.

Rojkind, M., and Kershenobich, D.: Hepatic fibrosis. Clin. Gastroent. 10:737, 1981.

Schiff, L.: Diseases of the Liver. 4th Ed. Lippincott, Philadelphia, 1975.

Sherlock, S.: Hepatic reactions to drugs. Gut 20:634, 1979.

Williams, R.L., and Benet, L.Z.: Drug pharmacokinetics in cardiac and hepatic disease. Ann. Rev. Pharmacol. Toxicol. 20:389, 1980.

Wright, R., Alberti, K., Karran, S., and Millward-Sadler, G. (eds.): Liver and Biliary Diseases. W.B. Saunders Co., Philadelphia, 1979.

Zakim, D., and Boyer, T. (eds.): Hepatology: A Textbook of Liver Diseases. W.B. Saunders Co., Philadelphia, 1979.

16

Disorders Affecting Muscle

Thousands of fibers course longitudinally for varying lengths to compose a single muscle (Fig. 16–1). These fibers consist of multinucleated cells whose length may run to 4 cm and whose diameter varies between 10 and 100 μm. Within the muscle cell cytoplasm (sarcoplasm), there are, in addition to organelles found in other cells, myofibrils. It is these fibrils that constitute the business end of muscle, and they are composed of the contractile proteins, actin and myosin, in association with two proteins that modulate their interaction, troponin and tropomyosin (Table 16–1).

NEUROMUSCULAR TRANSMISSION

The neuromuscular junction is the site of nervous input from the spinal cord or cranial nerve. Interference with information transfer, either anatomically or biochemically, at that point renders the muscle nonfunctional. Muscle cells share with nervous tissue the property of excitability, defined as a rapid change in transmembrane potential in response to adequate stimulation. This involves a rapid change of potential difference from -70 to -90 mv within the cell to $+25$ mv upon depolarization. The duration of this action potential is no more than a millisecond; the membrane becomes very much more permeable to potassium while sodium permeability diminishes drastically. Potassium efflux then brings about restoration of the normal transmembrane potential. When muscles are used in voluntary activity, nerve impulses arrive at the neuromuscular junction at rates approaching 50 per second. In response to each neural message the muscle develops an action potential, which engenders a contraction or twitch.

The neuromuscular junction or motor end-plate depends upon synaptic connections, as does the central nervous system, and hence there is a synaptic cleft at these junctions as well. Acetylcholine release from presynaptic vesicles is facilitated by calcium and inhibited by high concentra-

Table 16–1 MYOFIBRILLAR PROTEINS

Protein	M.W.	Physical and Chemical Characteristics	Localization	Function
Myosin	470,000	Shaped like golf clubs Shaft—light chain Head—heavy chain Composed of 6 polypeptides	Thick filament (A band)	Head is the crossbridge—contains myosin ATPase activity Contraction
Actin	42,000	Globular—55Å in diameter "like strings of beads in a necklace"	Thin filament (I band)	Contraction
Tropomyosin	35,000	Two α-helical chains in a linear coil Covers 7 actin molecules 450 Å long and 20Å in diameter	Thin filament	Regulation of actin-myosin interaction
Troponin	78,000	Globular with three subunits	Thin filament	T subunit binds tropomyosin C subunit binds Ca^{2+} I controls interaction of actin and myosin through position of tropomyosin

SKELETAL MUSCLE

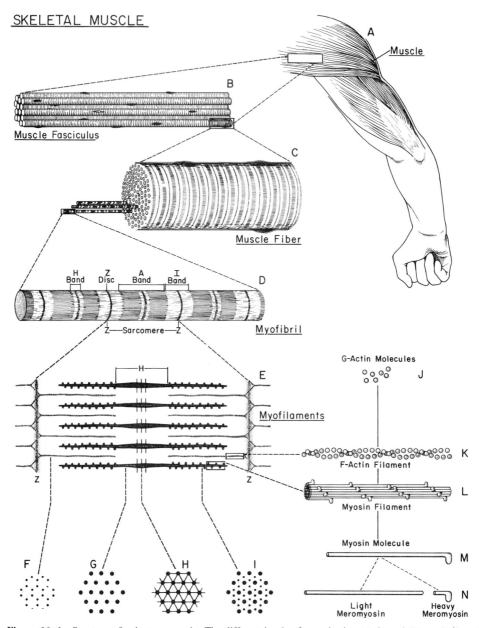

Figure 16–1 Structure of voluntary muscle. The different levels of organization (*A* through *N*) are indicated by the dashed lines. Note that *F* through *I* are cross-sections through a myofilament at the points shown. (Drawing by Sylvia Colard Keene. From Bloom W. and Fawcett D.W.: A Textbook of Histology. Philadelphia, W.B. Saunders Co. 1975.)

tions of magnesium, as well as by certain neurotoxins (e.g., botulinum toxin). Stimuli that are above the threshold for depolarization will produce an action potential that propagates across the surface of the sarcolemma. Activation of the contractile mechanism (actin-myosin sliding filaments) is mediated by signal propagation along the transverse tubules (Fig. 16–2). This tubular system is a continuation of the plasma membrane and because of its highly ramified nature assures that excitation leads to contraction. Actually, the sarcoplasmic reticulum is contiguous with, but separate from, the transverse tubules. Depolarization of the sarcoplasmic reticulum results in release of calcium with activation of the myosin ATPase.

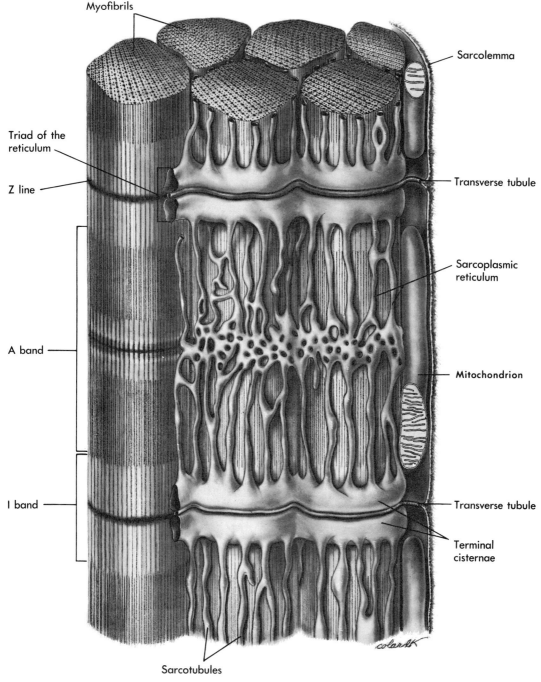

Figure 16-2 Relationship of the sarcoplasm to the transverse tubules. Propagation of the excitatory signal occurs through the extensive transverse tubular system in intimate contact with the muscle fiber. (From Bloom, W. and Fawcett, D.W.: A Textbook of Histology. Philadelphia, W.B. Saunders Co. 1975. Modified after Peachey: J. Cell Biol. 25:209, 1965. Drawn by Sylvia Colard Keene.)

Muscle Contraction

In the relaxed state, myosin is both phosphorylated and bound to a Mg^{2+}-ADP complex while troponin is bound to actin; consequently, tropomyosin is interposed physically between the actin and myosin molecules. This physical relationship ensures absence of any interaction between the two major contractile proteins. Addition of calcium to this system results in binding of this cation

Table 16–2 REACTIONS IN MUSCLE CONTRACTION*

Chemical Reactions	Action in Muscle	Mechanical Analogy
1. $Mg^{2+} \cdot ATP$ binds to head myosin		Loading gun by placing cartridge (ATP) in chamber (myosin head)
2. Myosin–$Mg^{2+} \cdot ATP$ complex converted into a "charged" form that binds actin in thin filament—Ca^{2+} sensitive step— the form is $Mg^{2+} \cdot ADP$ with the myosin being phosphorylated by P_i.	Actin linked to myosin	Cocking the gun
3. Hydrolysis of ATP with release of myosin–$Mg^{2+} \cdot ADP$ and P_i from myosin as soon as it attaches to actin. This brings about formation of contracted state.	Release of energy brings about a change in the angle of the cross-bridge with muscle shortening	Squeezing trigger to perform work on bullet
4. Detachment of cross-bridge occurs when a new ATP binds to the actin-myosin complex with dissociation to free actin and uncharged myosin-ATP. Therefore, relaxation requires presence of ATP.	Muscle resumes previous position of actin and myosin, i.e., relaxes	Ejecting spent cartridge

*Adapted from Murray, J.M., and Weber, A.: The cooperative action of muscle proteins. Sci. Am. 230(2):59, 1974.

to the troponin "C" subunit and cleavage of the troponin-actin bond. This, in turn, removes the interposed tropomyosin molecule, thus permitting interactions between actin and myosin. The troponin-tropomyosin complex therefore appears to function both as a circuit breaker and a means of information transfer (Table 16–2). As a consequence, cross-bridges form between the actin and myosin filaments, which slide past one another, producing a contraction. Should repolarization be interrupted because of persistence of acetylcholine at the end plate, paralysis ensues.

ATP furnishes the energy for contraction and hence must be replenished constantly. Phosphocreatine serves as the immediate source to rephosphorylate ADP by the enzyme creatine phosphokinase. Ultimately, oxidative phosphorylation serves as the process that provides for these energetic requirements. Before relaxation can be accomplished, as the actin and myosin filaments return to the precontracted position, the calcium that caused the initiation of the contraction must be again sequestered in the sarcoplasmic reticulum. As might be expected, reaccumulation is an energy-requiring process; it is the absence of ATP that accounts for the contracted state of muscle in rigor mortis.

THE FLOPPY INFANT

Hypotonia ought to be suspected when there is excessive joint mobility, a paucity of spontaneous activity, or a lack of resistance to passive movement. If such findings are not identified in the neonatal period, delay in reaching appropriate motor milestones may be the next feature to focus attention on the neuromuscular system.

In clinical assessment of such patients, a careful history and physical examination should help point the way to hypotonia either on a central basis or somewhere more peripheral in the neuromuscular system. Such a differential diagnosis based on the levels of neuromuscular axis affected is presented in Table 16–3. As noted there, a key point is whether or not the hypotonia is associated with a parallel decrease in muscle strength. Elevating the infant in the air and observing the ability to maintain extremities in an antigravity position or the ability to resist slipping down when held in the axilla should be useful for making that distinction.

Nerve conduction studies and electromyography will sometimes bolster the impression obtained by the evaluation of tendon reflexes and the search for pathological reflexes. If the lesion appears to be at the level of the muscle itself, it will be necessary to obtain a muscle biopsy, performed by an experienced individual, and to examine the specimen by electron microscopy and special histochemical techniques.

Birth anoxia or trauma causing central nervous system damage is the most common reason for central hypotonia. If motor milestone delay is prominent, careful evaluation demands establishing

Table 16–3 METABOLIC CAUSES OF HYPOTONIA

Physical Exam	Other	Level of Nervous System	Disorder
↑ DTRs, + Babinski, ankle clonus, strength intact		Cerebral cortex	Mental retardation (Down's) Atonic cerebral palsy Sphingolipidoses, mucopolysaccharidoses, mucolipidoses Hyperammonemia
Dystonia, choreoathetosis, clumsy child		Basal ganglia	Athetotic cerebral palsy Bilirubin encephalopathy
Ataxia, ↓ DTRs		Cerebellum	Ataxic cerebral palsy
↑ DTRs, + Babinski, sensory level		Spinal cord	Breech delivery
Absent reflexes, fasciculation, fibrillations		Anterior horn cell	Werdnig-Hoffman syndrome
↓ DTRs, ↓ nerve conduction velocity, strength diminished		Nerve fibers	Demyelinating neuropathies—infections, leukodystrophies, lead, diabetes, porphyria Familial dysautonomia Abetalipoproteinemia, ataxia-telangiectasia, Refsum's disease
Fluctuating decrease in strength, easy fatigability	Tensilon test	Neuromuscular junction	Myasthenia gravis
DTRs normal, sensation normal, strength diminished	Serum CPK, myoglobinuria	Muscle	Muscular dystrophy, myotonic dystrophy Glycogen storage diseases Malignant hyperthermia Congenital myopathies Polymyositis, thyrotoxic myopathy
DTRs normal, strength intact		Connective tissue	Congenital disorders of connective tissue—Ehlers-Danlos syndrome, Marfan's syndrome, osteogenesis imperfecta
		Systemic (probably multiple levels)	Scurvy, rickets, hypophosphatasia, malnutrition, hypothyroidism, chronic infection, renal tubular acidosis, hyperadrenalism

whether this muscle function abnormality exists alone or is associated with evidence of more global dysfunction, i.e., mental retardation. As noted in Table 16–3, Down's syndrome and the neurolipidoses and mucopolysaccharide storage disorders can cause hypotonia associated with severe intellectual deficit (see Chapters 30 and 32).

Muscle Disorders

Clinically, the various causes of congenital myopathies present in much the same manner, with variation in time of presentation being the most significant feature. Clinical presentation runs the

Table 16–4 MUSCLE CRAMPING

Usual Causes	Metabolic
Over-exertion	Muscle phosphorylase (McArdle's disease); Tarui's disease (muscle phosphofructokinase)
Tetany	Adynamia episodica hereditaria (hypokalemic periodic paralysis)
Hyponatremia	Myotonia congenita
Uremia	Myotonia dystrophy
Multiple sclerosis	Lipid metabolic disorders: Muscle carnitine palmityl acyl transferase deficiency; carnitine deficiency
Polymyositis	Wilson's disease
Toxins—thallium	Hartnup disease

gamut from the floppy infant or the child who manifests weakness when an antigravity posture is assumed all the way to the adolescent or young adult who first manifests difficulty after exercising.

Unfortunately, distribution of muscle weakness and assay of serum CPK levels or electromyography are rarely, if ever, helpful in making a specific diagnosis. Hence, muscle biopsy remains the most useful technique when coupled with special histochemical staining techniques and electron microscopy. Nonetheless, because of nonspecific changes in muscle, it too may fail to point to one diagnosis.

Metabolic derangements causing muscle cramping are presented in Table 16–4.

REFERENCES

Bessman, S.P., and Geiger, P.J.: Transport of energy in muscle: The phosphorylcreatine shuttle. Science 211:448, 1981.

Brooke, M.H., Carroll, J.E., and Ringel, S.P.: Congenital hypotonia revisited. Muscle and Nerve 2:84, 1979.

Buchthal, F., and Schmalbruch, H.: Motor unit of mammalian muscle. Physiol. Rev. 60:90, 1980.

Curtin, N.A., and Woledge, R.C.: Energy changes in muscular contraction. Physiol. Rev. 58:690, 1978.

Dubowitz, V.: Muscle Disorders in Childhood. W. B. Saunders Co., Philadelphia, 1978.

Eisenberg, E., and Greene, L.E.: The relation of muscle biochemistry to muscle physiology. Ann. Rev. Physiol. 42:293, 1980.

Ikemoto, N.: Structure and function of the calcium pump protein of sarcoplasmic reticulum. Ann. Rev. Physiol. 44:297, 1982.

Kassals, R., Mornet, D., Pantel, P., et al.: Structural aspects of actomyosin interaction. Biochimie 63:273, 1981.

Murray, J.M., and Weber, A.: The cooperative action of muscle proteins. Sci. Am. 230(2):59, 1974.

Sleep, J.A., and Smith, S.J.: Actomyosin ATPase and muscle contraction. Curr. Topics Bioenergetics 11:239, 1981.

Tada, M., Yamamoto, T., and Tonomura, Y.: Molecular mechanism of active calcium transport by sarcoplasmic reticulum. Physiol. Rev. 58:1, 1978.

Tregear, R.T., and Marston, S.B.: The crossbridge theory. Ann. Rev. Physiol. 41:723, 1979.

17

Neurological Disturbances

SEIZURES

A seizure is the clinical manifestation of an abnormal degree of synchronous electrical discharge of a large group of neurons in the brain. This has been termed "hypersynchronization." The ability to respond to an appropriate stimulus by propagating an orderly reversal in cell membrane electrochemical potential is conventionally termed "excitability." Inasmuch as neuronal excitability is the key property of the nervous system that allows it to respond to a stimulus (by reversal of the transmembrane electrical potential), it follows that a seizure must be an exaggeration of this normal property. Neuronal function is the sum total of excitatory and inhibitory signals arriving at a dendrite or soma. Hence, hyperexcitability or deficiency of inhibitors can result in the hypersynchronized state. As a general rule the location in the brain of the abnormal neurons, including the neurons that join in the abnormal spread of excitation will determine the clinical manifestations of the seizure activity.

The Nerve Impulse

When a neural membrane experiences a transient wave of increased ion permeability, the electrical potential reverses rapidly. This phenomenon constitutes the nerve impulse, which propagates at a finite velocity down the axon, proceeding by reversals in electrical potential (Fig. 17–1). Normally, the transmembrane potential is maintained (by active ion transport) between -70 and -90 mv. The magnitude of this potential difference is dependent upon the extracellular sodium concentration being 30 to 40 times higher than the potassium concentration, while the situation within the cell is reversed. When depolarization is brought about by stimulation, the potential difference becomes transiently positive (approximately $+25$ mv). This reversal in charge depends upon rapid influx of sodium ions across the membrane. Depolarization is a threshold phenomenon; that is, if a stimulus is adequate to initiate an action potential then the wave of depolarization follows. Thereafter, the membrane repolarizes through the action of transmembrane energy-linked ion pumps. At first potassium loss accounts for the decrease in intracellular positivity, but this is followed by active removal of sodium from the cell in exchange for potassium.

Excitability

A seizure (excessive synchronous firing of neurons) may be the result of one of several situations, shown in Table 17–1. Since both normal cerebral function and seizure activity depend upon the trans-synaptic spread of signals that generate an action potential, the factor that distinguishes a seizure is the spread to multiple cells, causing them to fire in synchrony. Hence, any process that decreases the membrane polarization would also lower the threshold for cell discharge.

The astute reader may already have wondered why, if all living cells actively maintain an electrochemical potential across their membranes, all cells do not possess the property of excitability? While the complete answer to this very germane question is not yet known, a partial response may be given. To begin with, it must be made clear that the processes responsible for maintenance

195

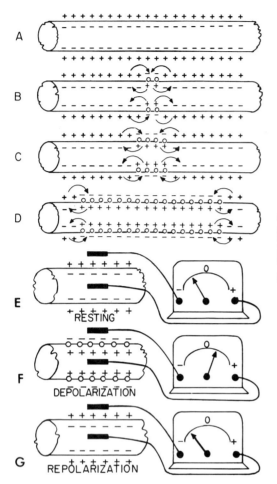

Figure 17–1 Schematic representation of propagation of action potential along a nerve fiber. Note the orderly progression of reversal in ionic charge (*A* to *D*). The electrical potentials recorded during the resting, depolarization, and repolarization states are shown in *E* to *G*. (From Guyton, A.C.: Textbook of Medical Physiology. 6th ed. Philadelphia, W.B. Saunders Co., 1981.)

of ionic gradients across all biological membranes are intrinsic to preservation of cell viability; hence, neuronal tissue must also carry out this basic function. The excitation phenomenon appears to be the result of subtle and discrete differences in the macromolecular membrane complex of neuronal cells in comparison with other types of cells. These differences, whatever they may be, permit two distinct membrane states to exist—resting and active. As in the muscle cell, calcium plays a vital role in the transition between these states (see Chapter 16). At least part of the role of this cation in neuronal transitions may be the alteration of Na^+ ion permeability during depolarization. Whatever the specific mechanism, we are ultimately driven to the conclusion that the specialized function of the neuronal cell membrane is yet another manifestation of the genetic endowment of the fertilized ovum, repressed in most other cell types (see Chapter 10).

Table 17–1   METABOLIC STATES ASSOCIATED
WITH SEIZURES

1. Enhanced membrane permeability to sodium or potassium
2. Decrease in threshold for influx of sodium
    Ca^{++} ion concentration modifies
    Possibility of abnormalities in transmembrane proteins
3. Abnormal functioning of Na^+, K^+ pump
    Hypoxia
    Hypoglycemia—decreased generation of high energy phosphates

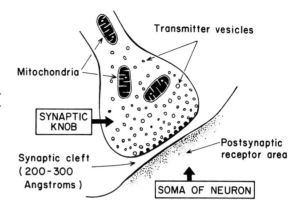

Figure 17-2 Schematic drawing of a synapse. (From Guyton, A.C.: Textbook of Medical Physiology. 6th ed. Philadelphia, W.B. Saunders Co., 1981.)

Synapses

The wiring diagram of the nervous system depends upon specialized areas of contact between axons and neurons—the synapses. It is at this point (Fig. 17-2) that a signal is transmitted. The signal may be excitatory or inhibitory. Chemical agents (neurotransmitters) are responsible for the trans-synaptic flow of information. These agents include acetylcholine, norepinephrine, dopamine, gamma-aminobutyric acid, and probably certain α-amino acids as well (e.g., glycine).

These chemicals are stored in vesicles localized at the synaptic cleft on the presynaptic side. When a signal brings about release of neurotransmitter, it enters the synaptic cleft and is there bound to a receptor on the postsynaptic membrane. This reception of information at the postsynaptic site then brings about the change in membrane permeability that propagates the wave of depolarization. Calcium ion concentration appears to be important in the process of transmitter release through a postulated effect on membrane pores. The mechanism of action of calcium on transmitter release is not well understood but may involve phosphatidyl inositol, which has been shown to undergo rapid turnover at both synaptic sites and endocrine membranes during their function. Indeed, the analogy between hormonal and nervous responsiveness may depend upon sharing a common mechanism, namely the rapid turnover of the head group of phosphatidyl inositol in response

Table 17-2 ETIOLOGIES OF SEIZURES ACCORDING TO AGE OF PRESENTATION

Newborn	First 1 to 2 Months of Life	Later Infancy and Childhood
Anoxia	Cerebral dysgenesis	Infection
Infection	Infection	Intracranial hemorrhage
		Anoxia
Intracranial hemorrhage	Subdural hematoma	Brain tumors
		Cerebral dysgenesis
		Febrile convulsions
Narcotic withdrawal		Breathholding, hyperventilation, syncope
Metabolic/Genetic	Metabolic/Genetic	Metabolic/Genetic
Hypoglycemia	Hypoglycemia	Hypoglycemia
Hyper- or Hyponatremia	Hyper- or hyponatremia	Hyper- or hyponatremia
Hypocalcemia	Hypocalcemia	Hypocalcemia
Bilirubin encephalopathy	Organic acidemias	Idiopathic
Organic acidemias	Urea cycle defects	Cerebral degenerative diseases
Urea cycle defects	Phenylketonuria and variants	Lysosomal defects
Nonketotic hyperglycinemia	Riley-Day syndrome	Unclassified
Lactic acidosis	Tuberous sclerosis	Drugs and poisons
Pyridoxine dependency	Alkalosis	Nephritis and hypertension
	Cerebral degenerative syndromes (rarely)	Uremia
		Alkalosis
		Pyridoxine dependency

to appropriate stimuli. Transmitter in the cleft space is removed by re-uptake or breakdown by enzymes. In some instances, diffusion may be the means of removal.

As noted above, dendrites and neuronal cell bodies receive both excitatory and inhibitory (hyperpolarizing) signals, the sum total of which controls the susceptibility to firing of the individual neuron. Actually, modulating influences are more complicated than the foregoing suggests; the result is a complex, orchestrated response of single neurons to a complex input of information. Such influences normally obviate the possibility of synchronous firing (a seizure). At the level of

Table 17–3 DISORDERS ASSOCIATED WITH
SEIZURES

Amino Acid Disorders
  Carnosinemia (3)*
  Homocystinuria (cystathionine-β-synthase) (3–5,7)
  Hydroxylysinemia (α-aminoadipic aciduria) (3)
  Hyper-β-alaninemia (3)
  Hyperleucinemia (3–5)
  Hyperlysinemia, episodic (3,4)
  Hyperlysinemia, persistent (3,7)
  Lysinuric protein intolerance (3,4,6,7)
  β-Mercaptolactate cysteine disulfiduria (3)
  Methionine malabsorption syndrome (2,3,7)
  Nonketotic hyperglycinemia (1,3,4)
  Phenylketonuria (phenylalanine hydroxylase) (3–5,7)
Organic Acidemias
  Isovaleric acidemia (1–3)
  β-Ketothiolase deficiency (2,3)
  Lactic acidosis (1,2)
  Maple syrup urine disease (1–3)
  Methylmalonic aciduria (1–3)
  Propionic acidemia (1–3)
Urea Cycle Defects
  Argininosuccinic aciduria (3,4,6,7)
  Carbamyl phosphate synthetase deficiency (3)
  Citrullinemia (3,4)
  Hyperargininemia (3,4,6)
  Hyperornithinemia (3)
  Hyperornithinemia, hyperammonemia, and homocitrullinuria (3)
  Ornithine transcarbamylase deficiency (3)
Carbohydrate Disorders
  Fructose diphosphatase deficiency (2,4,6)
  Glycogen storage disease (3,6)
  Glycogen synthetase deficiency (3)
  Hypoglycemia (3)
  Leigh's syndrome (2,3,7)
Neurodegenerative Disorders
  Sanfilippo syndrome (3–7)
  Gaucher's disease (3,5,6,7)
  Krabbe's disease (3,4)
  Niemann-Pick disease (3–7)
  Tay-Sachs disease (3–5)
  Ceroid lipofuscinosis (3–6)
  Neuronal-axonal dystrophy (3)
Other
  Hyper- or hyponatremia
  Hypocalcemia
  Hypophosphatasia (late manifestation of oxycephaly) (3,4)
  Menke's disease (3,7)
  Neonatal hyperbilirubinemia (3,4)
  Nephrogenic diabetes insipidus
  Pyridoxine dependency

*Associated findings: 1—catastrophic presentation in the neonate; 2—derangements of acid-base balance; 3—mental retardation; 4—other neurologic; 5—eye findings; 6—visceromegaly; 7—skin and/or hair findings.

the nervous system, such integrated processing of information determines the orchestrated functioning demanded by such processes as movement, memory, and thought.

Epilepsy

It follows from what we have said about synchronous firing of neurons that the multiple causes of epilepsy (Tables 17–2 and 17–3) share in common simultaneous firing of aggregates of neurons. Some of the neurons involved in this abnormal phenomenon may be normal but are made to depolarize because of a spreading wave emanating from the abnormal focus. Moreover, repetitive discharge of a neuron potentiates continued firing of that cell as well as other cells it depolarizes. The excessive synchronous neuronal discharge of epilepsy arises from two basic defects: decreased inhibition or increased excitation. Inhibitory neurotransmitters (e.g., GABA) cause hyperpolarization through enhanced K^+ efflux and Cl^- influx. Decrease of such a neurotransmitter could then be responsible for seizures because of the unopposed action of excitatory neurotransmitters.

Alternatively, increased synthesis or decreased removal of excitatory neurotransmitters could result in seizures. Experimentally, organophosphorus compounds bind to the postsynaptic membrane and inhibit acetylcholine esterase, the enzyme responsible for hydrolyzing acetylcholine.

The mechanism of convulsions in hypocalcemia seems to depend upon enhanced sodium entry into the cell. Although calcium is also necessary for release of neurotransmitter, the end result is usually heightened seizure potential. Occasionally, severe hypocalcemia may block transmitter release altogether, but with calcium administration seizures may appear as the excitatory effect begins to predominate again.

Abnormalities in the configuration of membrane proteins could modify the transport of Na^+ and K^+, separately or together, to accentuate the propensity to abnormal discharge of the membrane potential.

ATAXIA

Ataxia is a prime example of those abnormalities of either movement or posture caused by derangements in the basal ganglia and cerebellum. The cerebellum and brainstem normally interact to control the static postural background necessary for the execution of voluntary functions controlled by the corticospinal tracts. Together, the cerebellum and various interrelated areas of the brain comprising the basal ganglia are termed "the extrapyramidal system."

An ataxic patient suffers from movements that are not coordinated in range, speed, or strength.

Table 17–4 ETIOLOGIES OF ATAXIA

Anatomic	Metabolic/Genetic
Acute cerebellar ataxia	Abetalipoproteinemia
Cerebellar tumor	Aminoacidopathies: argininosuccinic aciduria, carbamyl phosphate synthetase
Hydrocephalus (progressive)	deficiency, hyperornithinemia with gyrate atrophy, maple syrup urine disease,
von Hippel-Lindau disease	ornithine transcarbamylase deficiency, persistent hyperlysinemia, pyroglu-
Degenerative	tamic aciduria, glutaric aciduria type I
Encephalomyelitis	Ataxia-telangiectasia
Subacute sclerosing panencephalitis	Cerebromacular degeneration
Infectious	Formiminoglutamic aciduria
Viral encephalitides	Friedreich's ataxia
	Hartnup disease
Intoxication (Drugs and Poisons)	Hypothyroidism
Anticonvulsants	Leigh's encephalopathy
Antihistamines	Lipidoses
Antimetabolites	Pelizaeus-Merzbacher disease
"Glue sniffing"	Pyruvate dehydrogenase deficiencies
Phenothiazines	Refsum's disease
Plumbism	Schilder's disease
	Wilson's disease

Table 17–5 ETIOLOGIES OF COMA

Drugs and Poisons	Metabolic/Genetic
Alcohol	Acidosis
Carbon monoxide	Diabetic ketoacidosis
Carbon tetrachloride	Organic acidemias
Insecticides	Renal tubular acidosis
Kerosene	Alkalosis
Lead	Fluid and electrolyte derangements
Mushroom	Adrenal crisis
Organic phosphate	Dehydration
Salicylates	Water intoxication (Inappropriate
Sedatives	ADH secretion, psychogenic
Hysteria	polydipsia)
Infection	Hyper- or hypocalcemia
Bacterial	Hyperglycinemia
Fungal	Hypoglycemia
Protozoan	Hyper- or hypomagnesemia
Tuberculosis	Hypoxia/hypercapnia
Viral	Liver failure/hyperammonemia
Postictal State	Cirrhosis with portosystemic shunts
	Reye's syndrome
Trauma	Urea cycle defects
Vascular	Myxedema
Cardiac (asystole)	Porphyria
Coagulopathy	Renal failure (uremia)
Emboli	Vitamin deficiencies
Hemorrhage	Niacin, Pyridoxine, Thiamine, B_{12}
Hyper- or hypotension	
Vasculitis	

In consequence, such individuals sway or stagger, manifesting robotlike movements, since complex acts are now executed in a stepwise fashion rather than in a fluid or "seamless" manner.

In general, motor disturbances arising from abnormalities of function of components of the extrapyramidal system are a manifestation of the unchecked actions of the voluntary motor system. Since the extrapyramidal system serves to steady volitional activities, in its absence one observes disturbances of tone and movement, including the loss of the ability to gauge the speed, distance, or power of a willed action. In children, this is often manifested by clumsiness and a tendency to

Table 17–6 CAUSES OF DEFECTIVE HEARING

Congenital/Infection	Metabolic
Meningitis	Cretinism
Encephalitis	Bilirubin encephalopathy
Recurrent otitis media	Lipid storage diseases
Tumors	Mucopolysaccharidoses
Trauma	Osteogenesis imperfecta
Vascular	Waardenburg's syndrome
Drugs and poisons	Refsum's disease
salicylates, aminoglycosides	Partial albinism
	Friedreich's ataxia
	Persistent hyperlysinemia
Congenital Defects	
Alport's syndrome	
Apert's acrocephalosyndactyly	
Cornelia de Lange syndrome	
Crouzon's disease	
Ectodermal dysplasia	
Leber's optic atrophy	
Retinitis pigmentosa	
Trisomy 15-16	
Trisomy 17-18	
Turner's syndrome	

Table 17-7 METABOLIC CAUSES OF HYPERTONIA

Demyelinating or degenerative diseases of the nervous system
    Tay-Sachs—late decerebrate rigidity
    Krabbe's—very spastic early
    Neimann-Pick—late spastic
    Gaucher's—retroflexion early followed by decerebrate state
    GM_1 gangliosidosis—spastic late
Phenylketonuria
Hypocalcemic tetany

Table 17-8 CONDITIONS ASSOCIATED WITH PERIPHERAL NERVE DISORDERS

Abetalipoproteinemia
Ataxia-telangiectasia
Chédiak-Higashi syndrome
Diabetes mellitus
Friedreich's ataxia
Heavy metal intoxication
Hypoglycemia
Krabbe's disease
Metachromatic leukodystrophy
Porphyria, acute intermittent
Refsum's disease
Tangier disease
Uremia
Vitamin deficiencies (acquired or inherited)

diminished activity because of a desire not to carry out motor activities that are poorly executed. It is the hallmark of all extrapyramidal manifestations that they are abolished by sleep. Table 17–4 lists those disorders that are commonly associated with severe disorders of the extrapyramidal system.

COMA

Coma is the most severe form of depressed consciousness representing the end of a spectrum of clinical states including inattention, confusion, and stupor. As these states reflect increasing degrees of impairment of consciousness, patients may manifest any or all of them during the course of an illness. They share as well an impairment in the functioning of neurons because of derangements in metabolic function of neurons. Central to many acquired processes is hypoxia (ischemia) with its well-known deleterious effects on brain function.

Other metabolic derangements caused either by acquired or inherited disease include hypoglycemia, acidosis, alkalosis, electrolyte abnormalities, hyperammonemia, and deficiencies of thiamine, nicotinic acid, vitamin B_{12}, pantothenic acid, and pyridoxine. Coenzyme abnormalities compromise the normal functioning of key metabolic pathways, while inborn errors are often associated with the accumulation of acids or toxins that interfere with cell function.

Table 17–5 lists the salient conditions that must be ruled out in the evaluation of the patient with coma. Certain clinical points are worth emphasizing. Hyperthermia may indicate heat stroke, while hypothermia may be the result of alcohol or barbituate intoxication. The presence of an odor is very important and may indicate diabetic ketoacidosis, uremia, or hepatic coma, as well as those

Table 17-9 METABOLIC DISORDERS MANIFESTING PSYCHIATRIC SYMPTOMS*

Acute intermittent porphyria
Fabry's disease
Wilson's disease
Metachromatic leukodystrophy
Hartnup disease
Homocystinuria (remethylation defect)
Persistent hyperlysinemia

*Often in association with neurologic findings.

Table 17-10 CONDITIONS ASSOCIATED WITH SUCKING AND SWALLOWING PROBLEMS*

Mental retardation
Muscular dystrophy
Myotonic dystrophy
Myasthenia gravis
Riley-Day syndrome
Organic acidemias (especially MSUD, IVA)
Neurodegenerative disorders
Storage diseases—lipidoses
Defect unknown (see Table 19–1 on Mental Retardation)

*Often manifested by excessive salivation.

inborn errors of metabolism associated with odor. Other metabolic disorders include certain urea cycle defects (see Chapter 22), hyperglycinemia (see Chapter 22), and branched-chain amino acid defects (see Chapter 34).

OTHER MANIFESTATIONS OF NEUROLOGICAL DYSFUNCTION

Other manifestations of neurologic dysfunction (e.g., defective hearing, hypertonia, peripheral nerve disorders, psychiatric symptoms, and sucking and swallowing problems) are listed in Tables 17–6 to 17–10.

REFERENCES

Brown, J.K.: Convulsions in the newborn period. Develop. Med. Child. Neurol. 15:823, 1973.

Cohen, M.M. (ed.): Biochemistry of Neural Disease. Harper & Row, New York, 1975.

Goldensohn, E.S.: The epilepsies. *In* Goldensohn, E.S., and Appel, S.H. (eds.): Scientific Approaches to Clinical Neurology. Lea & Febiger, Philadelphia, 1977. p. 654.

Hagiwara, S. and Byerly, L.: Calcium channel. Ann. Rev. Neuroscience 4:69, 1981.

Hawthorne, J.N., and Pickard, M.R.: Phospholipids in synaptic function. J. Neurochem. 32:5, 1979.

Hers, H.G.: α-Glucosidase deficiency in generalized glycogen storage disease (Pompe's disease). Biochem. J. 86:11, 1963.

Jennings, J.T., and Bird, T.D.: Genetic influences in the epilepsies. Am. J. Dis. Child 135:450, 1981.

Kark, R.A.P., Rosenberg, R.N., and Schut, L.J. (eds).: The Inherited Ataxias. Biochemical, Viral and Pathological Studies. Adv. Neurol. Vol. 21. Raven Press, New York, 1978.

Kintner, D., Costello, D.J., Levin, A.B., and Gilboe, D.D.: Brain metabolism after 30 minutes of hypoxic or anoxic perfusion or ischemia. Am. J. Physiol. 239:E501, 1980.

Lewis, A.J.: Mechanisms of Neurological Disease. Little, Brown & Co., Boston, 1976.

Nachmansohn, D.: Nerve excitability: Transition from descriptive phenomenology to chemical analysis of mechanism. Klin. Wschr. 55:715, 1977.

Plum, F., and Posner, J.B.: The Diagnoses of Stupor and Coma. 3rd ed. F. A. Davis, Co., Philadelphia, 1980.

Prince, D.A.: Neurophysiology of epilepsy. Ann. Rev. Neurosci. 1:395, 1978.

Putney, J.W., Jr.: Recent hypotheses regarding the phosphatidylinositol effect. Life Sci. 29:1183, 1981.

Stein, R.B.: Nerve and Muscle: Membranes, Cells and Systems. Plenum Press, New York, 1980.

Swaiman, K.F. and Wright, F.S. (eds.): The Practice of Pediatric Neurology. 2nd ed. C. V. Mosby, St. Louis, 1982.

Volpe, J.J.: Neurology of the Newborn. W.B. Saunders Co., Philadelphia, 1981.

18

Neurodegenerative Storage Diseases

Harold Finkel

Although clinical awareness of the neurodegenerative storage diseases dates from Tay and Sachs' description in the 1880's of what is now the disorder that bears their names, biochemical delineation of these and related disorders did not occur for another 80 years. During that period clinical descriptions associated with similar eponyms were ascribed to other degenerative diseases, which unfortunately added little to their accurate classification and, in fact, often impeded understanding of the underlying process. Many of these disorders are now known to be the result of defects in specific lysosomal enzymes, and prenatal diagnosis is possible in several, thus assuring the birth of an unaffected infant. Here we review the salient clinical evaluation of such patients and in Part III consider the biochemistry and specific clinical findings in each disease.

NEUROLOGICAL EVALUATION

The evaluation of neurological diseases should begin, as in all cases, with a detailed history. Attempts should be made to delineate the initial problem as well as the age of onset. One should then try to determine if the process is acute or chronic, static or progressive. A degenerative disease may evolve rather insidiously over a protracted period of time ranging from months to years. If the history suggests a delay in or failure of the acquisition of developmental milestones, progressive deviation from the normative curves, or regression of previously attained milestones, the physician should be alerted to the possibility of a neurodegenerative disorder.

Most progressive diseases present after an initial period of relatively normal development. Normally, the infant is continually acquiring new skills as he loses the primitive reflexes present after birth. Constant interaction with the environment is seen after a few weeks of life, and this accelerates the pace of psychomotor development. In the latter context, it is important to note that a sensorineural deficit in an otherwise normal infant often results in lack of such environmental interaction, thus producing a developmental lag. It is equally important to understand that development to a plateau (static) may be misinterpreted retrospectively as a progressive process, since failure of further development with advancing age will result in an increased discrepancy between actual and expected achievement.

Evaluation of the newborn is somewhat limited because the nervous system is not fully developed. As neuronal development and myelination proceed, additional parameters can be tested in the examination. Much of the examination as performed in the adult can be tested accurately in the child if a few tricks and patience are used.

The neurological evaluation should be performed methodically. *Cranial nerve* examination should note pupillary response to light and accommodation. Extraocular muscle function (III, IV, VI) is noted with doll's eye maneuver or by having the child follow a brightly colored object. In a similar manner, visual field determination can be evaluated by confrontation with bright or large objects. The fundoscopic examination can be quite informative if properly performed. Evidence of optic atrophy, macular changes, or chorioretinitis may suggest a specific diagnosis (see Eye Findings, Chapter 7). The trigeminal nerve sensory component is tested by corneal reflex and the motor components by ability to suck or chew. Facial symmetry (VII) is noted during crying or smiling. Auditory function can be grossly evaluated by acoustic blink response in the newborn and by turning toward sounds by 5 to 6 months. Vestibular testing is performed by rotational testing. Bulbar cranial nerve function is assessed by gag response and quality of cry. Hypoglossal dysfunction is noted by fasciculation or atrophy of the tongue.

Motor evaluation includes testing for tone, bulk, and strength. Muscle bulk is difficult to evaluate in the newborn due to the overlying subcutaneous fat. Tone and strength testing may be subjective. However, there should always be spontaneous symmetrical movements shortly after birth. The newborn is quite active and is constantly in motion while awake. Tone is the resistance offered during passive movements when the muscles are relaxed. The newborn normally has a suggestion of slightly increased tone, and a peak is found at 2 to 4 months, followed by a gradual return to a "normal" tone. Hyptonia, as in a "floppy" child, may suggest abnormalities in the central or peripheral nervous system (see Chapter 16). Spasticity is suggestive of an upper motor neuron disease and becomes increasingly prominent with progressive diseases (e.g. Krabbe's disease, metachromatic leukodystrophy).

Coordination requires the integrity of the posterior column and the cerebellum. Testing involves evaluating the ability to perform integrated movement (e.g., sitting, standing, and walking). Cephalic *titubation* (head-bobbing) and truncal ataxia should be sought.

Dysmetria (inability to arrest a motion) and dyssynergia (ataxia) are noted as the child reaches for objects. Nystagmoid movements may indicate cerebellar pathology as well.

Sensory testing by pin prick and touch and withdrawal response can be performed in the newborn; vibratory sense, two-point discrimination, stereognosis, and graphesthesia (recognition of figures drawn on the skin of the back) require the cooperation of the older child.

Deep tendon *reflexes* or muscle stretch reflexes can be obtained even in the infant. The increased flexor tone should enable the biceps, patellar, and Achilles reflexes to be elicited, but not the triceps. Outside of the immediate newborn period, increased reflexes as well as tone at 2 to 4 months of age are noted; unlike the newborn, all muscle stretch reflexes should be obtained. Ankle clonus up to 10 beats is normal in the immediate newborn period but diminishes shortly thereafter. The Babinski sign is variable up to one year of age and therefore may be of little help in confirming the presence of a progressive neurological disorder. Superficial abdominal reflexes are equivocal in infancy but the cremasteric response should be obtainable.

Examination of the infant may present some difficulties because of the constant evolution of the nervous system in early life. Primary reflexes present at birth consist of the Moro, grasp, lateral incurving or Galant's sign (contraction of abdominal muscles with tapping of anterior superior illiac spine), stepping response, crossed adductor to knee jerk, and tonic neck response. These findings as well as other signs in infancy may vary according to the time in relation to feedings, as well as temperature of the environment. Testing categories in the first few years should include *personal-social, language,* and *motor* evaluation. Repeated examination may be required for accurate assessment. Periodic assessment and comparisons of Denver Developmental evaluations are most helpful in this regard.

Evaluation of the child by such means allows the physician to assess maturation of the nervous system. Persistence of primary reflexes or their reappearance after an initial loss are suggestive of neurological dysfunction. Further testing should be pursued with a child who has a delay in the acquisition of the appropriate motor, social, or language skills, especially if no history of perinatal distress that might explain the findings can be obtained. Diseases affecting the basal ganglia are likely to begin with abnormal movements or dystonic posture. The floppy infant should be evaluated for disorders of the cerebellum, anterior horn cells, peripheral nerves or muscle itself.

CLINICAL SETTING IN WHICH TO CONSIDER THESE DISORDERS

Unfortunately, many children with these degenerative disorders do not follow the classical textbook presentation, and a high index of suspicion must be maintained in any infant or child whose normal neurological progression has slowed or appears to be regressing. Often this will require several months' observation before the physician is willing to confide his concerns to the parents. This requires sensitivity and support but should not be delayed when the physician is sure of the need to intensify his diagnostic efforts.

For example, hypotonia may be found in association with brisk reflexes, a situation that may occur with Tay-Sachs disease, Niemann-Pick disease, mannosidosis, and fucosidosis (see Chapter 30). Hyperammonemic states often have a significant central hypotonic component. Combinations of upper and lower motor neuron lesions are also found. These infants present with hypotonia, decreased muscle stretch reflexes, and a history of intellectual delay or deterioration. This may be found in infantile neuroaxonal dystrophy, metachromatic leukodystrophy, and Krabbe's disease. Additional physical findings such as enlarged viscera or an increased head circumference may suggest a specific storage disease.

As noted at the outset, recent advances in biochemistry have demonstrated a metabolic defect for many of these degenerative disorders. This is particularly true for those known as "lysosomal storage" diseases (see Chapter 30). The concept of lysosomal storage diseases was introduced by Hers in the 1960's when he proposed that these organelles contain hydrolytic enzymes that aid in the complete catabolism of specific proteins, carbohydrates, or complex lipids. In this view, these storage disorders are caused by a specific inherited defect in lysosome function, resulting in only partial degradation of endogenous substances. The lysosomes may then become engorged with the partially degraded material.

In the past because of the universally poor outlook and the fact that brain tissue for chemical analysis was often required, definitive diagnosis was not pursued. Today, determination of specific enzyme defects of many of the storage diseases can often be made from cultured skin fibroblasts, urine, and leukocytes. Vigorous pursuit of the diagnosis is important today in order to give the family accurate genetic counseling. More importantly, we may soon be able to afford therapeutic intervention in some of the inherited metabolic neurodegenerative diseases. In any child in whom such a diagnosis is suspected, a diagnostic evaluation is warranted.

LABORATORY EVALUATION

Initial screening tests can be performed easily because they are relatively inexpensive and cover a wide spectrum of etiologies. However, the possibility of false negatives (as discussed in the Appendix) must always be considered. Metabolic urinary screens consisting of ferric chloride, nitroprusside, dinitrophenylhydrazine, ketone, and reducing substance tests can be performed in most hospital laboratories and will aid in elimination of other groups of disorders. Serum electrolytes, complete blood count (with a search for intracellular inclusions), and BUN are also indicated. Other tests may be designed for more specific diagnostic testing: skull X-rays for intracranial calcifications seen in toxoplasmosis, cytomegalic inclusion disease, tuberous sclerosis, and so on; bone X-rays to demonstrate signs suggesting storage disease, such as long bone changes in Gaucher's disease or vertebral body changes in Hurler's disease.

More specific neurodiagnostic tests may be required to ascertain at which level of the CNS the effects are most striking. EEG's may substantiate a seizure disorder or give evidence of a chronic encephalopathy. EMG and nerve conduction time abnormalities may suggest evidence of a peripheral neuropathy as seen in metachromatic leukodystrophy. Lumbar puncture may be useful in some diseases; elevated CSF proteins are seen with some leukodystrophies, i.e., MLD and Krabbe's disease. In addition, spinal fluid studies for specific infections such as measles titers, for possible subacute sclerosing panencephalitis, should be considered. Other procedures such as visual evoked response, electronystagmography, and electroretinography are available to evaluate optic pathway abnormalities. Today, computerized tomography can demonstrate evidence of cortical atrophy and may differentiate structural defects in white or gray matter, dysmyelination (e.g., Pelizaeus-Merzbacher disease), or hereditary defects, (e.g., tuberous sclerosis).

Often the yield from such screening tests is low and more specific testing may be required.

Today, enzyme assay is the next step in many hospitals where such studies may be available. Indeed, occasionally the clinical picture will be clear enough that enzyme assays on leukocytes are warranted without amassing nonspecific substantiating data. At other times, these less specific studies are desirable because of the need to be selective in choosing which patients will require the more time-consuming enzyme studies. If storage is likely in an extra-CNS site, bone marrow evaluation may demonstrate Gaucher cells or foam cells and inclusion bodies in diseases such as GM_1 gangliosidosis or I cell.

Since definitive diagnosis of a number of the well-characterized lysosomal storage diseases can now be accomplished by assay of white cells or cultured skin fibroblasts, it is appropriate to request those studies when the clinical picture and/or ancillary data point to a progressive neurodegenerative disorder. Usually it is necessary to assay a number of the lysosomal hydrolases, since the clinical picture of very few are characteristic enough to be sure which enzyme is defective.

In those instances in which the enzyme assays have been unavailing, it may be necessary to perform a rectal biopsy for electron microscopy. Rarely, if ever, is a brain biopsy necessary. If the patient is so affected that a brain biopsy is contemplated, most often a post-mortem examination will suffice. It is essential that the discussion about the needs for an autopsy occur before death is imminent so that the highly emotional atmosphere attending the death of a child not prejudice this often very useful, and at that point, noninvasive study.

REFERENCES

DeJong, R.N.: The Neurological Examination. 4th ed. Harper & Row, Hagerstown, Maryland, 1979.
Farmer, T.W. (ed.): Pediatric Neurology. 2nd ed. Harper & Row, Hagerstown, Maryland, 1975.
Swaiman, K.F., and Wright, F.S. (eds.): The Practice of Pediatric Neurology. 2nd ed. C.V. Mosby, St. Louis, 1982.
Volpe, J.J.: Neurology of the Newborn. W.B. Saunders Co., Philadelphia, 1981.

19

Mental Retardation

The finely orchestrated events that occur within the central nervous system are exquisitely dependent upon the constancy of supply of oxygen and metabolic fuels as well as maintenance of the internal milieu. A broad spectrum of metabolic disorders can result in profound and often permanent disruption of cerebral function (Table 19–1). Nowhere is this more apparent than in the infant in whom the rapidly developing nervous system is particularly vulnerable to metabolic perturbations, with disruption in the normal pattern of development leading to permanent impairment of function. What is not known in many of the disorders causing mental retardation is the locus of the defect, i.e., is it at synapses, is it in myelin, or is it at the level of the integrated functioning of the nervous system? Here we will try to develop a coherent view of what is known about brain development and the way that it may be affected deleteriously. We will also try to develop some useful clinical-biochemical principles concerning the pathogenesis of mental retardation, recognizing at the outset that attempts at such a synthesis are tentative at best.

At every level of biological function the ability to receive and process information is fundamental. Cells possess receptor sites at which informational molecules (neurotransmitters, hormones) bind and elicit a biochemical response. The endocrine system and nervous system are two prime examples of information receipt and response generation. However, the integration of function and breadth of response in the nervous system has no counterpart in any other system of the body. The pattern of responsiveness that emerges points to two important organizational principles of the nervous system: (1) the inter-relationship between neural cells and so-called supporting tissues is crucial to normal function and (2) a full understanding of neural function requires an understanding of the integrated properties of billions of cells acting in concert to produce an effect (e.g., memory, consciousness) not achievable below some critical mass of cells and organization.

Certain inherited diseases, most particularly the lipid storage diseases (Chapter 30), cause profound mental deterioration in association with widespread disruption of cellular and subcellular organization. However, the majority of inborn errors associated with mental retardation do not cause such pervasive structural abnormalities and so the puzzle as to where they disrupt neural function is more difficult to decipher.

In man, as well as in the experimental animals from which much information has been derived, the brain undergoes a phase of accelerated growth in which an increase in brain weight and acceleration of other developmental processes reaches a crescendo—the growth spurt. It is a stage at which the neurons have attained the adult number and during which there is considerable multiplication of glial cells. Subsequently, myelination quickens, with a significant incorporation of cholesterol, glycosphingolipids, and phospholipids. Myelin appears to be an insulating material of paramount importance, ensuring the correct functioning of the complex network of neurons, axons, and dendrites. Concomitant with the increase of electrical activity and arborization of neurons of the developing brain is a notable increase in the amounts of neurotransmitters and gangliosides.

At a more macroscopic level, by term the infant's brain has achieved the adult complement of neurons but nonetheless weighs only about 400 g. With the continuing development of brain microcircuitry and insulation spoken of above the brain weighs about 1 kg by one year of age and by two years about 1.3 kg. Although myelination is substantially completed by the end of two years of age, it continues until the twenties.

A major factor in the unique vulnerability of the brain to deprivational and toxic perturbations during its growth and development is that many events occurring during this period either take place

Table 19–1   DISORDERS ASSOCIATED WITH MENTAL RETARDATION

Amino Acid Disorders
  Carnosinemia (3)*
  Gamma-glutamyl transpeptidase deficiency
  Hartnup disease (4,5,7)
  Histidinemia (4)
  Homocystinuria (cystathionine-β-synthase) (3–5,7)
  Hydroxylysinemia (α-aminoadipic aciduria) (3)
  Hyper-β-alaninemia (3)
  Hyperleucinemia (3–5)
  Hyperlysinemia, episodic (3,4)
  Hyperlysinemia, persistent (3,7)
  Hypervalinemia (1,4,5)
  Lysinuric protein intolerance (3,4,6,7)
  β-Mercaptolactate cysteine disulfiduria (3)
  Methionine malabsorption syndrome (2,3,7)
  Nonketotic hyperglycinemia (1,3,4)
  Pipecolic acidemia (4–6)
  Phenylketonuria (phenylalanine hydroxylase) (3–5,7)
  Tyrosine amino transferase deficiency (5,7)
  Tryptophanuria (4,7)
Organic Acidemias
  Glutaric aciduria (2)
  Isovaleric acidemia (1,2,3)
  β-Ketothiolase deficiency (2,3)
  Maple syrup urine disease (1,2,3)
  Methylmalonic aciduria (1,2,3)
  Propionic acidemia (1,2,3)
  Pyroglutamic aciduria (2,4)
  Pyruvate carboxylase deficiency (2)
  Pyruvate dehydrogenase deficiency (2,4)
Urea Cycle Defects
  Argininosuccinic aciduria (3,4,6,7)
  Carbamyl phosphate synthetase deficiency (3)
  Citrullinemia (3,4)
  Hyperargininemia (3,4,6)
  Hyperornithinemia (3)
  Hyperornithinemia, hyperammonemia,
    and homocitrullinuria (3)
  Ornithine transcarbamylase deficiency (3)

Carbohydrate Disorders
  Galactosemia (5,6)
  Glycogen storage diseases (3,6)
  Glycogen synthetase deficiency (3)
  Hypoglycemia (5)
  Leigh's syndrome (2,3,7)
Neurodegenerative Disorders
  Mucopolysaccharidoses
    β-Glucuronidase deficiency (5,6)
    Hunter's syndrome (5,6,7)
    Hurler's syndrome (5,6,7)
    Mucolipidoses (see Chapter 32)
    Mucopolysaccharidosis VIII (6)
    Sanfilippo's syndrome (3–7)
  Sphingolipidoses and Lipid Disorders
    Abetalipoproteinemia (4,5)
    Gaucher's disease (5,6,7)
    GM$_1$ gangliosidosis (5,6)
    Krabbe's disease (3,4)
    Metachromatic leukodystrophy (4,5)
    Niemann-Pick disease (3,4,5,6,7)
    Tay-Sachs disease (3–5)
  Defect Unknown
    Alexander's disease
    Canavan's disease
    Ceroid lipofuscinosis (3–5,6)
    Neuronal-axonal dystrophy (3)
    Schilder's disease (5)
Other
  Ataxia-telangiectasia (4,5,7)
  Cretinism (5,7)
  Familial dysautonomia (5)
  Formiminoglutamic aciduria (4)
  Hypophosphatasia (late manifestation
    of oxycephaly) (3,4)
  Lesch-Nyhan syndrome (4)
  Lowe's syndrome (5)
  Menkes' disease (3,7)
  Myotonic dystrophy (5)
  Neonatal hyperbilirubinemia (3,4)
  Nephrogenic diabetes insipidus
  Pseudo hypoparathyroidism (5)

*Associated findings: 1—catastrophic presentation in the neonate; 2—derangements of acid-base balance; 3—seizures; 4—other neurologic; 5—eye findings; 6—visceromegaly; 7—skin and/or hair findings.

when all the components are present, or they never take place. At a microscopic level this translates into a deficit of structural elements, such that the appropriate number and diversity of synaptic connections do not form. Hence, the immensely intricate "wiring diagram" of the normal brain is not achieved. To gauge what we are speaking of, in rat brain each neuron is engaged in several hundred to upwards of 20,000 synapses. Estimates of the neuronal population of rat brain run to 150,000,000; the human brain is 700 times heavier than rat brain. We are clearly confronted by a complexity beyond our present understanding.

PATHOGENESIS OF MENTAL RETARDATION IN INBORN ERRORS OF METABOLISM

Any theory that attempts to explain the pathogenesis of mental retardation in inborn errors must recognize that the consequence of the metabolic defect can be either a permanent structural defect or a reversible functional defect. While the pathogenesis of these two classes of sequelae may be different, at some threshold point a functional perturbation must be expressed as a permanent structural defect. The heightened liability of the infant and young child to retardation are referable then to the rapid growth of the CNS during that period of life. In analogy to our discussion of failure to thrive (see Chapter 10), "arrest" in the development of the CNS at a critical point may, depending on the severity of the perturbation, permanently impair the potential of that nervous system for normal function.

What has been discussed thus far should have prepared the reader for the view that abnormalities introduced during a critical and formative stage of cerebral development are very likely to be irreversible or at best only partially reversible. However, it is important to avoid the simplistic notion that "toxic" levels of normal metabolites are the direct cause of such abnormalities. In Part I of this text we discussed the complexity of metabolic regulatory mechanisms such as feedback or product inhibition, allosterism, and so on. Thus, it is entirely possible that deficits of metabolites distal to an enzyme defect may produce deficient synthesis of one or more critical brain elements. Alternatively, it is conceivable that it is the "toxic" effects of excess intermediates that inhibit enzymatic synthesis of those same elements. Generally, then, there are three potential means by which a given inborn error may result in cerebral dysfunction:

(1) a direct toxicity or lethality toward brain cellular elements, mediated by an inhibitory effect of the high levels of intermediates proximal to the defect upon one or more critical metabolic pathways;
(2) an indirect toxicity or lethality, mediated by deficient synthesis of compounds distal to the defect necessary for normal synthetic or regulatory metabolic pathways;
(3) a combination of 1 and 2 to varying degrees.

It is very likely that any given metabolic disease in which one sees cerebral dysfunction represents a combination of direct and indirect toxicity effects. Many published studies support this view.

Aminoacidopathies

While we must rely on measurements of plasma amino acids to diagnose many of the aminoacidopathies, it is important to note that such levels do not necessarily reflect the state of amino acid pools within the tissues. Indeed the bulk of the body's free amino acids are intracellular. Moreover, there are distinct differences in the amino acid composition of brain as opposed to other organs. Most particularly amino acids and amino acid metabolites with a putative neurotransmitter role are found in much higher concentrations in cerebral tissue. These include gamma-aminobutyric acid (GABA), N-acetylaspartate, glycine, glutamate, taurine, and glutathione. In contrast, methionine, isoleucine, tyrosine, phenylalanine, and ornithine are normally found in low concentrations in brain. This dichotomy in concentrations points, at least circumstantially, to a pathogenic role for elevation in concentration of those amino acids normally found in lowest concentration.

Not only are there regional differences within the brain in amino acid concentration; there are differences between cell types as well as among the organelles within the cells. Active transport-mediated uptake and concentration of a number of amino acids has been shown in subcellular preparations, the most striking of which are synaptic endings (synaptosomes). Indeed, organelles from cerebral cells are able to accumulate specific amino acids against a concentration gradient to a greater degree in vitro than are these organelles (lysosomes, mitochondria, and nuclei) isolated from kidney, liver, and muscle. Most assuredly this prodigious uptake capacity of brain organelles must give a clue to the activities that underlie neural function. At the least, precursor pools for protein synthesis (? memory) and neurotransmitter synthesis are most likely separate and under distinct controls within neurons.

Correlating in vitro experiments with in vivo levels of metabolites is a necessary first step in assigning physiological significance to abnormal intracellular levels of amino acids and metabolites. Where this has been done in phenylketonuria (PKU) and maple syrup urine disease (MSUD), the results support a pathophysiological role for the accumulated substances.

Support for a synthetic failure in the etiology of mental retardation due to inborn errors has come from investigations into the interdependence of structure and function. In PKU, for example, the total lipid content is lower and the ratio of cholesterol to galactolipid is significantly higher in white matter from patients with this disorder than in white matter from non-PKU individuals with mental retardation. This accords with an early arrest of myelination rather than demyelination. In maple syrup urine disease, as well, studies demonstrate amyelination. In general, such data, along with in vitro studies, point to a defect in elaboration of the protein structural elements of the brain with secondary effects on lipid components of myelin.

Investigations into the effect of the high levels of amino acids (>2 mM) on protein synthesis show that there is a general perturbation of the process whereby the particular aminoacyl tRNA synthetase joins with the amino acid to be incorporated into the growing protein. Indeed, in general, protein synthesis is not affected, nor is incorporation of aminoacyl tRNAs into protein. Polyribosomal disaggregation has been demonstrated, but this may be protein specific.

Serotonin synthesis is decreased in patients with PKU, most likely as a result of phenylalanine inhibition of tryptophan transport into the cell as well as competitive inhibition of the enzyme tryptophan hydrolase. How such an effect is translated into mental retardation (i.e., a permanent change) remains unclear. Phenylalanine has been shown to inhibit glycolysis at the pyruvate kinase step in human and rat brain. Fetal brain shows greater susceptibility than does mature brain. What has not been demonstrated is whether the postulated fall in ATP production, so necessary for biosynthetic reactions, actually occurs.

In another study, alpha-ketoisocaproate (the alpha-ketoacid derivative of leucine that accumulates in MSUD) has been shown to inhibit both the pyruvate and alpha-ketoglutarate dehydrogenase multienzyme complexes. As a consequence flux through the Krebs cycle would be greatly diminished and entry into the GABA shunt impaired. All of these studies suggest metabolite toxicity on related metabolic pathways. The literature, taken as a whole, supports the likelihood that mental retardation, at least in PKU and MSUD, results from a combination of direct and indirect effects of metabolites on the developing brain.

The Threshold for Neurological Deficit

It appears that there are several metabolic consequences to a single inborn error and that each may contribute to the brain dysfunction so common in these disorders. Complicating the matter still further is the total genetic endowment of an individual, which may permit some with a given inborn error nonetheless to escape, apparently intact neurologically. What biochemical traits in the genome of such individuals provide protection against deleterious effects that devastate most patients is more an enigma than the cause of mental dysfunction itself. For example, while most patients with PKU are retarded if not treated, there are some patients, apparently devoid of phenylalanine hydroxylase activity, who are not impaired neurologically despite the fact they have never been on a special diet. In homocystinuria, the relationship between the enzymic defect and development of mental retardation is also a puzzle. Clearly, there are factors yet to be understood that impinge on the ultimate prognosis for mental function. A realistic goal would be to be able to manipulate these other factors to improve the outcome for the patient.

REFERENCES

Cravioto, J., and Delicardie, E.R.: Nutrition, mental development and learning. *In:* Falkner, F., and Tanner, J.M. (eds.): Human Growth. Plenum Press, New York, 1979, p. 481.

Dobbing, J.: The later development of the brain and its vulnerability. *In* Davis, J.A., and Dobbing, J. (eds.): Scientific Foundations of Paediatrics. 2nd ed. Heinemann, London, 1981, p. 744.

Dobbing, J., and Sands, J.: Comparative aspects of the brain growth spurt. Early Hum. Dev. 3:79, 1979.

Gaull, G.E., Tallan, H.H., Lajtha, A., and Rassin, D.K.: Pathogenesis of brain dysfunction in inborn errors of amino acid metabolism. *In* Gaull, G.E. (ed.): Biology of Brain Dysfunction. Vol. 3. Plenum Press, New York, 1975, p. 47.

Gottlieb, D.I., and Glaser, L.: Cellular recognition during neural development. Ann. Rev. Neurosci. 3:303, 1980.

Katz, M.J., Lasek, R.J., and Nauta, H.J.W.: Ontogeny of the substrate pathways and the origin of the neural circuit pattern. Neuroscience 5:821, 1980.

Purves, D., and Lichtman, J.W.: Elimination of synapses in the developing nervous system. Science 210:153, 1980.

Raisman, G.: What hope for repair of the brain? Ann. Neurol. 3:101, 1978.

Reinis, S., and Goldman, J.: The Development of the Brain: Biological and Functional Perspectives. Charles C Thomas, Springfield, Illinois, 1980.

Rodier, P.M.: Chronology of neuron development: Animal studies and their clinical implications. Develop. Med. Child Neurol. 22:525, 1980.

Rose, S.P.R.: What should a biochemistry of learning and memory be about? Neuroscience 6:811, 1981.

Stent, G.S.: Strength and weakness of the genetic approach to the development of the nervous system. Ann. Rev. Neurosci. 4:163, 1981.

Tsukahara, N.: Synaptic plasticity in the mammalian central nervous system. Ann. Rev. Neurosci. 4:351, 1981.

Winick, M., and Morgan, B.L.G.: Nutrition and cellular growth of the brain. In Freinkel, N. (ed.): Contemporary Metabolism. Vol. I. Plenum Press, New York, 1979, p. 165.

20

Odor, Skin, and Hair

The use of the senses in physical diagnosis was described by the ancient physicians, dating as far back as the time of Hippocrates. Hippocrates himself used the sense of taste to diagnose a patient with diabetes mellitus. Every description of cystic fibrosis in medical testbooks includes a description of the stool as large, bulky, and "foul-smelling." Since the human nose is eminently more sensitive to odors than any laboratory equipment hitherto developed, every patient seen by a physician deserves the benefit of a "careful sniff or two" in the process of performing a physical examination, and parents should be questioned regarding atypical or abnormal odors of feces, urine, sweat, and so on. Sniffing should include urine, breath, and cerumen. In infants, leaving a finger in the baby's mouth for a few moments may facilitate identifying an unusual odor, which can be appreciated on the saliva.

OLFACTORY MANIFESTATIONS OF METABOLIC DISEASE

Detection of an odor signifies the presence of a volatile compound. Perhaps the most obvious clinical example is the acetonuria and the odor of acetone typically detected in the breath of a patient with diabetic ketoacidosis. In such a patient, the origin of the large amounts of acetone is the production of tremendous quantities of ketone bodies, one of which is acetoacetate. Acetoacetate is spontaneously and enzymatically decarboxylated to yield CO_2 and acetone. Since the respiratory tract is the major excretory organ for volatile compounds, it should surprise no one that acetone readily appears on the breath of the patient with ketoacidosis. In general, the pathophysiology of many diseases associated with odors follows a very similar pattern. A list of such disorders appears in Table 20–1.

In interpreting this table, it is important to recognize that the urine represents an extremely

Table 20–1 ODORS ASSOCIATED WITH METABOLIC DISORDERS

Disorder	Description
Maple syrup urine disease	Pancake syrup or burnt sugar
Isovaleric acidemia	Sweaty feet
Glutaric aciduria, Type II	
Phenylketonuria	Musty; mouse-urine
Tyrosinemia	Methionine (cabbage-like)
Methionine malabsorption (Oasthouse syndrome)	Malt or hops
β-Methylcrotonic aciduria	Tomcat urine
β-Hydroxy-β-methylglutaryl CoA lyase deficiency	
Uremia	Ammoniacal, fishy
Diabetic ketoacidosis	Decomposing fruit, acetone-like
Methylmalonic acidemia	Ammoniacal
Reye's syndrome	
Propionic acidemia	
Urea cycle defects	
Hawkinsinuria	Swimming pool (chlorine-like)
Trimethylaminuria	Fishy

concentrated sample of the blood, so that substances that may be present in trace amounts in blood are concentrated in easily detectable quantities in urine. Therefore, substances that are present in excess but are not highly volatile and are therefore not excreted primarily by the lung, may be present in quantities in urine sufficient to be detected by the olfactory sense. In this regard it is worthwhile to note that the musty odor of the urine of the phenylketonuric patient was the primary reason for the initial description of phenylketonuria as an inborn error of metabolism. The compound responsible for the musty odor is thought to be phenylacetic acid. Similarly in tyrosinemia, blood methionine levels may reach such extraordinary heights that the methionine itself gives off a characteristic (cabbage-like) odor.

Maple syrup urine disease often presents in the neonatal period with respiratory arrest of no apparent precedent cause, and the simple maneuver of smelling the freshly voided urine may give the physician a very strong clue as to the etiology of his patient's respiratory arrest. Such ease of diagnosis can hardly be equaled by any laboratory procedure. Finally, it is probably worth noting that a routine collection of urine for laboratory diagnosis in cases where an odor is detected is usually not adequate. This is an all too frequent reason for misdiagnosis. The volatility of the offending compounds may be so great that their presence will go utterly undetected by the time the routinely treated urine specimen reaches the responsible laboratory. It is therefore incumbent upon the concerned physician to contact the laboratory to which he plans to send the sample prior to its collection in order to establish the most expeditious means for diagnosis of his patient's disease (cf. Chap. 38).

SKIN AND HAIR MANIFESTATIONS OF METABOLIC DISEASE

As noted in the section on odor, the use of one's senses has a hoary tradition in medicine. Since the skin and hair (because of their ready accessibility) represent a window on the body, careful inspection and evaluation can be very helpful in gathering evidence for a generalized (met-

Table 20–2   SKIN INVOLVEMENT IN METABOLIC DISORDERS

Disorder	Skin Condition
Albinism	Hypopigmentation, light sensitivity
Chédiak-Higashi syndrome	Hypopigmentation
Cretinism (2,3)*	Dry, cool
Cutis laxa	Hyperextensible
Ehlers-Danlos syndrome	Fragility, extensibility
Farber's lipogranulomatosis	Skin papules
Gaucher's disease (1–3)	Hyperpigmentation
Hartnup disease (1)	Light-sensitive rash
Holocarboxylase synthetase deficiency (2)	Rash
Homocystinuria (1–3)	Mottling, malar flush
Hyperlipoproteinemias	
Type I	Eruptive xanthomatosis
Type IIA	Tendinous xanthomatosis
Type IIB	Xanthelasmata
Type III (3)	Xanthomata in creases of palms and interphalangeal creases of fingers
Hurler's syndrome (2,3)	
Niemann-Pick disease (1–3)	Hyperpigmentation
Phenylketonuria (1–3)	Eczema
Porphyria	Light-sensitive rash
Pseudoxanthoma elasticum (3)	
Refsum's disease	Hyperkeratosis
Riley-Day syndrome	Absence of sweating
Sanfilippo syndrome (1–3)	
Tyrosinemia, Oregon variant (3)	Hyperkeratosis, blistering

* Associated findings: 1—seizures; 2—mental retardation; 3—eye findings.

Table 20–3 HAIR CONDITIONS ASSOCIATED WITH
METABOLIC DISORDERS

Alopecia	**Abnormal Form**
Homocystinuria	Homocystinuria
Hyperlysinemia, persistent	Menkes' syndrome
Menkes' syndrome	Argininosuccinic aciduria
Progeria	
Thyroid deficiency	
Myotonic dystrophy	
Hirsutism	**Fair Hair**
Hunter's syndrome	Albinism
Hurler's syndrome	PKU
Scheie' syndrome	Homocystinuria
Porphyria	Histidinemia
Addison's disease	Isovaleric acidemia
	Cystinosis
	Menkes' syndrome

abolic) disorder (Tables 20–2 and 20–3). Expanding the evaluation of skin to a review of previous dermatological manifestations and questioning about sensitivity to sunlight or other exogenous agents also may prove to be very productive.

Further discussion about these dermatological manifestations can be found under the discussion of the specific disease entity in Part III.

REFERENCES

Odor

Hayden, G.F.: Olfactory diagnosis in medicine. Postgrad. Med. 67:110, 1980.

Skin

Der Kaloustian, V.M., and Kurban, A.K.: Genetic Disease of the Skin. Springer-Verlag, Berlin, 1979.
Fitzpatrick, T.B., Eisen, A.Z., Wolff, K., Freedberg, I.M., and Austen, K.F. (eds.): Dermatology in General Medicine. McGraw-Hill, New York, 1979.
Hurwitz, S.: Clinical Pediatric Dermatology. W.B. Saunders Co., Philadelphia, 1981.

21

Splenomegaly

The major functions of the spleen include: (1) removal or sequestration of red cells, platelets, and lymphocytes; (2) filtration of the blood for bacterial elements with concomitant production of opsonizing antibody; and (3) removal of the particulate elements from the cytoplasm of juvenile red blood cells.

Some disorders of the spleen manifested by splenic enlargement are intrinsic to the splenic cells themselves. Others result from an increased load on the splenic macrophages as a consequence of abnormalities elsewhere in the body. In still others the spleen is affected as a part of a multi-system disorder, such as in systemic lupus erythematosus, or on the basis of mechanical factors, such as in cirrhosis of the liver with portal hypertension. In this section, we will attempt to group the disorders listed in Table 20–1 into those categories and discuss one or two prototypic diseases in such a way as to illustrate the mechanisms underlying splenic enlargement in each category.

INTRINSIC SPLENIC DEFECTS

Disorders in this category are related by the common mechanism of a decreased rate of deg-radation of normally synthesized metabolic compounds. This decreased rate of catabolism is gen-erally attributable to the partial or complete absence of a catabolic enzyme. The prototype illustrat-ing these principles is Gaucher's disease or glucocerebrosidase deficiency (see Chapter 30).

The histopathologic basis for the gross enlargement of the spleen in Gaucher's disease is the presence of tremendous numbers of the so-called Gaucher cell. The Gaucher cell, usually between 20 and 100 μ in size, often with an eccentric nucleus, appears to derive from glucocerebroside engorgement of cells from the reticuloendothelial system. Although not entirely proven, the devel-opment of Gaucher cells is believed to result from a deficiency of glucocerebrosidase in reticuloen-dothelial cells of affected patients. The major source of glycolipid, the substrate for the glucocere-brosidase, derives from the membrane of red and white blood cells. The two relevant glycolipids are globoside from erythrocyte membrane and ceramide lactoside of the leukocyte membrane.

Since the spleen is the organ primarily responsible for monitoring the circulating red and white blood cells and removing those that are either damaged or senescent, it stands to reason that the spleen might undergo enlargement in a storage disorder. Although the glucocerebrosidase deficiency has been demonstrated in a variety of tissues, including peripheral leukocytes of affected individ-

Table 21–1 CAUSES OF SPLENOMEGALY

Intrinsic	Extrinsic
Cretinism	Pernicious anemia
Gaucher's disease	Hemolytic anemia
Gangliosidosis GM_1	Leukemia
Hemosiderosis	Sickle cell disease
Mucolipidoses	Galactosemia
Hurler's syndrome	Hereditary fructose intolerance
Multiple sulfatase deficiency	Thalassemia
Niemann-Pick disease	Tyrosinemia
Porphyria	
Sandhoff's disease	
Wolman's disease	

uals, there is no report of glycolipid storage in circulating, formed elements of the blood. Thus, the mechanism of development of the Gaucher cell is assumed to be a normal rate of red and white cell turnover that results in delivery of a normal load of neutral glycolipid to the reticuloendothelial system and its fixed cellular elements, with a deficiency of breakdown and subsequent lysosomal storage. Further discussion of the biochemistry of Gaucher's disease can be found in Chapter 30. The slowly increasing storage of partially degraded glycosphingolipids in the lysosomes of each reticuloendothelial cell within the spleen results in massive enlargement of the organ, sometimes to the point where it will occupy the entire left side of the abdomen. Other diseases included in this category of intrinsic enzymatic defects of the spleen manifest in a fashion very similar to that described for Gaucher's disease.

EXTRINSIC CAUSES OF INCREASED STORAGE

Many of these disorders also have as a biochemical basis an inherited enzymatic deficiency. However, this group of diseases differs from the preceding one because the genetic defect does not involve the cellular elements of the spleen but rather the cells of other tissue. Hemoglobinopathies, such as thalassemia major or sickle cell disease, are the prototypes of this category.

Strictly speaking, sickle cell disease does not result from a specific enzyme deficiency; it is due to a structurally abnormal protein with consequent abnormal oxygen-binding properties. Alteration of the coded sequence of the purine and pyrimidine bases of DNA results in the synthesis of a hemoglobin in which a valine residue is substituted for glutamic acid in the sixth position of the beta chain of the hemoglobin molecule. In a very real sense then, hemoglobin S disease reflects the interrelation between structure and function dealt with in Part I of this book. The presence of the single abnormal substitution in the globin molecule alters the hemoglobin molecules' conformation in such a fashion that when the alpha and beta chains interact during oxygenation and deoxygenation of the molecule, they cause the erythrocyte to assume a "sickle" form.

Hypoxia or acidosis, alone or in combination, will increase the rate of sickle formation. The sickled red cells form a clump that totally or partially obstructs small blood vessels. Sludging of the blood that ensues will aggravate a decrease in pH and an increase in the degree of hypoxia, thus enhancing the sickle effect. The net result of this process is the establishment of a microinfarct in the area supplied by the vessel. Because the driving force for blood flow through the red pulp of the spleen is essentially equal to portal venous pressure, the spleen is a target organ for establishment of microinfarcts in sickle cell disease. Initially, this process forces the spleen to step up its rate of breakdown and assimilation of of the damaged red blood cells, with consequent increase in the rate of storage of the red cell elements.

Thus, early in the disease, splenomegaly is a very common finding, based purely upon the increased rate of red cell destruction and the attendant storage of red cell constituents. Eventually, the extent of microinfarction in the spleen will result in destruction of functioning splenic tissue, with the final consequence being the process known as auto-infarction of the spleen. In patients with this degree of splenic damage, the spleen is often functionally and anatomically absent, so that splenomegaly is no longer a clinical finding.

Red cells that are abnormal either in the structure of their membrane, as in hereditary spherocytosis, or with respect to their intrinsic contents, as in the hemoglobinopathies, undergo accelerated removal by the spleen. Consequent increased breakdown of the red cells results in an increase in spleen size, manifested clinically as splenomegaly. Thus, the combination of splenomegaly with icterus, as a result of the overload of bilirubin sent from the spleen to the liver, should arouse suspicion of a hemolytic anemia.

Hypersplenism is another phenomenon that can account for a variety of disorders classified within this category. A typical example of hypersplenism is seen in the disorder known as tyrosinemia. Hypersplenism is characterized by splenomegaly accompanied by anemia, thrombocytopenia, and neutropenia together or in varying combinations. Characteristic of hypersplenism is the accentuation of normal breakdown processes carried out by the spleen, leading to the blood picture just described. Tyrosinemia is an excellent example in which one sees thrombocytopenia and frequently neutropenia, with anemia on occasion, perhaps due both to hypersplenism and to intravascular coagulation and a bleeding diathesis.

MISCELLANEOUS DISORDERS RESULTING IN SPLENOMEGALY

Included in this category are diseases of unknown etiology, as well as the disorders resulting in hepatic cirrhosis with secondary portal hypertension. One straightforward example of a mechanical cause for splenic enlargement is the development of hepatic cirrhosis.

In hepatic cirrhosis the pressure of the blood flowing towards the heart is exceeded by the resistance to its flow due to distortion of the hepatic lobular architecture. Thus, the intrahepatic increase in venous pressure is transmitted backwards into the portal vein. Since one of the major tributaries of the portal vein is the splenic vein, it is not surprising that in this disorder one regularly sees an increase in splenic size. It is highly probable that the increase in splenic size is exaggerated by the addition of hypersplenism, due to the large degree of stasis and hypoxia that exists because of poor blood flow through the red pulp of the spleen.

In other disorders, such as an arteritic-type disease like systemic lupus erythematosus, the perivascular infiltration in the spleen increases resistance to flow in a fashion similar to that seen in hepatic cirrhosis, with increasing stasis and a component of hypersplenism. Other disorders such as leukemia, with its tremendous infiltration of the splenic spaces by atypical white cells, may result in exaggerated breakdown of these atypical cells by the spleen, with subsequent development of what appear to be typical Gaucher cells.

REFERENCES

Green, M.: Pediatric Diagnosis: Interpretation of Symptoms and Signs in Different Age Periods. 3rd ed. W.B. Saunders Co., Philadelphia, 1980.

III

DISORDERS OF METABOLISM

22

Amino Acid Metabolic Disorders

DISORDERS OF PHENYLALANINE AND TYROSINE METABOLISM

Phenylketonuria (Defect: phenylalanine hydroxylase; Genetics: autosomal recessive; Prenatal Diagnosis: not accomplished)

Clinical Features

In 1934, Folling investigated two mentally retarded siblings who possessed an unusual odor. Initial studies revealed a compound in the urine that gave a green color with ferric chloride. Further studies showed this compound to be phenylpyruvic acid (the product of oxidative transamination of phenylalanine). This story represents medical detective work at its best and provided the first direct support for Garrod's predictions regarding inborn errors of metabolism. While classical phenylketonuria (PKU) is not one of the amino acid disorders that presents in the neonatal period, one may occasionally encounter vomiting and feeding difficulties in the first few weeks of life, often in association with pyloric stenosis, a relationship that is unexplained. Usually, early symptoms include excessive irritability and over-activity associated with a musty odor to the urine and sweat of the patients. Indeed, it is often the parents who are first to note the unusual odor so characteristic of these children. It is vital that the physician inquire of parents whether they have ever noted an unusual odor about their children. Eczematoid rashes seem to plague these infants and youngsters prior to the institution of a low phenylalanine diet. Intellectual development appears normal until between 3 and 5 months of age when the infant begins to demonstrate apathy and listlessness, often alternating with sporadic episodes of irritability.

As these children grow older, seizures occur in about 25 per cent. Hair and eyes are often less pigmented than in other members of the family. The behavior of these children seems to revolve around incessant activity. Uncontrollable temper tantrums are often set off by any stimulus. Such volatile behavior has often been the reason why these children have been admitted to institutions.

Biochemical Defects

The biochemical defect in classical PKU is the inability to carry out the normal hydroxylation of L-phenylalanine to tyrosine. The enzyme catalyzing this reaction is a so-called mixed function oxidase (phenylalanine hydroxylase), which is localized to liver, kidney, and pancreas only. Dietary phenylalanine and phenylalanine produced by the catabolism of tissue protein cannot be converted further into tyrosine; as a result, phenylalanine accumulates in body fluids. Minor catabolic pathways for phenylalanine come into play because of the accumulation of phenylalanine, which makes it possible for these pathways to be activated (Fig. 22–1). Such activation occurs through the metabolic regulation of enzyme activity, which is discussed in Chapter 2. As a consequence, in blood and urine one finds phenylpyruvate, phenyllactate, phenylacetate, and minor amounts of phenylethylamine, mandelic acid, and hippuric acid. An essential biochemical feature is the depres-

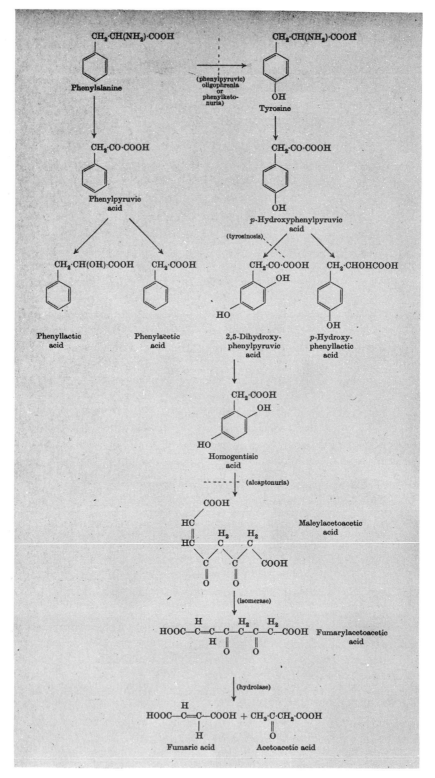

Figure 22–1 Major catabolic pathway for phenylalanine and tyrosine. The loci of known enzymatic defects are indicated by dashed lines. Note that hereditary tyrosinemia is now believed to be due to a defect in fumarylacetoacetate hydrolase, the final step in the pathway. (From Mazur, A., and Harrow, B.: Textbook of Biochemistry. Philadelphia, W.B. Saunders Co., 1971.)

sion in plasma of tyrosine levels because of the enzyme defect. The pigmentary defects in PKU appear to arise as a consequence of phenylalanine acting as a competitive inhibitor of tyrosinase, the enzyme responsible for production of melanin. It is curious that with the multiplicity of metabolites produced the only system severely deranged in phenylketonuria is the central nervous system. Considering the import of the brain to human conduct it is an important target organ indeed.

Damage to the developing central nervous system may be profound. Several studies indicate that the average loss in the development quotient during the first year of life in over 95 per cent of untreated patients is approximately 50 points. A consensus has thus developed that the earlier the diet is instituted the milder will be the effects on the brain.

Pathogenesis of Mental Retardation in Phenylketonuria

The noxious effects of PKU on the developing brain have been matters of great practical and experimental interest. Despite the enormous amount of research carried out on the pathogenesis of mental retardation in this disorder, it is not possible to point to any one factor as being causative (see Chapter 19). Research in this disease, and indeed in the general area of the inborn errors of amino acid metabolism, is severely hampered by the lack of a naturally occurring animal model that suffers the enzyme defect. Feeding high levels of phenylalanine results in elevated rather than depressed levels of tyrosine; use of the inhibitor p-chlorophenylalanine affects other enzymes as well, including pyruvate kinase. Additionally, it causes the formation of cataracts, a finding not encountered in PKU.

Minor metabolites that accumulate as a consequence of the alternate pathways utilized in phenylketonuria may normally serve either physiological or pharmacological roles in the nervous system. To aggravate the deficiency of tyrosine created by shunting into these minor pathways in PKU, phenylalanine inhibits tyrosine transport across biological membranes. In turn, this curtails the source of neuroactive tyrosine derivatives that can be synthesized, including tyramine, octopamine, and the catecholamines. One can speculate that such deficiencies could interfere with neurotransmitter action.

Elevated levels of phenylalanine have been shown to inhibit transport of other amino acids besides tyrosine. This might result in an imbalance of amino acids in brain that could disrupt protein synthesis or control of the synthesis of neurotransmitters. Several enzymes, including tyrosine hydroxylase, tryptophan hydroxylase, and pyruvate kinase, are inhibited in vitro by phenylalanine. Whether such phenomena obtain in the patient is not known; in four patients who died with PKU, catecholamine concentration and serotonin levels were much lower than in control brains from patients suffering mental retardation from other causes, a finding consistent with such a possible role in vivo.

Laboratory Diagnosis

The ferric chloride test can be used to suggest the diagnosis of PKU in an older child. It is positive in the presence of phenylpyruvic acid. However, during the first year of life, the test is often negative. This is the case when phenylpyruvic acid levels are less than 0.2 mg/ml, as may occur in very dilute urines or when protein intake has been very low for a period of time.

Several other metabolites, in particular from histidine and certain drugs such as chlorpromazine, may also produce a green color with the ferric chloride reagent. This test then is not an adequate screening test for PKU in infants. The method developed by Guthrie is now employed in all states in the United States as part of mandatory screening for this disorder. As performed in most screening labs the test will distinguish phenylalanine levels in excess of approximately 4 mg/dl in whole blood. Unfortunately, approximately 8 per cent of infants with classical PKU will have a negative Guthrie test within the first 3 days of life and it may not become positive until after the first week. Since there are occasional false negatives, the cautious physician is urged to consider the possibility of PKU in a child presenting with failure to thrive or any of the other symptoms discussed above. In such a situation a repeat Guthrie test is in order. The authors have encountered several such instances in which the initial testing by the state was negative but repeated testing, because of physician concern, was positive and led to the unequivocal diagnosis of phenylketonuria.

Variant Forms of Hyperphenylalaninemia

The most common cause of an elevation of the serum phenylalanine level above 4 mg per dl is the transient neonatal delay in development of the tyrosine oxidizing system (transient neonatal tyrosinemia). This condition, while far more common in low birth weight and premature infants, does occur occasionally in full-term infants as well. The elevation of phenylalanine is secondary to a block in the metabolism of tyrosine. Administration of 100 mg of ascorbic acid will reduce the tyrosine levels, but whether this is necessary is an area of some controversy.

In an infant with a serum phenylalanine concentration greater than 4 mg/dl Berry has recommended the following: (1) administration of 100 mg of ascorbic acid 24 hours prior to obtaining a repeat blood specimen, and (2) measurement of phenylalanine and tyrosine in blood and evaluation of urine for the presence of phenylalanine, O-hydroxyphenylacetic acid, and phenylpyruvic acid as well as tyrosine and tyrosine derivatives (p-hydroxyphenyllactic acid and p-hydroxyphenylpyruvic acid) by paper chromatography and spot tests. The majority of infants will be found to have a transient defect that will remit within two weeks of testing.

In a statewide screening program few infants will manifest persistent elevations of phenylalanine in the range of 4 to 20 mg/dl. Serum tyrosine will be low or normal, and the urine will be negative for phenylalanine metabolites. In all likelihood this represents a hyperphenylalaninemia variant or a delay in maturation of the hydroxylase system. Repetition of blood and urine screening while on an unrestricted diet should permit distinction. With classical phenylketonuria the serum phenylalanine will rise and urinary metabolites should appear. With delayed maturation of the hydroxylase system, as activity of the system increases serum phenylalanine concentrations will fall. By the age of three weeks if blood phenylalanine levels exceed 15 mg/dl regardless of the presence of metabolites in urine, restriction of phenylalanine intake is indicated. Multiple variant forms of PKU have been described.

Unfortunately, distinguishing among the various forms of PKU may not be possible by routine laboratory testing, and a number of workers have recommended the use of a phenylalanine loading test to separate the variant forms. The rationale and technique for performance of this loading test can be found in the references following this section. The test should only be performed in centers that are equipped to quantitate the specimens obtained and to embark upon the definitive care of affected infants through the restriction of phenylalanine in the diet.

Regarding the dihydropteridine reductase deficiency and defect in biosynthesis of biopterin (discussed below), further studies may be in order in some hyperphenylalaninemic infants.

Treatment

Treatment of PKU with a diet restricted in phenylalanine content is unquestioned in children whose phenylalanine levels are greater than 20 mg/dl and for whom the diagnosis of classical PKU appears to be unequivocal. Children whose diagnosis cannot be clearly delineated or who may have some variant of PKU pose great diagnostic difficulty for the expert in metabolic diseases. Diagnosis in such cases may require the use of either loading studies or enzyme assay in a liver biopsy. The use of diet therapy requires that phenylalanine be maintained above 3 mg/dl so that there not be any restriction of growth as a consequence of amino acid deficiency. This requires that children be treated in centers with a team that includes the pediatrician, nutritionist, and laboratory facilities to monitor amino acid levels. The diet for these children is severely restricted, requiring the creativity of nutritionist and parents to make it as palatable as possible in order to prolong treatment as long as necessary. At present, recommendations for duration of therapy vary from cessation in the fifth to cessation in the tenth year of life; current opinion leans toward keeping children on the diet longer because of possible deleterious effects on the developing central nervous system. Successfully treated female patients with PKU must resume the diet prior to conception because of the risk to the fetus (even if genetically normal) of the heightened level of phenylalanine and metabolites.

Dihydropteridine Reductase Deficiency

Clinical Features

In contrast to classical PKU, this variant is unresponsive to prompt institution of dietary phenylalanine restriction. Clinical recognition comes about because of the development of seizures, hypotonia, choreiform movements, and psychomotor retardation in a patient demonstrating elevated serum phenylalanine and depressed tyrosine. This is seen despite normalization of phenylalanine levels on a restricted diet.

Biochemical Defects

Assay of phenylalanine hydroxylase in a liver biopsy from one patient showed 20 per cent of normal adult control values, but dihydropteridine reductase activity (Fig. 22–2) was less than 1 per cent of normal in liver, brain, and other tissues. This latter deficiency prevents regeneration of tetrahydrobiopterin, the cofactor for the hydroxylase reaction. Since the reductase enzyme reaction regenerates the cofactor for both tyrosine and tryptophan hydroxylase, catecholamine and serotonin synthesis are compromised as well. Patient studies are scanty, but in one patient dopamine and serotonin were decreased in cerebrospinal fluid, brain, and various other tissues while norepinephrine metabolites were normal. This latter discrepancy is at present unexplained. While phenylalanine hydroxylase activity was lower than that of adult controls, it has not been determined whether this value represented significantly decreased activity in children.

By high-pressure liquid chromatography it is possible to show that patients with this variant of hyperphenylalaninemia excrete only oxidized forms of biopterin in their urine; normal children and those with phenylalanine hydroxylase deficiency excrete tetrahydrobiopterin predominantly.

Replacement therapy with L-dopa and 5-hydroxytryptophan has been suggested as the means to circumvent the block in synthesis of dopamine and serotonin. Ascorbate, which stabilizes tetrahydrobiopterin in vitro, may have some place in therapy as well.

Biopterin Deficiency—Hyperphenylalaninemia

Several patients have now been described with this variant of hyperphenylalaninemia. Neurological symptoms, particularly hypotonia and delay in motor development, are recognized earlier than with classical PKU. In spite of adequate control of serum phenylalanine levels deterioration continues unabated. Seizures have not been encountered in these patients as they have with dihydropteridine reductase deficiency. Since both tetrahydrobiopterin and dihydropteridine reductase are essential to the hydroxylases that synthesize dopamine, serotonin, and norepinephrine, it is not surprising that neurological symptoms are prominent in both defects. Why seizures occur in one and not the other is at present unanswered.

These patients can be diagnosed by administration of tetrahydrobiopterin, which will bring about a fall in the plasma phenylalanine level. Evidence thus far marshaled seems to support a defect in biosynthesis of biopterin, the precursor to tetrahydrobiopterin and the active cofactor for phenylalanine hydroxylase (Fig. 22–2).

Unfortunately tetrahydrobiopterin does not traverse the blood-brain barrier readily and so exogenous administration is not likely to be effective. At present L-dopa and 5-hydroxytryptophan administration are recommended to circumvent the block in neurotransmitter synthesis.

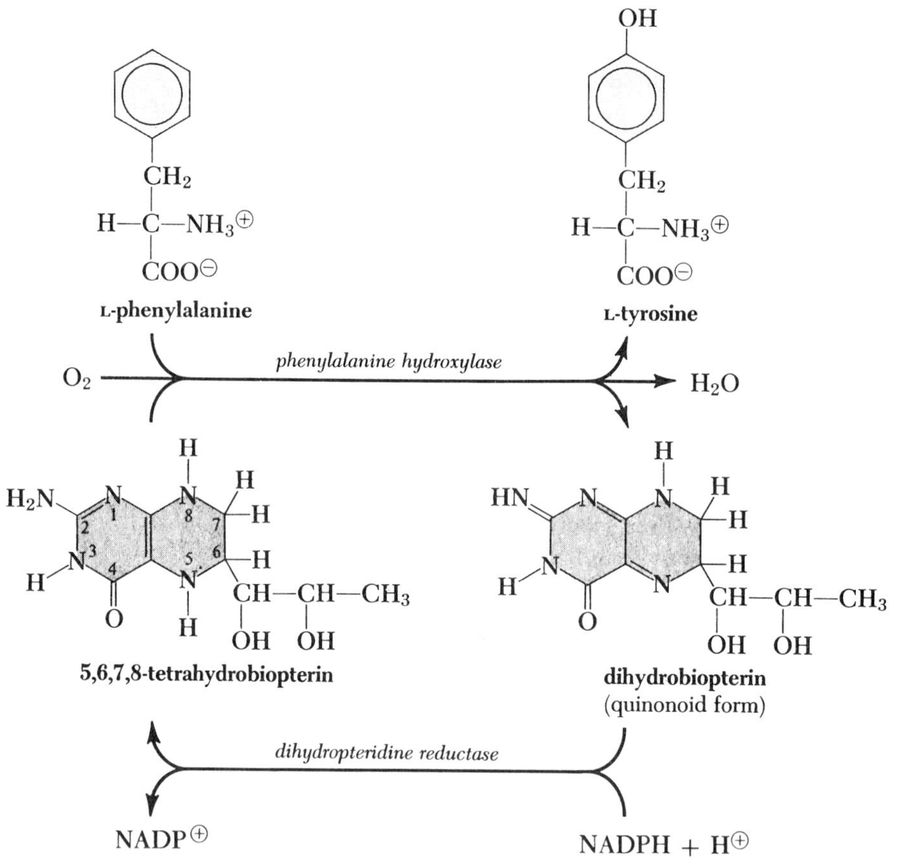

Figure 22–2 Pterin cofactor-dependence of phenylalanine hydroxylase. Tetrahydrobiopterin, synthesized from guanosine triphosphate, donates the electron required to convert molecular oxygen to H_2O and hydroxylate the ring of phenylalanine to produce tyrosine. The resulting dihydrobiopterin is recycled by conversion to tetrahydrobiopterin using NADPH. (From McGilvery, R.W.: Biochemistry: A Functional Approach. 2nd ed. Philadelphia, W.B. Saunders Co., 1979.)

Hereditary Tyrosinemia (Defect: Fumarylacetoacetate hydrolase; Genetics: autosomal recessive; Prenatal Diagnosis: not possible)

Clinical Features

Hereditary tyrosinemia is enigmatic, as methionine metabolism as well as tyrosine metabolism is affected. When the disease presents in the so-called "acute" form, the course is particularly malignant. Acute presentation is characterized by the appearance of symptoms within the first 6 months of life, with death due to liver failure in about 90 per cent of patients. Failure to thrive is almost universal, while hepatomegaly, jaundice, vomiting, a peculiar (methionine or cabbage-like) odor, ascites, fever, and bleeding episodes are also seen to varying degrees. Hypoglycemia due to islet cell hyperplasia has also been recorded, along with diarrhea and dyspnea.

Some patients do not present until later with a more slowly progressing form that includes failure to thrive, severe nodular cirrhosis, Fanconi syndrome, susceptibility to hypoglycemia, leukopenia, and thrombocytopenia. Many of these patients have come to medical attention because of hypophosphatemic rickets secondary to the Fanconi syndrome. Patients with the chronic form have a decided proclivity to develop hepatomas. As with many inborn errors hybrid forms exist, thus rendering a strict distinction between acute and chronic forms impractical.

Biochemical Defects

In this disorder, the biochemical cause remained enigmatic until very recently. A number of enzymes involved in methionine catabolism are defective in livers of such patients, but since all assays were performed on tissue that showed evidence of cirrhosis these findings were likely to be secondary rather than primary. As noted above, enormous elevations of plasma methionine may be seen in this disorder.

There is excessive formation and excretion of δ-aminolevulinic acid, and symptoms resembling acute porphyria occur in patients with the severe chronic liver failure of hereditary tyrosinemia. Documentation of p-hydroxyphenylpyruvic acid (p-HPPA) oxidase deficiency as the cause of this disorder has been unconvincing. There are no reports on the assay of this enzymatic activity in affected infants prior to the occurrence of hepatic damage.

Recently, Lindblad et al. have presented evidence to localize the defect at the last step of tyrosine catabolism, the fumarylacetoacetate hydrolase step. By gas chromatography-mass spectrometry these investigators have isolated and identified succinylacetone and succinylacetoacetate, which are thought to originate from maleylacetoacetate and fumarylacetoacetate, intermediates of the tyrosine catabolic sequence, which is blocked at the final step, i.e., fumarylacetoacetate hydrolase (Fig. 22–1). These authors attribute damage to liver and kidney to the accumulation of these compounds in the two organs; both possess significant activity of an earlier enzyme in this catabolic sequence, p-HPPA oxidase, that leads to maleylacetoacetate formation. Further, succinylacetone appears to be a potent inhibitor of porphobilinogen synthase, accounting for the increased excretion of 5-amino-levulinate in patients with hereditary tyrosinemia. These findings have now been confirmed at two other institutions. The cause of the hypermethioninemia is still conjectural.

Laboratory Diagnosis

Screening Tests. Tyrosine metabolites yield positive screening tests with Benedict's test, ferric chloride, and nitrosonaphthol. Abnormal blood chemistries are all referable to the deranged hepatic and renal tubular function seen in this disorder.

Urine. There is massive tyrosyluria with p-HPPA and p-HPLA predominating. Excessive tyrosine excretion persists even in the fasting state, as would be expected from protein breakdown. Amino acids showing particular elevation include tyrosine, proline, threonine, glycine, alanine, leucine, and methionine; δ-aminolevulinic acid may also be elevated.

Blood. Hypermethioninemia appears to be universal in this disorder, being especially marked in the acute phenotype, with levels of 1 to 5 mg/dl.

Treatment

The only known potentially effective approach to therapy in this disease is the dietary restriction of tyrosine, phenylalanine, and methionine in the acute stage during which hypermethioninemia is present. Vitamin C therapy has been tried and has not been successful. The original optimistic results reported with this diet have been tempered by further experience. With the acute form, liver dysfunction progresses relentlessly despite assiduous attention to dietary restriction.

Alcaptonuria (Defect: homogentisic acid oxidase; Genetics: autosomal recessive; Prenatal Diagnosis: not possible)

Clinical Features

When homogentisic (2,5-dihydroxyphenylacetic) acid cannot be further oxidized to maleyl-acetoacetate, the resulting disorder is termed alcaptonuria. Signs of the enzyme deficiency may become manifest soon after birth; the urine of such an infant will stain the diaper black, since homogentisic acid oxidizes in air and then polymerizes to a melanin-like compound. Homogentisic acid excretion is dependent upon the amounts of phenylalanine and tyrosine in the diet. During childhood alcaptonuria is the only manifestation of the defect and is without clinical import.

Before ochronosis (accumulation of the polymer in cartilage) can occur in tissues, there must be prolonged accumulation of homogentisic acid. Slate-blue discoloration of the ear and nose cartilage, and staining of the clothing in areas of excessive perspiration (such as the underarm) occur. Ochronosis can also be seen secondary to prolonged atabrine ingestion or transcutaneous absorption of carbolic acid. Since homogentisic acid is secreted into the tubular lumen, there is marked urinary homogentisate excretion without significant accumulation in plasma.

Biochemical Defects

The enzyme homogentisic acid oxidase catalyzes the cleavage of the ring structure of tyrosine, which is followed by formation of the cyclic compound (maleylacetoacetic acid). Subsequent conversion to fumarylacetoacetic acid, whose cleavage products are fumarate and acetoacetate (Fig. 22–1), allows entry to the tricarboxylic acid cycle. A deficiency of this oxidase results in release of homogentisate from cells into blood, leading to its excretion in large amounts in the urine. Apparently, because the enzymatic defect occurs below the point at which tyrosine is utilized for protein synthesis and conversion to specialized compounds (e.g., neurotransmitters), there are no significant immediate metabolic effects of the oxidase deficiency.

Laboratory Diagnosis

Screening Tests.   The patient's urine will darken, eventually turning black on standing in air or with the addition of alkali. Bile, porphyrins, myogloblin, and hemoglobin may also darken urine, thus giving a false positive reaction. Identification of homogentisate in the urine can be made by several different simple procedures: (1) adding alkali to urine will cause it to darken; (2) the Benedict's test produces a brown color with an orange precipitate; and (3) the ferric chloride test gives a purple-black reaction. The urine may not turn black spontaneously in alcaptonuria, particularly if the urine is acid or contains a large amount of reducing agent.

Radiological abnormalities apparent only in affected adults involve the vertebral bodies of the lumbar spine, which show degeneration of the intervertebral disc with narrowing of the intervertebral spaces and dense calcification of the remaining disc material. These changes are accompanied by variable fusion of the remaining vertebral bodies.

Definitive diagnosis rests with identification of homogentisate by a thin layer chromatography procedure or an enzymatic assay of the homogentisate in plasma.

Treatment

No effective treatment is known once ochronosis is established in alcaptonuria. However (by analogy with the dietary therapy for a number of amino acid disorders), it has been suggested that if homogentisic acid accumulation and polymerization can be curbed by restriction of phenylalanine and tyrosine intake beginning early in life, ochronosis might be prevented. Limitation of phenylalanine to 200 to 500 mg/day and a similar limitation of tyrosine might be successful if begun early in life.

Transient Neonatal Tyrosinemia

Clinical Features

Transient neonatal tyrosinemia is the commonest disorder of amino acid metabolism in man. While it occurs more frequently in premature infants than in full-term infants, it is not limited to small infants. Plasma tyrosine levels reach their apogee at the end of the first week of life and remain elevated for several weeks after birth in 0.5 per cent of surviving infants. Since plasma tyrosine levels in this disorder can exceed 2 mM (nl <0.7 mM), it is important to recognize that while considered harmless, some infants may manifest lethargy and obtundation during the time of the elevation. The most significant feature of this disorder is its early biochemical similarity to hereditary tyrosinemia. Hence it is essential to make the definitive diagnosis as early as possible in order to begin dietary therapy for the hereditary form.

Biochemical Defects

The enzyme defect in this disorder is diminished activity of *p*-hydroxyphenylpyruvic acid oxidase. This enzyme forms homogentisic acid through a complex series of reactions involving hydroxylation of the ring, migration of the pyruvyl side chain with conversion to an acetyl group, and liberation of carbon dioxide. In the premature infant the enzyme is subject to inhibition by its substrate resulting from the large quantities of tyrosine in the newborn diet. Relative deficiency of ascorbate in the diet and reduced amounts of enzyme in the cell contribute to decreased tyrosine clearance from the blood.

Laboratory Diagnosis

Screening tests will duplicate the results found in hereditary tyrosinemia, although abnormal blood chemistries are not usually found; when present, the latter represent prematurity rather than biochemical consequences of an enzyme deficiency. Abnormalities of urine and blood are similar to those described for hereditary tyrosinemia, but hypermethioninemia does not occur.

Definitive Diagnosis

The transient form may be distinguished from hereditary tyrosinemia either by reduction of protein intake to 2 to 3 g/day or by administration of 100 mg/day of vitamin C. Both of these maneuvers will decrease plasma tyrosine in the former while having no effect in the latter.

Hypertyrosinemia, Oregon Type, Type II (Defect: cytosolic tyrosine aminotransferase deficiency; Genetics: not known; Prenatal Diagnosis: not accomplished)

Clinical Features

This condition is much less common than hereditary tyrosinemia. Several patients have been described with mental retardation, microcephaly, hyperkeratotic skin lesions, cataracts, and keratotic eye lesions (pseudoherpetic keratitis). It is interesting that no renal or hepatic abnormalities have been encountered. Enzymatic studies in only 1 of 6 patients demonstrated a defect of cytosolic tyrosine transaminase.

Biochemical Defects

Owing to the high tissue tyrosine levels, transamination (or deamination) of the amino acid would be favored in extrahepatic sites that lack *p*-hydroxyphenylpyruvic acid oxidase activity. Thus the tyrosine metabolites, *p*-hydroxyphenylpyruvate, *p*-hydroxyphenyllactate, and *p*-hydroxyphenylacetate, would accumulate in blood and be excreted in the urine.

Laboratory Diagnosis

Tyrosine is increased in urine and plasma (higher than in hepatorenal tyrosinemia). Other amino acid concentrations are normal in plasma. About 75 per cent of the unoxidized tyrosine is excreted as the *N*-acetyl derivative, this compound being formed when tyrosine in blood exceeds 0.25 mM.

Treatment

As with the hepatorenal form of hereditary tyrosinemia, vitamin C administration has no effect on either plasma tyrosine levels or the keratotic lesions in this disease. However, unlike the former, dietary tyrosine restriction has been very beneficial in type II hypertyrosinemia, the skin and corneal lesions having promptly remitted. It is not yet known whether early tyrosine restriction in the affected neonate will prevent development of mental retardation.

NONKETOTIC HYPERGLYCINEMIA (Defect: glycine cleavage enzyme; Genetics: autosomal recessive; Prenatal Diagnosis: reported)

Clinical Features

The clinical features of this disease are not sufficiently unique as to make the clinical diagnosis obvious. In the neonatal presentation, patients exhibit listlessness, lack of spontaneous movement, opisthotonus, myoclonus and/or grand mal seizures, hiccups, and failure to thrive. Because of the neurological findings an EEG is often performed at this time. It usually shows hypsarrhythmias. One important diagnostic point is the lack of an acid-base disturbance in such catastrophically ill neonates, many of whom die in this early period. Others survive beyond the newborn stage but go on to develop a chronic seizure disorder and profound mental retardation. It is possible that many of the latter cases are entirely missed for lack of distinguishing biochemical features apart from elevated blood and urinary glycine levels, which may not always be measured.

Other severe neonatal diseases such as methylmalonic and propionic acidemias result in significant hyperglycinemia, the so-called "ketotic" form (see chapter 34). However, as Perry et al. have noted, it is clear that the hyperglycinemia, which persists in these conditions even with appropriate treatment for the organic acidemia, is not epileptogenic. These workers have shown that only in the nonketotic form of hyperglycinemia are glycine levels elevated in brain tissue and CSF. Since glycine is a putative inhibitory synaptic transmitter, it is possible that accumulation of this compound in the brain seriously impairs its function. Strychnine, a specific glycine receptor blocker, has been used in attempts at treatment, but the results have been equivocal.

Biochemical Defects

A major difficulty in elucidating the nature of the biochemical defect has been the enormous number of metabolic routes open to glycine (Fig. 22–3). As a nonessential amino acid, glycine can be synthesized from a number of sources; in turn, glycine can be converted to other amino acids or incorporated into purines, carbohydrates, lipids, or porphyrins. Glycine also serves as a methyl-group donor in reactions involving one-carbon transfer reactions.

$$\text{glycine} + NAD^+ + \text{tetrahydrofolate} \rightarrow NH_4^+ + CO_2 + 5,10\text{-methylene-tetrahydrofolate} + NADH$$

The first evidence that the glycine cleavage reaction (shown above) was deficient in nonketotic hyperglycinemia came from studies of Ando et al. and Baumgartner et al. These workers demonstrated defective conversion of ^{14}C-labeled glycine to $^{14}CO_2$ and to ^{14}C-serine in patients with nonketotic hyperglycinemia. Subsequently, assay of this enzyme in liver from patients confirmed the enzyme deficiency. However, it was still very difficult to conceptualize the pathogenesis of the disease until Perry et al. demonstrated that while affected liver tissue has a level of activity approximately 25 to 45 per cent of controls, affected brain has virtually undetectable enzyme activity. This discrepancy in enzyme activity may, indeed, account for the profound degree of cerebral

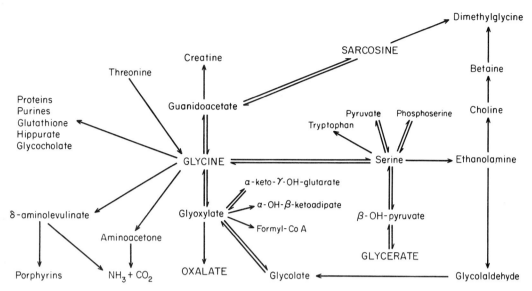

Figure 22–3 Metabolic fates of glycine. (From Bondy, P.K., and Rosenberg, L.E. (eds.): Metabolic Control and Disease. Philadelphia, W.B. Saunders Co., 1980.)

dysfunction associated with this disease. Further variations in residual brain enzyme activity may determine which affected individuals will survive the neonatal period.

Laboratory Diagnosis

The semiquantitative screening techniques involving paper or thin layer chromatography for urinary amino acids are minimally helpful, since glycinuria is a uniform and highly prominent finding in the newborn. Thus, the degree of glycinuria relative to the amounts of other urinary amino acids is highly significant. Furthermore, hyperglycinuria is a prominent associated finding in many neonatal organic acidemias and urea cycle disorders that must be excluded. This may be accomplished by demonstrating the absence of an anion-gap acidosis and by other screening tests such as *p*-nitroaniline, 2,4,-DNP, and so on. Quantitation of urinary amino acids will show glycine to be elevated 10 to 20 times normal, while blood glycine (the only significant affected amino acid) will be 3 to 5 times normal.

Definitive Diagnosis

Because glycine cleavage is not normally expressed to any significant degree in cultured skin fibroblasts or white cells, enzymatic confirmation must depend upon liver biopsy. However, when such tissue is available, the amount of residual enzyme activity is substantial and cannot unequivocally prove the diagnosis. Brain biopsy could provide the tissue for conclusive results, but such a procedure is unjustifiable in view of the bleak prognosis and lack of ability to use the information so obtained for prenatal diagnosis. Recently, Garcia-Castro et al. (1982) have reported prenatal diagnosis by measurement of the glycine/serine ratio in amniotic fluid. The efficacy of this method awaits confirmation.

Treatment

Because of the catastrophic presentation, cessation of protein feeds, attention to fluid balance, and exchange transfusions may be required. The last usually results in only minimal and transitory improvement, however. Sodium benzoate may lower glycine levels but has no effect on the clinical course. Recently, Gitzelmann et al. (1977) have reported on the successful treatment of this devastating disease with strychnine. However, subsequent attempts have resulted in less clear-cut improvement.

HISTIDINEMIA (Defect: histidase (L-histidine NH₃ lyase); Genetics: autosomal recessive; Prenatal Diagnosis: possible)

Clinical Features

Diagnosis of this disorder is not usually made until late in the first year of life or later; a defect in speech is the most common finding, probably secondary to a short auditory memory span. Mental retardation has been reported in two thirds of the patients. Patients range in I.Q. from 50 to well into the normal range, the latter having no other findings save elevated blood histidine. A typical patient profile has been developed: affected infants appear healthy initially but experience an increased incidence of infection in infancy and childhood as well as small stature, abnormal EEG, and seizures. While some patients show moderate to gross degrees of mental retardation, others manifest emotional lability and difficulty in school that may be deemed behavioral or psychological. Since clinical features are scanty, neuropsychiatric evaluation may be in order in a patient found to have histidinemia. Levy and co-workers have questioned the relationship of the enzyme defect to the clinical picture. It will require early biochemical detection and long-term follow-up to determine whether the biochemical features are directly related to the clinical findings.

Biochemical Defects

Histidine is an essential nutrient for the infant; growth will be compromised if it is in limited supply. The biochemical defect in histidinemia lies in the major degradative pathway for that amino acid. The pathway is initiated by nonoxidative deamination to form urocanic acid, a reaction catalyzed by histidase (Fig. 22–4). As a result of the deficiency histidine increases in plasma, with transamination of histidine assuming increasing importance as the catabolic route. When blood

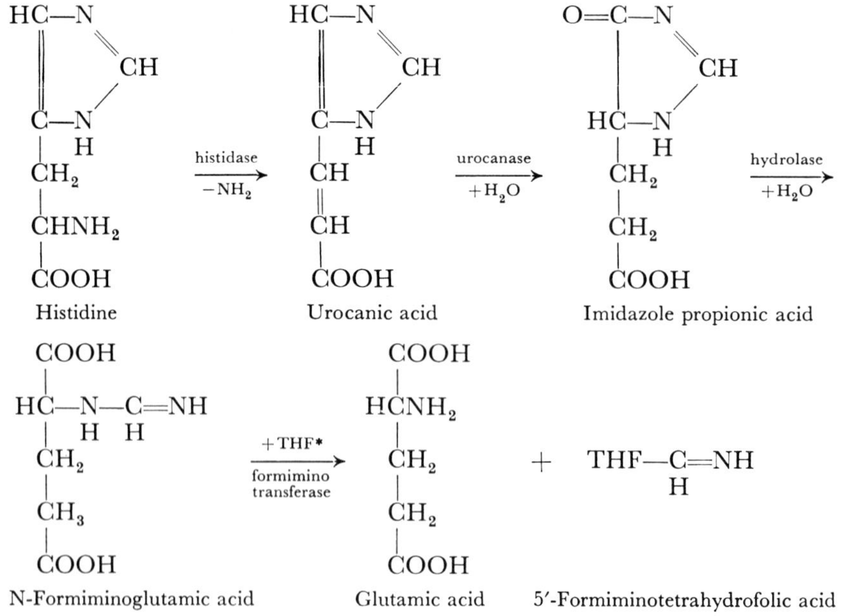

Figure 22–4 Catabolism of histidine. Decarboxylation of histidine (not shown) results in histamine. (From Kaldor, G.: Physiologic Chemistry of Proteins and Nucleic Acids in Mammals. Philadelphia, W.B. Saunders Co., 1969.)

histidine concentrations reach 6 mg/dl, this reaction results in formation of detectable amounts of imidazolelactic, imidazoleacetic, and imidazolepyruvic acids.

Laboratory Diagnosis

The ferric chloride test yields a green color due to imidazolepyruvate, but this usually requires that plasma histidine exceed 0.5 mM. This test is unreliable in the neonate, and accurate diagnosis requires demonstration of histidinuria followed by quantitation of blood. Plasma levels in patients have ranged from 2 to 27 mg/dl; normal levels are in the range of 0.4 to 1.0 mg/dl. A histidine loading test can be very helpful in sorting out individuals with decreased ability to handle histidine.

Definitive diagnosis depends upon direct or indirect evidence of impaired histidase activity in skin, but owing to genetic heterogeneity even this modality cannot be considered unequivocal.

Treatment

While blood histidine levels can be controlled by dietary means, it is not yet possible to judge whether such therapy leads to improvement. Levy and co-workers have cautioned that we do not yet know the biochemical ramifications of histidine deficiency, so that dietary treatment is not without potential hazard.

HOMOCYSTINURIA (Defect; cystathionine β-synthase; Genetics: autosomal recessive; Prenatal Diagnosis: possible)

Clinical Features

Patients with this most common form of homocystinuria show evidence of involvement of the eye, the skeletal system, the vascular system, and the brain. It is important to note that individuals with cystathionine β-synthase deficiency do not manifest any abnormalities at birth and that the affected pregnancies are uneventful. Thus, this disorder, as opposed to the rarer remethylation defect variants of homocystinuria (described below) is not usually part of the differential diagnosis of the catastrophically ill newborn. Ectopia lentis does not usually appear before the age of 3 years, but most patients have some manifestations by the age of 10. The initial recognition of ocular abnormalities may be an observation by parent or physician that the iris shakes when the head is moved rapidly. While there seems to be a predilection for downward dislocation of the lens, this is not invariant. In homocystinuria the defect is the result of thickening and fragmentation of the zonular fibers that attach the lens to the ciliary body, while in Marfan's syndrome these fibers are thin and elongated.

Osteoporosis is the most common abnormality of the skeleton, presenting usually after the first decade. Since bone tissue formation is disordered, one can expect and, indeed will find, scoliosis, genu valgum, and pes cavus, among other abnormalities.

Mental retardation is reported in about half of patients, and it is not uncommon for this problem to be the reason that medical assistance is first sought. Psychomotor delay may be perceived as early as the first year of life, but it may not be appreciated until later, since retardation is usually slowly progressive. Nonetheless, mental dysfunction is not the hallmark of this disease, and many patients are college graduates. Seizures occur in about 10 to 15 per cent of patients.

The complication of cystathionine β-synthase deficiency that is of most concern is the propensity to thromboembolism. This involves vessels of all diameters and is unpredictable as to when, where, and if it occurs. The malar flush and erythematous mottling of the extremities are also vascular manifestations of homocystinuria.

There is a wide spectrum of clinical manifestations in these individuals, and with heightened awareness of the disorder patients are being diagnosed who have lens abnormalities only. Still others are apparently normal siblings of known patients who on screening and subsequent quantitation manifest increased levels of homocystine in serum and urine.

Biochemical Defects

Methionine is an essential amino acid that has a unique role in the initiation of protein synthesis. In addition, by conversion to *S*-adenosylmethionine it serves as the major methyl group donor involved in the formation of creatinine and choline, in the methylation of bases in RNA, and as the source of the aminopropyl group in the formation of polyamines. Finally, in relationship to classical homocystinuria, it is converted to cysteine by way of homocysteine and cystathionine in a series of reactions termed the transsulfuration pathway.

The major steps in this pathway are shown in Figure 22–5. In the first step, *S*-adenosylmethionine is formed in a reaction catalyzed by methionine adenosyltransferase. This reaction involves transfer of the adenosyl portion of ATP to methionine, forming a sulfonium bond, which has a high group transfer potential, i.e., it is a so-called high-energy compound. Hence, each of the groups attached to this bond can participate in a transfer reaction, much as ATP does in so many reactions within the cell.

Homocysteine lies at a metabolic crossroad; it may condense with serine to form cystathionine or it may undergo remethylation, thereby conserving methionine. There are two pathways for remethylation in humans. In one, betaine provides the methyl groups while in the other 5-methyltetrahydrofolate is the methyl donor. This latter reaction is catalyzed by a B_{12}-containing enzyme, 5-methyltetrahydrofolate:homocysteine methyltransferase. Two defects in this latter mechanism may account for inability to carry out remethylation. In one, patients are unable to synthesize or accumulate methylcobalamin while others cannot produce the second cofactor, 5-methyltetrahydrofolate, because of a defect in 5,10-methylenetetrahydrofolate reductase.

As noted above, cystathionine formation is the other major fate of methionine. The condensation of homocysteine with serine is catalyzed by the vitamin B_6-requiring enzyme cystathionine β-synthase. In the last step of the transsulfuration sequence cystathionine undergoes cleavage to cysteine and α-ketobutyrate in yet another enzyme reaction that requires pyridoxal phosphate.

Since methionine has several pathways open to it, we would like to know what factors control the direction that its metabolism takes. Studies in young adults have shown that the utilization of methyl groups is normally accounted for chiefly by creatine-creatinine formation. This reaction

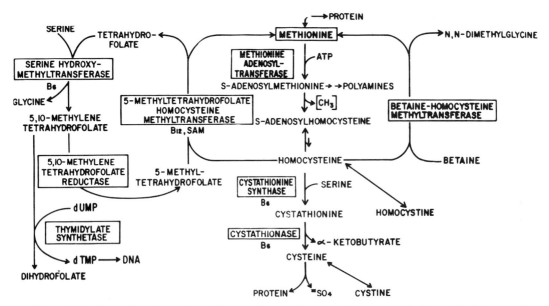

Figure 22–5 Transsulfuration pathway. The net effect of this pathway is the transfer of the sulfhydryl group from methionine to serine to form cysteine. Cystathionase is deficient in the brain of the neonate, thus making cysteine an essential amino acid in young infants. (From Fleisher, L.D., and Gaull, G.E.: Methionine metabolism in man: development and deficiencies. Clin. Endocrinol. Metab. 3:37, 1974.)

consumes more S-adenosylmethionine than all other transmethylations together. However, examination of enzyme activities from these two pathways in fetal animals leads to the conclusion that remethylation preponderates over transsulfuration. Indeed, since γ-cystathionase activity is unmeasurable in human fetal liver and brain, not only is the remethylation sequence favored but cysteine then becomes an essential amino acid for the fetus and infant.

As noted above, the predominant cause of homocystinuria is the absence of cystathionine β-synthase—a dimeric enzyme possessing two identical subunits in man. Several lines of evidence indicate that multiple mutations may affect this enzyme. There appear to be at least three distinct types of abnormal enzyme associated with homocystinuria: absent enzyme activity, reduced enzyme activity with normal ability to bind the cofactor pyridoxal phosphate, and reduced activity with diminished ability to bind the coenzyme.

As the name implies, renal clearance of abnormal levels of homocystine in the plasma causes excessive excretion of the amino acid in the urine. In cystathionine β-synthase deficiency plasma methionine concentrations are elevated as well—this serves as a point of distinction from the remethylation defects. At present it appears that the pyridoxal phosphate response may be explained by the fact that this vitamin increases the steady state concentration of the active enzyme by decreasing the rate of apoenzyme degradation and possibly by increasing the rate of holoenzyme formation. The explanation is not entirely satisfactory, however, since in vitro studies have shown detectable levels of enzyme activity in mutant fibroblasts that show no B_6 response, while in other mutant lines without detectable enzyme activity, B_6 response has occurred. Once again, a distressing lack of correspondence between in vivo observations and in vitro experiments forces investigators to probe the secrets of these diseases more deeply.

Pathophysiology

Research into the toxic effects of methionine and homocystine have uncovered a wide range of toxic effects on various organs. Nonetheless, a unifying hypothesis as to the deleterious mechanism of action of these amino acids has not yet emerged.

Evidence has accumulated showing that homocysteine interferes with formation of the normal cross-links of collagen. Most collagen molecules are composed of three polypeptide chains bound together by intramolecular cross links (see Chapter 27). Cross-link formation requires the generation of aldehydic groups by oxidation of epsilon-amino groups of the multiple lysyl or hydroxylysyl residues in the collagen monomers. Chemical interactions of these aldehyde groups, both by Schiff-base formation with amino groups of lysine or hydroxylysine on other chains and by aldol condensation between two aldehydes accounts for the cross-linking. How cross-link formation is disturbed in homocystinuria is not yet clear, but in vitro homocysteine forms stable thiazene ring compounds with aldehydes, thereby blocking the possibility of forming cross-links.

Harker et al. recently demonstrated a direct in vivo toxic effect of homocystine on the intima of large and medium-sized arteries in baboons subjected to a constant homocystine infusion. Platelets then adhered to the disrupted intimal surface, eventually resulting in thrombosis of the vessel. As measured by platelet turnover techniques, dipyridamole (an agent effective in prevention of platelet aggregation) was capable of preventing thrombosis but not the intimal damage. Platelet survival studies in homocystinuric patients gave comparable results. However, these data require further supporting documentation before dipyridamole can be used as an acceptable form of treatment in vitamin B_6-unresponsive homocystinurics.

Laboratory Diagnosis

Homocystine in urine is the biochemical hallmark of this disorder and can be detected by a positive urinary cyanide nitroprusside reaction. As other disulfides, including cystine and β-mercaptolactate-cystine, also react, amino acid paper chromatography will be required to distinguish these compounds from homocystine. Since there are two other forms of homocystinuria (discussed later)

Table 22–1 COMPARISON OF CLINICAL AND BIOCHEMICAL FEATURES
IN THREE FORMS OF HOMOCYSTINURIA*

Feature	Cystathionine β-Synthase Deficiency	Defective Cobalamin Coenzyme Synthesis	$N^{5,10}$-Methylene-tetrahydrofolate Reductase Deficiency
Mental retardation	common	common	common
Growth retardation	no	common	no
Dislocated optic lenses	almost always	no	no
Thromboembolic disease	common	no	rare
Megaloblastic anemia	no	rare	no
Homocystine in blood and urine	increased	increased	increased
Methionine in blood and urine	increased	normal or decreased	normal or decreased
Cystathionine in blood and urine	decreased	normal or increased	normal or increased
Methylmalonate in blood and urine	normal	increased	increased
Serum cobalamin	normal	normal	normal
Serum folate	normal or decreased	normal or increased	normal or decreased
Response to vitamin	pyridoxine	cobalamin (B_{12})	folate
Response to dietary methionine restriction	helpful	harmful	harmful

*From Bondy, P.K., and Rosenberg, L.E.: Metabolic Control and Disease. Philadelphia, W.B. Saunders Co., 1980.

in which plasma methionine is decreased, plasma amino acid evaluation is also in order (Table 22–1).

Deficiency of cystathionine β-synthase may be demonstrated in cultured fibroblasts, but it is not essential to the clinical diagnosis.

Treatment

Treatment in those patients who respond to pyridoxal phosphate is based on provision of approximately 250 to 500 mg/day. Folate deficiency may be avoided by addition of 5 mg/day to this regimen. In patients who do not respond to the coenzyme, dietary manipulation with a low methionine, cystine-supplemented diet may be helpful. Dipyridamole, an agent effective in decreasing platelet aggregation, has been used to prevent the thromboses, but there are no reports yet as to its effectiveness.

The therapy for this disorder is often unsatisfactory and requires management and follow-up in a center equipped to deal with inborn errors of metabolism. Thus, having made the diagnosis in a particular individual, it is essential that such children be followed periodically at a center. Since anesthesia increases the risk of intravascular coagulation, elective surgery under general anesthesia is absolutely contraindicated, as is angiography.

Defects in Homocystine Remethylation

Defective Activity of N^5-Methyltetrahydrofolate:Homocysteine Methyl-Transferase and Cobalamin Activation

Thus far four patients have been described with this defect in remethylation of homocysteine. The initial patient presented as a catastrophically ill newborn who died by 7 weeks of age. While homocystine levels were elevated in blood and urine, the level of methionine in blood was quite low. Of great interest was the presence of large amounts of methylmalonic acid in urine. Three other patients presented later in childhood, two of whom were retarded mentally. One of these patients also had severe megaloblastic anemia.

Since the coenzyme from vitamin B_{12} is required in two distinct enzyme reactions, i.e., remethylation of homocystine and catabolism of methylmalonic acid, the fundamental defect must involve a step in converting B_{12} to its coenzymes. Formation of both deoxyadenosyl B_{12} and methyl B_{12} requires a prior reductive step catalyzed by cobalamin reductase, which appears to be the defective enzyme in this variant.

Decreased N^{5,10} Methylenetetrahydrofolate Reductase Activity

Variability of presentation characterizes this homocysteine remethylation defect as well. Several patients have been reported from one family: one with seizures and muscle weakness, a second with schizophrenia and retardation, and a third who was asymptomatic. Subsequently patients with a more malignant neonatal presentation were reported, and hence both variants should be part of the differential diagnosis of "sepsis neonatorum."

Fibroblasts from each patient had markedly reduced levels of the above enzyme. The defect results in an inability to synthesize 5-methyltetrahydrofolate in amounts sufficient for the remethylation of homocystine to methionine. Homocystine accumulates in plasma, and the plasma methionine is decreased. As in the other remethylation defect there is accumulation of cystathionine. Treatment with high doses of folic acid has been beneficial in several patients.

CYSTINOSIS

Clinical Features

This autosomal recessive disease is perhaps one of the most distressing of all inborn errors to physicians, parents, and investigators. Individuals born with the infantile nephropathic form are normal as neonates and for the first six months of life. Thereafter, a symptom complex slowly evolves; there is polyuria, polydipsia, fevers of unknown origin, a rapidly increasing degree of failure to thrive, and a loss of appetite. Despite all of this, the infant's mental development proceeds at a completely normal rate; in our experience these children are usually above average in intelligence.

At the time of initial onset of symptoms, a routine physical examination will most often be entirely unrevealing. However, the astute clinician who includes a urinalysis as a part of every child's physical may uncover an alkaline pH, together with mild to moderate glucosuria and proteinuria. The findings are referable to the renal tubular dysfunction, known as Fanconi syndrome (see Chapter 23), which is a constant feature of this disease. Urinary amino acid screening may not show a generalized aminoaciduria at the outset.

At about one year of age, the infant may refuse to walk or stand, directing attention toward the rickets that has slowly evolved. This is a consequence of renal tubular involvement. At this time, a careful history may elicit information indicating photophobia, and a slit-lamp examination will reveal crystalline deposits in the cornea and a "salt and pepper" type retinopathy. Urinary screen will show a marked glucosuria (with a normal blood glucose), proteinuria, and generalized aminoaciduria. From this time on, the natural history of the disease involves diminishing renal function, increasing photophobia, frequent bouts of moderate to severe metabolic acidosis with intercurrent infection, and a striking growth failure. The worsening renal function increases dependence upon exogenous vitamin D (or its analogues) for prevention of rachitic changes, even with the minimal degree of growth evident in these patients. Without other forms of medical intervention these individuals die in chronic renal failure around the end of the first decade.

Two other forms of cystinosis have been described: (1) an adolescent (juvenile) type, in which the onset of symptoms is delayed until middle childhood with a slower progression than the infantile form but with a similar prognosis, and (2) an adult form, in which the only clinical findings are photophobia, headache, and lacrimation, with the kidney totally unaffected.

Biochemical Defects

The pathological findings (including crystal deposition in kidney, liver, bone marrow, spleen, lymph nodes, cornea, rectal mucosa, and peripheral leucocytes) have long been attributed to a defect resulting in increasing cystine storage with age. However, measurement of tissue cystine content in kidney from an affected fetus showed levels equivalent to those found in kidney from an older cystinotic child. This, at the very least, calls into question a quantitative relationship between age and cystine deposition; it also casts doubt upon the concept that increasing cystine storage is related directly to diminished renal function. The duration of cystine storage or increasing biochemical vulnerability to storage of cystine (or a related toxic metabolite) may underlie the pathogenesis of this disorder. Nonetheless, despite intensive investigation the biochemical defect in this puzzling disease remains unelucidated.

Diagnosis

The finding of proteinuria, glucosuria, or an alkaline urine pH in an acidotic infant should alert the physician to the possibility of Fanconi syndrome. Demonstration of a normal blood glucose, hyperchloremic acidosis, and a generalized aminoaciduria on metabolic screen will provide sufficient evidence for this diagnosis. Any patient with a Fanconi syndrome should be evaluated for the presence of cystine crystals in eye, rectal mucosa, or bone marrow.

Measurement of cystine content of cultured fibroblasts from an affected individual provides definitive diagnostic evidence. Levels range from 80 to 100-fold normal. By this means, both heterozygote and prenatal detection can also be carried out.

Treatment

Until recently, symptomatic treatment was all that was available up to the point of end-stage renal disease, when renal transplantation could be offered. Interestingly, successful renal transplants do not subsequently manifest tubular dysfunction; this is clearly due to the fact that the donor genotype remains operative within the recipient. Within the last year or two, cysteamine (a sulfhydryl binder) has been used successfully to diminish levels of intracellular cystine in vivo. This was reflected in slowing of the progression of renal disease in some but not all of the patients studied. Further experience is necessary with this form of therapy before it can be recommended routinely.

DISORDERS OF LYSINE METABOLISM

The major catabolic pathway for lysine (Fig. 22–6) commences not with transamination (as for most amino acids) but with condensation with α-ketoglutarate followed by reduction to saccharopine. These two reactions are catalyzed by one enzyme, lysine-ketoglutarate reductase. In the next step saccharopine is split oxidatively, releasing glutamate and 2-aminoadipate semialdehyde. The latter cyclizes spontaneously and then undergoes oxidation to form 2-aminoadipate. Transamination with L-glutamate yields 2-ketoadipate; subsequently glutaryl CoA is formed.

Persistent Hyperlysinemia

Clinical Features

As the name implies there is a persistent elevation in plasma lysine ranging up to 5 times normal in this disorder. Apart from this consistent finding, the clinical presentation has varied widely. Significant mental retardation appears to be a frequent finding, although Woody et al. have reported 3 siblings of whom none was retarded. More recently Levy, Shih, and McReady have reported a child with normal intelligence at the age of 5 years who was diagnosed at birth. Other clinical findings include abnormal facies, synophrys, short stature, deafness, convulsions, joint laxity, webbed toes, and autistic type behavior. Such a wide spectrum of clinical presentation raises the possibility of a variety of defects underlying the persistent hyperlysinemia.

Biochemical Defects

The major biochemical finding is defined by the name of the disorder. Absence of a concomitant hyperammonemia distinguishes between the persistent and periodic hyperlysinemic syndromes.

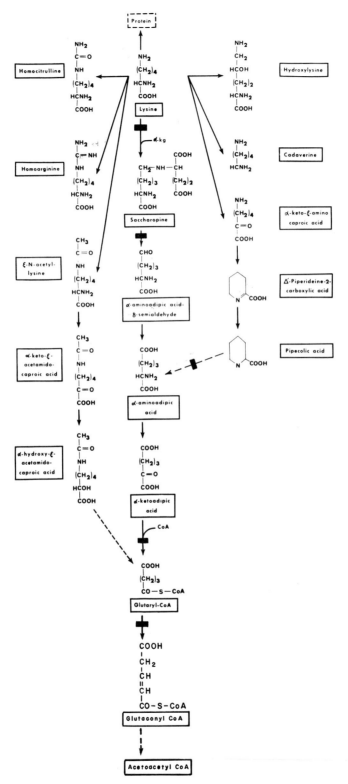

Figure 22–6 Pathways for lysine metabolism. The vertical path directly below lysine is the major catabolic route. Broken lines indicate less well-defined steps; known enzymatic defects are denoted by solid blocks. (From Bondy, P.K., and Rosenberg, L.E. (eds.): Metabolic Control and Disease. Philadelphia, W.B. Saunders Co., 1980.)

Plasma lysine levels in persistent hyperlysinemia can range from 1 to 5 times the upper limit of normal; there is a corresponding hyperlysinuria. There appears to be no correlation between clinical findings and the height of plasma lysine levels in any given patient. Lysine levels are also elevated in cerebrospinal fluid, although here again there is no clinical correlation. The hyperlysinuria is an isolated, overflow-type aminoaciduria; there are no other dibasic amino acids present in the urine in excess. The fact that there is only an elevation in plasma lysine without other metabolites being affected implies a metabolic block rather early in the catabolic pathway. This is further supported by the finding in several patients of intermediates of the minor lysine pathways. Confirmation of the foregoing suspicion was obtained by Dancis et al. who found that the activity of lysine:alpha-ketoglutarate reductase, which is responsible for conversion of lysine to saccharopine, was markedly reduced in fibroblast extracts from two patients with persistent hyperlysinemia. Finally, it is the concomitant absence of saccharopine and of hyperammonemia that delineates biochemically one particular form of persistent hyperlysinemia.

Carson and co-workers reported a patient who in addition to persistent hyperlysinemia also showed small amounts of saccharopine and homocitrulline in the serum. Since saccharopine formation is one step beyond the lysine:alpha-ketoglutarate dehydrogenase block demonstrated by Dancis, this patient appeared to represent another form of persistent hyperlysinemia. Measurements of the lysine:alpha-ketoglutarate dehydrogenase in skin fibroblasts from Carson's patient showed an activity in the range of 37 per cent of control. On the other hand, saccharopine dehydrogenase activity was entirely absent. Therefore, this patient represents an entirely separate enzymatic defect. Two patients have been reported with absence of both lysine reductase and saccharopine dehydrogenase activities in liver. Defects in sequential enzymes are distinctly rare (orotic aciduria). In the case of these two enzymes of lysine catabolism, any explanation involving possible shared protein subunits must acknowledge that lysine reductase employs NADP as coenzyme in a reduction while saccharopine dehydrogenase employs NAD in an oxidation.

A third type of persistent hyperlysinemia has been reported. Although the precise nature of the enzymatic defect has yet to be elucidated, it is thought to be deficiency of α-ketoadipic acid decarboxylase. Patients with this third form of the disease excrete large amounts of alpha-aminoadipic acid in the urine as well as α-ketoadipic acid.

Thus, it is likely that persistent hyperlysinemia, as originally described, consists of a number of distinct enzymatic defects that are only recently becoming delineated. It appears that the designation persistent hyperlysinemia embraces a heterogeneous group of disorders.

Pathophysiology

As in most of the amino acid catabolic disorders, the precise nature of the pathophysiological events leading to the clinical syndrome is not well understood. However, lysine is one of the several essential amino acids in human beings; hence a defect in its metabolism might be expected to cause clinical disease. What role, if any, high levels of lysine play in the development of CNS symptoms is not known. However, the disorder cystinuria, in which there may be defective CNS epithelial transport of cystine and the dibasic amino acids, including lysine, has been thought for some time to be associated with some degree of CNS dysfunction. It may be that the presence of excess amounts of lysine are equally damaging to the developing CNS.

Laboratory Findings

Plasma lysine levels range from 1 to 5 times the normal upper limit of approximately 4.7 mg of lysine/dl. Correspondingly, hyperlysinuria is also present, with urinary lysine excretion over 24 hours ranging up to 15 to 20 times the upper limit of normal.

Lysine loading using 150 mg L-lysine/kg body weight has been used to define an abnormal response in such patients, but should not be considered part of the routine work-up of such patients. Investigation of urinary excretion of metabolites of the minor pathways for lysine catabolism are usually unrewarding, since special techniques must be utilized in order to verify the presence of pipecolic acid or ϵ-N-acetyl-lysine. Therefore, patients with persistent hyperlysinemia and hyperlysinuria should be referred to a metabolic unit for definitive diagnosis.

Presently definitive diagnosis of persistent hyperlysinemia depends upon demonstration of a deficiency of one of three enzymes: either lysine:alpha-ketoglutarate dehydrogenase, α-ketoadipic acid decarboxylase, or saccharopine dehydrogenase activity. These may be demonstrated in skin fibroblasts grown from the affected individual.

Periodic Hyperlysinemia Associated With Hyperammonemia

Information about this disorder comes essentially from one well-studied patient who was hospitalized at the age of 2½ months with dehydration and coma. Other clinical findings included spasticity and vomiting. EEG examination showed a diffusely abnormal pattern, although spinal fluid examination disclosed no abnormality. Clinically, there was a one to one correspondence between the onset of feedings and the presentation of the symptom complex. When dietary protein was decreased to 1.5 g/kg/day there was a dramatic improvement in general condition and no further episodes of coma. Throughout the periods of coma, blood ammonia concentrations varied from 500 to 600 μg/dl. An additional finding was the increased plasma concentration of lysine and arginine. Although the inhibition of arginase by lysine was postulated to explain this, the patient's plasma lysine level was considerably lower than has been seen in others with persistent hyperlysinemia unassociated with hyperammonemia. Of course, it is the intracellular concentration of lysine that would bring about such inhibition, and since most tissues concentrate amino acids, intracellular levels usually exceed plasma concentrations. Hence, other factors as yet undefined may be involved in intracellular accumulation of lysine. Other biochemical studies in the hospital were within normal limits. At the age of 10 months the patient was spastic with an inability to sit or hold up her head. At the present time there is no good explanation for the biochemical manifestations outlined above. Although the authors of the report implicated L-lysine dehydrogenase as the deficient enzyme, their determinations showed that the enzyme was present in the patient's liver biopsy specimen at a level which was approximately 25 to 30 per cent of normal activity. This is generally considered to be a level which is adequate for the prevention of clinical symptomatology in most inborn enzymatic disorders.

Pipecolic Acidemia

To date there have been two patients reported with this disorder. Both children showed early onset of feeding problems with persistent vomiting, poor head control, progressive central nervous system deterioration, and finally, death within the first two years of life. Each had hepatomegaly with generalized hypotonia. Examination of the eye grounds revealed a peripheral pigmentation of the retina most marked around the macula area.

The suspicion of pipecolic acidemia derived from the finding of an abnormal spot on the plasma paper chromatogram that stained blue with ninhydrin and showed a red fluorescence with UV light. There was no hyperlysinemia present in either patient. That pipecolic acid is derived at least in part from lysine was shown by Woody by injection of L-lysine ^{14}C into 2 patients with lysine:alpha-ketoglutarate reductase deficiency. They found pipecolate ^{14}C in the plasma and urine of these patients. The biochemical nature of the defect is thought to be deficiency of aminoadipic semialdehyde oxidase. It is not possible to project the likely pathophysiological events leading to the clinical picture at this time.

Glutaric Aciduria, Type I

To date, two different forms of glutaric aciduria have been described. The clinical manifestations as well as the biochemical findings are so different in the two types that it is best to consider them as separate disorders.

Clinical Features

The clinical hallmark of Type I glutaric aciduria is generally acknowledged to be a striking dystonia accompanied by choreo-athetotic movements. The patients with this disease are generally normal in the neonatal period with the first appearance of symptoms sometime within the first year of life. There is generally a severe impairment of motor development, perhaps attributable to the same etiology as the dystonia and choreo-athetosis. Severe metabolic acidosis has been conspicuously absent in others. Mental retardation, appearing later in life, is a variable finding in this disease. In the patients in whom mental retardation has not been thought to be present there is a severe dysarthria. It may be that this dysarthria has complicated testing in the patients in whom mental retardation was thought to be present.

Laboratory Findings

Because of the varied presentation of this disease it is difficult to outline specific laboratory abnormalities. However, in those patients who are not acidotic at the time of initial presentation there are no routine clinical laboratory abnormalities identifiable. Most patients such as these have been identified by a more involved search for the cause of their dystonia and choreo-athetosis. On the other hand, the patients who have been reported with infantile onset marked by severe metabolic acidosis have shown, in addition to chemical evidence of acidosis, significant ketonuria. All other laboratory studies have generally been reported as normal. Remarkably, the plasma levels of lysine, tryptophan, and hydroxylysine have been uniformly reported as normal. There is a fairly constant elevation among all these patients of glycine and alanine. Urinary amino acids, however, are much more reflective of a severe metabolic disruption. There is a massive elevation in glutamine and glutamic acid in the urine together with increases in alpha-aminoadipic acid, glycine, and saccharopine.

Demonstration of glutaric aciduria depends upon gas chromatography. By this means, all patients with this disorder have shown enormous elevations in urinary glutaric acid, β-hydroxyglutaric acid, and glutaconic acid. These compounds are not found in urine from normal patients.

Pathophysiology

Pathological findings in a patient with this disorder, who expired at the age of 10 years, revealed a liver of normal size with lobular architecture intact. All hepatocytes contained fatty, cytoplasmic globules, and the mitochondria showed swelling and disruption in the normal cristae. There was no evidence of inflammation or fibrosis. Examination of the brain disclosed bilateral shrinkage and a grey discoloration of the putamen. Approximately three fourths of the putamen showed chronic degeneration with severe loss of neurons and gliosis. Similar changes were found in the lateral margins of the caudate nucleus.

These pathological changes in the brain correspond anatomically to the dystonia and choreo-athetosis that are the hallmarks of this disease. Recently, Stokke and co-workers have investigated the inhibition of brain glutamate decarboxylase by glutaric acid, glutaconic acid, and β-hydroxyglutaric acid. These investigations were based on the speculation that the movement disorder in glutaric aciduria might result from decreased levels of GABA, an inhibitory neurotransmitter, as a consequence of inhibition of brain glutamate decarboxylase by the accumulating 5-carbon dicarboxylic acids. All three dicarboxylic acids tested were found to be potent inhibitors of the glutamate decarboxylase in rabbit brain. However, these findings need to be confirmed.

Definitive Diagnosis

The site of the metabolic block in this disease is thought to be glutaryl CoA dehydrogenase. This enzyme has been assayed in leukocytes, in cultured skin fibroblasts, and in mitochondria isolated from human liver. In addition, Christensen and Brandt have demonstrated the presence of glutaryl CoA dehydrogenase activity in amniotic fluid cells that is of the same order as skin fibroblasts. This observation provides the basis for prenatal diagnosis in this disease.

UREA CYCLE DEFECTS

Carbamyl Phosphate Synthetase Deficiency

Clinical Features

As noted in the section on hyperammonemia, there are three general modes of clinical presentation for the defects of ureagenesis. First there is presentation in the neonatal period often after milk feeding, with a fulminating course marked by coma, neutropenia, and convulsions. Earlier symptoms may include irritability, lethargy, poor feeding and vomiting, depressed neurological status, tachypnea without obvious cause, myoclonic spasms, and hypothermia. A *subacute form* presenting within the first few months of life is characterized by vomiting, feeding difficulties, and failure to thrive. Akinetic seizures, bilateral spiking on EEG, and delayed development are also seen. The third form usually does not present until after the first year of life, when a catabolic event leads to overt symptoms, although delayed development with or without seizures may have been present.

Biochemical Defects

Entry of ammonia into the urea cycle is dependent on the formation of carbamyl phosphate from ammonia, bicarbonate, and ATP, in a reaction catalyzed by mitochondrial carbamyl phosphate synthetase. The hyperammonemia found in these patients is a direct consequence of deficient formation of carbamyl phosphate from the ammonia derived from protein catabolism. This compound is a precursor not only for the formation of urea but also for the formation of pyrimidines, a process that is catalyzed by a different enzyme in the cytosol.

Laboratory Diagnosis

The best screening test for this disorder is a blood ammonia, which in the affected neonate may be in the range of 1000 to 3000 μg/dl. In the older child a two-hour postprandial measurement may be necessary, since elevation may depend upon protein ingestion. There are no specific amino acid abnormalities noted in blood or urine, although in some cases blood glutamine, alanine, and lysine have been increased. Glutamine elevation is likely the result of condensation of the accumulating ammonia with glutamic acid. Confusion with the organic acidemias is possible but they can be ruled out by urinary organic acid screening. In these latter disorders the blood ammonia is usually only a fraction of that encountered in carbamyl phosphate synthetase deficiency, but this point alone cannot be employed as an invariant distinction. Definitive diagnosis depends on hepatic and leukocytic enzymatic studies.

Treatment

In the past, rigorous restriction of protein, exchange transfusions, and peritoneal dialysis have been of little benefit to neonates with this disorder. More recently, hemodialysis has been shown to be more effective.

A biochemical therapy—provision of benzoic or phenylacetic acids (250 to 350 mg/kg PO or IV) to encourage formation of the corresponding amino acid acylation product, i.e., hippurate and phenylacetylglutamine—has met with some success in several patients (Fig. 22–7). Keto acid analogues of essential amino acids have also been employed but have been less efficacious than benzoate and phenylacetate (see below, Overview of Treatment of Urea Cycle Defects).

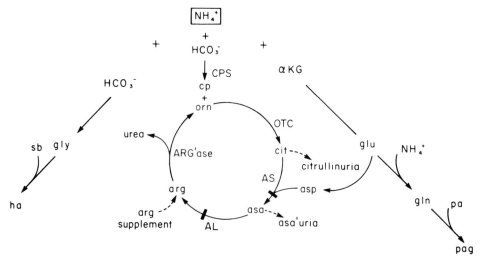

Figure 22-7 Normal and alternative pathways of waste nitrogen excretion: ha, hippuric acid; sb, sodium benzoate; pag, phenylacetylglutamine; pa, phenylacetic acid; ep, carbamylphosphate; asa, argininosuccinic acid. (From Batshaw, M.L., Thomas, G.H., and Brusilow, S.W.: New approaches to the diagnosis and treatment of inborn errors of urea synthesis. Pediatrics 68:290, 1981. Copyright American Academy of Pediatrics 1981.)

Ornithine Transcarbamylase Deficiency

Clinical Features

This disorder is inherited as a sex-linked dominant. Thus, in an affected XY male we should expect the full-blown syndrome, since there is no accompanying X chromosome to code for normal enzyme synthesis. Indeed, in male infants the usual presentation is as a neonatal catastrophe with survival past the first month of life a rarity. The situation with respect to females is more complicated. Since the female has one X chromosome coding for an abnormal enzyme and one coding for a functional enzyme, her liver should contain more enzyme activity than the liver of an affected male and the clinical expression of the disease should be milder. In addition, because of random inactivation of X chromosomes (so-called lyonization) (see Chapter 2) we should expect to encounter much variability from female to female, an expectation that is fulfilled. Although affected females are often mentally retarded, they usually survive beyond the neonatal period.

In some girls (and women) the only symptoms may be episodic nausea, vomiting, abdominal pain, and a very severe headache. This constellation of symptoms closely resembles those of the migraine syndrome and has prompted some observers to suggest that many individuals with migraine are heterozygotes for one of the hyperammonemic syndromes. Since the mother of a girl with a sex-linked dominant disorder ought herself to be affected, a history of protein intolerance or headache with protein loading is occasionally elicited.

Less than one third of female patients reported have died. Most have shown recurrent vomiting and feeding difficulties presenting at various ages. These episodes may be accompanied by headaches, confusion, emotional outbursts, and slurring of speech, probably related to the hyperammonemia. Male infants are usually normal at birth but within several hours or days develop difficulty feeding, lethargy, protein intolerance, vomiting, irritability, coma, and seizures. Rarely do they recover from their comatose state, and respiratory arrest is usually the terminal event. In those patients who have survived beyond the initial neonatal presentation, severe mental retardation has been the rule. Although onset in the male is usually very early, this is not invariable.

Biochemical Defects

The second step of the urea cycle is the formation of citrulline from carbamyl phosphate and ornithine, a reaction catalyzed by the enzyme ornithine transcarbamylase. It is this enzyme that is deficient in type II congenital hyperammonemia.

Laboratory Diagnosis

Quantitation of postprandial blood ammonia is the most direct screening test; in the neonatal form persistent elevation without protein feeding is the rule. When the blood ammonia has become elevated there is a corresponding increase in the SGOT and SGPT levels in the blood as well.

Urinary glutamine and lysine are often increased, and orotic acid crystals are often found on urine microscopic examination. The orotic aciduria that is characteristic of most cases of this syndrome is worthy of comment. Orotic acid is a precursor in the pathway of pyrimidine synthesis. The carbamyl phosphate that accumulates because of the defect in urea synthesis is shunted instead into the pathway of pyrimidine synthesis. The result is an increase in the synthesis of orotic acid, which then spills over into the urine where it forms typical needle-like crystals. The absence of orotic acid crystals in urine in carbamyl phosphate synthetase deficiency helps to distinguish it from OTC deficiency. While paper chromatography of urinary amino acids is unrevealing in carbamyl phosphate synthetase or ornithine transcarbamylase deficiencies, other urea cycle defects do manifest abnormalities. Differentiation between ornithine transcarbamylase deficiency and Reye's syndrome may be exceedingly difficult. Definitive diagnosis requires assay of ornithine transcarbamylase activity in liver or jejunal mucosa biopsy samples.

Treatment

Patients with partial deficiency of ornithine transcarbamylase will usually respond to protein restriction (1.0 to 1.5 g/kg/day), but with complete absence of enzyme activity more drastic measures must be attempted. These include hemodialysis, non-nitrogen analogues of essential amino acids, and citrate to augment α-ketoglutarate formation. Sodium benzoate may be a useful adjunct to therapy of hyperammonemic crises in this disorder.

Citrullinemia

Clinical Features

This is a rare disorder—about 50 cases have been described. The patterns of clinical expression range from death in the neonate to the healthy adult with hypercitrullinemia without hyperammonemia. The neonate shows poor feeding and often develops a depressed neurological state with poor tone, loss of the Moro reflex, and either hyper- or hypotonicity. Convulsions may be followed by coma and death. While symptoms generally begin after the first milk feeding, onset can be on the first day of life before any feeding is offered. In such a case, this may serve as a distinguishing feature from the organic acidemias, which do not usually present until the end of the first week of life.

In the subacute presentation, appetite and vigor of feeding decrease and vomiting is often associated with protein ingestion. Lethargy may progress to tremulousness, ataxia, and convulsions, with delayed psychomotor development. Liver enlargement is occasionally noted.

Biochemical Defects

Argininosuccinate synthetase catalyzes the condensation of aspartic acid and citrulline. As a consequence of the defective enzyme, citrulline accumulates behind the block. Two types of enzyme deficiency have been documented in this disorder: in one form the affinity of the enzyme for the substrate is altered so that the enzyme binding of citrulline is manyfold less than normal. In the second variant no enzyme activity can be detected.

Laboratory Diagnosis

While the postprandial blood ammonia is usually increased, this is not invariably so, and the BUN is characteristically normal. Paper chromatography of urine is a very useful study in this disorder. It will show a slight increase in neutral and acidic amino acids in the urine, presumably because citrulline shares the same renal transport system as the neutral amino acids. A striking accumulation of citrulline in the urine will be seen, as it is elevated from several hundred times normal in infants (nl = 1 mg/dl) to several thousands times normal in older patients. Plasma citrulline is also greatly elevated. Spraying a ninhydrin-treated chromatogram with Ehrlich's aldehyde reagent will reveal a bright yellow or peach-colored spot where citrulline is present. Some infants show a metabolic acidosis with hyperglycinemia and hypocalcemia, along with hypertransaminemia. Osteoporosis has been described on radiological examination.

The definitive diagnosis rests on assay of argininosuccinic acid synthetase in leukocytes, skin fibroblasts, or needle biopsy specimen of liver tissue.

Treatment

Protein restriction and keto analogues have been tried in this disorder with clinical improvements. Recently, the successful use of sodium benzoate and arginine supplements has been described.

Argininosuccinicaciduria

Clinical Features

This is the most common type of urea cycle defect. As with the other defects there is more than one phenotype. In the *neonatal type,* there is poor feeding, lethargy, tachypnea, and respiratory alkalosis (a distinctly unusual finding in an inborn error). In this form there is a rapidly fatal neonatal course with seizures and respiratory distress. Survival beyond three months has been most unusual. Feeding difficulties punctuate the presentation of the *subacute type,* which manifests in early infancy. Failure to thrive, delayed developmental milestones, and seizures are also likely. Hepatomegaly unassociated with significant microscopic abnormalities characterizes the hepatic findings. Some patients have abnormal hair (described below). Finally, in the *late onset type,* which accounts for most of these patients, excessive irritability and difficulties with feeding presage developmental delay and ataxia, which may not appear until the second year of life.

About half of these patients have thin, friable hair called *trichorrexis nodosa* owing to the tiny nodes present on the hair shafts. Although suggestive, this finding is not specific for argininosuccinicaciduria, as it is found in other diseases of the hair. Interestingly, some children with very friable hair, but without any evidence of hyperammonemia or protein intolerance, will excrete minute amounts of argininosuccinic acid in the urine.

Biochemical Defects

Argininosuccinase is responsible for cleavage of argininosuccinic acid to arginine and fumarate. By this reaction fumarate may enter the citric acid cycle. Arginine, the other product, will form urea and regenerate ornithine in the final step of the pathway.

Laboratory Diagnosis

Argininosuccinic acid is present in large amounts in the urine (2 to 9 g/24 hour), even during periods of clinical well-being, so that paper chromatography will usually reveal the distinctive argininosuccinic acid spot.

In the newborn form of this disorder there is commonly a marked hyperammonemia. In such patients there is also often a generalized hyperaminoacidemia with glutamine, alanine, and lysine being particularly elevated. Alkaline phosphatase and SGOT levels are usually increased when hyperammonemia is present. Orotic aciduria is sometimes seen as well.

The definitive diagnosis depends upon the demonstration of deficiency of argininosuccinase in red cells or white cells, liver, kidney, and fibroblasts.

Treatment

Protein restriction and arginine (500 mg/day) may ameliorate the biochemical and clinical abnormalities. The latter therapy exploits the high urinary excretion of argininosuccinic acid, a metabolite that contains both the amino groups that would normally leave the body as urinary urea. By providing adequate arginine to regenerate ornithine, ammonia can be removed from the body as argininosuccinic acid, thereby circumventing the block in argininosuccinase deficiency. It is worthy of note that the increased intracellular argininosuccinic acid levels that result from this therapy ameliorate the toxicity seen in this disease. This fact underscores the extremely toxic nature of free NH_3 in the human relative to the pathway intermediates that are increased as a consequence of the enzyme deficiency.

Arginase Deficiency

Clinical Features

Most patients with this very rare disorder have succumbed as neonates. It appears to be characterized by a spastic diplegia and severe psychomotor retardation and hepatomegaly. The vomiting so characteristic of protein intolerance is seen as well. As with the other hyperammonemic states, later onset forms occur, but the outcome is not always favorable. In one such patient who did not manifest symptoms until 3 years there was developmental delay, deterioration, and death.

Biochemical Defects

Arginase completes the urea cycle by splitting arginine into urea while regenerating the ammonia acceptor, ornithine.

Laboratory Diagnosis and Treatment

Arginine is greatly elevated in blood, urine, and CSF. Paper chromatography may suggest cystinuria, but the clinical histories are very different and a negative cyanide nitroprusside (for cystine) with elevated postprandial plasma ammonia should point in the direction of a urea cycle defect. Red cells serve as a readily available source to assay arginase activity, but skin or liver may also be used. Protein restriction has resulted in lowering of blood ammonia.

Hyperornithinemia

Protein intolerance and irritability alternating with lethargy and convulsions have characterized the few patients described. Ataxia has been common as well. Chemical abnormalities include the triad of hyperornithinemia, hyperammonemia, and homocitrullinuria.

Ornithine Aminotransferase Deficiency

This is an unusual defect of ornithine catabolism with gradual loss of visual acuity beginning at the end of the first decade and culminating in blindness during adulthood. Mental retardation is not a component of the clinical picture.

Retinal and choroidal atrophy are the causes of the visual problems, and recently interference with formation of guanidinoacetate and creatinine by ornithine has been demonstrated in such patients. Sipilä et al. speculate that limitation of high-energy phosphates (including phosphocreatine) may be the cause of these degenerative changes. Why patients with hyperornithinemia (see above) do not present with these findings is at present unexplained.

The enzyme ornithine aminotransferase that transaminates ornithine to glutamate semialdehyde appears to be defective in this disorder. Ornithine levels are increased in plasma, with an overflow ornithinuria as an associated finding.

Table 22–2   UREA CYCLE DEFECTS AND HYPERAMMONEMIA SYNDROMES

Condition	Genetics	Clinical Findings	Blood Ammonia*	Amino Acid Elevations in Plasma	Urinary Metabolites	Enzyme Defect (Tissue to Assay)	Treatment
Carbamyl Phosphate Synthetase Deficiency	AR	Neonatal catastrophe	3+	Glutamine, alanine, lysine	Normal orotic acid	Carbamyl phosphate synthetase (liver, jejunum)	Hemodialysis or peritoneal dialysis ↓Protein intake Benzoate or phenylacetate Keto-analogues
Ornithine Transcarbamylase Deficiency	XD	1. Neonatal catastrophe 2. Hypotonia, lethargy secondary to protein intolerance 3. Variability in female	2+ to 3+	Glutamine, alanine, lysine	Orotic acid↑	Ornithine transcarbamylase (liver, jejunum)	Same as above
Citrullinemia	AR	Severe neonatal presentation Subacute Occasional normal adults	Usually 2+ to 3+ after protein	Citrulline	3+ Citrulline + Neutral and acidic amino acids	Argininosuccinic acid synthetase (white blood cells, skin fibroblasts, liver)	Protein restriction, benzoate, arginine
Argininosuccinicaciduria	AR	Severe Subacute Ataxia, convulsions Friable hair	2+ after protein normal fasting	Argininosuccinic acid	Argininosuccinic acid, glutamine, alanine, lysine, ± orotic acid†	Argininosuccinase (red and white blood cells)	Protein restriction, benzoate Arginine
Hyperargininemia	AR	Neurological, hepatomegaly	2+	Arginine	Arginine, cystine, lysine, ornithine	Arginase (red blood cells)	Protein restriction
Hyperornithinemia	AR	Protein intolerance Lethargy, ataxia, convulsions	2+	Ornithine	Homocitrulline, ornithine		
Ornithinemia with Gyrate Atrophy	AR	↓Visual acuity → blindness	normal	Ornithine	Ornithine	Ornithine amino transferase	Protein restriction, creatine
Lysinuric Protein Intolerance	AR	Protein intolerance, mental retardation	2+	Ornithine	Lysine, cystine, citrulline, arginine	Defective transport of dibasic amino acids	Citrulline

*Degree of elevation: + mildly elevated; 2+ moderately elevated; 3+ markedly elevated.
† ± occasional finding.

248

Treatment

Low protein diets have not decreased plasma ornithine. Exogenous creatine may be indicated to supply adequate phosphocreatine.

Transient Hyperammonemia of the Preterm Infant

This recently described hyperammonemic condition occurring in the first two days of life presents much as the catastrophic inborn errors of the urea cycle. Indeed, blood ammonia levels may reach 7000 μg/dl. Nonetheless, this condition is apparently acquired, rather than inherited, and therefore responds to exchange transfusion or peritoneal dialysis. Clinically the distinguishing feature of the syndrome is the maintenance of a normal blood ammonia level after emergency therapy—even on a full protein ration. Moreover, no abnormal metabolites are seen in urine. The pathogenesis of this not uncommon hyperammonemic syndrome is undefined at present.

Overview of Treatment of Urea Cycle Defects

Protein should be restricted to the amount needed for growth and normal brain function. High carbohydrate intake will minimize endogenous protein breakdown. One significant source of blood ammonia is the action of the bacterial enzyme urease on urea present in the large intestine (see Chapter 11). Enemas are therefore used to sterilize the large intestine and to wash out from the bowel as much protein and amino acid as possible. During the acute phase of deterioration fluid management is key to facilitating removal of excess amounts of amino acids that may have accumulated. Hemodialysis appears to be more efficacious in lowering blood ammonia than peritoneal dialysis or multiple exchange transfusions.

Amino acid acylation with benzoic acid and phenylacetic acid and supplementation with arginine have been discussed above (see Fig. 22–7). The acylation products, hippurate and phenylacetylglutamine, can serve as acceptors for the amino groups normally destined to leave the body as urea. Arginine supplementation can provide substrate to form argininosuccinic acid, which bears both amino groups normally removed as urea. It has the added therapeutic advantage of having a clearance from the body equal to the glomerular filtration rate.

Both these types of intervention provide a "sink" for excess amino groups not able to be removed as urea. Use of α-keto analogues of the essential amino acids also seemed like a very promising approach to therapy notwithstanding their initial general unavailability. However, therapeutic success with these agents depends upon no dramatic increments in nitrogen catabolism, as occur with infection or vomiting with cessation of oral intake. In such instances the α-keto acids cannot "accept" sufficient ammonia by the following reaction,

$$\alpha\text{-keto acid} + NH_3 \rightarrow \text{amino acid}$$

to keep ammonia levels in the nontoxic range.

Hence, while they may be useful as an adjunct to the other therapies discussed above and outlined in Table 22–2, they cannot be employed alone. Further background and discussion of therapy of the urea cycle disorders can be found in the article by Batshaw and associates (1982).

REFERENCES

Amino Acid Metabolic Disorders—General

Rosenberg, L.E., and Scriver, C.R.: Disorders of amino acid metabolism. *In* Bondy, P.K. and Rosenberg, L.E. (eds.): Metabolic Control and Disease. 8th ed. W.B. Saunders Co., Philadelphia, 1980, p. 583.
Rowe, P.B.: Inherited disorders of folate metabolism. *In* Stanbury, J.B., Wyngaarden, J.B., Fredrickson, D.S., et al. (eds.): The Metabolic Basis of Inherited Disease. 5th ed. McGraw-Hill, New York, 1983, p. 498.

Wellner, D., and Meister, A.: A survey of inborn errors of amino acid metabolism and transport in man. Ann. Rev. Biochem. 50:911, 1981.

Phenylalanine and Tyrosine

Berger, R., Smit, G.P.A., Stoker-de Vries, S.A., et al.: Deficiency of fumarylacetoacetase in a patient with hereditary tyrosinema. Clin. Chim. Acta 114:37, 1981.
Berry, H.K., Sutherland, B.S., and Umbarger, B.: Diagnosis and treatment: interpretation of results of blood screening studies for detection of phenylketonuria. Pediatrics 37:102, 1966.
Cohn, R.M., Yudkoff, M., Yost, B., and Segal, S.: Phenylalanine-tyrosine deficiency syndrome as a complication of the management of hereditary tyrosinemia. Am. J. Clin. Nutr. 30:209, 1977.
Goldsmith, L.A.: Tyrosinemia and related disorders. *In* Stanbury, J.B., Wyngaarden, J.B., Fredrickson, D.S., et al. (eds.): The Metabolic Basis of Inherited Disease. 5th ed. McGraw-Hill, New York, 1983, p. 287.
La Du, B.N.: Alcaptonuria. *In* Stanbury, J.B., Wyngaarden, J.B. and Fredrickson, D.S. (eds.): The Metabolic Basis of Inherited Disease. 4th ed. McGraw-Hill, New York, 1978, p. 268.
Lane, J.D., and Neuhoff, V.: Phenylketonuria: Clinical and experimental considerations revealed by the use of animal models. Naturwiss. 67:227, 1980.
Lenke, R.R., and Levy, H.L.: Maternal phenylketonuria and hyperphenylalaninemia: An international survey of the outcome of untreated and treated pregnancies. N. Engl. J. Med. 303:1202, 1980.
Lindblad, B., Lindstedt, S., and Steen, G.: On the enzymic defects in hereditary tyrosinemia. Proc. Natl. Acad. Sci. USA 74:4641, 1977.
Milstein, S., Kaufman, S., and Summer, G.K.: Hyperphenylalanemia due to dihydropteridine reductase deficiency: Diagnosis by measurement of oxidized and reduced pterins in urine. Pediatrics 65:806, 1980.
O'Flynn, M.E., Holtzman, N.A., Blaskovics, M., et al.: The diagnosis of phenylketonuria: A report from the collaborative study of children treated for phenylketonuria. Am. J. Dis. Child 134:769, 1980.
Scriver, C.R., and Clow, C.L.: Phenylketonuria and other phenylalanine hydroxylation mutants in man. Ann. Rev. Genet. 14:179, 1980.
Scriver, C.R., and Clow, C.L.: Phenylketonuria: Epitome of human biochemical genetics. N. Engl. J. Med. 303:1336, 1980.
Tourian, A.Y., and Sidbury, J.B.: Phenylketonuria. *In* Stanbury, J.B., Wyngaarden, J.B., Fredrickson, D.S., et al. (eds.): The Metabolic Basis of Inherited Disease. 5th ed. McGraw-Hill, New York, 1983, p. 270.
Wilchen, B., Hammond, J.W., Howard, N., et al.: Hawkinsinuria: A dominantly inherited defect of tyrosine metabolism with severe effects in infancy. N. Engl. J. Med. 305:865, 1981.
Witkop, C.J., Jr., Quevedo, W.C., Jr. and Fitzpatrick, T.B.: Albinism. *In* Stanbury, J.B., Wyngaarden, J.B., Fredrickson, D.S., et al. (eds.): The Metabolic Basis of Inherited Disease. 5th ed. McGraw-Hill, New York, 1983, p. 301.

Nonketotic Hyperglycinemia

Ando, T., Nyhan, W.L., Gerritsen, T. et al.: Metabolism of glycine in the nonketotic form of hyperglycinemia. Pediatr. Res. 2:254, 1968.
Baumgartner, R., Ando, T., and Nyhan, W.L.: Nonketotic hyperglycinemia. J. Pediatr. 75:1022, 1969.
Garcia-Castro, J.M., Isales-Forsythe, C.M., Levy, H.L., et al.: Prenatal diagnosis of non-ketotic hyperglycinemia. N. Engl. J. Med. 306:79, 1982.
Gitzelmann, R., Steinmann, B., Otten, A. et al.: Nonketotic hyperglycinemia treated with strychnine, a glycine receptor antagonist. Helv. Pediatr. Acta 32:517, 1977.
Hiraga, K., and Kikuchi, G.: The mitochondrial glycine cleavage system. J. Biol. Chem. 255:11664, 11671, 1980.
Hiraga, K., Kochi, H., Hayasaka, K., et al.: Defective glycine cleavage system in nonketotic hyperglycinemia. J. Clin. Invest. 68:525, 1981.
Kikuchi, G.: The glycine cleavage system: Composition, reaction mechanism, and physiological significance. Molec. Cell. Biochem. 1:169, 1973.
Nyhan, W.L.: Nonketotic hyperglycinemia. *In* Stanbury, J.B., Wyngaarden, J.B., Fredrickson, D.S., et al. (eds.): The Metabolic Basis of Inherited Disease. 5th ed. McGraw-Hill, New York, 1983, p. 561.
Perry, T.L., Urquhart, N., Hansen, S., and Mamer, O.A.: Studies of the glycine cleavage enzyme system in brain from infants with glycine encephalopathy. Pediatr. Res. 12:1192, 1977.
Warburton, D., Boyle, R.J., Keats, J.P., et al.: Nonketotic hyperglycinemia: Effects of therapy with strychnine. Am. J. Dis. Child. 134:273, 1980.

Histidine

La Du, B.N.: Histidinemia. *In* Stanbury, J.B., Wyngaarden, J.B., and Fredrickson, D.S. (eds.): The Metabolic Basis of Inherited Disease. 4th ed. McGraw-Hill, New York, 1978, p. 317.
Levy, H.L., Shih, V.E., and Madigan, P.M.: Routine newborn screening for histidinemia. New Engl. J. Med. 291:1214, 1974.
Levy, H.L., Shih, V.E., and McReady, R.A.: Inborn errors of metabolism and transport: prenatal and neonatal diagnosis. Abstracts of the 13th International Congress of Pediatrics, Vienna, 1971, Part V, pp. 1–16.

Homocystine

Fowler, B., Kraus, J., Packman, S., and Rosenberg, L.E.: Homocystinuria: Evidence for three distinct classes of cystathionine β-synthase mutants in cultured fibroblasts. J. Clin. Invest. 61:645, 1978.

Gaull, G.E., Tallan, H.H., Lonsdale, D., et al.: Hypermethioninemia associated with methionine adenosyltransferase deficiency: Clinical, morphologic, and biochemical observations on four patients. J. Pediatr. 98:734, 1981.

Harker, L.A., Slichter, S.J., Scott, C.R., and Ross, R.: Homocystinemia: Vascular injury and arterial thrombosis. N. Engl. J. Med. 291:537, 1974.

Harpey, J.P., Rosenblatt, D.S., Cooper, B.A., et al.: Homocystinuria caused by 5,10-methylenetetrahydrofolate reductase deficiency: A case in an infant responding to methionine, folinic acid, pyridoxine, and vitamin B_{12} therapy. J. Pediatr. 98:275, 1981.

Lipson, M.H., Kraus, J., and Rosenberg, L.E.: Affinity of cystathionine β-synthase for pyridoxal 5'-phosphate in cultured cells: A mechanism for pyridoxine-responsive homocystinuria. J. Clin. Invest. 66:188, 1980.

Mudd, S.H., and Levy, H.L.: Disorders of transsulfuration. In Stanbury, J.B., Wyngaarden, J.B., Fredrickson, D.S., et al. (eds.): The Metabolic Basis of Inherited Disease. 5th ed. McGraw-Hill, New York, 1983, p. 522.

Schulman, J.D., Mudd, S.H., Schneider, J.A., et al.: Genetic disorders of glutathione and sulfur amino-acid metabolism. Ann. Intern. Med. 93:330, 1980.

Valle, D., Pai, G.S., Thomas, G.H., and Pyeritz, R.E.: Homocystinuria due to cystathionine β-synthase deficiency: Clinical manifestations and therapy. Johns Hopkins Med. J. 146:110, 1980.

Cystinosis

Schneider, J.A., and Schulman, J.D.: Cystinosis. In Stanbury, J.B., Wyngaarden, J.B., and Fredrickson, D.S., et al (eds.): The Metabolic Basis of Inherited Disease. 5th ed. McGraw-Hill, New York, 1983, p. 1844.

States, B., Harris, D., and Segal, S.: Patterns of cystine reduction by fibroblasts from normal and cystinotic children. Pediatr. Res. 11:685, 1977.

States, B., Lee, J., and Segal, S.: Uptake of cystine by cystine-depleted fibroblasts from patients with cystinosis. Biochem. Biophys. Res. Commun. 98:290, 1981.

Yudkoff, M., Foreman, J.W., and Segal, S.: Effects of cysteamine therapy in nephropathic cystinosis. N. Engl. J. Med. 304:141, 1981.

Lysine

Carson, N.A.J., Scally, B.G., Neill, D.W., and Carré, I.J. Saccharopinuria: a new inborn error of lysine metabolism. Nature 218:679, 1968.

Dancis, J., Hutzler, J., Cox, R.P., and Woody, N.C.: Familial hyperlysinemia with lysine-ketoglutarate reductase insufficiency. J. Clin. Invest. 48:1447, 1969.

Ghadimi, H.: The hyperlysinemias. In Stanbury, J.B., Wyngaarden, J.B., and Fredrickson, D.S. (eds.): The Metabolic Basis of Inherited Disease. 4th ed. McGraw-Hill, New York, 1978, p. 387.

Liebel, R.L., Shih, V.E., and Goodman, S.I., et al.: Glutaric acidemia: a metabolic disorder causing progressive choreoathetosis. Neurology 30:1163, 1980.

Stokke, O., Goodman, S.I., Moe, T.G.: Inhibition of brain glutamate decarboxylase by glutarate glucaconate and β-hydroxyglutarate: explanation of the symptoms in glutaric aciduria? Clin. Chim. Acta 66:411, 1976.

Woody, N.C., and Pupene, M.B.: Excretion of pipecolic acid by infants and by patients with hyperlysinemia. Pediatr. Res. 4:89, 1970.

Glutamate

McIntyre, T.M., and Curthoys, N.P.: The interorgan metabolism of glutathione. Intl. J. Biochem. 12:545, 1980.

Prusiner, S.B.: Disorders of glutamate metabolism and neurological dysfunction. Ann. Rev. Med. 32:521, 1981.

Urea Cycle

Ballard, R.A., Vinocur, B., Reynolds, J.W., et al.: Transient hyperammonemia of the preterm infant. N. Engl. J. Med. 299:920, 1978.

Batshaw, M.L., Roan, Y., Jung, A.L., et al.: Cerebral dysfunction in asymptomatic carriers of ornithine transcarbamylase deficiency. N. Engl. J. Med. 302:482, 1980.

Batshaw, M.L., Thomas, G.H., and Brusilow, S.W.: New approaches to the diagnosis and treatment of inborn errors of urea synthesis. Pediatrics 68:290, 1981.

Batshaw, M.L., Brusilow, S., Waber, L., et al.: Treatment of inborn errors of urea synthesis: Activation of alternative pathways of waste nitrogen synthesis and excretion. N. Engl. J. Med. 306:1387, 1982.

Brusilow, S.W., and Batshaw, M.L.: Arginine therapy of argininosuccinase deficiency: Lancet I:124, 1979.

Cederbaum, S.D., Shaw, K.N.F., Spector, E.B., et al.: Hyperargininemia with arginase deficiency. Pediatr. Res. 13:827, 1979.

Hsia, Y.E.: Inherited hyperammonemic syndromes. Gastroenterology 67:347, 1974.

Kline, J.J., Hug, G., Schubert, W.K., and Berry, H.: Arginine deficiency syndrome. Am. J. Dis. Child 135:437, 1981.

LaBrecque, D.R., Latham, P.S., Riely, C.A., et al.: Heritable urea cycle enzyme deficiency—liver disease in 16 patients. J. Pediatr. 94:580, 1979.

Mantagos, S., Tsagaraki, S., Burgess, E.A., et al.: Neonatal hyperammonemia with complete absence of liver carbamyl phosphate synthetase activity. Arch. Dis. Child. 53:230, 1978.

Naylor, S.L., Klebe, R.J., and Shows, T.B.: Argininosuccinic aciduria: Assignment of the argininosuccinate lyase gene to the pter→q22 region of human chromosome 7 by bioautography. Proc. Natl. Acad. Sci. USA 75:6159, 1978.

O'Donnell, J.J., Sandman, R.P., and Martin, S.R.: Gyrate atrophy of the retina: Inborn error of 1-ornithine:2-oxoacid aminotransferase. Science 200:200, 1978.

Oyanagi, K., Sogawa, H., Minami, R., et al.: The mechanism of hyperammonemia in congenital lysinuria. J. Pediatr. 94:255, 1979.

Palekar, A.G., and Mantagos, S.: Human liver argininosuccinase purification and partial characterization. J. Biol. Chem. 256:9192, 1981.

Pierson, D.L., and Brien, J.M.: Human carbamyl-phosphate synthetase I. J. Biol. Chem. 255:7891, 1980.

Rajantie, J., Simell, D., Rapola, J., and Perheentupa, J.: Lysinuric protein intolerance: A two-year trial of dietary supplementation therapy with citrulline and lysine. J. Pediatr. 97:927, 1980.

Rubio, V., Britton, H.G., and Grisolia, S.: Mechanism of carbamoyl-phosphate synthetase. Eur. J. Biochem. 93:245, 1979.

Sipilä, I., Simell, D., and Arjomaa, P.: Gyrate atrophy of the choroid and retina with hyperornithinemia. Deficient formation of guanidinoacetic acid from arginine. J. Clin. Invest. 66:684, 1980.

Snodgrass, P.J.: Biochemical aspects of urea cycle disorders. Pediatrics 68:273, 1981.

Snyderman, S.E.: Clinical aspects of disorders of the urea cycle. Pediatrics 68:284, 1981.

Symposium on Urea Cycle Enzymes and Ammonia Metabolism. Enzyme 26:225–259, 1981.

Valle, D., and Simell, D.: The hyperornithinemias. In Stanbury, J.B., Wyngaarden, J.B., Fredrickson, D.S., et al. (eds.): The Metabolic Basis of Inherited Disease. 5th ed. McGraw-Hill, New York, 1983, p. 382.

Walser, M.: Urea cycle disorders and other hereditary hyperammonemic syndromes. In Stanbury, J.B., Wyngaarden, J.B., Fredrickson, D.S., et al. (eds.): The Metabolic Basis of Inherited Disease. 5th ed. McGraw-Hill, New York, 1983, p. 402.

Walser, M., Batshaw, M., Sherwood, G., et al.: Nitrogen metabolism in neonatal citrullinemia. Clin. Sci. Molec. Med. 53:173, 1977.

Wiegand, C., Thompson, T., Bock, G.H., et al.: The management of life-threatening hyperammonemia: A comparison of several therapeutic modalities. J. Pediatr. 96:142, 1980.

Williamson, J.R., Steinman, R., Coll, K., and Rich, T.L.: Energetics of citrulline synthesis by rat liver mitochondria. J. Biol. Chem. 256:7287, 1981.

Yudkoff, M., Yang, W., Snodgrass, P.J., and Segal, S.: Ornithine transcarbamylase deficiency in a boy with normal development. J. Pediatr. 96:441, 1980.

23

Disorders of Amino Acid Transport

The cell membranes of all cells possess mechanisms for the transport of solutes from the extracellular to the intracellular environment. Indeed, the transport of solutes across the cell membranes is the initiating event in the metabolism of many compounds, and most cells derive their nutrient material from the extracellular environment. Besides the ubiquity of such transport systems for general cell homeostasis, there are groups of cells in the intestine and in the renal proximal tubule whose membranes are specialized into a microvillus brush border especially for the transport of amino acids and other solutes. These cells are responsible for reabsorption or absorption of compounds from the lumen of the renal tubule or the intestinal lumen, across the cell and into the blood stream. As such they function for the homeostasis of the entire organism.

A number of inherited disorders have been described in which an abnormality exists in the function of the microvillus membrane of the proximal renal tubule cells as well as of that of the intestinal mucosa. Many of these disorders affect both the intestinal absorptive and the renal reabsorptive capacity in the same patient. The genetic disorders of amino acid transport as a group are among some of the most common inherited abnormalities. These disorders include classical cystinuria, dibasic aminoaciduria without cystinuria, cystinuria without dibasic aminoaciduria, Hartnup's disease, iminoglycinuria, methionine and tryptophan malabsorption syndromes, and a large group of diseases of various etiologies that result in aminoaciduria, glycosuria, and phosphaturia, which are known as the Fanconi syndrome.

DISORDERS OF CYSTINE AND DIBASIC AMINO ACID TRANSPORT

Cystinuria

The most common of the inherited disorders of amino acid transport is classical cystinuria, which has been recognized since the early nineteenth century. It is also the transport disorder with the highest morbidity as a consequence of formation of urinary tract cystine stones with the resultant complications of pain, hematuria, and on occasion, obstruction of the urinary tract. Classical cystinuria is characterized by elevated urinary levels of cystine, lysine, ornithine, arginine, and a cysteine-homocysteine disulfide. On a molar basis, there appears to be three to four times as much lysine excreted as cystine. The diagnosis of this condition depends on demonstrating the typical pattern of amino acid excretion and is not dependent on the presence of urinary calculi or any of the concomitant clinical findings.

The presence of excessive amounts of cystine and dibasic amino acids in the urine of affected patients is related to a genetic defect in the transport of these amino acids. The molecular mechanism of this defect is not yet understood. The associated excretion of cystine and dibasic amino acids has led to the postulate that there is a shared transport system for these four amino acids that is defective. Animal studies indeed demonstrate in isolated renal tubules and in isolated brush border membrane vesicle preparations that there is a system shared by cystine and the dibasic amino acids. There also appears to be a second system for cystine as well as for each of the individual dibasic amino acids that is not shared by the others. In vitro studies with slices of renal cortex from affected kidneys have clearly demonstrated a defective transport of lysine and arginine. The physiology of the hyperexcretion of cystine, however, appears to be more complicated than merely the absence of a shared transport system, since renal clearance studies have demonstrated that cystine clearance exceeds the glomerular filtration rate by as much as twofold. Such a result indicates secretion of cystine by the kidney. The mechanisms of cystine secretion are as yet not well understood.

Investigative efforts into the underlying abnormality have focused on a study of intestinal transport of cystine and the dibasic amino acids because of evidence for an intestinal defect and the ready availability of intestinal mucosa acquired by peroral biopsy. The studies of the in vitro uptake of cystine and the dibasic amino acids by jejunal mucosa have revealed three different patterns of transport defects corresponding to three different cystinuric phenotypes (Table 23–1). These findings have suggested that the three types of cystinuric defects are allelic, i.e., they have the same chromosomal locus. There has been some question that the type III homozygote is not a unique entity and that this might be a compound or mixed heterozygote of the first and second type of cystinuria. The issue awaits resolution.

The liability for clinical disease derives from the presence in the urine of excessive amounts of cystine, the least soluble of all naturally occurring amino acids. Cystine solubility is about 300 mg per liter of urine at pH less than 7.5. Stone formers excrete over 250 mg per gram of creatinine with a range of total 24-hour excretion of cystine of 0.5 to over 1.5 g. Crystalluria and a tendency to stone formation are more likely to occur during the hours of sleep when little water is ingested and urine volumes are small. Renal dysfunction in these patients is due entirely to cystine calculus formation, and no abnormality results from the hyperexcretion of lysine, arginine, and ornithine.

Newborn screening studies for cystinuria place the incidence of homozygous disease at about 1 in 7000 births. Affected individuals usually present later in life in the second, third, and fourth decades with clinical signs and symptoms of urinary tract stones. Cystine calculi, however, have been found in patients as early as the first year of life and as late as in the ninth decade. The stones formed are usually composed of cystine but contain other substances. On occasion, urate stones may be observed in association with cystinuria. Examination of the urine for the presence of hexagonal crystals can be very helpful in making the diagnosis.

The cyanide nitroprusside test is the most reliable screening procedure available for the detection of excessive cystine in the urine; it produces a positive burgundy color reaction when cystine concentrations are greater than 75 mg/l. Under ideal circumstances this test should be performed on a portion of a 24-hour urine collection, which, if positive, can then be quantitated for cystine and the dibasic amino acids. Quantitation is necessary to distinguish the carrier from the homozygous individual. The carrier for types I and II cystinuria will have an excessive excretion of cystine and

Table 23–1 CYSTINURIC PHENOTYPES

Observations	Type I	Type II	Type III
Intestine:			
Carrier-mediated transport (in vitro)	Absent for cystine, lysine, and arginine; normal for cysteine	Absent for lysine; decreased for cystine	Low to normal for cystine and lysine
Oral cystine loading	No elevation of plasma cystine	No elevation of plasma cystine	Slower than normal rate of increase in plasma cystine
Kidney:			
Carrier-mediated transport (in vitro)	Normal for cystine and cysteine; decreased for lysine	Unknown	Normal for cystine; decreased for lysine
Urinary amino acid excretion	Increased cystine, lysine, arginine, and ornithine	Increased cystine, lysine, arginine, and ornithine	Increased cystine, lysine, arginine, and ornithine
Urinary amino acid excretion in obligate heterozygotes	Normal	Increased cystine and lysine	Increased cystine and lysine

lysine but little or no hyperexcretion of ornithine and arginine. Only about one third of carriers for cystinuria are this type. The remaining two thirds of carriers for type I cystinuria will reveal no abnormality in the urine.

As regards the homozygote, it is important to quantitate the excretion of cystine before treatment is begun. The most common cause of a false positive cyanide nitroprusside test is the presence of ketonuria; such a result may also be obtained in individuals with homocystinuria or in those who have a generalized aminoaciduria with a concomitant hyperexcretion of cystine. The presence of cystine in the urine can be distinguished by a modification of a nitroprusside test, and a generalized aminoaciduria would be detected by various types of chromatographic procedures. Individuals with positive nitroprusside tests not caused by hyperexcretion of cystine normally do not form calculi. Moreover, it should not be difficult to distinguish their phenotype from those affected by classic cystinuria.

Since the pathogenesis of kidney damage in cystinuria is dependent upon the excessive amounts of this relatively insoluble material in the urine, any treatment regimen must focus on decreasing cystine excretion or increasing its solubility. The simplest method for increasing the solubility has consisted of increasing the amount of solvent in which the cystine is dissolved. This has been accomplished by increasing fluid intake to as much as 4 liters of fluid per day to keep urinary cystine below 300 mg/l. This regimen requires that patients arise at least once a night to drink water. This type of therapy has been successful in up to 70 per cent of the patients in some series. Its success depends on the ability of patients to maintain a regimen of excessive fluid and water intake. Alkalinization of the urine has been used as an adjunct for increasing the solubility of cystine. However, the solubility does not increase appreciably above pH 7.5, and it is difficult to maintain an alkaline urine with a pH above 7.5 for long periods of time, a situation that has rendered this method of limited utility. Moreover, precipitation of calcium salts is favored by maintaining an alkaline urine pH, further decreasing the benefit of such an approach.

An effective therapeutic approach that has relied upon decreasing the actual excretion of cystine and on the formation of mixed disulfide compounds has been accomplished by the use of D-penicillamine (β-β-dimethylcysteine). Oral administration of this compound to cystinuric patients results in the excretion in the urine of a product of a disulfide exchange (cysteine-penicillamine mixed disulfide), which is much more soluble than cystine itself. The administration of penicillamine also causes a decrease in plasma cystine levels that results in the urinary excretion of less cystine by decreasing the filtered load presented to the kidney. As a consequence of both these mechanisms there is a marked decrease in the amount of urinary cystine. The goal of maintaining urinary cystine levels below 200 mg/g of creatinine can usually be accomplished by administration of 1 to 2 g of D-penicillamine per day in 3 or 4 equally divided doses. Extensive experience with this form of therapy has documented its efficacy in preventing stone formation. D-Penicillamine therapy may also bring about dissolution of stones already present in the urinary tract and thus obviate the need for surgical intervention to remove calculi from the urinary tract. In monitoring the efficacy of treatment by urinary amino acid quantitation, it is important to remember that many methods of amino acid measurement will not distinguish between the cysteine moiety of cysteine-penicillamine disulfide and free cystine in the urine, the latter being the critical substance to measure.

Rare Disorders of the Cystine-Dibasic Amino Acid Transport System

Isolated Hypercystinuria

This entity was reported in 1966; no further reports have appeared subsequently. It is noteworthy that the existence of hyperexcretion of cystine in humans provides very strong evidence in favor of the conclusion that cystine is transported by at least one system that is not shared with the dibasic amino acids in the renal tubule.

Hyperdibasic Aminoaciduria (Lysinuric Protein Intolerance)

Lysinuric protein intolerance is a defect of diamino acid transport in both kidney and intestine and is characterized by renal hyperdiaminoaciduria and hyperammonemia following protein ingestion. Inheritance is autosomal recessive. In contrast to cystinuria, cystine excretion is characteristically normal with low to normal plasma levels of lysine, ornithine, and arginine but enormously elevated urinary levels of these three amino acids. Hyperammonemia is thought to be due to decreased intestinal absorption of lysine, ornithine, and arginine, creating a depletion of body stores. This results in a slowing of the urea cycle because of the ornithine deficiency, with a consequent build-up of ammonia. Since ornithine acts as the initial ammonia acceptor in the urea cycle and arginine cleavage yields urea while regenerating ornithine, supplementation of the diet with either arginine or ornithine should normalize urea production in the face of a normal dietary protein load. This has been shown to be efficacious, leading to a remarkable increase in growth in affected children. A variant of this disorder has been reported in which affected individuals do not have clinical disease.

Disorders of Neutral Amino Acid Transport

Hartnup Disease

Hartnup disease is characterized by a pellagra-like skin rash, a reversible cerebellar ataxia that is usually most severe when skin lesions are florid, frequent and persistent headache, psychiatric symptoms ranging from emotional lability to frank delirium and hallucinations, and constant aminoaciduria of renal origin.

Exacerbations of clinical findings with recrudescence especially during childhood have been reported in association with a variety of physiological stresses including intercurrent febrile illness and inadequate nutrition. The pivotal role of nutrition in exacerbations coupled with the diminution in frequency and severity of attacks as these children get older suggests relative deficiency of some dietary component during the rapid growth phases of childhood. Indoleacetic acid, a degradative product of tryptophan metabolism, is generally present in the urine of these patients, especially during periods of clinical relapse. There are also large amounts of the parent compound tryptophan. The major metabolic route for tryptophan is conversion to nicotinic acid and NAD, leading to the conclusion that it is either tryptophan or niacin that is relatively deficient in Hartnup disease.

Renal clearances of the neutral amino acids, including alanine, serine, threonine, valine, leucine, isoleucine, phenylalanine, tyrosine, tryptophan, histidine, glutamine, and asparagine, ranging from 8 to 20-fold normal levels in the presence of normal plasma amino acid levels is characteristic of this disorder. These data indicate that the renal tubule of patients with Hartnup disease manifests an inherited defect in the reabsorptive mechanism of the neutral amino acids, and led Milne and co-workers (1960) to investigate the possibility that this defect might include the intestinal epithelium as well. They demonstrated that patients with Hartnup disease have a defect in intestinal absorption of tryptophan. Navab and Asatoor (1970) further demonstrated that oligopeptides containing tryptophan, in combination with other amino acids, are absorbed normally in the intestines of these patients, accounting for the presence of a relative rather than absolute deficiency of tryptophan in these patients.

Definitive diagnosis of this disorder is dependent upon urinary amino acid chromatography. Quantification of amino acid excretion by ion-exchange chromatography is not necessary, since the pattern of the amino acids excreted in excess is pathognomonic of the disease. Paper chromatography of 10 to 20 microliters of urine from the 24-hour collection that has been stained with ninhydrin will usually suffice to make the diagnosis. Obligate heterozygotes for Hartnup disease do not have excessive amino acid loss in urine as sometimes occurs in carriers with cystinuria; hence no further studies are indicated to distinguish the homozygous state.

Because the clinical findings appear to derive from inefficient intestinal absorption and increased urinary loss of amino acids, the most rational and innocuous approach to treatment consists of placing the patient on a high protein intake. Supplementation of such a diet with 40 to 200 mg of oral nicotinamide per day is recommended as well, since such treatment usually produces marked improvement of both skin and central nervous system involvement. In view of the possibility that bacterial breakdown products of tryptophan, such as indole, which are absorbed, may interfere with the endogenous conversion of tryptophan to NAD, Milne has recommended sterilization of the gut with oral neomycin during exacerbations.

Other Disorders of Amino Acid Transport

Tryptophan Malabsorption (Blue Diaper Syndrome)

This is a rare disease characterized by recurrent febrile episodes, growth retardation, irritability, constipation, and blue-stained diapers. Detailed investigation suggests a defect in tryptophan absorption with a complete absence of tryptophan in the urine. Hypercalcemia and nephrocalcinosis accompany the intestinal defect in tryptophan absorption, resulting in azotemia. The blue coloration of the diapers is caused by indigotin, an oxidation product of indican. This compound is found in increased amounts in the urine in association with other indole derivatives. Neomycin administration will reduce excretion of indolic urinary constituents.

The inheritance pattern of this syndrome is not known, nor has any treatment been defined. In the blue diaper syndrome the lack of nicotinamide deficiency symptoms seen in Hartnup disease is the result of the defect in intestinal absorption of tryptophan not being compounded by an increased urinary loss as well.

Methionine Malabsorption Syndrome (Oasthouse Urine Disease)

This rare disorder supports the existence of a separate transport system in kidney and gut for methionine, and possibly phenylalanine and tyrosine. The clinical picture is striking. The affected infant has white hair, edema, hyperpneic attacks, mental retardation, convulsions, and a urinary odor characteristic of a brewery (Oasthouse). The urine of the first patient reported contained increased amounts of methionine, the branched-chain amino acids (leucine, isoleucine and valine), phenylalanine, and tyrosine. Additionally, large amounts of α-hydroxybutyric acid were found in the urine, this acid being a reduced form of an α-keto acid produced during the conversion of methionine to cysteine. The urine of the second child contained only the hydroxy acid while she was on a normal diet. However, when an oral methionine loading study was performed, excretion of α-hydroxybutyric acid and the keto acid metabolites of the branched-chain amino acids increased. Excretion of methionine in stool, while usually high, increased enormously with loading as did the α-hydroxybutyric acid.

The first patient reported appears to represent an example of abnormal renal transport of methionine, with an inferred defect in intestinal absorption as well. In contrast, the second child appears to have had a defect in methionine transport in gut only, with renal tubule transport normal, as evidenced by the absence of aminoaciduria even after an oral methionine load. By analogy with types I and II cystinuria these two patients could represent two mutations rather than one. The limited information about this condition does not permit discussion of either inheritance or treatment.

DISORDERS OF GLYCINE AND IMINO ACIDS

Familial Iminoglycinuria

Although not clinically significant, the value of detection and study of this autosomal recessive condition lies in a clarification of the normal processes for glycine, proline, and hydroxyproline reabsorption in the renal tubule as well as an improvement in our understanding of the way in which the genome determines the specificity characteristic of membrane transport systems (see Chapter 2). Because of the asymptomatic nature of this disorder, affected patients are likely to be detected only by means of a mass screening program. Persons with the homozygous condition are likely to be detected without difficulty by these means, since the presence of any detectable free proline or hydroxyproline in the urine beyond the first three months is a distinct abnormality. If the definitive diagnosis has been made, no treatment is necessary. However, there are other disorders, not at all benign, in which hyperglycinuria is a prominent laboratory finding and leads to a problem in differential diagnosis.

Hyperglycinuria Associated With Other Disorders

These conditions are generally associated with overt clinical symptoms, the most important entities being ketotic and nonketotic hyperglycinemia. Although hyperglycinuria in these inborn errors of metabolism is only secondary to the extremely high blood levels of glycine (overflow aminoaciduria), they are essential diagnoses to make, since at least one form of ketotic hyperglycinemia is potentially responsive to therapy with biotin and protein restriction and may otherwise be fatal (Chapter 34).

Hyperglycinuria, associated with calcium oxalate urolithiasis, has been reported as a sex-linked dominant trait through three family generations. However, whether the aminoaciduria was related to the pathogenesis of the urolithiasis was not established. Although these patients did not manifest a systemic acidosis, it is possible such patients represented an incomplete form of renal tubular acidosis with urolithiasis. Indeed, incomplete distal renal tubular acidosis was unknown until the report of Wrong and Davies in 1959. Subsequently, a number of reports have shown that patients with the incomplete form of distal tubular acidosis can present with urolithiasis in the absence of a systemic acidosis.

Hyperglycinuria has also been reported in association with renal glycinuria, familial hypophosphatemic rickets, hyperprolinemia, cystinuria, and renal tubular injuries from heavy metals. In addition, increased glycine clearance may be part of the Fanconi syndrome and often appears in severe metabolic acidosis, particularly in infants.

FANCONI SYNDROME

This constellation of findings represents a generalized tubular dysfunction consisting of mellituria, generalized aminoaciduria, hyposthenuria, phosphaturia, hypercalciuria, hypernatriuria, proximal renal tubular acidosis with bicarbonaturia, proteinuria, and rickets that is resistant to vitamin D. Historically, the description of the Fanconi syndrome has been tied to the description of cystinosis, although it is now recognized that cystinosis is not the only cause. Compounding the initial confusion, a distinction between cystinosis and cystinuria was also not made until much later, so that some early descriptions of the Fanconi syndrome include nephrolithiasis, which is not a characteristic of either the Fanconi syndrome or cystinosis. Proper designation of the syndrome is the Toni-Debre-Fanconi syndrome, as a tribute to the three authors whose cases contributed to full recognition of the clinical picture.

While Fanconi syndrome is usually thought of as a secondary finding in a variety of diseases, both inherited and acquired, a significant number of cases occur in which the underlying etiology, be it acquired or inherited, eludes the physician. Such cases of idiopathic Fanconi syndrome, while not having a well-established genetic basis, have been reported to be both autosomal recessive and autosomal dominant traits. It behooves the physician to undertake an extensive etiological search in every case before labeling the child with the diagnosis of "idiopathic" Fanconi syndrome. In childhood the commonly seen type is the secondary form; the most common cause is cystinosis, with other potential causes listed in Table 23–2 following far behind.

The hallmark of the Fanconi syndrome is a generalized aminoaciduria, entirely unlike the

Table 23–2 ETIOLOGIES OF THE FANCONI SYNDROME

Genetic/Metabolic	Acquired/Toxic
Idiopathic	Acute tubular necrosis
Cystinosis	Chemical ingestion
Busby's syndrome	Lysol
Galactosemia	Maleic acid (in rats)
Hereditary fructose intolerance	Nitrobenzene
Glycogen storage disease, type 1	Chemical ingestion
Lowe's syndrome	Salicylates
Luder-Sheldon syndrome	Tetracycline (outdated)
Nephrotic syndrome (congenital)	Methyl-3-chromosome
Osteogenesis imperfecta	Streptozotocin
Renal tubular acidosis	Severe burns
Sickle cell disease	Heavy metal poisoning
Spherocytosis	Bismuth
Thalassemia	Cadmium
Tyrosinemia	Lead
Wilson's disease	Mercury
	Uranium
	Severe hypokalemia
	Protein malnutrition
	Hyperparathyroidism
	Vitamin deficiency (B_{12}, C, D)
	Multiple myeloma
	Transplant rejection

specific genetic amino acid transport disorders with which we have dealt previously. In this case, there is no apparent selectivity, and amino acids of the acidic, basic, neutral and iminoglycine groups are excreted in excess. Because of the global nature of the transport defect (amino acids, ions, hexoses, and so on) the various transport systems must be affected in a way that destroys their integrity (perhaps by an effect on the genome) or their ability to utilize energy required for the transport process. Either inhibitory process would be consistent with an acquired metabolic toxicity as opposed to a hereditary defect. Segal has suggested that the generalized aminoaciduria, glycosuria, and phosphaturia are the result of disruption of either the luminal or the basal membrane, resulting in a secondary disruption of transport function. A recent report suggests that interference by a biochemical intermediate with intracellular metabolic changes, occurring with development, is the underlying etiology for the Fanconi syndrome.

Although any of the clinical consequences of the Fanconi syndrome may bring the patient to the physician's attention, usually parents seek medical consultation because of unexplained fevers, growth failure, and obvious bowing of the lower extremities due to rickets. Since the first two features are frequent manifestations of urinary tract infection in infancy, the physician would do well to consider the Fanconi syndrome as a part of the differential diagnosis, even in the absence of clinical rickets. The demonstration of hyperchloremic metabolic acidosis, hypophosphatemia, glycosuria, and generalized aminoaciduria gives sufficient grounds for preliminary diagnosis and further etiological investigation. Slit-lamp examination of the cornea will often reveal the presence of cystine crystals, thus assuring the diagnosis of cystinosis (see Chapter 7).

Treatment is symptomatic and is directed toward the effects of tubular dysfunction. Correction of the acidosis by administration of sodium potassium citrate (modified Shohl's solution) in doses of 40 to 60 ml/day in divided doses is essential. Despite this therapy some patients will not elevate their plasma CO_2 above 20 mmol/l no matter how much alkali is given. Occasionally one encounters a patient in whom provision of adequate amounts of potassium as modified Shohl's solution will result in hypernatremia. In such a case, a changeover to sodium citrate and a KCl solution will permit the two cations to be regulated independently. Large doses of vitamin D are usually required to promote healing of the rickets. We begin with an initial dosage of 5000 I.U./day, with a simultaneous correction of the acid-base abnormality. Such doses will bring about x-ray evidence of healing of the rickets in most patients. Some advocate starting at 10,000 to 15,000 I.U./day, but we have not resorted to such high doses except in cases in which the diagnosis is made late in childhood or in the rare patient with such a low bicarbonate threshold that complete correction of the acidosis is not possible.

REFERENCES

Amino Acid Transport—General

Crane, R.K.: The gradient hypothesis and other models of carrier-mediated active transport. Rev. Physiol. Biochem. Pharmacol. 73:99, 1977.

Erlit, D.: Solute transport across isolated epithelia. Kidney Int. 9:76, 1976.

McNamara, P.D., and Ozegovic, B.: Membrane structure and transport systems. *In* Herman, R.H., Cohn, R.M., and McNamara, P.D. (eds.): Principles of Metabolic Control in Mammalian Systems. Plenum Press, New York, 1980, p. 373.

Oxender, D.L.: Membrane transport. Ann. Rev. Biochem. 47:777, 1972.

Quinn, P.J., and Chapman, D.: The dynamics of membrane structure. CRC Crit. Rev. Biochem. 8:1, 1980.

Roth, K.S., and Segal, S.: Tubular aspects of hereditary and developmental disorders of the kidney. *In* Hamburger, J., Crosnier, J. and Grunfeld, J.P. (eds.): Nephrology. Wiley-Flammarion, New York and Paris, 1979, p. 945.

Wilson, D.B.: Cellular transport mechanisms. Ann. Rev. Biochem. 47:933, 1978.

Disorders of Cystine and Dibasic Amino Acid Transport

Desjeux, J.F., Rajantie, J., Simell, O., et al.: Lysine fluxes across the jejunal epithelium in lysinuric protein intolerance. J. Clin. Invest. 65:1382, 1980.

Foreman, J.W., McNamara, P.D., and Segal, S.: Transport of cystine by isolated renal tubules and brushborder membrane vesicles. *In* Belton, N.R., and Toothill, C. (eds.): Inherited Transport Disorders, MTP Press, England, 1981, p. 263.

Gold, R.J.M., Dobrinski, M.J., and Gold, D.P.: Cystinuria and mental deficiency. Clin. Genet. 12:329, 1977.

Kato, T.: Renal handling of dibasic amino acids and cystine in cystinuria. Clin. Sci. Molec. Med. 59:9, 1977.

McNamara, P.D., Pepe, L.M., and Segal, S.: Cystine uptake by rat renal brushborder vesicles. Biochem. J. 194:443, 1981.

Oyanagi, K., Sogawa, H., Minami, R., et al.: The mechanism of hyperammonemia in congenital lysinuria. J. Pediatr. 94:255, 1979.

Rajantie, J., Simell, O., and Perheentupa, J.: Intestinal absorption in lysinuric protein intolerance. Gut 21:519, 1980.

Rosenberg, L.E., Downing, S., Durant, J.L., et al.: Cystinuria: Biochemical evidence of three genetically distinct diseases. J. Clin. Invest. 45:365, 1966.

Scriver, C.R., Whelan, D.T., and Clow, C.L.: Cystinuria: increased prevalence in patients with mental disease. N. Engl. J. Med. 283:783, 1970.

Segal, S.: The nature of amino acid transport disorders. Proc. Fifth International Pediatric Nephrology Congress, in press.

Silk, D.B.A., Perrett, D., Stephens, A.D., et al.: Intestinal absorption of cystine and cysteine in normal human subjects and patients with cystinuria. Clin. Sci. Molec. Med. 47:393, 1974.

Smith, A., and Procopis, P.G.: Cystinuria and its relationship to mental retardation. Med. J. Aust. 2:932, 1975.

Segal, S., and Thier, S.: Cystinuria. *In* Stanbury, J.B., Wyngaarden, J.B., Fredrickson, D.S., et al. (eds.): The Metabolic Basis of Inherited Disease. 5th ed. McGraw-Hill, New York, 1983, p. 1774.

Disorders of Neutral Amino Acid Transport

Buehler, B.A.: Inherited disorders of amino acid transport in relation to kidney. Ann. Clin. Lab. Sci. 11:274, 1981.

Leonard, J.V., Marrs, T.C., Addison, J.M., et al.: Intestinal absorption of amino acids and peptides in Hartnup disorder. Pediatr. Res. 10:246, 1976.

Milne, M.D., Crawford, M.A., Girad, C.B., et al.: The metabolic disorder in Hartnup disease. Quart. J. Med. 29:407, 1960.

Navab, F., and Asatoor, A.M.: Studies on intestinal absorption of amino acids and a dipeptide in a case of Hartnup disease. Gut 11:373, 1970.

Wong, P.W.K., Lambert, A.M., Pillal, P.M., et al.: Observations on nicotinic acid therapy in Hartnup disease. Arch. Dis. Child. 42:642, 1967.

Other Disorders of Amino Acid Transport

Drummond, K.N., Michael, A.F., Ulstrom, R.A., et al.: The blue diaper syndrome: familial hypercalcemia with nephrocalcinosis and indicanuria. Amer. J. Med. 37:928, 1964.

Kitagawa, T., Akatsuka, A., Owada, M., et al.: Biologic and therapeutic effects of 1-α-hydroxycholecalciferol in different types of Fanconi syndrome. Contr. Nephrol. 22:107, 1980.

Roth, K.S., Foreman, J.W., and Segal, S.: The Fanconi syndrome and mechanisms of tubular transport dysfunction. Kidney Int. 20:705, 1981.
Roth, K.S., Goldmann, D.R., and Segal, S.: Developmental basis for maleic acid-induced Fanconi syndrome. Pediatr. Res. 12:1121, 1978.

Other Disorders of Amino Acid Transport

Smith, A.J., and Strang, L.B.: An inborn error of metabolism with the urinary excretion of α-hydroxybutyric acid and phenylpyruvic acid. Arch. Dis. Child. 33:109, 1958.
Wrong, O., and Davies, H.E.F.: The excretion of acid in renal disease. Quart. J. Med. 28:259, 1959.

24

Bilirubin Disorders

CONGENITAL NONHEMOLYTIC NONCONJUGATED HYPERBILIRUBINEMIA

Type I

The hallmark of this disorder, described by Crigler and Najjar in 1952, is a serum unconjugated bilirubin level greater than 20 mg/dl unaccompanied by any conjugated bilirubin. Subsequently, milder forms of this disorder have been described. However, because of individual variations in the ability of neonates to eliminate bilirubin, it often requires some time to ascertain whether an affected infant suffers from the complete or partial absence of glucuronyl transferase (Fig. 24–1). For both diagnosis and therapy, the key distinction is the ability of phenobarbital to induce UDP-glucuronyl-transferase enzyme activity with the partial defect. In the complete defect, stools are of normal color and there is bilirubin in the urine. In contrast, the bile is frequently colorless, containing no bilirubin glucuronides. As a result of the hyperbilirubinemia early in infancy, there is unequivocal evidence of bilirubin encephalopathy and at autopsy of kernicterus. While most die,

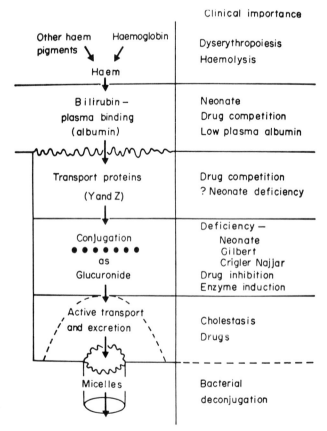

Figure 24–1 The relationship between bilirubin metabolism and its disorders. (From Sherlock, S.: Diseases of the Liver and Biliary System. 6th ed. Oxford, Blackwell Scientific Publications, 1981.)

survivors suffer choreoathetosis as a result of the toxicity of bilirubin to nervous tissue during this vulnerable period of brain growth and functional maturation (see Chapter 19).

Complete absence of UDP-glucuronyltransferase activity, unresponsive to phenobarbital therapy, characterizes this disorder. Other liver function tests are normal, including investigation of bilirubin turnover, hepatic uptake, and storage.

Type II

In this variant unconjugated bilirubin levels usually do not exceed 20 mg/dl, and some monoglucuronide can be detected in the serum. While no activity of the bilirubin UDP-glucuronyltransferase can be detected on in vitro enzyme assays, these patients show an increase in conjugating ability in response to phenobarbital. Within 2 to 3 weeks, administration of 3 to 5 mg/kg/day in children will produce a decrease in the plasma bilirubin concentration. Persistent suppression of bilirubin levels requires continuation of therapy. The liability of the brain to develop bilirubin encephalopathy is greatest during the first weeks or months of life, so that vigorous therapy is most vital at that time. It is not unusual for individuals with this variant form to be first diagnosed in adolescence or early adulthood; hence, prognosis for normal intellectual development is often quite good.

In practice, it is not always easy to distinguish these disorders from the normal neonate presenting with "physiological jaundice of the newborn." However, as the hyperbilirubinemia persists beyond the acceptable period for physiological jaundice of the normal neonate, suspicion of an abnormality is likely to be aroused. Distinction from biliary atresia and neonatal hepatitis is accomplished by the elevated conjugated bilirubin that occurs in bile outflow problems and hepatocellular damage. Additionally, the question of hypothyroidism in circumstances of hyperbilirubinemia is always an important one to answer.

Since response to phenobarbital serves both a diagnostic and a therapeutic function, it represents the best means for distinguishing the two forms of this disorder.

Treatment

Definitive diagnosis of defects of UDP-glucuronyltransferase activity are not likely to be made until it becomes clear that phototherapy and exchange transfusion are unable to maintain serum bilirubin below 20 mg/dl. At that point one of the two forms of congenital nonhemolytic unconjugated hyperbilirubinemia should be strongly suspected; to distinguish them one administers phenobarbital, in a dose of 5 to 8 mg/kg/day for a period of two to three weeks, while monitoring the therapeutic response. Several authors recommend that because of the liability of the brain to permanent damage by bilirubin, phototherapy should be continued, although it may obscure interpretation of the pharmacological response. Nonetheless, such a delay is justified because the integrity of the brain is at stake. Vitamin D supplementation is indicated during prolonged phenobarbital administration because of accelerated catabolism of this hormone by other enzymes induced by phenobarbital.

Infants with complete absence of the UDP-glucuronyltransferase will not respond to phenobarbital, but phototherapy and exchange transfusion may nonetheless protect the brain from bilirubin toxicity. During that period of enhanced CNS vulnerability these procedures can decrease bilirubin levels to the innocuous range of 4 to 8 mg/dl. Several studies have shown that after the first few months of life either continuous or intermittent phototherapy for 12 hours daily over several years can maintain the bilirubin concentrations between 10 and 17 mg/dl. Such levels are compatible with normal development.

Cholestyramine and agar, drugs that impede the intrahepatic circulation of bilirubin, can augment the effectiveness of phototherapy and indeed decrease the duration of required daily phototherapy.

MILD NONHEMOLYTIC UNCONJUGATED
HYPERBILIRUBINEMIA (Gilbert's Syndrome)

While Gilbert's syndrome is the most common of all types of congenital nonhemolytic unconjugated hyperbilirubinemia, diagnosis is not usually made until early adulthood. Indeed, a history of prolonged neonatal jaundice is a rarity in the clinical histories of these patients. Often such patients are first discovered when they undergo routine screening as part of an annual physical with an associated blood chemistry profile. Longevity and quality of life are probably unaffected by this disorder. Steady-state bilirubin levels are usually less than 5 mg/dl, with a range of 0.8 to 10 mg/dl.

When performed, liver biopsy shows accumulation of a granular, golden-brown pigment, which appears to be lipofuscin. However, biopsy is rarely required. Approximately 50 per cent of the conjugated bilirubin is in the mono-glucuronide form. When these patients are treated with phenobarbital, the bilirubin level usually will fall to within the normal range. The pathogenesis of Gilbert's syndrome is still poorly understood, but the defect may reside in either defective hepatic bilirubin uptake or defective conjugation.

Chronic Familial Conjugated Hyperbilirubinemia

Dubin-Johnson and Rotor's syndromes are characterized by jaundice and liver enlargement (50 per cent) and nonspecific symptoms such as weakness, fatigability and decreased appetite. These latter symptoms may not be unequivocally related to the underlying disorder. Bilirubin levels are in the range of 2 to 5 mg/dl, with over half direct reacting. Urinary excretion of bile pigments occurs, but hypertransaminemia, pruritus, and acholic stools do not.

The defect in these disorders is poorly defined but involves the transport of conjugated bilirubin and other low molecular weight anions by the hepatocyte into the bile. As a consequence, bromsulphalein (BSP) transport is abnormal, evincing characteristic but different patterns for each of these syndromes. In Dubin-Johnson syndrome the plasma level of dye at 90 minutes is greater than at 45 minutes, indicating regurgitation of conjugated bromsulphalein into the plasma. In Rotor syndrome elimination of dye is diminished, with 30 to 50 per cent retention at 45 minutes but without the rise at 90 minutes seen in the Dubin-Johnson syndrome.

Another point of distinction relates to the pattern of urinary coproporphyrin excretion. In Dubin-Johnson syndrome levels in urine are normal or slightly increased, but more than 80 per cent is the I isomer. In Rotor's syndrome urinary levels are about 6 times normal, with about 60 per cent as the I isomer. Studies on the nature of the pigment stored in liver in Dubin-Johnson syndrome indicate that it is neither a melanin variant nor a porphyrin. Finally, oral cholecystography fails to visualize the gallbladder in Dubin-Johnson, again indicative of decreased organic anion handling by the hepatocytes. Probably no therapy is required save for reassurance that the condition will not affect the quality or length of life.

REFERENCES

Berk, P.D., Jones, E.A., Howe, R.B., and Berlin, N.I.: Disorders of bilirubin metabolism. *In* Bondy, P.K., and Rosenberg, L.E. (eds.): Metabolic Control and Disease. 8th ed. W.B. Saunders Co., Philadelphia, 1980, p. 1009.

Crigler, J.F., and Najjar, V.A.: Congenital familial nonhemolytic jaundice with kernicterus. Pediatrics 10:169, 1952.

Ezhuthacan, S.G., and Gartner, L.M.: Physiology of bilirubin metabolism. *In* Lifshitz, F. (ed.): Clinical Disorders in Pediatric Gastroenterology and Nutrition. M. Dekker, New York, 1980, p. 3.

Karp, W.B.: Biochemical alterations in neonatal hyperbilirubinemia and bilirubin encephalopathy: A review. Pediatrics 64:361, 1979.

Woolkoff, A.W., Chowdhury, J.R., and Arias, I.M.: Hereditary jaundice and disorders of bilirubin metabolism. *In* Stanbury, J.B., Wyngaarden, J.B., Fredrickson, D.S., et al. (eds.): The Metabolic Basis of Inherited Disease. 5th ed McGraw-Hill, New York, 1983, p. 1385.

Valaes, T.: Bilirubin metabolism. Review and discussion of inborn errors. Clin. Perinatol. 3:177, 1976.

25

Disorders Affecting Bone

RICKETS

Rickets may be defined by the situation in which the matrix for bone is normal in composition and amount but fails to calcify at a normal rate. In other words, the mineral-osteoid (or cartilage) ratio is decreased, and the rate of removal of mineral from bone is not increased. It follows that rickets is a disorder that presents during periods of growth, since it is in such circumstances that a discrepancy between unabated matrix elaboration (by osteocytes and osteoblasts) and subsequent calcification can develop. The causes for rickets are manifold, and the particular cause must be found in each patient before therapy is initiated. Bone biopsy reveals excessive accumulation of uncalcified osteoid or cartilage, which results in flaring of the ends of bones and softening of their shafts, the latter producing the pronounced tendency to bending seen in rickets.

Clinical symptoms are often subtle at first, with apathy and hypotonia with weakness most common. Thereafter, irritability becomes more prominent, with the infant preferring not to be touched. Signs involving bones include frontal bossing, delay in closure of the anterior fontanelle, and limb and rib deformities. Tetany is rare, and when it occurs is a late manifestation.

Biochemistry

Rickets, with its defect in normal mineralization of bone (Table 25–1), results from disordered calcium, magnesium, and phosphate metabolism. Nutritional rickets is the result of inadequate exposure to sunlight or exclusion of vitamin D from the diet. In the absence of adequate vitamin D, dietary calcium absorption from the gut is greatly diminished. To continue to provide calcium for body needs, PTH secretion increases, thereby augmenting mobilization of calcium from bone. In the absence of vitamin D the permissive effect on parathyroid (PTH) mediated osteolysis is not expressed. Consequently, both plasma calcium and phosphate fall. Decrease in plasma calcium engenders increased PTH secretion, which augments bone mobilization, thereby raising plasma calcium. However, because of the PTH effect on kidney phosphaturia is also increased, further exacerbating the tendency to hypophosphatemia (Table 25–2). As this process continues a point is reached at which plasma phosphate levels are too low to support normal mineralization. Since collagen production continues unabated, there accumulates a mass of uncalcified osteoid.

In addition to nutritional deficiency, there are two main general causes of rickets: (1) abnormalities in vitamin D activation of metabolism, and (2) abnormalities of target tissue (Table 25–3).

When $1,25\text{-}OHD_3$ is deficient, secondary hyperparathyroidism supervenes. Moreover, the normal regulatory role of vitamin D on PTH secretion is not expressed. The extent to which the latter contributes depends upon the chronicity of the process as well as on plasma phosphate levels. Excessive secretion of PTH produces aminoaciduria and phosphaturia. Hepatic disease and chronic administration of anticonvulsant medications, especially diphenylhydantoin and phenobarbital, interfere with vitamin D metabolism. In the latter cases, the drugs are believed to induce microsomal enzymes that accelerate metabolism of vitamin D metabolites to inactive forms.

The second group, target cell abnormalities, is characterized by phosphaturic states that lead

Table 25-1 OSTEOPENIC SYNDROMES

Syndrome	Definition	Histology of Undecalcified Bone	Causes	X-ray Findings	Laboratory
Osteoporosis	Total bone mass ↓ Mineral-osteoid ratio is normal, bone composition is normal Predominantly affects vertebrae and ends of long bones (trabecular bones)	Decrease in trabecular bone in relation to total bone volume Osteoid not increased	Primary—senile, juvenile idiopathic Secondary—immobilization, chronic renal failure, steroids, Turner's syndrome, homocystinuria, Riley-Day syndrome, Menkes' syndrome, osteogenesis imperfecta, chronic liver disease, malabsorption, heparin therapy	When advanced, density of aorta may be as great as or greater than that of vertebral bodies; findings are not diagnostic	Normal—Ca, P, alkaline phosphatase
Osteomalacia (Rickets)	Mineral-osteoid ratio ↓ Failure of mineralization Bone mass may be normal, ↑, or ↓	Osteoid greatly increased	Lack of vitamin D Phosphate depletion Inactivation D-anticonvulsant therapy Chronic renal disease RTA Chronic liver disease Vitamin D-resistant rickets	In adults, cannot be distinguished from osteoporosis unless pseudofractures present (5–10% of patients) In children, knobbing and prominence of epiphyses of wrists and ankles	Ca normal or ↓ P↓ or ↓↓ Alkaline phosphatase ↑ Low serum 25-vitamin D
Osteitis Fibrosa Cystica	↓ Mineralized bone, replaced by fibrous tissue and loosely textured woven bone (abnormal)		Hyperparathyroidism—osteoblasts advance in distance forming large resorption spaces in cortex		Ca ↑ P ↓ Alkaline phosphatase ↑

Table 25–2 STAGES IN DEVELOPMENT
OF VITAMIN D–DEFICIENCY RICKETS

1. Serum Ca^{++} decreased, P normal because of D lack; engenders PTH response, which leads to:
2. ↑Serum Ca^{++} to normal, P decreased, aminoaciduria. As bone loses ability to respond to PTH stage 3 supervenes:
3. Both serum Ca^{++} and P are decreased.

to hypophosphatemia. In these phosphopenic states rickets is a result of inadequate phosphate for mineralization.

Vitamin D–Dependent Rickets

This variant of rickets usually presents by the end of the second year of life but may be evident as early as six months of age. These infants manifest hypotonia and weakness and delay in growth and attainment of motor milestones. They are more likely to manifest tetany and convulsions than are vitamin D-deficient individuals. Particular note should be made of the generalized aminoaciduria that is a constant feature of this variant. In contrast to the Fançoni syndrome and X-linked hypophosphatemic rickets, provision of adequate vitamin D (10,000 to 50,000 I.U./day) will restore normal growth rate with calcification of the uncalcified matrix.

Vitamin D–Resistant Rickets (X-Linked Hypophosphatemic Rickets)

Onset of this variant is usually in infancy or childhood, with growth failure and deformities of the long bones of the legs accounting for the shortened stature. Occasionally a dental exam will disclose poorly formed teeth associated with gingival disease. This may be the initial tip-off to the

Table 25–3 DISORDERS OF BONE
MINERALIZATION

Rickets
I. Deficiency of 25-HCC or 1,25-DHCC accompanied by secondary hyperparathyroidism
  A. Deficiency of Vitamin D
    1. Lack of adequate intake
    2. Lack of sunlight
    3. Malabsorption
      a. Sprue
      b. Hepatic or biliary dysfunction
    4. Chronic renal insufficiency
    5. Vitamin D dependency
    6. Drugs which enhance conversion to inactive forms
      a. Diphenylhydantoin
      b. Phenobarbital
II. Phosphaturic states
  A. Fanconi syndrome
    1. Cystinosis
    2. Wilson's disease
    3. Galactosemia
    4. Hereditary fructose intolerance
    5. Hereditary tyrosinemia
  B. Renal tubular acidosis
  C. Oculo-cerebral-renal syndrome
Hypophosphatasia
I. Pseudohypophosphatasia

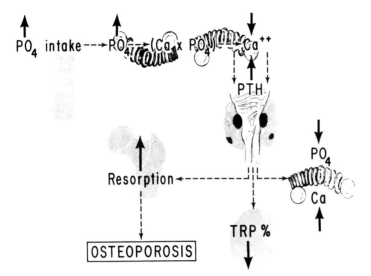

Figure 25–1 One possible mechanism for the development of osteoporosis. Increased phosphate intake is reflected by elevations in serum PO_4, which in turn depresses serum calcium. In response to lowered serum calcium, parathyroid hormone is released; thus calcium is resorbed from bone, serum calcium rises, and tubular reabsorption of PO_4 in kidney is decreased. (From Jowsey, J.: Metabolic Diseases of Bone. Philadelphia, W.B. Saunders Co., 1977.)

underlying bone diathesis of vitamin D-resistant rickets. The muscular weakness and convulsions so common in the other causes of rickets are usually not features of this form.

Therapy with high doses of vitamin D (100,000 to 500,000 I.U.) will bring about healing of the uncalcified osteoid, but it does not improve the short stature or the hypophosphatemia.

SECONDARY HYPERPARATHYROIDISM AND BONE DISEASE

In renal insufficiency, the conversion of 25-hydroxycholecalciferol (25-HCC) to 1,25-dihydroxycholecalciferol (25-DHCC) is diminished for at least two reasons: decreased functioning renal mass and increased levels of inorganic phosphate in renal cortex and serum. As a consequence of the diminution of the "D" effect on gut, calcium malabsorption and secondary hyperparathyroidism supervene. Hyperparathyroidism causes fibrous replacement of the demineralized bone—the

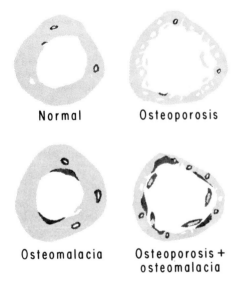

Figure 25–2 Relationship of bone to osteoid in health and disease. (From Jowsey, J.: Metabolic Diseases of Bone. Philadelphia, W.B. Saunders Co., 1977.)

major lesion in chronic renal failure. In addition, osteomalacia is also usually present in this situation because of decreased 1,25-dihydroxycholecalciferol production. The skeletal picture can be further complicated by the presence of osteoporosis as well as osteosclerosis with metastatic calcification.

Osteoporosis (Fig. 25–1)

Osteoporosis represents a state of insufficient calcified bone and can be caused by a number of disease states (Table 25–1). While the bone mass is decreased in osteoporosis, the mineral to osteoid ratio is normal. This contrasts with the situation in osteomalacia where the mineral to osteoid ratio is decreased (Fig. 25–2). Postmenopausal osteoporosis is brought about by a chronic imbalance between the rates of bone formation and bone resorption in favor of resorptive activity. The degree of imbalance need only be slight since a calcium loss of 30 mg/day over a period of 30 years would produce clinically detectable osteoporosis.

Impaired collagen synthesis may also be a cause of osteoporosis since this process is integrated with the deposition of mineral during the formation of bone. As seen in Table 25–1, a number of the rare disorders associated with osteoporosis may share as their abnormality a derangement in the formation of mature (cross-linked) collagen (see Chapter 27).

REFERENCES

Avioli, L.V., and Raisz, L.G.: Bone metabolism and disease. *In* Bondy, P.K. and Rosenberg, L.E. (eds.): Metabolic Control and Disease. 8th ed. W.B. Saunders Co., Philadelphia, 1980, p. 1709.

Goldring, S.R., and Krane, S.M.: Disorders of calcification; osteomalacia and rickets. *In* DeGroot, L., Cahill, G.F., Jr., Martini, L., et al. (eds.): Endocrinology. Grune and Stratton, New York, 1979, p. 853.

Jowsey, J.: Metabolic Diseases of Bone. W.B. Saunders Co., Philadelphia, 1977.

Lovinger, R.D.: Rickets. Pediatrics 66:359, 1980.

Rasmussen, H.: Hypophosphatasia. *In* Stanbury, J.B., Wyngaarden, J.B., Fredrickson, D.S., et al. (eds.): The Metabolic Basis of Inherited Disease. 5th ed. McGraw-Hill, New York, 1983, p. 1497.

Rasmussen, H., and Anast, C.: Familial hypophosphatemic rickets and vitamin D-dependent rickets. *In* Stanbury, J.B., Wyngaarden, J.B., Fredrickson, D.S., et al. (eds.): The Metabolic Basis of Inherited Disease. 5th ed. McGraw-Hill, New York, 1983, p. 1743.

Riggs, B.L.: Osteoporosis—A disease of impaired homeostatic regulation? Min. Electrol. Metab. 5:265, 1981.

Teitelbaum, S.L., and Bullough, P.G.: The pathophysiology of bone and joint disease. Am. J. Pathol. 96:283, 1979.

26

Carbohydrate Disorders

In this chapter we consider those inborn errors caused by congenital deficiency of a specific enzyme or membrane transport system necessary for the metabolism of a particular sugar. Patterns of clinical presentation vary widely. On the one hand, there is the asymptomatic child with essential pentosuria or benign fructosuria, who is evaluated only because a reducing agent has been detected in his or her urine. On the other hand are the galactosemic patients, who may die because of inanition and liver failure, or infants afflicted with the glucose-galactose malabsorption syndrome, who may succumb to severe diarrhea and dehydration. Such tragedies can be avoided if the diagnosis is made promptly and the offending sugar is removed from the patient's diet. It is possible for the clinician who is a careful historian to make the presumptive diagnosis by tests, of both urine and stool, for a reducing agent. Definitive diagnosis usually requires in vitro demonstration that the suspected enzyme or membrane transport system is absent or defective.

All of these syndromes, save for lactase deficiency, are rare and are inherited according to an autosomal recessive pattern. Intestinal lactase deficiency may occur after infancy and apparently affects most of the world's adult population.

SYNDROMES OF CARBOHYDRATE MALABSORPTION: THE DIARRHEAL SYNDROMES

Pathophysiology

Dietary carbohydrate is composed of starches and sugars, with the former predominating in the diet of adults and children and the latter in the diet of young infants. The salivary glands, pancreas, and intestinal brush border produce a spectrum of enzymes that catalyze the hydrolytic breakdown of complex carbohydrates primarily into glucose, galactose, and fructose, which then are transported across the small intestinal epithelium to the portal circulation. Thus, salivary and pancreatic alpha-amylase facilitate the conversion of the starches amylose and amylopectin to the dissaccharide maltose (95 per cent) and the oligosaccharide isomaltose (5 per cent) (Fig. 26–1). These oligosaccharides and disaccharides are then acted upon by the maltase and isomaltase of the intestinal brush border, which convert them into the monosaccharide glucose. Lactose and sucrose are hydrolyzed by brush border lactase and sucrase to their respective monosaccharide constituents. (Fig. 26–1) The glucose and galactose liberated by these sequential cleavages are transported from the intestinal lumen into the blood stream by an energy-dependent active process that is coupled to the movement of Na^+ across the intestinal cell membrane. Fructose, in contrast, is transported by a separate sodium-independent system. This latter point offers a means of therapeutic intervention for the glucose-galactose malabsorption syndrome.

Two distinct types of genetic defects account for the carbohydrate malabsorption syndromes. There may be a deficiency of either a specific brush border disaccharidase or a monosaccharide transport system. In either instance sugar accumulates within the intestinal lumen, where it increases the osmolality of the succus entericus, drawing additional water into the lumen. The distended bowel contracts spasmodically, causing abdominal pain. Diarrhea and abdominal distension are also very common. Some undigested sugar may be detected in the diarrheal stool, which gives a positive reaction with the copper sulfate (Clinitest) tablets. Metabolism of some of this carbohydrate by colonic bacteria to organic acids results in an acid stool, which can be detected by diphenylhydra-

LUMEN   INTESTINAL CELL

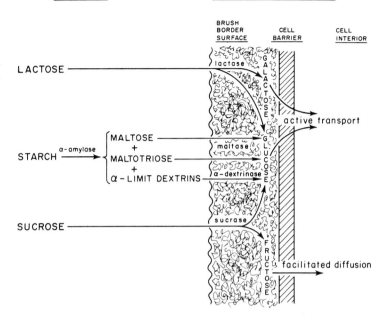

Figure 26–1 Mechanism of carbohydrate digestion. Digestion of starch commences intraluminally, with hydrolysis to maltose and iso-maltose. These and other dietary disaccharides are hydrolyzed further within the intestinal brush border and then transported into the cell proper by an active transport mechanism. (From Sleisenger, M.H., and Fordtran, J.S.: Gastrointestinal Disease: Pathophysiology, Diagnosis, and Management. Philadelphia, W.B. Saunders Co., 1978.)

zine paper. Mellituria is an inconstant finding. It is caused by passive diffusion of disaccharide across the intestinal epithelium. The salient features of the carbohydrate malabsorption syndromes are given in Table 26–1.

Oral carbohydrate tolerance tests combine a high degree of accuracy in making a diagnosis with minimal discomfort for the patient. The patient is fed a 2 g/kg dose of the carbohydrate in question (up to 50 g) in a 10 per cent solution. Blood is obtained at 0, 30, 60, 90, 120, and 150 minutes. The normal response to such carbohydrate administration is an elevation of blood glucose of 50 mg/dl over fasting values. Patients with a carbohydrate malabsorption syndrome typically show a rise of less than 20 mg/dl. Stool should also be collected and tested for pH and the presence of a reducing agent. It is important that the patient be asymptomatic when the test is performed. Previous carbohydrate intake should have been high enough (20 to 50 g daily) to insure adequate hepatic glycogen stores. The patient should be lying down and relaxed.

If the rise of blood glucose is small enough (less than 50 mg/dl) to suggest intestinal disaccharidase deficiency, the test should be repeated, offering the constituent monsaccharides as the diagnostic challenge. If the monosaccharide tolerance test produces an appropriate rise of blood glucose while the disaccharide load does not, it is likely that the defect is enzymatic, i.e., an intestinal disaccharidase deficiency rather than a transport deficiency for a monosaccharide.

Table 26–1   CHARACTERISTIC FEATURES OF CARBOHYDRATE
MALABSORPTION SYNDROMES

1. Diarrhea, bloating, and abdominal pain following the ingestion of the offending sugar
2. Remission of symptoms once the sugar is removed from the diet
3. Acid stool (pH < 6)
4. Positive copper sulphate (Clinitest) reaction of stool (Method: dilute with water 1:2, centrifuge, add tablet to 15 drops of supernatant)
5. Growth failure
6. Irritability
7. Mellituria (intermittent; only if diarrhea severe)
8. No rise of blood glucose following oral load of suspected sugar
9. Demonstration of absent enzyme activity or transport system on intestinal mucosa obtained by peroral biopsy

Primary Glucose-Galactose Malabsorption Syndrome

This rare disorder becomes clinically manifest soon after the newborn infant has received the first feedings. The presenting symptom is profuse, watery diarrhea leading rapidly to dehydration and acidosis. Appetite may be undiminished. The outcome may be fatal if therapy is not instituted promptly. Most dietary carbohydrates contain glucose or galactose and will perpetuate the diarrhea. An important exception is fructose. When this hexose is administered orally, blood glucose rises promptly. The oral administration of glucose itself has little effect on blood glucose and may indeed perpetuate the diarrhea, while a sucrose load causes only a modest rise.

Brush border disaccharidase activity is normal. The cause of the syndrome is the congenital absence of an intestinal transport system that is shared by glucose and galactose. Some glucose transport capacity is retained, although it is only about 10 per cent of normal. This probably suggests the presence of more than one intestinal glucose transport system. Fructose absorption, which is mediated by a carrier system distinct from those serving glucose and galactose transport, is normal. Spontaneous remission of symptoms with age may occur.

Diagnosis can be strongly suspected on the basis of the relationship of onset of symptoms early on with ingestion of lactose-containing milk, failure of relief of symptoms with oral glucose, and demonstration of galactose and glucose in the stool. If fructose-containing fluids are administered and symptoms abate, the diagnosis is strongly supported. Glucose and galactose tolerance tests performed at a time the patient's condition permits should provide clinical diagnosis, especially when coupled with the previous excellent response to fructose.

Some suggest that definitive diagnosis depends upon the in vitro demonstration of normal intestinal disaccharidase activity coupled with the failure of intestinal mucosa to concentrate either radioactive glucose or galactose. We believe that the clinical tests outlined above should make such studies unnecessary as a routine. When contemplated, however, they should be performed at a center that specializes in such investigation.

Congenital Lactase Deficiency

Considering that human breast milk contains about 7 g/dl of lactose while cow's milk contains 5 g/dl, the neonate consumes approximately 50 to 60 of lactose daily. Hydrolysis of the disaccharide to glucose and galactose is mediated by brush border lactase. In infants with lactase deficiency enzyme activity is markedly diminished, with the result that symptoms begin consequent upon milk feeding to the neonate. They include severe, persistent diarrhea and failure to thrive. An oral lactose load causes a rise of blood glucose of less than 50 mg/dl. Blood glucose concentration rises appropriately following the oral administration of either glucose or galactose. The stool shows an acid pH and contains lactose. Some lactosuria may also be present if the diarrhea has been unremittent and severe.

The syndrome of congenital lactase deficiency should be distinguished from the acquired lactase deficiency sometimes encountered in children in association with infectious enteritis, malnutrition, sprue, and inflammatory bowel disease. This should not be difficult, since congenital lactase deficiency characteristically presents during the first few days of life. It also must not be confused with the intestinal lactase deficiency that is common to many healthy older children and adults around the world. Almost all of these individuals have had normal intestinal lactase activity during early infancy, when they are able to tolerate an oral lactose load without any clinical difficulty. The ingestion of lactose in later life, when intestinal lactase activity is diminished, may cause diarrhea and a sense of bloating.

The response to a lactose-free diet helps to confirm the diagnosis and to distinguish congenital lactase deficiency from the glucose-galactose malabsorption syndrome, which also becomes clinically apparent during early infancy. Perhaps the most current and accurate means of detecting intestinal lactase deficiency is the hydrogen breath test. The basis for this test is the habitation of the bowel by bacteria that are capable of producing H_2 from lactose; a positive correlation has been shown to exist between the amount of lactose delivered to the colon and the amount of H_2 excreted through the lungs. Since the vast majority of lactose is broken down into sugar monomers and absorbed in the upper small bowel, a lactase deficiency will be reflected by a large increase in lactose delivery to the colonic flora. The fact that the study is noninvasive gives it great potential in its application to pediatric bowel disease.

Sucrase-Isomaltase Deficiency

This diagnosis must be considered in any older infant or child with chronic diarrhea, irritability, and growth failure. The typical patient is asymptomatic as long as human breast milk or infant formula is the source of carbohydrate. Neither preparation contains a significant amount of sucrose. Symptoms appear once sucrose or starches are added to the diet. There is considerable variation in severity of the syndrome. This probably reflects the amount of residual enzyme activity still present. The ingestion of starches provokes a milder symptomatology than does the ingestion of sucrose, perhaps because the limit dextrins formed from the incomplete hydrolysis of starch have a relatively high molecular weight (about 1500) and would therefore exert only about 10 per cent of the osmotic effect of a corresponding amount of sucrose. Affected children learn to avoid sweets, although some tolerance to sucrose may develop when they mature. Lactose digestion is normal. In general, the clinical course is milder than that characteristic of the carbohydrate malabsorption syndromes presenting during early infancy.

All patients have had diminished activity of both sucrase and isomaltase (alpha-dextrinase) in their brush border. It is not clear whether this dienzyme complex is truly absent or whether there exists a structural abnormality of the enzyme protein. Nor is it certain if the absence of two distinct enzymes denotes a biological control mechanism common to both or the presence of two enzyme activities on a single protein molecule. It is known that the sucrase and isomaltase activities do not share the same active site.

Diagnosis is suggested by the history and by the failure of blood glucose concentration to rise following an oral sucrose load. The stool pH is acid, but the copper sulphate (Clinitest) reaction of stool is negative because sucrose is not a reducing sugar. Other sugars—glucose, fructose, maltose, lactose—are tolerated well. Sucrosuria is an inconstant finding. Biochemical analysis of intestinal mucosa obtained by peroral biopsy shows a markedly diminished sucrase-isomaltase activity and normal activity of other disaccharidases.

Lactose Intolerance Without Lactase Deficiency

The biochemical cause of this syndrome is not known. It is included among the carbohydrate malabsorption syndromes because it is frequently confused with congenital lactase deficiency.

Untreated patients follow a malignant course. The onset of symptoms occurs during the first few days of life when severe diarrhea, vomiting, and acidosis are apparent. A substantial lactosuria has been a characteristic finding, and aminoaciduria, proteinuria, and renal tubular acidosis are common. Post-mortem examination of the first reported case showed adrenal and hepatic atrophy and degeneration of the renal tubules. Presumably, the pathophysiology relates in some obscure way to lactose toxicity, since withdrawal of lactose from the diet results in a prompt cessation of symptoms and even minimal amounts of lactose will evoke the clinical syndrome. The lactose tolerance test, however, is normal. Intestinal lactase activity is either normal or only transiently depressed.

The diagnosis should be suggested by the age of onset, the relationship to lactose ingestion, remission of symptoms when lactose is removed from the diet, heavy lactosuria, and normal intestinal lactase activity.

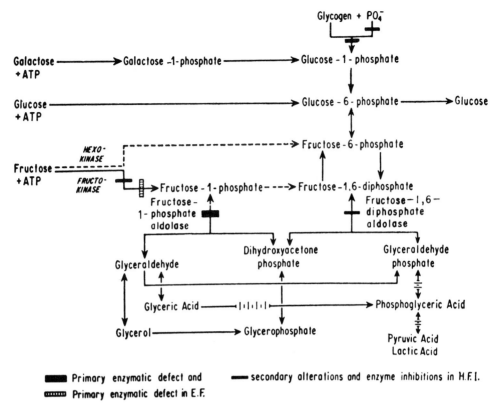

Figure 26–2 Scheme of carbohydrate metabolism. The primary enzyme defects of essential fructosuria and hereditary fructose intolerance (HFI) are shown. Note the secondary enzyme effects exerted by accumulated fructose-1-PO₄ in HFI. (From Froesch, E.R.: Disorders of fructose metabolism. Clin. Endocrinol. Metab. 5:599, 1976.)

DISORDERS OF FRUCTOSE METABOLISM

Essential Fructosuria (Fructokinase Deficiency)

Patients with fructokinase deficiency are unable to convert fructose to fructose-1-phosphate (Fig. 26–2). Consequently, fructose accumulates in the blood and spills over into the urine where it may be detected with Clinitest tablets. No clinical symptoms are associated with this enzyme deficiency. It is important that this harmless condition not be confused with diabetes mellitus. The glucose oxidase (Glucostix) reaction is specific for glucose and is useful in distinguishing the cause of the mellituria. The presence of fructose in urine may be demonstrated with paper, thin layer, or gas chromatography. When properly performed, Seliwanoff's test is a useful colorimetric procedure, especially when the presence of glucose in the urine has been ruled out by Glucostix. A liver biopsy to definitely demonstrate the absence of the enzyme in this benign condition does not seem warranted.

Hereditary Fructose Intolerance

Clinical Features

Typically the affected infant grows normally while fructose is absent from the diet, as when ingesting breast or cow's milk. When fructose, sucrose, or sorbitol (the sugar alcohol of fructose) is ingested, most often in fruits or juices, symptoms may appear.

Clinical manifestations of this disorder range in severity from profound failure to thrive with progressive liver dysfunction to the adolescent or adult enjoying apparently good health save for occasional vomiting, abdominal pain, and hypoglycemia on ingesting offending foods. Nonetheless, fructose intolerance may have serious and even fatal consequences because of hepatic dysfunction.

Often, within 30 minutes of ingesting sufficient fructose the patient will manifest vomiting, abdominal pain, profuse sweating (hypoglycemia), diarrhea, and even coma and convulsions. This acute picture includes a rapid fall in serum phosphorus, rises in magnesium and urate, hypoglycemia, hyperfructosemia and fructosuria, and elevation of serum transaminase. Another component of fructose toxicity is renal tubular acidosis with bicarbonate wastage.

Sometimes the association of acute onset of symptoms with sweet foods is recognized by the individual and he excludes sweets from the diet. Such a historical fact is key in pointing to a diagnosis of food intolerance. The affected child who thus avoids sweets benefits by having exceptionally good teeth—another clue to the diagnosis.

Sometimes in infants or youngsters, continued feeding of fructose will cause a chronic syndrome of hepatic failure and renal tubular dysfunction reminiscent of tyrosinemia. Poor feeding, failure to thrive, hepatomegaly, jaundice, anemia, bleeding, and renal tubular acidosis are then seen. The worsening renal tubular function (amino aciduria) and hepatic function (hyperaminoacidemia) conspire to produce abnormal urinary and plasma profiles with particular elevations of tyrosine and methionine. However, fructose intolerance is far more responsive to dietary management than is hereditary tyrosinemia, so that cirrhosis need not result in the former as it usually does in the latter condition. Although hypoglycemia follows fructose ingestion, mental retardation is not a feature of this disease. Generally, because of the aversion to sweets adults limit their intake with amelioration of all signs and symptoms.

Biochemical Defects

The defect is a deficiency of the enzyme fructose-1-phosphate aldolase, which mediates the hydrolysis of fructose-1-phosphate to glyceraldehyde and dihydroxyacetone phosphate. The hypophosphatemia engendered by fructose ingestion is predominantly the result of sequestration of phosphate as fructose-1-phosphate in the liver. Phosphaturia as well contributes to this loss. It seems reasonable that the hypophosphatemia reflects intracellular ATP depletion. Further support for this contention comes from the hypermagnesemia, seen concomitantly, which is probably caused by the release of magnesium from ATP to which it had been bound. The hypoglycemia is caused by both defective glycogenolysis and defective gluconeogenesis. Adequate stores of phosphate and ATP are needed for normal functioning of either pathway.

Additionally, there is evidence that fructose-1-phosphate has an inhibitory action on phosphorylase on the one hand and the gluconeogenic function of aldolase A and phosphohexose isomerase on the other. Hypersecretion of insulin does not play a role in the causation of the hypoglycemia.

Under normal circumstances fructose is metabolized more rapidly than glucose, causing a more rapid depletion of intracellular Pi (noted above) than occurs with glucose administration. Glucose metabolism by liver is modulated by insulin, and the enzyme phosphofructokinase is inhibited by ATP and citrate. This latter metabolite provides information regarding the conduct of the citric acid cycle, while ATP is the final product of oxidative phosphorylation, the process normally linked to the metabolic events occurring in the citric acid cycle. Fructokinase, the first enzyme in fructose metabolism, is under no such constraints and so fructose metabolism is not integrated with the conduct of the citric acid cycle and levels of ATP. Hence, inorganic phosphate can become sequestered in these patients as fructose-1-phosphate. The hypophosphatemia and decreased ATP levels may serve as signals to bring about breakdown of adenine nucleotides to replenish the intracellular phosphate. This chain of events leads to heightened levels of inosine monophosphate and consequent accumulation of uric acid with hyperuricemia, a finding that distinguishes hereditary fructose intolerance from galactosemia and tyrosinemia.

Diagnosis and Laboratory Findings

As with so many inborn errors, heightened suspicion will lead the physician to ascertain whether a particular patient has fructose intolerance. One should search for a history that relates clinical deterioration to the ingestion of fructose. Not infrequently such infants require hospitalization for "unexplained" liver disease. If insufficient attention is paid to the inciting circumstances, undue focus will be directed to the hepatic dysfunction without considering the need to find out whether there is hypophosphatemia, hyperuricemia, hypoglycemia, and fructosuria. Because hereditary fructose intolerance and galactosemia both give a positive urine test for a reducing agent such testing is mandatory. Chemical and chromatographic techniques will further identify fructose or galactose. Diagnosis ultimately depends upon a fructose tolerance test, the intravenous route being preferred over the oral because it causes less gastrointestinal upset. One infuses 250 mg/kg over a 5-minute period. At this level the response should be reflected in the blood without overt symptoms. The fructose challenge should elicit hypophosphatemia, hypertransaminasemia, and hyperuricemia as well as modest lowering of blood glucose, usually without clinical findings. Nonetheless, one must always be on the look-out for the possibility of frank hypoglycemia. Enzymatic diagnosis can be accomplished on liver, kidney, or intestine but should not usually be necessary.

Treatment

The patient must avoid all foods containing fructose, sucrose, or sorbitol. This will require careful dietary counseling, since fructose is abundant, not only in sweets and fruits but also in many vegetables, including potatoes, cucumbers, and broccoli. It is not unheard of for these patients to develop symptoms to ingestion of anything sweet.

Fructose-1,6-Diphosphatase Deficiency

This disorder resembles hereditary fructose intolerance in that the ingestion of fructose evokes a syndrome of hypoglycemia, metabolic acidosis, hyperlactatemia, hypophosphatemia, and hepatomegaly. There is no progression toward liver failure, however, and patients do not avoid sweet foods. The diagnosis is suggested by the temporal relationship of hypoglycemia and mellituria to fructose ingestion. Fructose in urine may be identified by the methods described above. Fructose-1,6-diphosphatase activity is markedly diminished in patient's liver. It is a key enzyme in the gluconeogenic pathway (Fig. 26–2), and hypoglycemia is an expected result when the enzyme is missing.

DISORDERS OF GALACTOSE METABOLISM

Transferase Deficiency Galactosemia

The infant with deficiency of galactose-1-phosphate uridyltransferase presents a picture not dissimilar from that of fructose intolerance and tyrosinemia. Since human milk and cow's milk contain lactose, symptoms appear early in life (usually within a few days of the first feedings), the patient developing diarrhea, vomiting, and dehydration. In contrast to physiological jaundice of the newborn, hyperbilirubinemia is of the direct variety and persists beyond the first few days of life. While hemolysis is a contributing factor, hepatic dysfunction is the primary cause of the increase in the conjugated fraction. Further evidence for liver damage is provided by hepatomegaly, elevation of serum transaminase, and occasional prolongation of clotting times. In such a patient slit-lamp examination of the lens is mandatory. In galactosemia punctate nuclear cataracts may be seen that will be missed by conventional ophthalmoscopy. Again, as in hereditary fructose intolerance and tyrosinemia, renal dysfunction is evidenced by aminoaciduria, proteinuria, and renal tubular acidosis. In contrast to these other disorders the brain is at risk in transferase deficiency. Unless galactose is removed promptly from the patient's diet, severe inanition occurs and mental retardation results. Indeed, the outcome can be fatal.

There are now several variants of transferase deficiency galactosemia; among these is a form in black patients who are able to oxidize significant amounts of galactose. While erythrocyte transferase activity is undetectable, these patients possess about 10 per cent of normal activity in liver and small intestine. These patients show little in the way of liver or gastrointestinal symptoms but sometimes have delayed development. Nonetheless, there is an infantile galactose toxicity syndrome often seen in these patients.

Another variant (Duarte) manifests about 50 per cent of normal enzyme activity in the red blood cells in the homozygous state. With that degree of residual activity they are completely asymptomatic. Mixed heterozygotes for the Duarte variant and classical transferase deficiency have about 25 per cent of normal enzyme activity in their erythrocytes. Such individuals have an abnormal galactose tolerance test but are usually symptom free. Electrophoretic mobility can differentiate the Duarte enzyme from the normal enzyme. Other variants, termed Rennes, Indiana, and Los Angeles are less well defined clinically.

Biochemical Defects

The cause of this syndrome is deficiency of galactose-1-phosphate uridyltransferase, the enzyme that catalyzes the formation of uridine diphosphate (UDP)-galactose and glucose-1-phosphate from galactose-1-phosphate and UDP-glucose (Fig. 26–3). As a consequence of this block in the sugar nucleotide pathway galactose-1-phosphate accumulates in the lens, liver, brain, and kidney. Galactitol, the sugar alcohol of galactose, also accumulates because of the action of the enzyme aldol reductase. The cataracts so common in this disorder appear to be the result of intralenticular accumulation of galactitol, which draws water into the lens, with consequent disruption of the zonular fibers. Galactose-1-phosphate is believed to play a role in the generation of liver and cerebral dysfunction. One avenue of support for this view comes from patients with galactokinase deficiency galactosemia (see below) in whom no galactose-1-phosphate accumulates. While they develop cataracts because of galactitol buildup, they suffer no permanent damage to the liver, kidney, or brain. Moreover, growth of fibroblasts from transferase-deficient patients is inhibited by galactose. Kidney of patients with transferase deficiency shows elevated levels of galactitol and galactose-1-phosphate. Feeding galactose to pregnant rats causes a decrease in concentration of DNA, amino acids, glucose, and serotonin receptors in the pup's brain. Recently, diminished responsiveness of synaptic endings to acetylcholine has been demonstrated in such animals.

Laboratory Tests and Diagnosis

Transferase deficiency galactosemia is treatable and is therefore an important diagnosis to consider in any neonate who develops jaundice, diarrhea, vomiting, and failure to thrive while receiving a diet that contains lactose. The diminished dietary intake as a consequence of these symptoms may cause galactosuria to disappear. Normal full-term newborns may have up to 60 mg of galactose per 100 ml of urine during the first week of life. Thus, galactosuria cannot be considered pathognomonic of the disease. Galactose will give a positive Clinitest reaction with a negative glucose oxidase. There are now available strips impregnated with galactose oxidase (Galactostix) that permit identification of the sugar as galactose. It is best to test urines after several milk feedings have been given, i.e., late in the day. Galactose tolerance tests are contraindicated because of hazards to the patient. Gas chromatography can be used to measure urinary and blood galactose concentrations, but since galactosuria and lactosuria may be a consequence of severe liver disease, from any cause, such quantitation is of limited usefulness. Moreover, it is not uncommon to find galactosuria (and glucosuria) in low birth weight infants secondary to immaturity of the renal glucose-galactose transport system. Hence, one should never make the diagnosis of transferase deficiency galactosemia solely on the basis of liver disease and mellituria. Assay of red cell galactose-1-phosphate uridyltransferase activity is mandatory. Several methods and kits for this assay are available.

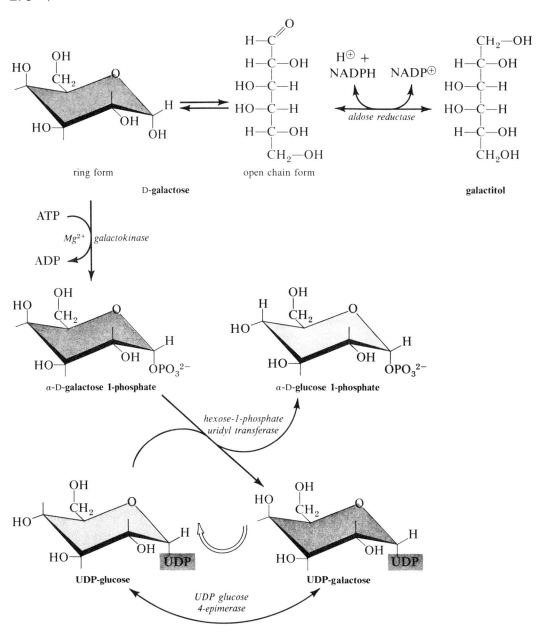

Figure 26–3 Pathways of galactose metabolism. (From McGilvery, R.W.: Biochemistry: A Functional Approach. 2nd ed. Philadelphia, W.B. Saunders Co., 1979.)

Pending results of the enzyme assay, galactose ingestion in any form must be suspended. One should see prompt improvement in vigor and appetite and disappearance of renal tubular dysfunction. Hepatic abnormalities will respond more slowly. In the past casein-base formulas (e.g., Nutramigen or soybean milks) have been substituted, since they were believed to contain negligible amounts of galactose. However, recently this has been questioned, and, indeed, use of Nutramigen in the first year of life has been cautioned against. Moreover, lactose is used as a filler in many foods like bread, frankfurters, sausage, and some candies, and so parents must be on guard constantly for such adulterated foods. In addition to improvement in renal and liver function on a stringently managed diet, the cataracts may resolve if they are not very far advanced. Prompt institution of therapy is considered to be key to a successful outcome of neurological development. Nonetheless, difficulties with perceptual ability and a shortened attention span occur even in children who were treated from early infancy and whose mothers were on low galactose diets when pregnant. During later childhood and especially adolescence it is necessary to liberalize the diet, although milk ought never to be permitted.

Galactokinase Deficiency Galactosemia

This variant of galactosemia usually presents with visual impairment secondary to the formation of cataracts. In contrast to transferase deficiency no renal or hepatic dysfunction is seen. Pseudotumor cerebri was reported in one affected child, presumably because of the intracerebral accumulation of osmotically active galactitol. Absent from this form are the profound inanition and neurological disability characteristic of untreated patients with transferase deficiency galactosemia. Nonetheless, the course may not always be so benign (Segal et al., 1979). Any child with cataracts ought to have a work-up for both forms of galactosemia. Demonstration of galactose in the urine in the absence of liver disease suggests galactokinase deficiency. The enzyme can be assayed in erythrocytes.

Treatment is as for transferase deficiency, i.e., interdiction of all forms of galactose from the diet. With such a regimen the cataracts usually regress if the diagnosis is made before they are advanced.

Uridine Diphosphate Galactose-4-Epimerase Deficiency Galactosemia

One family has now been described with this disorder. Hypergalactosemia and galactosuria were noted, but the affected individuals have been free of symptoms. It is important that this condition not be confused with galactosemia secondary to deficiency of either galactokinase or transferase enzymes.

DISORDERS OF PENTOSE METABOLISM

Essential Pentosuria

Individuals with this disorder excrete 1 to 4 g of D-xylulose daily. The excretion is independent of diet. D-Xylulose is an intermediate of the glucuronic acid pathway:

$$\text{glucose-6-phosphate} \rightarrow \text{D-glucuronic acid} \rightarrow \text{D-xylulose} \rightarrow \text{D-ribose}$$

The deficient enzyme, xylitol dehydrogenase, may be assayed in erythrocytes. No symptoms are associated with this condition. An occasional patient has been treated with insulin when the mellituria was assumed mistakenly to represent glycosuria. Virtually all patients have been Jews of central or eastern European origin.

The diagnosis is suggested by a positive urinary Benedict's reaction: at 55°C D-xylulose, a powerful reducing agent, will reduce copper sulfate at this low temperature while most other sugars will not. Fructose is another important exception. The chromatographic identification of D-xylulose is not difficult, since the sugar stains red with the orcinol-trichloracetic reagent.

REFERENCES

Baerlocher, K., Gitzelmann, R., Steinmann, B., and Gitzelmann-Cumarasamy, N.: Hereditary fructose intolerance in early childhood: a major diagnostic challenge. Helv. Paediatr. Acta 33:465, 1978.
Berry, G., Yandrasitz, J.R., and Segal, S.: Experimental galactose toxicity: Effects on synaptosomal phosphatidylinositol metabolism. J. Neurochem. 37:888, 1981.

Bond, J.H., and Levitt, M.D.: Quantitative measurement of lactose absorption. Gastroenterology 70:1058, 1976.

Burman, D., Holton, J.B., and Pennock, C.A. (eds.): Inherited Disorders of Carbohydrate Metabolism. MTP Press Ltd. Lancaster, England, 1980.

Cohn, R.M., and Segal, S.: Galactose metabolism and its regulation. Metabolism 22:627, 1973.

Felig, P.: Disorders of carbohydrate metabolism. *In* Bondy, P.K., and Rosenberg, L.E. (eds.): Metabolic Control and Disease. 8th ed. W.B. Saunders Co., Philadelphia, 1980, p. 276.

Getzelmann, R., Steinmann, B., Van Den Berghe, G.: Essential fructosuria, hereditary fructose intolerance, and fructose-1,6-diphosphatase deficiency. *In* Stanbury, J.B., Wyngaarden, J.B., Fredrickson, D.S., et al. (eds.): The Metabolic Basis of Inherited Disease. 5th ed. McGraw-Hill, New York, 1983, p. 118.

Gray, G.M.: Intestinal disaccharidase deficiencies and glucose-galactose malabsorption. *In* Stanbury, J.B., Wyngaarden, J.B., Fredrickson, D.S., et al. (eds.): The Metabolic Basis of Inherited Disease. 5th ed. McGraw-Hill, New York, 1983, p. 1729.

Paige, D.M., and Bayless, T.M. (eds.): Lactose Digestion: Clinical and Nutritional Implications. Johns Hopkins University Press, Baltimore, 1981.

Segal, S.: Disorders of galactose metabolism. *In* Stanbury, J.B., Wyngaarden, J.B., Fredrickson, D.S., et al. (eds.): The Metabolic Basis of Inherited Disease. 5th ed. McGraw-Hill, New York, 1983, p. 167.

Segal, S., Rutman, J.Y., and Frimpter, G.W.: Galactokinase deficiency and mental retardation. J. Pediatr. 95:750, 1979.

Warfield, A., and Segal, S.: Myoinositol and phosphatidylinositol metabolism in synaptosomes from galactose fed rats. Proc. Natl. Acad. Sci. USA 75:4568, 1978.

27

Collagen Disorders

Connective tissues are structural and functional aggregates of collagen, elastin, glycoproteins, and protein polysaccharides. Different connective tissues may be distinguished qualitatively by the different structural elements and quantitatively by the amount of each element. At a higher level of organization the physicochemical interaction of these macromolecules also contributes to the distinctive characteristics of a particular connective tissue. Because of this interdependence, disorders affecting collagen, elastin, glycoaminoglycans, and glycoproteins may affect connective tissues and bone as part of their clinical expression. Phenocopies are particular problems in differential diagnosis of these disorders, as, for example, with Marfan's syndrome and homocystinuria.

COLLAGEN

Structure and Composition of Collagen

Collagen is an aggregate of three left-handed polypeptide alpha chains containing about 1000 amino acids, with approximately three amino acids per turn (Fig. 27–1), 1.5 nm in diameter and 300 nm in length. The three helices twist around each other like a rope to form a right-handed helix. Finally these triple helices associate to form fibrils, such association depending upon hydrophobic interactions, interchain hydrogen bonds, and specific side-chain interactions (all noncovalent forces; see Part I).

Collagen is unique among proteins, since every third amino acid is glycine. Apparently approximation of the three chains precludes an amino acid with a side chain, a sterochemical require-

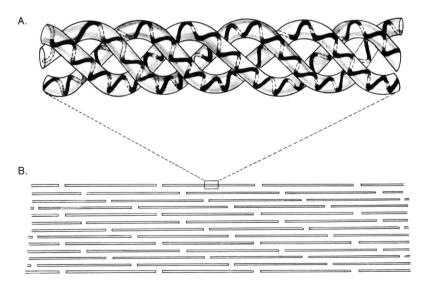

Figure 27–1 The collagen molecule. *A*, Three polypeptide chains, associated through noncovalent forces, combine to form a triple helix as shown. *B*, The general configuration of multiple triple-helices within a collagen fibril. (From Flickinger, C.J. et al.: Medical Cell Biology. Philadelphia, W.B. Saunders Co., 1979.)

ment satisfied by glycine. The general formula $(X-Y-Gly)_{333}$ describes the composition of collagen. Other unusual aspects include the presence of approximately 100 proline residues in the X position and 100 hydroxyproline residues in the Y position. Both these amino acids are rigid rings, which favor formation of a triple helix, while hydroxyproline is crucial to stabilizing the triple helix. Finally, hydroxylysine is also found in collagen, serving both as a site for formation of covalent cross-links as well as for attachment of carbohydrate residues. Hydroxylation of proline and lysine is a post-translational event in the formation of collagen (see below).

Functions of Collagen

Distribution of collagen throughout the body is widespread with collagens of different composition serving distinctive functions (Table 27–1). Examination of the table reveals a gamut of structural as well as more subtle discriminatory functions, e.g., tendons, ligaments, bone, cartilage, basement membrane (glomeruli), and cornea (light transmission). The cardiovascular and gastrointestinal systems also depend upon collagen for much of their function (heart valves, arterial walls, and wall of the G.I. tract).

Biosynthesis and Processing of Collagen

Collagen is a derivative of a precursor protein, precollagen, which consists of three pro α chains and which possesses additional peptides at both the amino and carboxyl termini. Synthesis occurs intracellularly on the rough endoplasmic reticulum; hydroxylation of proline and lysine residues and glycosylation occur intracellularly as well. In addition, the procollagen chains associate and undergo both noncovalent and covalent interactions, the latter involving formation of interchain disulfide bonds. All of these processes ensure the formation of the procollagen triple helix, an obligatory step to extracellular secretion.

Conversion of procollagen to collagen appears to be an extracellular process requiring removal of the additional peptides of the pro α chains. These processes are outlined in Table 27–2.

Hydroxylation of Peptidyl Proline and Lysine

Hydroxylation of prolyl and lysyl residues within the procollagen molecule is mediated by prolyl-4 hydroxylase and lysyl hydroxylase, respectively. Ascorbic acid is required for the prolyl

Table 27–1 COLLAGEN TYPES

Type	Tissue Distribution	Protein Units	Chemical Composition
I	Bone, tendon, skin, ligament, fascia, cornea, arteries, uterus, heart valves	Two identical chains plus one nonidentical fiber; bundles in parallel	67% hydroxylysine; 1% carbohydrate; no cysteine
II	Cartilage, nucleus pulposus, neural retinal tissue, vitreous body	Three identical chains	Abundant hydroxylysine and carbohydrate
III	Skin, arteries, uterus, lung, liver, intestine	Three identical chains; forms circumferential helical network in hollow tissues	High hydroxyproline; hydroxylysine and carbohydrate content similar to type I; interchain disulfide bonds
IV	Basement membranes (glomeruli, cornea)	Three identical chains	High hydroxylysine; hydroxyproline; three hydroxyproline and carbohydrate interchain disulfide bonds

Table 27–2 STEPS IN BIOSYNTHESIS OF COLLAGEN AND ASSOCIATED DISEASE STATES

Process	Comment	Associated Disease State
Intracellular		
Protein synthesis of pre-procolla-gen	Determines linear sequence (primary structure), which contains information for higher order folding (see Part I)	Regulation of synthesis deranged in osteogenesis imperfecta, Ehlers-Danlos type IV (ecchymotic)
Processing		
1. Removal of peptide sequences from pre-procollagen	Proteases remove "signal" sequences to form procollagen from pre-procollagen	
2. Hydroxylation		
Proline residues	Most hydroxylated by prolyl-4-hydroxylase (requires ascorbate, acts only on residues in Y position)	Ehlers-Danlos type VI Osteogenesis imperfecta Scurvy
	Smaller percentage by prolyl-3-hydroxylase (residues in X-position only if Y position is 4-hydroxyproline)	? Alcaptonuria
Lysine residues	Lysyl hydroxylase—sites for addition of carbo-hydrates—required for cross-link formation (see below)	
3. Glycosylation of hydroxyly-sine	Mediated by glycosyl and galactosyl transfer-ases	
4. Association of three pro α chains with formation of interchain disulfide bonds	Process may be spontaneous or enzyme mediated (not known)	
5. Formation of triple helix	Spontaneous association (information inherent in primary structure)	
6. Secretion into extracellular space	Procollagen must be in triple helix conformation; may involve microtubules	
Extracellular		
1. Procollagen→Collagen	Removal of additional sequences at amino and carboxy termini by proteases	Ehlers-Danlos, type VII
2. Collagen molecules assemble into fibrils	Spontaneous process—these fibrils lack tensile strength of final collagen	Ehlers-Danlos, type I
3. Cross-link formation to achieve tensile strength	Formation of reactive aldehydes at certain lysyl and hydroxylysyl residues—mediated by lysyl oxidase (Cu-containing protein)	Cutis laxa, X-linked Ehlers-Danlos, type V Menke's syndrome
	Synthesis of covalent cross-links (condensation of two aldehydes; or condensation aldehyde and amino group of lysine or glycosylated hydroxylysine	Homocystinuria Alcaptonuria

hydroxylase, functioning either to maintain iron in the reduced state or to protect sulfhydryl groups in the enzyme.

Covalent Intermolecular Cross-links in Collagen

The tensile strength and insolubility of collagen fibers are a function of an extensive system of cross-links that form between adjoining collagen molecules. Enzymatic generation of reactive aldehydes from specific lysyl and hydroxylysyl residues in the collagen molecule is accomplished by the enzyme lysyl oxidase. These aldehyde groups thence undergo spontaneous (nonenzymatic) formation of aldimines (Schiff bases). This step is a prerequisite to formation of even more stable cross-links between these reactive groups and amino acids located on contiguous collagen molecules. Until recently it was believed that the final cross-links were di- and tri-functional lysine derivatives. However, a new cross-link, a 3-hydroxy-pyridinium derivative, probably formed from three hydroxylsyl residues, has been described. Eyre has proposed a mechanism for its formation, whch is depicted in Figure 27–2. This new derivative appears to be the most stable cross-link in collagen.

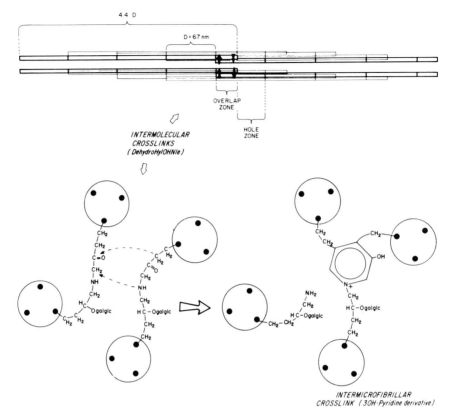

Figure 27–2 Scheme showing the formation of a 3-hydroxypyridinium cross-link from two dihydroxylysinonorleucine cross-links. The upper diagram demonstrates how the contiguous alignment of microfibrils fosters the spontaneous formation of intermolecular cross-links. (From Eyre, D.R.: Collagen: a molecular diversity in the body's protein scaffold. Science 207:1315–1322, 1980. Copyright 1980 by the American Association for the Advancement of Science.)

DISORDERS OF COLLAGEN METABOLISM

Consonant with the ubiquitous distribution of collagen types throughout the tissues of the body, disorders of connective tissues are associated with skeletal deformities, fragile skin, poor wound healing with abdominal scar formation, vascular and gastrointestinal perforation, and hyperextensible joints.

While some order is being imposed in this heterogeneous group of inherited and acquired disorders, certain enigmas remain, for example, deficient lysyl oxidase activity both in a form of Ehlers-Danlos syndrome and a variant of cutis laxa. At present it seems that the recessive forms of these collagen diseases involve processing enzymes, while the dominant forms are likely to involve structural defects. However, much remains to be learned about these disorders before unifying principles can be applied with certainty.

Ehlers-Danlos Syndrome

This is a heterogeneous group of disorders of type I or III collagen (Table 27–3). They share certain common manifestations, including fragility, easy bruisability, hyperextensibility of skin, and hypermotility of joints. While each disorder has a distinctive fundamental biochemical lesion, the end result of each is a deleterious effect on the stability of the collagen fibril.

Cutis Laxa

This disorder of collagen can be subdivided into three disease entities on the basis of genetic inheritance. The most severe of the three is the autosomal recessive disease, in which there is lung,

Table 27–3 EHLERS-DANLOS SYNDROMES

Type	Major Clinical Manifestations	Skin	Bruising	Joint Mobility	Inheritance	Biochemical Defect
I Gravis	Musculoskeletal deformities, prematurity due to membrane rupture, venous varicosities, heart valve abnormalities	3+ extensibility 3+ fragility Velvet feel, cigarette paper scars	2+, hyperpigmentation from heme	3+	AD	Undefined
II Mitis	Rarely mitral valve prolapse	2+ extensibility 2+ fragility	2+	2+	AD	Undefined
III Benign; Hypermobile		2–3+ extensibility + fragility Soft, not velvety	+	3+	AD	Undefined
IV Ecchymotic	Arterial rupture, intestinal perforation; skin torn easily	+ extensibility 2+ fragility	3+	0–+	AD AR	Undefined Deficient synthesis of type III collagen
V X-linked	Cigarette-paper, floppy cardiac valves, short stature, inguinal hernias	2+ extensibility + fragility	+	Digits only	X-linked	Lysyl oxidase, deficiency of type III collagen cross-link formation
VI Ocular	Musculoskeletal deformity, marfanoid habitus, ocular fragility, keratoconus, rupture of globe	3+ extensibility 2+ fragility	2+	3+	AR	Lysyl hydroxylase—interferes with cross-link formation
VII	Short stature, hip dislocation (arthrochalasis multiplex congenita)	2+ extensibility + fragility	2+	3+	AR	Structural mutation pro $\alpha 2$ chain-inhibits cleavage of aminopeptide → poor tensile strength ?Procollagen peptidase

+—mild
2+—moderate
3+—marked

Table 27–4   OSTEOGENESIS IMPERFECTA

Type	Clinical Features	Fractures At Birth	Inheritance	Additional Features	Biochemistry
I	Scoliosis, "codfish" deformity of vertebrae, fractured and bowed long bones, hyperextensible joints, blue sclera, normal dentition, deafness	No	AD	Easy bruisability	↓ Type I collagen relative to type III
II	Low birth weight, often premature, multiple fractures (most intrapartum), disordered cranial ossification, femurs misshapen ("crumpled"), deep blue sclera	Yes	AR	Invariably fatal in infancy	↓ Synthesis of type I collagen; ↑ bone-OH-lysine content
III	Normal birth weight, scoliosis, long bone deformities, hyperextensible joints, poor dentition, blue sclera in infancy, normal sclera in adult years	Yes	AR (sporadic)	Easy bruisability, occasional deafness	Altered ratio of type I:type III collagen
IV	Normal birth weight, fractures generally uncommon, osteoporosis with variable bony deformities, sclera normal, dentition strikingly abnormal	No	AD	Normal auditory acuity	Altered ratio of type I:type III collagen

bladder, and gastrointestinal involvement, with early death resulting from emphysema and cor pulmonale. In addition, there is obvious involvement of the skin, the hallmark of all three forms of cutis laxa, causing loss of normal elasticity and conferring hyperextensiveness. While the autosomal dominant form results only in the skin manifestations, the X-linked type is more severe and causes venous varicosities and abnormalities of the ribs and long bones. None of the three types causes easy bruisability or joint hypermobility, a major differential point separating cutis laxa from Ehlers-Danlos syndrome.

Although the biochemical lesion has not been definitively demonstrated in all three forms, the defect seems to reside in different aspects of function of the enzyme lysyl oxidase.

Osteogenesis Imperfecta

This disorder, best known for its congenital fractures and blue sclerae, has now been classified into four types based upon the clinical varieties and hereditary patterns (Table 27–4). Since type I

Table 27–5   CLINICAL FEATURES OF HOMOCYSTINURIA AND MARFAN'S SYNDROME

System	Homocystinuria	Marfan's Syndrome
Ocular	Ectopia lentis (usually downward), glaucoma, myopia, retinal detachment, cataracts	Microphakia, ectopia lentis (usually upward), glaucoma, retinal detachment
Skeletal	Osteoporosis, genu valgum, dolichostenomelia, pes cavus, flatfeet, scoliosis, pectus excavatum, abnormal dentition, arachnodactyly	Arachnodactyly, flatfeet, genu valgum, joints hyperextensible, pectus excavatum, exceptionally tall
CNS	Cerebral dysfunction, seizures, abnormal EEG, spasticity, focal neurological signs, psychiatric disturbance	Normal to mild retardation
Cardiovascular	Arterial and venous thrombosis, malar flush, livedo reticularis	Cystic medial necrosis of aorta, aneurysm, atrial septal defect
Other	Hair (light, sparse, brittle), liver (fatty changes)	Hair (fine, friable), face (long, narrow)

Table 27–6 VARIANTS OF PSEUDOXANTHOMA ELASTICUM

Variant	Skin	Ocular Findings	Cardiovascular
Dominant I	Papular rash on flexor surfaces Imparts ''plucked chicken'' effect Skin may hang in folds, e.g., blood- hound features Mucous membranes may be involved	Angioid streaks—may undergo hemorrhage with loss of vi- sion Chorioretinitis may also lead to blindness	Fibrous proliferation and calcifi- cation in media of arteries Peripheral pulses diminished Intermittent claudication Angina pectoris Abdominal angina Precocious myocardial infarction Hypertension (renal vessels) Increased tendency to hemor- rhage, especially in G.I. tract
Dominant II	Milder skin manifestation	Mild retinal involvement	No findings
Recessive I	Similar findings to dominant I	←———————— Milder than dominant I ————————→	
Recessive II	Generalized cutaneous laxity	No findings	No findings

collagen is essentially the only collagen in bone, it is likely that a structural defect of the collagen molecule will be found to underlie the autosomal dominant forms, while an enzyme defect in synthesis, cross-linking, or degradation will be shown to cause the autosomal recessive types of disease.

Marfan's Syndrome

Despite the familiarity on the part of many physicians with what they remember to be the findings of patients with Marfan's syndrome, clinics with wide experience in disorders of connective tissue have accumulated persuasive evidence that this disorder manifests wide heterogeneity of clinical findings. Nonetheless, the gratuitous use of terms such as forme fruste confuse the issue, since only in textbooks do patients with Marfan's manifest all of the findings that cumulatively have come to be associated with the syndrome.

Three systems are affected predominantly in Marfan's syndrome: skeletal, cardiovascular, and ocular (Table 27–5). In many series when the diagnosis is suspected, echocardiography almost always shows evidence of cardiovascular involvement. Marfan's syndrome is not a diagnosis to be made solely on clinical findings unless all systems are involved and even then further cardiovascular evaluation is mandatory. The table presents features that allow differentiation from homocystinuria. This is important from a therapeutic point of view.

Recently Boucek et al. (1981) have presented evidence for a defect in the $\alpha2$ (I) peptide of collagen, resulting in a defect in cross-linked formation. How such a defect arises and leads to the wide-ranging manifestations of this syndrome remains to be elucidated.

Pseudoxanthoma Elasticum

This nosology embraces several disorders of connective tissue that affect skin, eyes, and the cardiovascular system. The underlying defect has not been defined in any of the forms. They are compared in Table 27–6.

REFERENCES

Bornstein, P., and Byers, P.H.: Disorders of collagen metabolism. *In* Bondy, P.K., and Rosenberg, L.E.(eds.): Metabolic Control and Disease. 8th ed. W.B. Saunders Co., Philadelphia, 1980, p. 1089.
Bornstein, P., and Sage, H.: Structurally distinct collagen types. Ann. Rev. Biochem. 49:957, 1980.
Boucek, R.J., Noble, N.L., Gunja-Smith, Z., and Butler, W.T.: The Marfan syndrome: A deficiency in chemically stable collagen cross-links. N. Engl. J. Med. 305:988, 1981.
Byers, P.H., Siegel, R.C., Holbrook, K.A., et al.: X-linked cutis laxa: Defective cross-link formation in collagen due to decreased lysyl oxidase activity. N. Engl. J. Med. 303:61, 1980.

Eyre, D.R.: Collagen: Molecular diversity in the body's protein scaffold. Science 207:1315, 1980.

Helseth, D.L., Jr., and Veis, A.: Collagen self-assembly in vitro. J. Biol. Chem. 256:7118, 1981.

Pinnell, S.R. and Murad, S.: Disorders of collagen. *In* Stanbury, J.B., Wyngaarden, J.B., Frederickson, D.S., et al. (eds.): The Metabolic Basis of Inherited Disease. 5th ed. McGraw-Hill, New York, 1983, p. 1425.

Prockop, D.J., Kivirikko, K.I., Tuderman, L., and Guzman, N.A.: The biosynthesis of collagen and its disorders. N. Engl. J. Med. 13:77, 1979.

Pyeritz, R.E., Murphy, E.A., and McKusick, V.A.: Clinical variability in the Marfan syndromes. Birth Defects 15:155, 1979.

Sandberg, L.B., Soskel, N.T., and Leslie, J.G.: Elastin structure, biosynthesis, and relation to disease states. N. Engl. J. Med. 304:566, 1981.

Steinmann, B., Tuderman, L., Peltonen, L., et al.: Evidence for a structural mutation of procollagen type I in a patient with the Ehlers-Danlos syndrome type VII. J. Biol. Chem. 255:8887, 1980.

28

Glycogen Storage Diseases

GLYCOGEN AS A FOOD STORE

Polysaccharides act as food stores and as structural elements. Here we will consider their role as food stores (glycogen); in Chapter 32 they are considered as structural components. Owing to their small size, high concentrations of monosaccharides would increase osmotic pressure (see Chapter 2) to unphysiological levels were they to serve as carbohydrate food stores. This would have profoundly deleterious effects on metabolic processes. Through polymerization the chances for noncovalent intermolecular interactions are increased greatly over their unlikely occurrence with monomers. As a result, solubility decreases, thereby diminishing any effect on solvent availability in the cell, and the polymer is stored as granules. Construction of glycogen as an open, branched structure permits easy access to enzymes involved in addition and subtraction of monomers. Interestingly, at least some of the enzymes that subserve these functions are themselves bound to the surface of the glycogen granules, providing an organized structural-functional interaction.

Glycogen serves as a ready source of fuel for "flight or fight" in muscle. In liver, which utilizes fatty acids as its primary fuel, glycogen is broken down and released to serve the relentless glucose demands of brain and red cells. This distinction emphasizes the central role played by the liver in total body glucose homeostasis.

Before embarking on a description of the heterogeneous group of glycogen storage disorders, it is essential to review the salient features of glycogen metabolism so that the diseases may be understood in the context of these metabolic reactions. Glycogen is a polymer of D-glucose subunits linked by 1,4-ether linkages into straight chains that branch with 1,6-linkages (Fig. 28–1). The enormous molecular weight of most native glycogen molecules, consistent with their storage function, is in the neighborhood of 100 to 200 million. It now appears that the synthesis and degradation of glycogen are carefully controlled, coordinated events, and they cannot really be understood in isolation from each other. Before we attempt to describe some of the complexities of regulation we must first review the synthetic and degradative pathways involving glycogen (Fig. 28–2).

Glucose monomers, as uridine diphosphate (UDP) glucose, are incorporated into a glycogen chain by the enzyme glycogen synthase, water being lost as two glucose moieties condense. As noted above, glycogen is a highly ramified polymer, and branches are added as 1,6-ether linkages by the branching enzymes (α-glucan-glycosyl-4,6-transferase). Exclusion of water permits more concentration of energy-yielding molecules per unit of cellular volume. However, the hydrophilic nature of the glucose monomers places an upper limit on this storage process that is easily exceeded by essentially hydrophobic lipid molecules (see Chapter 31).

Glycogen molecules aggregate to form particles, observable on electron microscopy; these particles are associated, probably by noncovalent linkage, with the enzymes mediating synthesis and degradation of the polysaccharide. Normally, liver contains up to 4 per cent glycogen and muscle up to 2 per cent on a wet weight basis.

Degradation of glycogen commences with the action of phosphorylase, which is subject to regulation by phosphorylation-dephosphorylation, the phosphorylated form being active. This enzyme cleaves terminal 1,4-glucosidyl bonds but is unable to cleave residues that are not at least four residues removed from a branch point. Phosphorylase action alone produces a so-called "limit-

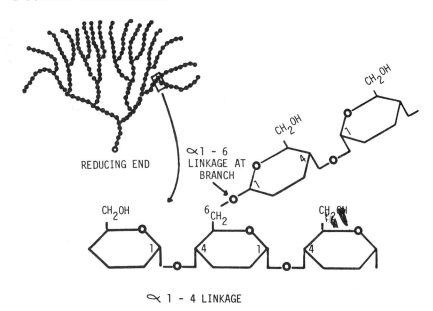

Figure 28–1 Structure of glycogen. The molecule is basically a straight-chain glucose polymer connected by 1,4-glycosidic linkages. Branching occurs approximately every 12 glucose units by formation of a 1,6-glycosidic bond. (From Mahler, R.F.: Disorders of glycogen metabolism. Clin. Endocrinol. Metab. 5:579, 1976.)

dextrin," in a reaction that requires inorganic phosphate and liberates glucose-1-phosphate in the process.

Owing to the specificity requirements of phosphorylase, continued sequential degradation of glycogen requires the "debranching enzyme," amylo-1,6-glucosidase, which is somewhat unusual in that it is a multi-functional enzyme catalyzing two successive reactions. First, acting as a glycosyl-(1,4→1,4)-transferase, it transfers three glycosyl residues from a branch point to a chain terminus, thereby lengthening it to seven so that phosphorylase can again cleave off residues up to four from a branch point. The second catalytic activity of debrancher is the hydrolysis of the single residue at the branch that is in alpha-1,6-linkage, the specific configuration required by this enzyme. Here free glucose is released.

Glucose-1-phosphate released by phosphorylase is converted to glucose-6-phosphate by phosphoglucomutase. Glucose-6-phosphate can then enter glycolysis or the pentose pathway or be hydrolyzed by glucose-6-phosphatase to glucose.

Control of Glycogen Metabolism in Liver

The glycogen catabolic and synthetic sequences are under the control of hormones and other effectors, several of which act on key enzymes of the sequence through reversible covalent modification by phosphorylation-dephosphorylation. To coordinate glycogen metabolism so that a signal directs either synthesis or degradation, the activities of the two key enzymes of these sequences (i.e., glycogen synthase and phosphorylase) must change in opposite directions as a consequence of phosphorylation. Indeed, phosphorylation increases the activity of phosphorylase while decreasing the activity of the synthase. Phosphorylation is mediated by kinases and dephosphorylation by phosphatases.

We content ourselves here with a simplified version of the controls in liver. The reviews by Hers (1976), Cornblath and Schwartz (1976), and Fletterick and Madsen (1980) should be consulted for more details of this extremely complex sequence. When glucose is in short supply, pancreatic alpha cells secrete glucagon, which binds to liver cells and stimulates adenyl cyclase to produce cAMP, in turn activating protein kinase. The protein kinase phosphorylates glycogen phosphorylase

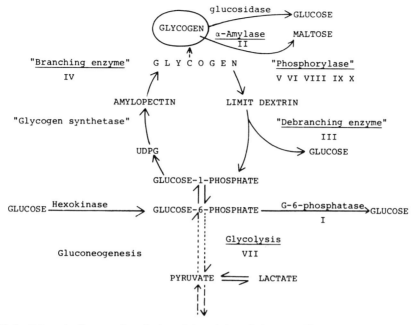

Figure 28–2 Schematic diagram of synthesis and degradation of glycogen. The roman numerals correspond to the affected enzymes in various types of glycogen storage disease. Types II and VII are not shown. (From Mahler, R.F.: Disorders of glycogen metabolism. Clin. Endocrinol. Metab. 5:579, 1976.)

to its active form while converting glycogen synthase to its inactive form. Ultimately, glucose is liberated in the blood through the degradative sequence.

On the other hand, in times of glucose excess, after a carbohydrate meal, the pancreas secretes insulin. This hormone causes activation of glycogen synthase. The consequent cellular glucose influx enhances glucose binding to phosphorylase, which causes partial inhibition of that enzyme. A proposed mechanism for the inhibitory action of glucose on phosphorylase has been reviewed by Fletterick and Madsen. Hence, glycogen synthesis and storage from the entering glucose is promoted. Figure 28–3 shows these processes and the signals that control their activity.

GLYCOGEN STORAGE DISEASE

Type I Glycogen Storage Disease

Clinical Features

The most prominent clinical features of this disease are failure to thrive in association with hepatomegaly, hypoglycemia, hyperlactatemia, profound hypertriglyceridemia, and hyperuricemia. It is not uncommon for initial presentation to be due to a prolonged bleeding episode resulting from impairment of platelet function. Children with this defect have characteristic china-doll-like faces. Enlargement of the kidney is frequent but may be appreciated only with an abdominal flatplate because of the hepatomegaly. There may be associated glycosuria and a generalized aminoaciduria, with impairment of energy-requiring transport processes in the renal tubule (see Chapter 23). Transient ketonuria may be seen, but ketoacidosis is not a feature of this disorder. Later in life xanthomata may appear as a consequence of the persistent triglyceride elevation.

Biochemical Defects

The cause of the variegated symptoms encountered in this glycogen storage disease is a defect in the multifunctional enzyme glucose-6-phosphatase, which serves as the terminal step in the glu-

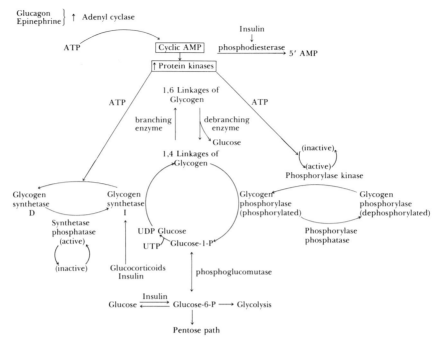

Figure 28–3 Regulation of glycogen metabolism. (From Villee, D.B.: Human Endocrinology: A Developmental Approach. Philadelphia, W.B. Saunders Co., 1975.)

coneogenic sequence. This enzyme provides more than 90 per cent of the glucose released by liver; hence it occupies a central role in normal glucose homeostasis. Glucose, supplied either by the breakdown of glycogen or through the gluconeogenic pathway, is converted to glucose-6-phosphate (G-6-P). Before free glucose can be released into the blood stream to serve the needs of glucose-requiring organs, it must undergo cleavage of the terminal phosphate group to form free glucose. While the debranching enzyme (amylo-1,6-glucosidase) can maintain some of the glucose needs by its hydrolysis of branch points, the bulk of the G-6-P release enters glycolysis, forming lactate. Additionally, it enters the pentose phosphate pathway, forming 5-ribosylpyrophosphate (5-RPP), a precursor of uric acid (see Chapter 36). Urate synthesis has been shown to be increased in affected individuals. The increased production and elevated blood levels of lactate contribute to the hyperuricemic state by inhibiting renal tubular urate secretion. However, an additional factor, hitherto shown to be important in the hyperuricemia associated with hereditary fructose intolerance (see Chapter 26), appears to be important in glucose-6-phosphatase deficiency as well. This factor is depletion of ATP and Pi during glycogenolysis and glycolysis, which brings about the degradation of preformed nucleotides to uric acid. The molecular mechanism is the activation of adenylate deaminase, which degrades AMP to inosinic acid; the lack of AMP in turn activates 5-RPP amidotransferase, the first committed step in purine biosynthesis. In patients who lack glucose-6-phosphatase, the G-6-P resulting from phosphorolysis of glycogen enters the glycolytic pathway instead of being released into the blood stream as free glucose. Trapped in the liver, it utilizes ATP for the glycolytic sequence and is converted to lactate. Greene and co-workers (1978) suggest that this chain of events accounts for part of the uric acid production, a later phase being the result of compensatory increased flux through the pentose phosphate pathway.

Hypertriglyceridemia seems to be a consequence of both increased formation of very low-density triglyceride and decreased activity of lipoprotein lipase. The following factors contribute to the enhanced triglyceride formation. Since hypoglycemia is a persistent problem in von Gierke's disease, insulin levels are correspondingly and appropriately low. In consequence, lipolysis is activated and lipoprotein lipase activity (which is modified by insulin) is decreased. Metabolism of G-6-P by glycolysis leads to the trioses dihydroxyacetone phosphate and glyceraldehyde phosphate. In the next step, glyceraldehyde is converted to 1,3-diphosphoglyceric acid in a reaction that also produces NADH. Augmentation of NADH levels stimulates the formation of alpha-glycerol phosphate from dihydroxyacetone phosphate, which can then form triglyceride by condensation with fatty acids. The increased glucose-carbon flux through pyruvate increases the acetyl CoA pool, which raises intracellular levels of malonyl CoA. The latter compound regulates entry of fatty acids into mitochondria, slowing their oxidation and causing net fatty acid synthesis (see Chapter 13). Thus, the supply of fatty acids for triglyceride formation is significantly increased.

Recently, the defect in a subtype of this disorder (pseudo glycogen storage disease type I) with apparently normal glucose-6-phosphatase activity, on in vitro assay, has been clarified. Studies by Lange et al. (1980) demonstrated that an intact membrane in vivo is essential to the hydrolysis of G-6-P by this microsomal enzyme. This is so because of the role of a G-6-P-specific translocase as a prerequisite to cleavage by the enzyme. Freezing tissue disrupts the membrane, thereby circumventing the selectivity of the translocase. When glucose-6-phosphatase was assayed in fresh tissue from a patient with the subtype, activity was 10 per cent of normal. However, on a frozen specimen activity was increased to about 30 per cent of normal.

Laboratory Findings

The triad of hypoglycemia, hyperlactatemia, and hyperuricemia leads to the strong suspicion of von Gierke's disease. The glucagon stimulation test will generate a trifling increase in blood glucose but will further increase the blood·lactate, owing to failure to release G-6-P and consequent increased glycolysis. Intravenous administration of galactose, fructose, or glycerol also causes little increase in blood glucose. Fructose or galactose will end up as G-6-P; owing to the absence of the phosphatase, there is no glucose release, hence no increase in the blood sugar. Consequently, this test can be employed to distinguish von Gierke's disease from debrancher deficiency (see below). Again, it should be noted that the acidosis encountered in glucose-6-phosphatase deficiency is a lactic acidosis and not a ketoacidosis. Apparently, the increased pyruvate is either carboxylated to furnish oxaloacetate for complete oxidation or oxidatively decarboxylated to acetyl CoA with probable stimulation of net fatty acid synthesis. Elevation of intracellular levels of malonyl CoA also has important inhibitory effect on ketogenesis. Although enzyme assay on liver obtained by open biopsy provides a definitive diagnosis, it is rarely necessary to perform those studies in order to embark upon a therapeutic regimen.

Treatment

Although chemical hypoglycemia is commonplace, symptomatic hypoglycemia is rare, a fortunate discrepancy that has been attributed to the utilization of lactate or β-hydroxybutyrate by the brain. Sucrose and lactose are best avoided because the monosaccharides that comprise them (galactose and fructose) undergo rearrangement to glucose-6-phosphate, leading to further glycogen storage. Recently, Greene et al. (1980) have shown that continuous nasogastric feedings overnight by pump with glucose and glucose oligosaccharides can decrease the size of the liver while preventing recurrences of hypoglycemia. This noninvasive therapy now supplants portacaval shunt as the therapy of choice. Physicians contemplating this therapeutic regime should study the paper by Greene et al.

Type II Glycogen Storage Disease (Acid Maltase Deficiency, Pompe's Disease)

This form of glycogen storage disease differs from all others in that it involves a defect of a lysosomal enzyme. Symptoms appear early in the first year of life with failure to thrive, irritability, hypotonia, dyspnea, and occasionally even cyanosis. Enlargement of the tongue is quite common but not invariable. Consonant with cardiac involvement, chest X-ray reveals an enlarged globular heart; the EKG may actually provide the diagnosis, revealing left axis deviation, short P-R interval, a huge QRS, and T wave inversion. Downhill progression is rapid, and no therapy forestalls the demise of the patient.

Milder variants affecting striated muscle only and not presenting until late childhood or early adulthood have been described as well.

Biochemical Defects

Acid maltase (α-1,4-glucosidase) is a lysosomal enzyme that mediates cleavage of glycogen to glucose, acting on both 1,6 and 1,4 linkages. In the absence of this enzyme, glycogen accumulates within lysosomes and ultimately within the cytosol of the cell. The physiological role of this enzyme is not certain, but it has been proposed that during the normal lysosomal housekeeping functions some glycogen is taken into the lysosome along with other supramolecular components that undergo degradation therein. In this disorder absence of this enzyme leads to intralysosomal accumulation of glycogen.

Laboratory Diagnosis

Biochemical diagnosis depends upon showing the absence of acid maltase activity in either liver or muscle. Leukocyte activity is unfortunately too variable to be employed for diagnosis. Prenatal diagnosis is possible using cultured amniotic cells and should be performed in a laboratory having experience with this assay.

Treatment

At present there is no therapy, other than supportive measures, for this relentlessly fatal disorder.

Type III Glycogen Storage Disease (Limit Dextrinosis, Cori's Disease, Forbes' Disease)

Children with type III glycogen storage disease often possess doll-like faces like those seen in von Gierke's disease, in addition to hepatomegaly, muscle weakness, and fasting hypoglycemia (the latter being associated infrequently with symptoms). There is no renal enlargement in this form of glycogen storage disease. It carries with it a better prognosis than type I. Splenic enlargement is occasionally seen. Xanthoma may occur, but serum lipids may return to normal around puberty. Indeed, there is an unexplained amelioration of symptoms at that time. Recently, DiMauro et al. (1979) have reported five patients manifesting predominant myopathic symptoms who did, nonetheless, have biochemical evidence of hepatic debrancher dysfunction as well.

Biochemical Defects

The enzymatic defect involves the multifunctional debranching enzyme amylo-1,6-glucosidase. Absence of this enzyme permits glycogen breakdown to continue until the outermost branch points are reached, at which point further degradation is not possible.

Laboratory Diagnosis

Laboratory findings are similar to those of type I and include hypoglycemia, hypertriglyceridemia, hypercholesterolemia, and hyperuricemia. Hypoglycemia, while present, rarely represents a clinically important problem. Glucagon or epinephrine administration after a long fast serves to distinguish this form from glucose-6-phosphatase deficiency. In type III such stimulation fails either to cause a rise in the blood sugar or to increase the blood lactate level, in contrast to the situation seen with glucose-6-phosphatase deficiency. However, such patients manifest a rise in blood sugar when either galactose, fructose, or glycerol is administered, since glucose-6-phosphatase is active. Definitive biochemical diagnosis may, however, require enzyme assay on liver biopsy.

Treatment

Optimal dietary therapy involves a high protein diet with frequent feedings. Night feedings during infancy and during intercurrent infections are essential.

Type IV Glycogen Storage Disease (Amylo Pectinosis, Andersen's Disease)

Clinical Features

This is a rare and severe form of glycogen storage disease. Hepatic cirrhosis with jaundice and liver failure beginning during infancy characterizes this disorder. While glycogen deposition occurs as well in heart, kidney, spleen, lymph nodes, skeletal muscle, and intestinal mucosa, it is the liver that suffers the most as the consequence of glycogen deposition. Nonetheless, muscle weakness is not uncommon and may antedate severe hepatic dysfunction.

Biochemical Defects

As reviewed above, amylo-1,4-1,6-transglucosidase (brancher enzyme) mediates the transfer of a terminal fragment of 6 or 7 glucosyl residues to the 6 hydroxyl group of glucose on a glycogen chain, forming an α-1,6 linkage. As a result of the enzyme defect, an abnormally structured glycogen results, possessing excessively long outer branches with a paucity of branch points.

Laboratory Diagnosis

Enzyme assay can be accomplished on leukocytes and should be considered in any infant or child with liver failure in whom galactosemia, hereditary fructose intolerance, tyrosinemia, and Wilson's disease have been ruled out.

Treatment

Thus far there is no therapy, other than supportive, for this disorder.

Type V Glycogen Storage Disease (Myophosphorylase Deficiency, McArdle's Disease)

Clinical Features

This disease has an interesting history; the first case was diagnosed as a psychosomatic disorder. Patients are asymptomatic while at rest but experience muscle cramping after moderate exercise. Onset of symptoms is usually not until around age 20, when it may present as an episode of myoglobinuria, particularly after strenuous exercise. It is not clear yet whether the current jogging craze will uncover a quiescent defect in previously sedentary individuals.

Biochemical Defects

Muscle phosphorylase, an enzyme distinct from liver phosphorylase, is deficient in this disease. Deposition of normal glycogen occurs in muscle; the liver is uninvolved. Predictably, there is no lactic acid production with ischemic exercise, a point that is helpful in diagnosis.

Laboratory Diagnosis

Several hours following strenuous exercise, muscle enzymes (including LDH, aldolase, and CPK) are increased in serum. The increase in serum lactic acid expected with exercise is not observed because fatty acids alone rather than glucose serve the energetic needs of the muscles in this disorder. Unequivocal diagnosis would require enzyme assay on a muscle biopsy, but a diagnosis can usually be made on clinical and routine laboratory tests and so it is probably not justified, particularly since the disorder need not be incapacitating.

Treatment

In harmony with the above, the patient should avoid severe exercise, thereby permitting fatty acids to serve the energy requirements of moderately, as against maximally, exercising muscle.

Type VI Glycogen Storage Disease (Hepatic Phosphorylase Complex Deficiency, Hers' Disease)

Patients afflicted with disorders of the enzymes mediating activation of phosphorylase or of the phosphorylase molecule itself manifest hepatomegaly, slight growth retardation, and glycogen storage; clinical manifestations are less severe than with types I and III. Since these children are the most mildly affected of those with hepatic glycogen storage disease, it is likely that the defect is only partial.

Biochemical Defects

As reviewed above, the activation of the phosphorylase complex is accomplished in three separate steps. In the first step, adenylate cyclase mediates formation of cyclic AMP, which then activates a protein kinase by the removal of an inhibitory unit from that enzyme. In the next step, the kinase then carries out phosphorylation of the phosphorylase kinase, which converts glycogen phosphorylase into an active form. Hence, at least three genetic defects are possible and, indeed, defects of the (1) protein kinase, of the (2) phosphorylase kinase, and of the (3) phosphorylase itself have been discovered. Most patients thus far described appear to lack phosphorylase kinase.

Laboratory Diagnosis

Hypoglycemia is not usually encountered, but glucagon does not elicit a hyperglycemic response. Transaminase levels may be abnormal. Diagnosis is suggested by the mildness of the disorder and can be proved by assay of the enzyme system in peripheral white cells. Obviously, assay of enzyme in a liver biopsy is also possible but does not seem justified for this assay alone.

Treatment

Dietary therapy can defend against the occasional hypoglycemia; the prognosis is excellent, with mental development being normal. A high protein diet (15 to 20 per cent of calories) administered on a frequent basis is the mainstay of therapy. Fats should account for 30 to 35 per cent of calories and carbohydrate, mainly as starch, dextromaltose, and glucose the remainder. Liver enlargement regresses as the patient reaches adolescence.

Type VII Glycogen Storage Disease (Defect of Muscle Phosphofructokinase)

Clinical Features

This disorder is similar to McArdle's disease in that strenuous exercise fails to elicit an increase in blood lactic acid and pyruvate levels. After such exercise, the patient may experience pain and muscle destruction with concomitant myoglobinuria. Phosphofructokinase activity may be assayed with erythrocytes; the liver enzyme is normal. Avoidance of symptoms requires that the patient restrict activity only to mild or moderate exercise.

REFERENCES

Burman, D., Holton, J.B., and Pennock, C.A. (eds.): Inherited Disorders of Carbohydrate Metabolism. MTP Press Ltd., Lancaster, England, 1980.

Cornblath, M., and Schwartz, R.: Disorders of Carbohydrate Metabolism in Infancy. 2nd ed. W.B. Saunders Co., Philadelphia, 1976.

D'Ancona, G.G., Wurm, J., and Croce, C.M.: Genetics of type II glycogenosis: Assignment of the human gene for acid alpha-glucosidase to chromosome 17. Proc. Natl. Acad. Sci. USA. 76:4526, 1979.

DiMauro, S., Hartwig, G.B.., Hays, A., et al.: Debrancher deficiency: Neuromuscular disorder in 5 adults. Ann. Neurol. 5:422, 1979.

Dombrádi, V.: Structural aspects of the catalytic and regulatory function of glycogen phosphorylase. Int. J. Biochem. 13:125, 1981.

Fletterick, R.J., and Madsen, N.B.: The structure and related functions of phosphorylase a. Ann. Rev. Biochem. 49:31, 1980.

Greene, H.L., Slonim, A.E., Burr, I.M., and Moran, J.R.: Type I glycogen storage disease: Five years of management with nocturnal intragastric feeding. J. Pediatr. 96:590, 1980.

Greene, H.L., Wilson, F.A., Hefferan, P. et al.: ATP depletion, a possible role in the pathogenesis of hyperuricemia in glycogen storage disease type I. J. Clin. Invest. 62:321, 1978.

Hays, A.P., Hallett, M. Delfs, J., et al.: Muscle phosphofructokinase deficiency: Abnormal polysaccharide in a case of late-onset myopathy. Neurology 31:1077, 1981.

Hems, D.A., and Whitton, P.D.: Control of hepatic glycogenolysis. Physiol. Rev. 60:1, 1980.

Hers, H.G.: The control of glycogen metabolism in the liver. Ann. Rev. Biochem. 45:167, 1976.

Howell, R.R., and Williams, J.C.: The glycogen storage diseases. *In* Stanbury, J.B., Wyngaarden, J.B., Fredrickson, D.S., et al. (eds.): The Metabolic Basis of Inherited Disease. 5th ed. McGraw-Hill, New York, 1983, p. 141.

Lange, A.J., Arion, W.J., and Beaudet, A.L.: Type Ib Glycogen storage disease is caused by a defect in the glucose-6-phosphate translocase of the microsomal glucose-6-phosphatase system. J. Biol. Chem. 255:8381, 1980.

Matcham, G.W.J., Patil, N.B., Smith, E.E., and Whelan, W.J.: The glycoprotein nature of liver glycogen. *In* Esmann, V. (ed.): Fed. Europ. Biochem. Soc. Vol. 42. Pergamon Press, London, 1978, p. 305.

Powell, R.C., Wentworth, S.M., and Brandt, I.K.: Endogenous glucose production in type I glycogen storage disease. Metabolism 30:443, 1981.

29

Lactic Acidosis

Of late, lactic acidosis has received increasing notice in the internal medicine literature. While great emphasis has been placed on those conditions and disorders associated with lactic acidosis in the adult, relatively little attention has been paid to the inborn errors of metabolism associated with lactic acidosis in the infant and child. Here we wish to direct our attention especially to those situations in which lactic acidosis assumes importance in the pediatric age group.

Since lactic acid represents a dead-end product of the anaerobic metabolism of glucose via the glycolytic pathway, lactic acidosis in reality represents a defect in the handling of pyruvate through the several pathways open for its disposal (Fig. 29–1). Although no unambiguous definition of lactic acidosis exists (a situation that may seem somewhat surprising to the reader), there seems to be general agreement that lactic acidosis occurs when the serum lactate level is persistently raised above 5 mM, such elevation being associated with a decrease in the arterial blood pH. For many years there seemed to be a view that the predominant cause of lactic acidosis was over-production of lactate. However, as discussed below, in a number of instances underutilization by the liver and kidney, particularly because of defects in gluconeogenesis, can be of greater importance than over-production.

LACTATE AND PYRUVATE METABOLISM

Lactate, the final product of anaerobic metabolism of glucose, exists in equilibrium with pyruvate through the reaction catalyzed by the enzyme lactate dehydrogenase:

$$Pyr + H^+ + NADH \xrightarrow{LDH} Lac + NAD^+ \tag{1}$$

or,

$$\frac{L}{P} = k\frac{[NADH]\,[H^+]}{[NAD^+]} \tag{2}$$

Note that the conversion of pyruvate to lactate as shown in equation (1) consumes two hydrogen ions (by complete oxidation of pyruvate) and thus subserves an important function. Twenty times as many hydrogen ions would otherwise be liberated during the dissociation of pyruvic acid as from an equimolar quantity of lactic acid (pK is 3.8). Much interest has been focused on the lactate/pyruvate ratio, which, as shown in equation (2), is dependent upon 3 cytosolic variables: pyruvate concentration, the NADH/NAD$^+$ ratio (which reflects the redox state of the cytosol), and the hydrogen ion concentration in the cytosol. Of course, the NAD$^+$/NADH couple is a major source of reducing potential within the cell and hence occupies a position of great importance in the regulation of metabolism. Abundant experimental data exist to show that normally the mitochondria are 50 to 100-fold more reduced than the cytosol. This discrepancy between the state of reduction of the cytosol and that of the mitochondria renders the use of the serum lactate/pyruvate ratio as an indicator of the tissue lactate/pyruvate ratio of limited validity. Neither can it be used as an accurate determinant of tissue redox states, according to equation (2). With this caveat in mind measurement of lactate and pyruvate may nonetheless be useful in defining certain acquired and inherited disorders of lactate and pyruvate metabolism; the serum values of those metabolites should not be taken as representing a one to one correspondence with the likely tissue levels.

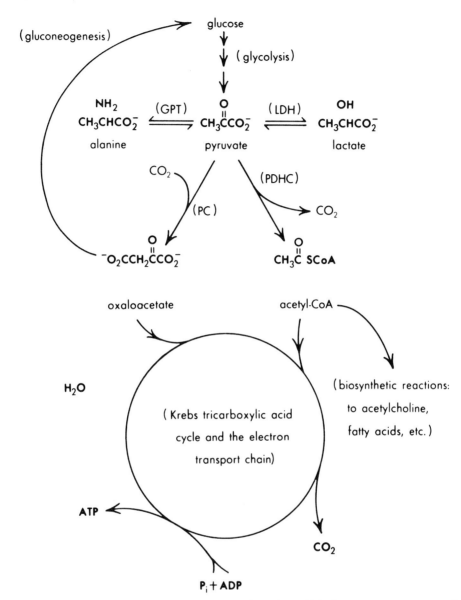

Figure 29–1 Relationship of Lactate to Pyruvate Metabolism. The multiple fates open to pyruvate are shown. Enzymes are abbreviated as follows: GPT = glutamic-pyruvic transaminase, LDH = lactate dehydrogenase, PC = pyruvate carboxylase, PDHC = pyruvate dehydrogenase complex. (From Blass, J.P.: Disorders of pyruvate metabolism. Neurology 29:280, 1979.)

Pyruvate is a metabolite of such central importance in intermediary metabolism that it (and several others such as glucose-6-phosphate and acetyl CoA) is called a "crossroads metabolite," emphasizing its pivotal role in a multiplicity of metabolic processes. Four major processes provide for the utilization of pyruvate: transamination to form alanine, reduction to lactate (which has been discussed above), carboxylation to oxaloacetate in the gluconeogenic sequence, and oxidative decarboxylation to acetyl CoA (Fig. 29–2). Defects in gluconeogenesis and the pyruvate dehydrogenase multi-enzyme complex then can be expected to interfere with pyruvate utilization, with the consequence that lactic acid may accumulate in the serum. The third determinant of the lactate concentration in the cytosol was noted to be the hydrogen ion concentration. Available evidence indicates that as pH in the extracellular fluid falls this engenders a fall in intracellular pH that

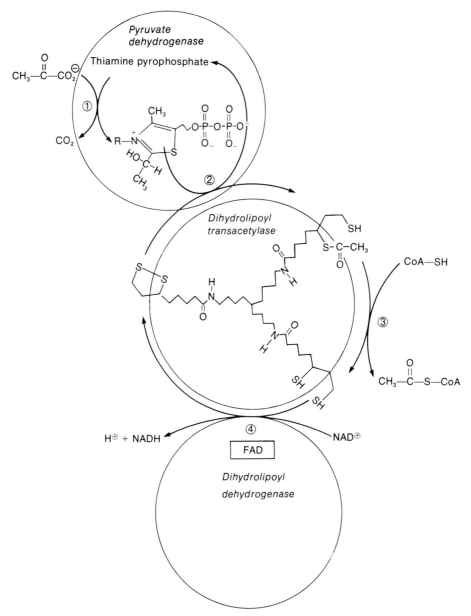

Figure 29–2 Mechanism of the pyruvate conversion to acetyl CoA. Pyruvate dehydrogenase is the multienzyme complex responsible for this reaction. The reaction occurs in a stepwise fashion, as shown. Cofactors required are thiamine pyrophosphate, CoASH, NAD, lipoic acid, and FAD. (From Flickinger, C.J., et al.: Medical Cell Biology. Philadelphia, W.B. Saunders Co., 1979.)

inhibits the key gluconeogenic enzyme pyruvate carboxylase, impairing its ability to produce oxaloacetate. Hence, either by intracellular acidosis or more rarely as a consequence of an inherited defect of the enzyme pyruvate carboxylase one may expect to find an accumulation of lactic acid. In addition, alterations in the cellular redox state generated by intracellular pH changes can adversely affect the activity of the pyruvate dehydrogenase enzyme complex, thus decreasing entry of pyruvate into the Krebs cycle, diminishing ATP production, and further inhibiting pyruvate carboxylase activity.

Acidosis

As noted above, lactic acid is a strong acid and when formed at body pH dissociates completely with the hydrogen ion titrating available intracellular and extracellular buffers. When lactate undergoes reconversion to glucose or complete oxidation through the citric acid cycle, hydrogen ions are consumed in this process, thereby balancing the previous hydrogen ion surfeit. Hence, any imbalance between rates of production or rate of utilization of lactate can lead to either a transitory or a more permanent state of lactic acidosis as defined earlier.

Lactate Formation and the Cori Cycle

While all tissues are capable of carrying out glycolysis, the predominant lactate producers of the body are erythrocytes, muscle, renal medulla, intestinal mucosa, retina, and when present, tumor tissue. Balanced against this production are the liver and the kidney, which are the main lactate consumers of the body. In the main the process of gluconeogenesis in liver and kidney accounts for the bulk of lactate consumption by those organs. The Cori cycle links these two groups of organs by transport of lactate through the blood from the producers to the consumers, as is shown in Figure 29–3. As noted before, an imbalance occasioned by either over-production or diminished utilization at either limb of this cycle can lead to the accumulation of lactate in the blood. Not shown in this figure is an additional safety gap for the removal of lactate from the blood, i.e., the excretion of lactate by the kidney when it exceeds a threshold of about 7 mEq/l.

While under normal circumstances the liver is the main organ mediating the removal of lactate from the blood, when liver oxygenation is compromised conversion of pyruvate to acetyl CoA by the pyruvate dehydrogenase multi-enzyme complex is inhibited and lactate is produced instead. Since inadequate ATP is being generated as a consequence of the diminished oxygenation, ATP is unavailable for the energy needs of gluconeogenesis, the other pathway that would normally remove the accumulated lactate. We note again that a decrease in the intracellular pH adversely affects the activity of the key gluconeogenic enzyme pyruvate carboxylase.

Clinical Classification of Lactic Acidosis

The classification proposed by Cohen and Woods (1976) in their monograph on lactic acidosis has gained wide acceptance in the medical community. In their system, type A, which is by far the most common cause of lactic acidosis, is associated with compromise of oxygen or blood supply to tissue, as is found in shock. Here we are concerned with one variation of the so-called type B, associated with inborn errors of gluconeogenesis and of the pyruvate dehydrogenase multi-enzyme complex. Hypoglycemia often, but not invariably, attends these defects, as do central ner-

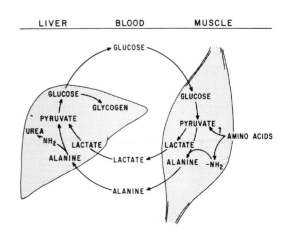

Figure 29–3 The Cori cycle and its relationship to the alanine cycle. The Cori cycle is responsible for overall conversion of lactate from muscle metabolism of glucose and/or glycogen back to glucose. The alanine cycle represents the means for carriage of ammonia (from muscle metabolism of amino acids) to the liver for urea synthesis. Note that removal of the ammonia results in pyruvate formation from alanine, thus permitting entry into the Cori cycle. (From Bondy, P.K., and Rosenberg, L.E. (eds.): Metabolic Control and Disease. Philadelphia, W.B. Saunders Co., 1980.)

Table 29–1 CONDITIONS ASSOCIATED WITH LACTIC ACIDOSIS

Defect/Condition	Clinical Features and Lab Findings	Biochemical Defect	Comments and References
Disorders of Gluconeogenesis			
Glucose-6-phosphatase deficiency	Hypoglycemia, hyperlipemia, hyperuricemia, hepatomegaly, xanthomas, failure to thrive		see Chapter 28
Fructose-1,6-diphosphatase	Hypoglycemia, failure to thrive, seizures, hepatomegaly		see Chapter 26
Pyruvate carboxylase	Variable hypoglycemia, failure to thrive, mental retardation, acidosis, variable hepatomegaly, seizures		Robinson et al., 1980
PEPCK	Hypoglycemia, hypotonicity, hepatomegaly, developmental delay, failure to thrive		Robinson et al., 1980
Disorders of Pyruvate Catabolism			
Pyruvate dehydrogenase multienzyme complex	Neurologic manifestations—spectrum from intermittent ataxia, chorea to coma and death, mental retardation, hepatomegaly, acidosis, hypoglycemia, variable optic atrophy	Different components of multienzyme complex involved in various patients	Neurological findings reported in different patients vary widely; Blass, 1980
E_3-Dihydrolipoyl dehydrogenase	Elevation lactate, α-ketoglutarate and branched-chain amino acids, optic atrophy, lethargy, hypertonia, stridor	E_3 component of pyruvate, α-ketoglutarate and branched-chain keto acids dehydrogenase is same enzyme	Robinson et al., 1980
Leigh's subacute necrotizing encephalopathy	Seizures, vomiting, mental retardation, weakness, blindness, peculiar sobbing respirations	One patient had pyruvate carboxylase defect Others—defective activation of PDH complex	DeVivo et al., 1979
Pyruvate dehydrogenase phosphatase	Tachypnea, hypotonia, lethargy, seizures, coma, death No hypoglycemia, ketoacidosis		Robinson and Sherwood, 1975

vous system manifestations and a prominent anion gap (see Chapter 12). In contrast to type A lactic acidosis the peripheral circulation is usually intact in these inborn errors of metabolism, and the defects appear to reside at the level of the key enzymes of gluconeogenesis or pyruvate disposal rather than in the electron transport chain. Defects in branched-chain amino acid metabolism including methylmalonic aciduria and propionic acidemia may also be associated with lactic acidosis, presumably by interfering with gluconeogenesis, most likely at the pyruvate carboxylase step, although definitive data for this proposal are lacking.

Table 29–1 lists the more important inborn errors of metabolism associated with lactic acidosis. The reader is referred to the chapters discussing these particular disorders in this text for information regarding diagnosis and treatment.

References

Blass, J.P.: Disorders of pyruvate metabolism. Neurology 29:280, 1979.

Blass, J.P.: Pyruvate dehydrogenase deficiencies. *In* Burman, D., Holton, J.B., and Pennock, C.A. (eds.): Inherited Disorders of Carbohydrate Metabolism. MTP Press, Lancaster, England, 1980, p. 239.

Blass, J.P.: Inborn errors of pyruvate metabolism. *In* Stanbury, J.B., Wyngaarden, J.B., Fredrickson, D.S., et al. (eds.): The Metabolic Basis of Inherited Disease. 5th Ed. McGraw-Hill, New York, 1983, p. 193.

Bleile, D.M., Hackert, M.L., Pettit, F.H., and Reed, L.J.: Subunit structure of dihydrolipoyl transacetylase component of pyruvate dehydrogenase complex from bovine heart. J. Biol. Chem. 256:514, 1981.

Cohen, R.D., and Woods, H.F.: Clinical and Biochemical Aspects of Lactic Acidosis. Blackwell, London, 1976.

Denton, R.M., and Halestrap, A.P.: Regulation of pyruvate metabolism in mammalian tissues. Essays in Biochemistry 15:37, 1979.

DeVivo, D.C., Haymond, M.W., Obert, K.A., et al.: Defective activation of the pyruvate dehydrogenase complex in subacute necrotizing encephalomyelopathy (Leigh disease). Ann. Neurol. 6:483, 1979.

Hochachka, P.W.: Living Without Oxygen. Harvard University Press, Cambridge, Mass., 1980.

Kreisberg, R.A.: Lactate homeostasis and lactic acidosis. Ann. Intern. Med. 92:227, 1980.

Oh, M.S., Phelps, K.R., Traube, M., et al.: D-lactic acidosis in a man with the short-bowel syndrome. N. Engl. J. Med. 301:249, 1979.

Park, R., and Arieff, A.I.: Lactic acidosis. Adv. Intern. Med. 25:33, 1980.

Plaitakis, A., Whetsell, W.O., Cooper, J.R., and Yahr, M.D.: Chronic Leigh disease: A genetic and biochemical study. Ann. Neurol. 7:304, 1980.

Robinson, B.H., and Sherwood, W.G.: Pyruvate dehydrogenase phosphatase deficiency: A cause of congenital chronic lactic acidosis in infancy. Pediatr. Res. 9:935, 1979.

Robinson, B.H., Taylor, J., Kahler, S.G., and Kirkman, H.N.: Lactic acidemia, neurologic deterioration and carbohydrate dependence in a girl with dihydrolipoyl dehydrogenase deficiency. Eur. J. Pediatr. 136:35, 1981.

Robinson, B.H., Taylor, J., and Sherwood, W.G.: The genetic heterogeneity of lactic acidosis: Occurrence of recognizable inborn errors of metabolism in a pediatric population with lactic acidoses. Pediatr. Res. 14:956, 1980.

Tanaka, K., and Rosenberg, L.E.: Metabolism of amino acids and organic acids. *In* Freinkel, N. (ed.): Contemporary Metabolism, Vol. 1. Plenum Press, New York, 1979, p. 461.

30

Lipidoses

The brain is a lipid-rich organ; in fact, myelin has the highest concentration of lipid of any normal tissue except adipose tissue. Brain substance is composed of cholesterol, sphingolipids, and glycerophospholipids. Gray and white matter vary both in concentration and distribution of the various lipids, white matter being predominantly myelin. On the basis of wet weight, there is almost three times as much lipid in white matter as in gray matter. Gangliosides are characteristically found in the gray matter, whereas white matter is richer in galactolipids and relatively poor in phospholipids.

During myelination of the central nervous system substantial changes occur in gray and white matter composition. An elevation in the galactocerebroside concentration, an important constituent of nerve sheath, is seen with increased myelination. Elevation in the concentration of gangliosides in the nerve cell membrane is proportional to the increased arborization of the axons and dendrites that occurs as the nervous system achieves its mature form.

Sphingolipids, as components of various membranes, are found in almost all tissues of the body. Their structure is based upon a C_{18} long-chain amino alcohol called sphingosine (Fig. 30–1), to which other components are added through the amino or hydroxyl groups. A long-chain fatty acid joined by an amide bond to the nitrogen atom of C_2 of sphingosine is called a ceramide. It is a hydrophobic lipid moiety. Hydrophilic groups can be introduced into the ceramide through the C_1 alcohol, thereby modifying the properties of the membrane component. For example, substitution of a hydrophilic hexose such as glucose or galactose to the ceramide produces a cerebroside, whereas substitution of phosphocholine produces a sphingolipid called sphingomyelin. Galactocerebroside and a sulfated derivative, cerebroside sulfatide, are the main glycolipid constituents of myelin.

The gangliosides are acidic glycosphingolipids containing neuraminic acid (sialic acid). They are polyanionic compounds (negatively charged). They abound in the neurons of the CNS and have been shown to play a role in the cell membrane receptor for cholera toxin, thyrotropin, and serotonin. The predominant gangliosides of the brain share a common carbohydrate component attached to the ceramide moiety, namely, glucose-galactose-N-acetyl-galactosamine-galactose. This tetrahexosyl pattern is designated "1" and further nomenclature is derived as follows: G-ganglioside, M-monosialo, 1-tetrahexosyl, GD_1-ganglioside disialo, and so on. GM_2, the ganglioside that accumulates in Tay-Sachs disease, has three hexosyl groups and is termed 2. Extraneural ganglioside in erythrocytes is in the form of hematoside [GM_3], which contains a sialic acid and lignocerate as the major fatty acid. Table 30–1 (a guide to the sphingolipids) demonstrates the composition and nomenclature of these neural lipids.

LYSOSOMAL FUNCTION

Lysosomes are a class of subcellular organelles, widely distributed among cell types, that contain an array of acid hydrolases. These enzymes function to degrade intracellular and extracellular polymers—proteins, polysaccharides, complex lipids, and nucleic acids—into their simple precursors. Material to be degraded within the lysosome gains entrance in a roundabout fashion, since the lysosomal membrane is impermeable to molecules with a molecular weight above 200. Cellular components destined to be broken down, as well as foreign material taken up through phagocytosis, are encapsulated in vacuoles that may then fuse with the lysosome. By virtue of the sequential

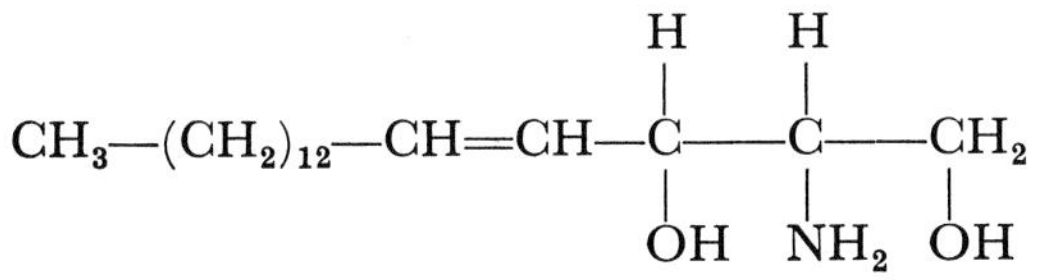

$$CH_3-(CH_2)_{12}-CH=CH-\underset{\underset{\displaystyle OH}{|}}{\overset{\overset{\displaystyle H}{|}}{C}}-\underset{\underset{\displaystyle NH_2}{|}}{\overset{\overset{\displaystyle H}{|}}{C}}-CH_2$$
$$|$$
$$OH$$

Sphingosine

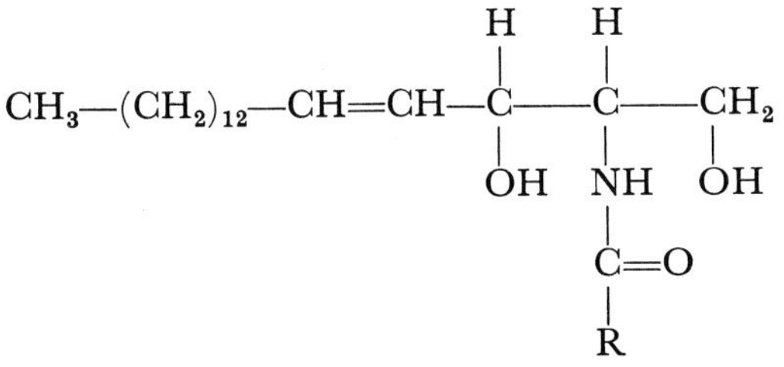

$$CH_3-(CH_2)_{12}-CH=CH-\underset{\underset{\displaystyle OH}{|}}{\overset{\overset{\displaystyle H}{|}}{C}}-\underset{\underset{\displaystyle NH}{|}}{\overset{\overset{\displaystyle H}{|}}{C}}-CH_2$$

Ceramide

$$CH_3-(CH_2)_{12}-CH=CH-C-C-CH_2-O-P-O-CH_2-CH_2-N^+-(CH_3)_3$$

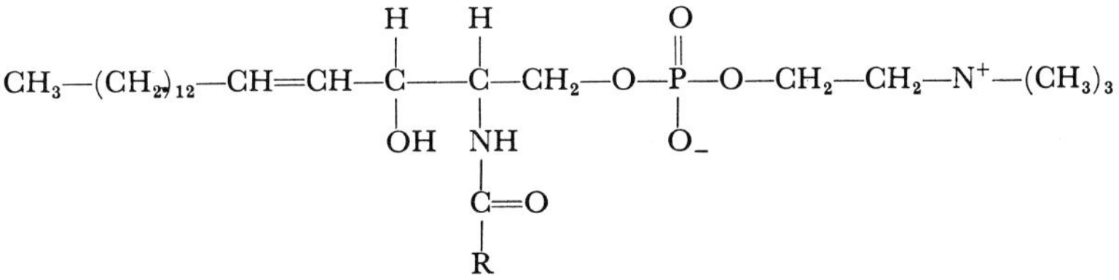

Sphingomyelin

Figure 30–1 Structures of various sphingolipids. (From Mason, E.J.: Physiological Chemistry of Lipids in Mammals. Philadelphia, W.B. Saunders Co., 1968.)

Table 30–1 A GUIDE TO THE SPHINGOLIPIDS

Sphingosine: C_{18} amino diol with one unsaturated bond

Ceramide: Sphingosine acylated with long chain fatty acids (C_{14}–C_{26}; C_{18} predominates; hydroxy acids found)

Cerebrosides:
  Galactocerebroside: Cer-Gal
  Glucocerebroside: Cer-Glc

Sulfatide: Cer-Gal-3-sulfate

Ceramide Oligosaccharides (2–4 hexoses):
  Globoside: Cer-Glc-Gal-Gal-GalNAc
  Trihexoside: Cer-Glc-Gal-Gal

Gangliosides

Cer-Glc-Gal-GalNAc-Gal
        |
     NANA
	GM$_1$	monosialotetrahexosylceramide

Cer-Glc-Gal-GalNAc-Gal
       | |
    NANA   NANA
	GD$_{1a}$	disialotetrahexosylceramide

Cer-Glc-Gal-GalNAc-Gal
        |
     NANA
     |
     NANA
	GD$_{1b}$	disialotetrahexosylceramide

Cer-Glc-Gal-GalNAc
       |
    NANA
	GM$_2$ (Tay-Sachs ganglioside)	monosialotrihexosylceramide

Abbreviations: Cer = ceramide; Gal = galactose; Glc = glucose; GalNAc = N-acetylgalactosamine; NANA = N-acetylneuraminic acid; G = Ganglioside; M = monosialo; D = disialo-; 1 = tetrahexosyl; 2 = trihexosyl; 3 = dihexosyl.

breakdown of these oligomers and polymers, the small molecular constituents pass into the cytoplasm where they may be reutilized by the cell.

In many of the neurodegenerative disorders there is a defect in the catabolism of a particular lipid as a result of defective or absent enzymatic activity of a specific lysosomal hydrolase (Fig. 30–2). Accumulation of abnormal amounts of partially degraded, normally occurring material, because of the enzyme defect, results in lipid storage, which causes brain dysfunction. The true proximate cause of the brain dysfunction in such circumstances is enigmatic, but it may involve anatomical and functional disruption of the normal three-dimensional brain organization (see below). To date, there are almost a dozen discrete disorders of sphingolipid metabolism identified that result in specific neurodegenerative diseases as a result of impaired catabolism.

A number of these lysosomal hydrolases manifest specificity for a particular functional group and specific configuration of (α versus β); hence, they function in a sequential fashion to degrade polymers containing these bonds. Examples of such polymers include glycosphingolipids, glycos-

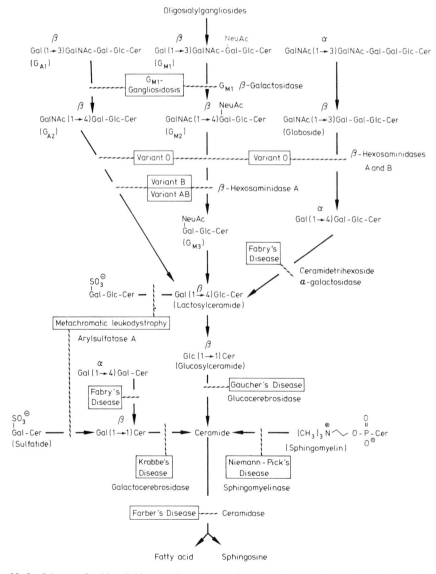

Figure 30–2 Scheme of sphingolipid catabolism. Enzymatic defects of major diseases are denoted. (From Sandhoff, K., and Christomanou, H.: Biochemistry and genetics of gangliosidoses. Human Genetics 50:107, 1979.)

aminoglycans, and glycoproteins. It should be clear that such a wide range of hydrolytic activity (glycosidases, lipases, amidases, sulfatases, neuraminidases) underscores a relative specificity for the bond and neighboring constituents, with limited selectivity for the rest of the molecule. If the normal process of breakdown to component building blocks is impeded, the undegraded material will accumulate, engendering the formation of storage bodies. Eventually these entities engorge the cell and, in an as yet unknown manner, cause cell death.

Internalization of Acid Hydrolases into the Lysosome

If, as discussed in Chapter 2, protein synthesis occurs in the endoplasmic reticulum (E/R), we then have to explain how the acid hydrolases find their way into the lysosome. This problem has practical (clinical) import. In the first place, failure of incorporation of these hydrolases into lysosomes appears to account for I-cell disease (see below), with the consequent accumulation of several different cell constituents. Moreover, were such enzymes to remain free in the cytosol, they could cause damage to cellular constituents.

As presently conceived all glycoprotein enzymes destined for export from the cell, or into the lysosome, bear "signal" saccharide sequences that contain the recognition information for export from the cell. Lysosomal hydrolases have, in addition, phosphomannosyl residues that serve as a definitive signal that directs these enzymes into the lysosome. When this sequence is not added on to the enzyme in a post-translational modification step, they are secreted extracellularly instead. In this fashion the genetic code directs the ultimate destination of the synthesized protein as well as its structure.

Pathogenesis of Mental Dysfunction in Lysosomal Storage Diseases

Two general consequences of accumulation of undegraded cell constituents appear to bear upon the pathogenesis of mental dysfunction in the lysosomal storage diseases. Cell dysfunction and cell death occur at some point when storage exceeds a critical threshold. While the threshold has not been quantified, it must relate to the disruption of organization of cellular components as well as possible toxic effects of some of the "detergent-like" materials that accumulate.

An additional factor in the mental dysfunction relates to distortion of the intricately laid out neuronal geometry that must be fundamental to the myriad connections that underlie the integrated (orchestrated) development and functioning of the nervous system. Abnormal, very large neuronal processes termed meganeurites form as a response to accumulation of undigested cell constituents in neurons. These meganeurites are often larger than the parent cell body and with their multiple spines ramify in a haphazard fashion, forming aberrant contacts with other neurons, dendrites, and meganeurites. In this way they have a profoundly deleterious effect on the normal "wiring diagram" of the brain and the integrated firing of synapses. Apparently this elaboration of haphazardly oriented dendrites occurs subsequent to normal synaptogenesis as a consequence of lysosomal storage.

A Note on Therapy

While replacement therapy with purified enzyme or enzyme encapsulated in liposomes is being attempted in various centers, thus far results have not been very encouraging from a clinical point of view. Because of the lack of definitive therapy for these devastating neurodegenerative disorders great sensitivity is called for on the part of the physician in dealing with parents of the affected child. It has been said that such a child dies three times: in the minds of the parents when the diagnosis is made, when and if the child is institutionalized, and finally when the child in fact succumbs. The family should be given the benefit of on-going psychiatric support throughout the child's course and beyond if necessary. The devastating effects on a marriage, of rapid deterioration

Table 30–2 CLINICAL MANIFESTATIONS OF THE GM₁
GANGLIOSIDOSES

	Infantile	Late Infantile
Onset	birth	7 months
Death	1½ to 2 years	3 to 10 years
Hepatomegaly	+	−
Splenomegaly	+	−
Macrocephaly	+	−
Facies	coarse	normal
Macula	cherry-red (50%)	normal
Early Neurological Findings	poor suck, weak cry, lethargy, exaggerated startle	ataxia, dysarthria
Deafness	late	NI
Blindness	early	late
Tone	↓ (late ↑)	↓ (late ↑)
DTR's	↑	↑
Brain Stem	preterminal	NI
Seizures	late	late
Acousticomotor Response	+	+
Marrow	foam cells	foam cells
X-ray (bones)	MPS-like	minimal Δ's
CSF Protein	normal	normal
Urine	MPS+, foam cells	variable MPS-uria
Nerve Conduction	normal	normal

+ = present; − = absent; NI = no information.

and inevitable death in a previously normal baby cannot be over-emphasized. To ignore them is to deny the family the only effective means of therapy yet available in a number of these diseases.

LIPID STORAGE DISEASES

Generalized Gangliosidosis*

Clinical Features

Neglecting forms of intermediate severity, there are two general modes of clinical presentation of generalized gangliosidosis (Table 30–2). Signs and symptoms of infantile GM₁ gangliosidosis may be noted shortly after birth because of neurological and visceral manifestations. Psychomotor delay is noted from birth with hypotonicity and poor suck, weak cry, and poor appetite. The infant is hypoactive and consequently may be perceived by his parents to be a "good baby" because he is not irritable, cries infrequently, and sleeps a great deal of the time. Hepatic and splenic enlargement account for the visceromegaly. These infants manifest early onset (often at birth but in any event no later than 6 months of age) of tissue involvement similar to that seen with mucopolysaccharidoses: dysmorphic features, frontal bossing, increased distance between nose and upper lip, gingival hypertrophy, macroglossia, and facial edema. By 8 to 9 months of age, the child is unable to sit or crawl, movements are uncoordinated, and nystagmus may develop. The previously hypotonic infant now manifests brisk reflexes and spasticity with flexion contractures of the joints. Dorsolumbar kyphoscoliosis is quite common. The fingers are short and stubby. Tonic clonic seizures develop later. By 12 months of age, the child may become deaf and dysphagic. Decerebrate posturing is noted terminally.

The bone marrow demonstrates *foam cells* or vacuolated lymphocytes. Foam cells are also found in the lungs, which may account for the repeated bouts of pneumonia typical of this disease. Cherry-red spots are noted in approximately 50 percent of the patients with infantile GM₁ gangliosidosis.

---

*Prepared by Harold Finkel.

X-rays demonstrate bony changes in the vertebral column and sella turcica. Mucopolysacchariduria, although present, is not as great as in the mucopolysaccharidoses.

Pathologically there is ventricular dilation and atrophy of the brain due to neuronal loss. Glycolipid accumulates in the brain: 90 percent as GM_1 ganglioside and 1 to 2 percent as asialo GM_1. Mucopolysaccharides are abundant in the visceral tissues as well.

Differential diagnosis of the infantile form of GM_1 gangliosidosis includes Hurler's syndrome, Niemann-Pick disease, I-cell disease, and the other mucolipidoses. Onset is earlier with GM_1 than with Hurler's syndrome or Niemann-Pick disease, corneal clouding is usually absent, and bony and facial abnormalities are greater in GM_1 than in Niemann-Pick disease.

Juvenile-onset GM_1 gangliosidosis is distinguished by the lack of visceral involvement and minimal or absent bony abnormalities. The onset is generally late in the first year of life and death occurs from 3 to 10 years of age. The child presents with rapid developmental regression; ataxia and dysarthria develop. The initially hypotonic child quickly develops spastic quadriparesis. Seizures are prominent and difficult to control.

Differential diagnosis includes metachromatic leukodystrophy and juvenile GM_2 gangliosidosis. Clinical differentiation may not be easy, and enzymatic studies are necessary for a definitive diagnosis.

Biochemical Defects

Generalized (GM_1) gangliosidosis is an autosomal recessive disorder due to deficiency of β-galactosidase activity, which cleaves the terminal galactose from GM_1 ganglioside. Accumulation of the normal monosialoganglioside as well as a small increase in the asialo derivative results. In addition there is accumulation of keratan sulfate-like mucopolysaccharide.

Owing to the defect of the β-galactosidase for GM_1 ganglioside there is significant accumulation of this lipid in gray matter and liver. The asialo form also accumulates in brain. A mucopolysaccharide similar to keratan sulfate is stored, and there is glycoprotein storage as well. Presumably this enzyme is involved in the catabolism of a number of larger molecules containing β-galactosyl linkages, accounting for the variety of partially degraded molecules that are stored.

Tay-Sachs Disease*

Infantile GM_2 is known to have an ethnic predilection for Ashkenazi Jews and manifests a less variable picture clinically than is seen with any of the other lipidoses (Table 30–3). The affected child develops normally for the first 5 to 6 months, although an exaggerated startle response may be observed (a myoclonic jerk that the child develops when a noise of any intensity is made). The child acquires the ability to sit and crawl and may develop a social smile. By six months a relative hypotonia develops, and the child fails to walk. After 1 year of age there is a rapid and progressive deterioration. The child no longer sits or transfers objects, and weakness progresses to paralysis. Brisk reflexes develop, progressing to spasticity. By 18 months the child has severe visual impairment or central blindness, associated in 90 percent of patients with development of the classical cherry-red spot of the macula. This characteristic finding is due to storage of ganglioside in the cells around the macula and as a result the normal red color of the macula appears more intense in contrast with the pale background of the fundus. Death occurs in the second year.

A juvenile form of this disorder occurs in the non-Jewish population and has a slower progression. Classified as type III, it was first described by Bernheimer and Seitelberger, whose names are associated with the eponym. The onset is at 2 to 6 years and the chief presenting complaints are ataxia and dysarthria. Later, athetoid posturing of the extremities and spasticity develop, progressing to decerebrate rigidity. Blindness is noted to occur late in the disease and no cherry-red maculas

---

*Prepared by Harold Finkel.

Table 30–3 CLINICAL MANIFESTATIONS OF THE GM_2 GANGLIOSIDOSES

	Tay-Sachs Disease	Sandhoff's Disease	Juvenile (type III)
Onset	4–6 months	3–6 months	2–6 years
Death	2 years	11–40 months	5–15 years
Hepatomegaly	–	mild	–
Splenomegaly	–	–	–
Macrocephaly	late	+	–
Facies	doll-like	doll-like	normal
Macula	cherry-red (90%)	+/– cherry-red, optic atrophy	optic atrophy
Early Neurological Findings	exaggerated startle ←——— myoclonic jerk ———→ developmental plateau then regression		ataxia, dysarthria, athetoid posturing
Deafness	+	+	–
Blindness	early	+	+
Tone	late ↓	late ↓	+
DTR's	↑	↑	↑
Brain Stem	late	late	+
Seizures	late	late	+
Acousticomotor Response	+	+	+/–
Marrow	normal	normal	normal
X-ray (bones)	normal	normal	normal
CSF Protein	normal	normal	normal
Urine	normal	normal	normal
Nerve Conduction	normal	normal	normal
Ethnicity	Jewish	varied	varied

+ = present; – = absent.

have been observed. Death occurs at 5 to 15 years as a result of repeated pneumonic bouts due to aspiration.

GM_2 type II variant or Sandoffs disease presents in a clinically identical manner to GM_2 type I. There does not appear to be a Jewish heritage in type II. Neuronal swelling with concentric layers of cytoplasmic inclusion bodies are noted in both types I and II, but the asialoganglioside GM_2 of nervous tissue is found in higher concentrations in type II. In addition there is also an increased concentration of globoside, the glycosphingolipid of mesenchymal tissue, in the visceral organs; kidney storage of this substance on pathological examination is much more pronounced than in classical Tay-Sachs disease.

A rare form, termed the AB variant, has been associated with mental deterioration, seizures, and difficulties in walking, first manifesting at about 6 years of age. There are no visual or ocular findings.

Biochemical Defects

Inability to cleave the terminal N-acetyl-β-galactosamine residue from GM_2 ganglioside is the cause of the accumulation of this ganglioside in Tay-Sachs disease and its variant forms. The enzyme responsible for this hydrolytic reaction is a hexosaminidase and exists in two isoenzyme forms, A and B. In Tay-Sachs disease (type I) Hex A is deficient but Hex B is elevated, whereas in Sandhoff's disease (type II) both forms are deficient. Juvenile Tay-Sachs (type III) is apparently the result of a partial deficiency of Hcx A.

While some question remains as to the number of subunits composing isoenzymes A and B, it seems generally agreed upon that form A is composed of differing polypeptides, α and β, whereas form B is made up of identical β units only. Recently the AB variant has been ascribed to absence of an activator protein, which is essential as a surfactant, acting probably through formation of a mixed micelle composed of GM_2 ganglioside and activator protein.

Defective catabolism of the ganglioside results in storage in the brain and to a lesser extent in the viscera. Ballooning of the neuronal cytoplasm with GM$_2$ ganglioside in cytoplasmic membrane bodies develops throughout the nervous system, and central demyelination occurs. Astrocyte proliferation results and may account for the megalencephaly noted late in the disease. Normally GM$_2$ ganglioside is a trace constituent of brain tissue, but in Tay-Sachs disease it accounts for 6 to 12 per cent of brain dry weight. By an as yet undefined process acting on the accretion of normal brain constituents these brains suffer a striking decrease of cerebroside and sulfatide.

In Sandhoff's disease there is also a striking increase in GM$_2$ ganglioside, but in this variant the asialo derivative is greatly increased as well. Liver, kidney, and spleen also evidence accumulation of the lipid globoside, which is a constituent of erythrocyte and kidney membrane.

Niemann-Pick Disease*

Clinical Features

There are at least four clinical variants of Niemann-Pick disease (Table 30–4), but absence of sphingomyelinase has been defined only in two. Infantile or type A presents by 3 months of age with difficulty in feeding, failure to thrive, and neurological deterioration. Enlargement of the liver precedes splenic involvement in contrast to Gaucher's disease, although this is not sufficiently invariant to be diagnostic by itself. The skin develops a yellow hue as a result of defective catabolism of a chromogenic analogue of sphingomyelin. Bone changes are noted, but they are not as severe as in Gaucher's disease. There is widening of the medullary cavity and thinning of the cortex. Severe malnutrition resulting in a cachetic habitus is the norm for this disease.

Neurological deterioration occurs usually as hypotonia, listlessness, loss of developmental milestones, and failure to attain new motor skills. These infants are apathetic, often with a protruding tongue reminiscent of Down's syndrome or hypothyroidism. Loss of auditory acuity early on contrasts with the "acoustic-motor-startle" reflex characteristic of Tay-Sachs disease. Cherry-red

Table 30–4 CLINICAL MANIFESTATIONS OF THE NIEMANN-PICK VARIANTS

	A Acute Infantile	B Visceral	C Mixed	D Nova-Scotia
Onset	early infancy (insidious)	variable	4–20 years	childhood
Death	2–3 years	normal life span	childhood	12–20 years
Hepatomegaly	2+	+	+/−	+/−
Splenomegaly	+	+	+/−	+/−
Macrocephaly	−	−	−	−
Facies	frontal bossing	−	−	−
Macula	cherry-red (50%)	−	−	−
Early Neurological Findings	difficulty feeding, apathy	−	jaundice, poor coordination, tremor, personality Δ's, intellectual regression	intellectual regression
Deafness	+	−	−	−
Blindness	+	−	−	−
Tone	↓	normal	↓ early, spasticity (late)	↓ early
DTR's	↑	normal	↑	↑
Seizures	uncommon	−	+	+
Acousticomotor Response	−	−	−	−
Marrow	N-P foam cells	−	foam cells	foam cells
X-ray (bones)	demineralization	−	NI	NI
CSF Protein	normal	normal	normal	normal

+ = present; − = absent; NI = no information.

*Prepared by Harold Finkel.

spots occur in approximately 50 per cent. Blindness is progressive but is unassociated with optic atrophy. Progressive retardation with loss of environmental contact and diminished hearing may occur late in the disease. Seizures are unusual.

Vacuolated lymphocytes on peripheral blood smear are a very helpful diagnostic finding, especially in conjunction with Niemann-Pick foam cells (15 to 19 μ in diameter) found in bone marrow aspirates and liver biopsy.

Atrophy of the brain, with diminished gray matter volume and patchy areas of demyelination, is found. Microscopically there is neuronal distention with lipid material and displacement of the nucleus. Cerebellar atrophy is also found.

Form B is a chronic disorder free of neurological involvement. Splenomegaly usually becomes apparent between 2 and 6 years of age, with hepatomegaly and pulmonary involvement occurring later on.

Type C is of later onset, with neurovisceral involvement heralded by hepatosplenomegaly. Neurological abnormalities develop after visceral involvement. Hypotonia with brisk DTR's may be the initial finding; later on spasticity is noted. Intention tremor, dyssynergia along with extensor plantar response, and extrapyramidal signs develop later in the course. Progressive signs of dementia are noted. Type D is similar to C but is confined to individuals of Nova Scotian extraction; it is not clear that they are different diseases. Myoclonic seizures are common.

Biochemical Defects

A defect in the lysosomal hydrolase sphingomyelinase has been demonstrated in types A and B. The enzyme cleaves the bond linking phosphorylcholine through the C_1 of ceramide. Sphingomyelin is found in plasma membranes, endoplasmic reticulum, and mitochondria. In addition it is a component of myelin nerve sheaths. The enzyme activity in the classic infantile form of Niemann-Pick disease is less than 7 per cent of normal and in the type B, 15 to 18 per cent of control. While sphingomyelin levels in spleen in types C and D are three to four times normal, enzyme assays of sphingomyelinase have failed to reveal a decrease in activity. One possible explanation is that an in vivo factor is required that is not necessary in the in vitro assay because of the use of detergents. Another is that types C and D are misclassified as Niemann-Pick disease variants.

Recently an animal model of type A has been described in Siamese cats. This should allow investigators to study the pathobiochemistry of this devastating lipidosis.

Gaucher's Disease*

Clinical Features

Deficiency of β-glucosidase activity results in accumulation of glucocerebroside, with deposition in the reticuloendothelial cells of liver, spleen, and bone marrow. This disease was described in 1882 by Gaucher; since then various forms of the defect have been described and clinical severity appears to depend upon the percentage of residual enzyme activity (Table 30–5). The infantile or type II form is the most devastating and begins with prominent neurovisceral involvement. Presentation is usually not until 3 to 4 months of age, but it occasionally occurs in the neonatal period or as late as into the second year. A feeble cry, poor suck, and absent Moro reflex with hepatosplenomegaly are noted initially. Dysphagia and strabismus develop, and the child maintains the head in a retroflexed position. By 9 months of age the child is quite spastic with hyperactive muscle stretch reflexes, clonus, and rigidity. Progressive loss of bulbar functions ensues, and the child usually succumbs as a result of repeated bouts of aspiration pneumonia.

In addition there is prominent visceral involvement. Splenomegaly and occasionally hepatomegaly develop as a result of accumulation of Gaucher cells in the reticuloendothelial system.

---

*Prepared by Harold Finkel.

Table 30–5 CLINICAL MANIFESTATIONS OF GAUCHER VARIANTS

	Infantile (Acute Neuronopathic)	Juvenile	Adult
Onset	<6 months	preteen	late child to adult
Death	2 years	about 2 years after onset of neurological signs	variable
Hepatomegaly	+	+	+
Splenomegaly	2+	+	2+
Macrocephaly	−	−	−
Facies	normal	normal	normal
Macula	normal	normal	normal, pinquecula
Early Neurological Findings	poor suck and swallow, weak cry, squint, regression of development	tremor, progressive dementia	non-neurological
Deafness	−	−	non-neurological
Blindness	−	−	non-neurological
Tone	↑ (late ↓)	variable	non-neurological
DTR's	↑	variable	non-neurological
Brain Stem	cranial nerve	cranial nerve	non-neurological
Seizures	late	early	non-neurological
Acousticomotor Response	−	−	non-neurological
Marrow	Gaucher cell	Gaucher cell	Gaucher cell
X-ray (bones)	Erlenmeyer flask	variable	Erlenmeyer flask/fractures
CSF Protein	normal	normal	normal
CBC	pancytopenia	normal	pancytopenia
Ethnicity	varied	varied	Ashkenazi Jews (50%)

+ = present; − = absent.

Marrow infiltration results in erosion of cortices in the long bones. Serum acid phosphatase activity is elevated and a secondary pancytopenia may result. The Gaucher cell is a result of the accumulation of glucocerebroside in the histiocyte. This accumulated substance causes the nucleus to be placed eccentrically; intracytoplasmically the accumulated material is reminiscent of wrinkled tissue paper or a meringue on a pie.

The most common lipid storage disease is the type I non-neuronopathic adult form of Gaucher disease. There is a predilection for Ashkenazi Jews, but this disease is not limited to this group. Onset is usually in childhood with hepatosplenomegaly, hypersplenism, and thrombocytopenia with a tendency to bleeding and anemia. Bone lesions are quite common and include fractures, widening of lower femur ("Erlenmeyer flasks"), and episodes of bone pain (often excruciating) that may last for days or weeks. The latter are probably due to encroachment on blood supply by expanding masses of lipid storage cells. Some patients suffer pulmonary and cardiac symptoms as well, secondary to infiltration with lipid-laden macrophages. Neurological manifestations are conspicuously absent.

A third variant (juvenile, type III) usually presents with splenomegaly, usually by the second year of life, and is followed by a silent period of three to seven years before overt neurological manifestations appear. Often the first neurological findings are quite subtle, e.g., persistent strabismus followed by development of myoclonic seizures. This form is the least common and fraught with the greatest variability in clinical expression; hence authoritative statements regarding mode of presentation and course are not possible.

Biochemical Defects

The glucocerebroside that accumulates in Gaucher's disease is of extraneural origin, since the predominant cerebroside in the brain is galactocerebroside. Sources are lactosylceramide from leukocytes, and globoside (cer-glu-gal-gal-NAcgal), the principal neutral glycolipid of the erythro-cytes. Gangliosides that have cer-gal linkages may also be sources of the glucocerebroside. Calculations by Kattlove et al. (1969) suggest that the much shorter life span of granulocytes vis-à-vis erythrocytes makes them the single major source of glycolipids that accumulate in Gaucher's disease. Patients with chronic myelogenous leukemia may also have Gaucher cells, presumably from glucocerebroside accumulation that exceeds catabolic capacity, as a result of increased leukocyte turnover.

At least 8 to 9 per cent glucocerebrosidase activity is required to prevent central nervous system dysfunction resulting from accumulation of the acidic glycolipid. Patients with infantile Gaucher's disease have less than 5 per cent of normal enzyme activity and patients with the adult form have levels that vary from 18 to 40 per cent of normal. The CNS histopathological examination demonstrates neuronal loss, with few Gaucher cells found in the areas of abnormality. This is in contrast to Tay-Sachs and Niemann-Pick diseases, in which neuronal cytoplasmic distention is prominent. Pathological changes are limited to the pyramidal and ganglionic layers in the cerebral cortex. The brainstem also shows depletion of the nerve cells with neuronophagia. The spinal cord demonstrates similar changes in the ventral horn, which accounts for the flaccidity apparent late in the clinical course of the disease. Characteristically, again in contrast to GM_1 and GM_2 gangliosidosis, myelin changes are not found.

Prenatal Diagnosis and Treatment

Prenatal diagnosis is possible on cultured amniotic fluid cells obtained in the second trimester. No therapy is available for the infantile neuronopathic form. Administration of purified glucocerebrosidase to patients with the adult form has resulted in decrease of lipid stored in liver. Whether such therapy or administration of enzyme encapsulated in liposomes will reverse the clinical manifestations is currently under investigation.

The adult form, with its severe bony involvement, will require the attention of orthopedic surgeons as well as other members of a team to minister to these often gravely incapacitated individuals.

Metachromatic Leukodystrophy*

Clinical Features

As with several of the lipid storage diseases a number of clinical variants have now been described, all apparently with the same enzyme involved (Table 30–6). In this case it is the sulfatase that cleaves the sulfate group from sulfatide (see below). The late infantile variant usually presents insidiously during the second year of life, with irritability and fretfulness. In a child who previously may have walked, difficulty in walking and standing are encountered. Thereafter, the pace of intellectual development begins to slow down, and the hypotonia gives way to a hypertonic state with increased DTR's. Cranial nerve involvement is manifested by oculomotor palsies, paucity of facial movements, and depressed gag reflex. Ataxia is prominent as is difficulty with speech. A gray coloration of the macula with a red center has been described; it is reminiscent of the cherry-red macula but is not as obvious. CSF protein is increased in this disorder, and conduction times on electromyography are prolonged. After a period, varying from 6 months to 2 years, the child exists in a state of extensor spasticity with frequent myoclonic seizures. Depending on the quality of care, this stage can persist for several years.

A juvenile form of metachromatic leukodystrophy presents with ataxia and intellectual deterioration between the ages of 5 and 20 years. Symptoms may be quite subtle. Indeed, school failure because of inattentiveness or emotional difficulties may be the cause of referral to the pediatrician. Difficulties in walking may also occur at this time or soon thereafter, coupled with the development of postural abnormalities and nystagmus. A third variant, the adult form (arbitrarily defined as

---

*Prepared by Harold Finkel.

Table 30–6 CLINICAL MANIFESTATIONS OF THE VARIANTS OF METACHROMATIC LEUKODYSTROPHY

	Infantile	Juvenile	Adult	Multiple Sulfatase
Onset	12–18 months	3–10 years	3rd decade	1–2 years
Death	2–4 years	5–12 years	4–5th decade	3–12 years
Hepatomegaly	–	–	–	+
Splenomegaly	–	–	–	+
Macrocephaly	–	–	–	+/–
Facies	–	–	–	coarsened
Macula	cherry-red, optic pallor	–	–	
Early Neurological Findings	loss of ability to walk, clumsy, nystagmus	difficulty walking, weakness, peripheral neuropathy	ataxia, dysarthria, dementia, schizophrenia	delayed development
Deafness	–	–	–	–
Blindness	–	–	–	–
Tone	late ↓	↓	↑	+
DTR's	↓/absent	↓	↑	
Brain Stem	late	+	+	
Seizures	late	+	late	+
Acousticomotor Response	+/–	–	–	–
Marrow	normal	normal	normal	inclusions (also in peripheral WBC's)
X-ray (bones)	normal	normal	normal	MPS-like
CSF Protein	↑	↑	normal	↑
Urine	metachromatic granules	metachromatic granules	metachromatic granules	MPSuria
Nerve Conduction	prolonged	prolonged	prolonged	prolonged

+ = present; – = absent.

commencing after age 21), presents with a picture similar to the juvenile but with a prominent psychotic component. Indeed, several adults with metachromatic leukodystrophy were first diagnosed as having a psychiatric disorder. Progression is much slower than with the infantile and juvenile forms.

Another form of sulfatase deficiency exists in which in addition to deficiency of lysosomal sulfatase A and B, there is also dysfunction of microsomal arylsulfatase C. As a result, there is accumulation of sulfates that occur as part of sphingolipids, glycosaminoglycans, and steroids. Patients have clinical onset at 1 to 2 years with symptoms and signs of both metachromatic leukodystrophy and the mucopolysaccharidoses, the latter being manifested by dysostosis multiplex and hepatosplenomegaly. Death occurs usually by the end of the first decade.

Biochemical Defects

Cerebral white matter is rich in certain asialo glycosphingolipids not found in significant quantities in other areas of the body. In particular, sulfatide and cerebroside have a major role in myelin structure and, presumably, function.

Catabolism of sulfatide to galactocerebroside requires the enzyme arylsulfatase A (cerebroside sulfatase). The accumulation of sulfatides occurs in metachromatic leukodystrophy, which derives its name from the ability of a particular sulfatide to act as a chromatrope, i.e., to induce a color change in staining properties of certain catonic dyes. Color of a longer wavelength than expected is transmitted because of this interaction. While sulfatide also accumulates in kidney, liver, and gall bladder, it does not appear to impair the function of these organs.

The loss of myelin occurs in oligodendrocytes of the central nervous system and loss of myelin sheath in the peripheral nervous system. How accumulation of sulfatide leads to disruption of the myelin sheath is at present an unanswered question. Granular and lamellar inclusions are found in

Table 30–7 Table 30–7   ENZYME DEFECTS IN MULTIPLE SULFATASE DEFICIENCY

Enzyme	Presumed Substrates	Inheritance
Arylsulfatase A (glycoprotein)	Galactosyl sulfatide Lactosyl sulfatide	Autosomal
Arylsulfatase B (glycoprotein)	UDP-N-acetylgalactosamine-4-sulfate in dermatan and heparatan sulfate	Autosomal
Arylsulfatase C (lipoprotein)	Steroid sulfates	Autosomal
Iduronate sulfate sulfatase (Hunter)	DS, HS	X-linked
Sulfamidase (San Filippo)	HS	Autosomal
N-Ac galactosamine-6-sulfate sulfatase (Morquio)	KS,C6S	Autosomal
N-Ac glucosamine-6-sulfate sulfatase (MPS VIII)	HS:KS	Autosomal

the Schwann glial and neuronal cells. Metachromatic granules accumulate within kidney tubules, and sulfatides are greatly increased in urine.

The biochemical derangements in multiple sulfatase deficiency are confusing, since the enzymes shown to be deficient (Table 30–7) are located either on the autosomes or on the X-chromosomes. A ready explanation for such a widespread genetic and biochemical defect is not forthcoming presently.

Krabbe's Disease*

Clinical Features

Absence of galactosylceramide β-galactosidase appears to be responsible for Krabbe's disease, a leukodystrophy characterized by symptoms of central demyelination (Table 30–8). Clinical presentation occurs early in the first year (mean age 4 months), usually with irritability and hypertonicity, and rapidly thereafter developmental retardation ensues. Reflective of white matter involvement, long-tract signs include spastic quadriparesis, brisk DTR's, and a positive Babinski sign. Later optic atrophy with blindness, myoclonic jerks, and acousticomotor hyperresponsiveness, similar to that of Tay-Sachs disease, is present. Poikilothermia is a notable and not uncommon finding. Preterminally severe mental impairment is found with the hypertonicity giving way to hypotonicity manifested by flaccid quadriparesis and decreased DTR's. Death occurs from 3 months to 2½ years. There is some evidence of a peripheral neuropathy, but this is not as prominent as in metachromatic leukodystrophy.

The white matter demonstrates large amounts of globoid histiocytes (macrophages) in areas of demyelination about small blood vessels. There is a decreased number of oligodendroglial cells with concomitant gliosis. Peripheral nerve undergoes axonal degeneration with accumulation of foamy histiocytes. Cerebrospinal fluid protein content is elevated as a result of peripheral demyelination; this points to a leukodystrophy.

Biochemical Defects

Discussion of pathogenesis in this disease must explain the lack of galactocerebroside build-up despite the absence of the enzyme required for its degradation. Psychosine (galactosyl sphingosine) does accumulate in the brains of these patients (10 to 100 times normal), and there is evidence that this compound exerts a toxic effect on oligodendroglial cells, the cells that elaborate the myelin sheath. Such a proposition could explain the destruction and absence of myelin in the brain of patients with this disease, through a cytotoxic effect as well as an inhibition of the formation of galactosylceramide.

---

*Prepared by Harold Finkel.

Table 30–8 CLINICAL MANIFESTATIONS OF KRABBE VARIANT

	Infantile	Late Infantile
Onset	4–6 months	2–5 years
Death	7 months–3 years	3–8 years
Hepatomegaly	–	–
Splenomegaly	–	–
Macrocephaly	–	–
Facies	normal	normal
Macula	optic atrophy	
Early Neurological Findings	irritability, constant crying, general-ized paresis, loss of motor skills	hemiparesis, spastic diplegia
Deafness	–	–
Blindness	+/–	+
Tone	spasticity ↑, late flaccid	↑
DTR's	depends on stage	depends on stage
Brain Stem	pseudobulbar (breathing, swal-lowing)	bulbar
Seizures	+	+
Acousticomotor Response	+	
Marrow	normal	normal
X-ray (bones)	normal	normal
CSF Protein	↑	normal/↑
Urine	renal epithelial cells	–
Nerve Conduction	prolonged	normal

+ = present; – = absent.

Diagnosis

Definitive diagnosis requires assay of the enzyme in white blood cells or cultured fibroblasts. Elevation of protein in the cerebrospinal fluid and abnormal electromyography may be suggestive, but no clinical findings or ancillary tests are sufficiently diagnostic to obviate the need for enzymatic studies.

Prenatal Diagnosis and Therapy

While no therapy is available, prenatal diagnosis and genetic counseling can be offered to parents.

Fabry's Disease

Clinical Features

Fabry's disease, which is the result of deficiency of α-galactosidase A, differs from the other sphingolipidoses in several ways: first, inheritance is X-linked recessive; second, renal rather than neurological involvement is the preponderant clinical manifestation; and third, storage is predominantly in vascular endothelium.

The hemizygote male is affected by a debilitating array of symptoms and signs as a consequence of glycolipid accumulation. Onset of symptoms is usually in childhood or adolescence with so-called "Fabry crises" characterized by excruciating burning pain in palms and soles. As the disease progresses, this pain may become unbearable for some of those afflicted. Abdominal pain may also occur, further complicating the diagnostic possibilities.

The classical skin lesions of this disorder, the angiokeratomas, may present in childhood. They are usually distributed symmetrically and are found over the hips, thighs, back, buttocks, and genitals. Mucosal involvement occurs as well.

As lipid accumulation increases with increasing age, deposition in the cardiovascular system and kidneys becomes the major cause of disability. Symptoms include angina, myocardial infarction, and valvular lesions. Renal involvement is manifested by proteinuria, worsening function eventuating in uremia by middle age. Hypertension is probably on a renal basis and exacerbates the cardiac findings as well as contributing to the vascular abnormalities in the central nervous system. Cerebral manifestations include thrombosis and occasionally hemorrhage, seizures, hemiplegia, aphasia, and even frank psychosis. Corneal opacities may be observed.

Heterozygous females are usually mildly affected but may be as severely affected as the hemizygous male (see Chapter 2).

The deficiency of α-galactosidase A leads to the accumulation of Gal-Gal-Glc-Cer, Gal-Gal-Cer, and blood group B substances in the tissues affected.

Treatment and Prenatal Diagnosis

Episodes of pain have responded to therapy with diphenylhydantoin and carbamazepine. Renal transplantation has been effective in preventing the demise through kidney failure and in a few patients has also provided a means to catabolize accumulated glycolipid. The biochemical results are by no means universal. Therapy with purified enzyme is being attempted, and while results are encouraging, the infused enzyme has a short half-life.

Prenatal diagnosis has been accomplished and must for the present remain the mainstay of any therapy the physician can offer a family with an affected member.

Farber's Lipogranulomatosis

This rare disorder is the result of absence of the lysosomal enzyme ceramidase, which hydrolyzes the fatty acid attached to the sphingosine backbone of glycosphingolipids. Clinical expression varies from mildly affected individuals to severely affected patients who manifest signs and symptoms beginning at 3 to 4 months of age. These latter unfortunate souls suffer painful joint swelling with nodule formation, hoarseness and noisy respiration, failure to thrive, and intermittent fever. Growth disturbances may be exacerbated by swallowing and respiratory difficulties caused by epiglottic and laryngeal granulomas. As the disease progresses flexion contractures develop at the knees, wrists, and fingers. Mental impairment is inconstant, and peripheral nerve involvement is frequent. Seizures are not associated with this disorder. Ocular findings similar to those of metachromatic leukodystrophy have been reported, i.e., grayish opacification of retina surrounding the foveola. Dysphagia, vomiting, and recurrent pneumonitis punctuate the worsening course, with pulmonary deterioration the terminal event, usually by age two.

Ceramide accumulates in subcutaneous nodules, kidney (10-fold normal), and liver (60-fold normal). Pathological examination of a subcutaneous nodule reveals the presence of PAS-positive material extractable with lipid solvents. These findings will distinguish these nodules from those seen in rheumatoid arthritis, the major condition to be differentiated from Farber's lipogranulomatosis. Thin-layer chromatographic procedures can isolate ceramide extracted from such nodules, and quantitation has been accomplished by estimation of the sphingosine content. High-pressure liquid chromatography and GC-mass spectrometry have also been employed.

This enzyme can be assayed in cultured skin fibroblasts and white cells, with the latter being the diagnostic method of choice.

At present there is no specific therapy.

Refsum's Disease (Phytanic Acid α-Hydroxylase)

Refsum's disease is caused by deficiency of phytanic acid α-hydroxylase and is one of the heredoataxic syndromes. The most characteristic findings are cerebellar ataxia, peripheral neuropathy, retinitis pigmentosa with night blindness, and elevated CSF protein. Most patients present by age 20, but the time of onset is variable. Other findings include nerve deafness, ichthyotic changes of palms and soles and occasionally of the trunk.

Phytanic acid is a 20-carbon acid whose source is entirely from ingested greens containing the chlorophyll molecule. The defect is the absence of the enzyme phytanic acid α-hydroxylase that carries out the first step in the catabolism of phytanic acid. Diagnosis can be made by fatty acid quantitation in serum with gas chromatography; phytanic acid will account for as much as 30 per cent of the fatty acids there. Normally, only trace amounts are encountered.

Elimination of phytanate from the diet is effective in reducing serum and tissue levels. Some neurological manifestations improve (peripheral neuropathy), but cranial nerve functions apparently do not. Obviously the earlier dietary therapy is begun, especially before significant demyelination has occurred, the more likely are clinical abnormalities to be reversed. Plasmaphoresis has also been utilized to diminish phytanate levels acutely.

Wolman's Disease (Acid Cholesteryl Ester Hydrolase Deficiency)

Wolman's disease is due to the absence of the lysosomal acid lipase that catalyzes the degradation of cholesteryl esters and glycerides. Symptoms begin early in life and include pernicious vomiting and abdominal distension, failure to thrive, anemia, and steatorrhea. Moderate to marked hepatosplenomegaly appearing in the neonatal period is almost universal. Adrenal calcification, evident on X-ray is virtually pathognomonic of this disorder. Neurological symptoms seem to be limited to a decrease in spontaneous activity, there being a paucity of abnormal neurological signs. The downhill course, characterized by increasing vomiting and diarrhea, ends in the death of the infant usually before 6 months of age.

An allelic defect, of a milder nature, is the cause of the cholesteryl ester storage disease, which is compatible with survival to adulthood. While lipid deposition and hypercholesterolemia occur, atherosclerosis is not invariant; some patients manifest hepatosplenomegaly only. Thus, this disease should be part of the differential diagnosis of glycogen storage disease. Adrenal calcification is not usual.

Neither disorder manifests routine laboratory findings to a specific nature. Diagnosis requires assay of the enzyme in leukocytes or cultured skin fibroblasts. There is no therapy available.

Mucolipidoses

As the name implies these disorders are defects in the catabolism of mucopolysaccharidoses and sphingolipidoses. It follows then that signs and symptoms would include those associated with both classes of disorders, i.e., visceromegaly, coarsened features, mental retardation, and neurological deterioration. Mucopolysacchariduria is not a feature of these disorders, but in some oligosacchariduria is prominent.

Mucolipidosis I

Mild coarsening of features and minimal to moderate mental retardation with delay in motor development are associated with visceromegaly and dysostosis multiplex. A cherry-red macula spot has been described. Several patients have had myoclonic seizures. Absence of neuraminidase (sialidase) has been described in several of these patients.

Mucolipidosis II (*I-Cell Disease*)

This disorder and mucolipidosis III are unusual in that there is a deficiency of multiple lysosomal enzymes needed to degrade mucopolysaccharides and mucolipids associated with a marked elevation of these enzymes in blood. The designation I-cell derives from the inclusions seen on electron microscopy in cultured fibroblasts. I-cell disease is reminiscent clinically and radiologically of Hurler's syndrome but is distinguished by its presentation at birth with hepatomegaly, coarsened facial features, gingival hyperplasia, and bone changes. Corneal clouding is minimal, and mucopolysacchariduria may be absent. The clinical course is one of deterioration, with death by age 2.

Mucolipidosis III

This mucolipidosis does not manifest clinically until age 2 to 4 years when stiffness in hands and shoulders suggests juvenile rheumatoid arthritis. However, there is no inflammation. The claw-hand deformity so characteristic of this class of disorders is present by age 6 to 8 years. A decrease in stature and mild coarsening of facial features are also present. Mental dysfunction may be mild. Skeletal X-rays show evidence of dysostosis multiplex, but urine shows no mucopolysacchariduria. Assay of several lysosomal hydrolases in serum will make the presumptive diagnosis.

Biochemical Defects

These two disorders show marked elevation of lysosomal hydrolases in body fluids (diagnostic) and a partial deficiency of these enzymes in fibroblasts. In consequence of these abnormalities the catabolism of mucopolysaccharides, glycolipids, and glycoproteins is deranged. Why these enzymes are not located within the lysosomes is at present unknown, but it has been speculated that these enzymes may lack the phosphomannosyl traffic signal groups added after protein synthesis (posttranslational modification), which are required to direct uptake of the enzyme into the lysosome (see page 307).

Mucolipidosis IV

The first sign of this disorder is corneal clouding, often detected in the neonate. It differs from the other mucolipidoses by the absence of facial coarsening, dysostosis multiplex, and visceromegaly. Mental retardation is moderate to severe. Recently it has been shown that a soluble form of ganglioside neuraminidase was defective in one patient studied. It remains to be seen whether this is a primary or secondary abnormality.

Fucosidosis

This defect in lysosomal α-L-fucosidase affects the degradation of fucose-containing glycolipids, glycoproteins, and glycosaminoglycans. Thus far two different phenotypes have been described—an infantile form exhibiting findings associated with the mucopolysaccharidoses and a juvenile form akin to Fabry's disease.

The infantile form is characterized by progressive deterioration of mental and motor function associated with thickened skin and elevated sweat sodium and chloride (in the range encountered with cystic fibrosis).

Individuals with the juvenile variant are less retarded and have normal sweat electrolytes but manifest angiokeratoma corporis diffusum, a finding more commonly associated with Fabry's disease.

Mannosidosis

Patients with mannosidosis due to deficiency of lysosomal α-mannosidase exhibit a number of findings generally associated with the mucopolysaccharidoses, including coarsened features, corneal clouding, cataracts, psychomotor retardation, and bony changes. In addition some patients have been found to have decreased serum immune globulins and a defect in leukocyte chemotaxis. Whether these abnormalities are the cause of or contributory to the propensity to frequent upper respiratory infections in these individuals is not yet defined.

Mannose-containing oligosaccharides and glycoproteins in urine are quite elevated, but glycosaminoglycans are in the normal range. Examination of a peripheral blood smear will reveal vacuolated lymphocytes.

REFERENCES

Assmann, G., and Fredrickson, D.S.: Acid lipase deficiency: Wolman's disease and cholesteryl ester storage disease. *In* Stanbury, J.B., Wyngaarden, J.B., Fredrickson, D.S., et al. (eds.): The Metabolic Basis of Inherited Disease. 5th ed. McGraw-Hill, New York, 1983, p. 803.

Beaudet, A.: Disorders of glycoprotein degradation: mannosidosis, fucosidosis, sialidosis, and aspartylglycosanunuria. *In* Stanbury, J.B., Wyngaarden, J.B., Fredrickson, D.S., et al. (eds.): The Metabolic Basis of Inherited Disease. 5th ed. McGraw-Hill, New York, 1983, p. 788.

Brady, R.O., and Barranger, J.A.: Glycosyl ceramide lipidosis: Gaucher's disease. *In* Stanbury, J.B., Wyngaarden, J.B., Fredrickson, D.S., et al. (eds.): The Metabolic Basis of Inherited Disease. 5th ed. McGraw-Hill, New York, 1983, p. 842.

Brady, R.O.: Sphingomyelin lipidosis: Niemann-Pick disease. *In* Stanbury, J.B., Wyngaarden, J.B., Fredrickson, D.S.,et al. (eds.): The Metabolic Basis of Inherited Disease. 5th ed. McGraw-Hill, New York, 1983, p. 831.

Brady, R.O.: The Sphingolipidoses. *In* Bondy, P.K., and Rosenberg, L.E. (eds.): Metabolic Control and Disease. 8th ed. W. B. Saunders Co., Philadelphia, 1980, p. 523.

Daniels, L.B., and Glew, R.H.: β-Glucosidase assays in the diagnosis of Gaucher's disease. Clin. Chem. 28:569, 1982.

Desnick, R.J., and Sweeley, C.C.: Fabry's disease (α-galactosidase A deficiency). *In* Stanbury, J.B., Wyngaarden, J.B., Fredrickson, D.S., et al. (eds.): The Metabolic Basis of Inherited Disease. 5th ed. McGraw-Hill, New York, 1983, p. 906.

Drenckhahn, D., and Lullmann-Rauch, R.: Drug-induced experimental lipidosis in the nervous system. Neuroscience 4:697, 1979.

Farooqui, A.A.: Sulfatases, sulfate esters and their metabolic disorders. Clin. Chem. Acta. 100:285, 1980.

Farrell, D.F., and MacMartin, M.P.: GM_1 gangliosidosis: Enzymatic variation in a single family. Ann. Neurol. 9:232, 1981.

Farrell, D.F., and Ochs, U.: GM_1 gangliosidosis: Phenotypic variation in a single family. Ann. Neurol. 9:225, 1981.

Fischer, H.D., Gonzalez-Noriega, A., Sly, W.S., et al.: Phosphomannosyl-enzyme receptors in rat liver. J. Biol. Chem. 255:9608, 1980.

Hechtman, P., and Kachra, Z.: Interaction of activating protein and surfactants with human liver hexosaminidase A and GM_2 ganglioside. Biochem. J. 185:583, 1980.

Kattlove, H.E., Williams, J.C., Gaynor, E., et al.: Gaucher cells in chronic myelocytic leukemias: An acquired abnormality. Blood 33:379, 1969.

Kelley, T.E., Bartoskesky, L., Harris, D.J., et al.: Mucolipidosis I (acid neuroaminidase deficiency). Am. J. Dis. Child. 135:703, 1981.

Kolodny, E.H., and Moser, H.W.: Sulfatide lipidosis: Metachromatic leukodystrophy. *In* Stanbury, J.B., Wyngaarden, J.B., Fredrickson, D.S., et al. (eds.): The Metabolic Basis of Inherited Disease. 5th ed. McGraw-Hill, New York, 1983, p. 881.

Moser, H., and Chen, W.W.: Ceramidase deficiency: Farber's lipogranulomatosis. *In* Stanbury, J.B., Wyngaarden, J.B., Fredrickson, D.S., et al. (eds.): The Metabolic Basis of Inherited Disease. 5th ed. McGraw-Hill, New York, 1983, p. 820.

O'Brien, J.S.: The gangliosidoses. *In* Stanbury, J.B., Wyngaarden, J.B., Fredrickson, D.S., et al. (eds.): The Metabolic Basis of Inherited Disease. 5th ed. McGraw-Hill, New York, 1983, p. 945.

Pentchev, P.G., and Barranger, J.A.: Sphingolipidosis: molecular manifestations and biochemical strategies. J. Lipid Res. 19:401, 1978.

Percy, A.K., Shapiro, L.J., and Kaback, M.M.: Inherited Lipid Storage Diseases of the Central Nervous System. Current Problems in Pediatrics IX:6, 1979.

Purpura, D.P.: Ectopic dendritic growth in mature pyramidal neurones in human ganglioside storage disease. Nature 276:520, 1978.

Purpura, D.P., and Suzuki, K.: Distortion of neuronal geometry and formation of aberrant synapses in neuronal storage disease. Brain Res. 116:1, 1976.

Rosenberg, R.N.: Biochemical genetics of neurologic disease. New Engl. J. Med. 305:1181, 1981.

Sandhoff, K.: The biochemistry of sphingolipid storage disease. Angew Chem. Int. Ed. Engl. 16:273, 1977.

Sandhoff, K., and Christomanou, H.: Gangliosidoses. Human Genetics 50:107, 1979.

Silverstein, S.C., Steinman, R.M., and Cohn, Z.A.: Endocytosis. Ann Rev. Biochem. 46:669, 1977.

Sly, W.S.: Saccharide traffic signals in receptor-mediated endocytosis and transport of acid hydrolases. *In* Svennerholm, L., Mandel, P., Dreyfus, H., Urban, P. (eds.): Structure and Function of the Gangliosides. Plenum Press, New York, 1980, p. 433.

Steinberg, D.: Phytanic and storage disease. Refsum's disease. *In* Stanbury, J.B., Wyngaarden, J.B., Fredrickson, D.S., et al. (eds.): The Metabolic Basis of Inherited Disease. 5th ed. McGraw-Hill, New York, 1983, p. 731.

Suzuki, K., and Suzuki, Y.: Galactosylceramide lipidosis: Globoid cell leukodystrophy (Krabbe's disease). *In* Stanbury, J.B., Wyngaarden, J.B., Fredrickson, D.S., et al. (eds.): The Metabolic Basis of Inherited Disease, 5th ed. McGraw-Hill, 1983, p. 857.

Svennerholm, L., Vanier, M.T., and Mansson, J.E.: Krabbe disease: a galactosylsphingosine (psychosine) lipidosis. J. Lipid Res. 21:53, 1980.

Vidgoff, J., Lovrien, E.W., Beals, R.K., and Buist, N.R.M.: Mannosidosis in three brothers. A review of the literature. Medicine 56:335, 1977.

Waheed, A., Hasilik, A., and von Figura, K.: Processing of the phosphorylated recognition marker in lysosomal enzymes. J. Biol. Chem. 256:5717, 1981.

Wenger, D.A., Sattler, M., Kudoh, T., et al.: Niemann-Pick disease: A genetic model in Siamese cats. Science 208:1471, 1980.

31

Lipids and Lipoprotein Disorders

LIPID STRUCTURE

The lipids represent a varied group of substances that are insoluble in water but soluble in nonpolar solvents such as ether, chloroform, benzene, and hydrocarbons. It is worth emphasizing that, for the most part, lipids are part of macromolecular entities, either in association with protein or in association with carbohydrate. As such, they represent a key component of membranes, with lipid-protein interactions representing a crucial factor in the expression of the catalytic activity of membrane-bound enzymes. The main forces holding lipids together in such supramolecular entities are noncovalent forces—generally hydrophobic interactions; these seem to make the major contribution to lipid-lipid and lipid-protein bonding. The resulting structures are quite malleable. Presumably, it is such plasticity that enables these supramolecular aggregations of lipids to carry out their in vivo functions, particularly as they interact with proteins. However, disruption of their native habitat in membranes makes it difficult to study their functions in vitro. Of course, another role is as a food store of enormous potential size.

While the lipids do not share a homogeneous structure, as do proteins or nucleic acids, most lipids contain a long hydrocarbon chain, which may number from 14 to 24 carbon atoms. Straight-chain fatty acids are either saturated or unsaturated and usually have an even number of carbon atoms. Unsaturated fatty acids are almost always in the *cis* form rather than in the *trans* form, since the carbon-carbon double bond allows only restricted rotation. As a result, geometrical isomers are produced with side chains on the same side of the double bond in the *cis* form and on opposite sides in the *trans* form (Fig. 31–1). A *cis* double bond interposes a kink in the molecule, setting such unsaturated acids apart sterically from saturated and *trans*-unsaturated fatty acids. The kink in the chain impairs side-group approximation and therefore interchain hydrophobic interactions. In consequence of hindered interchain interactions, *cis*-unsaturated acids have a lower melting point than

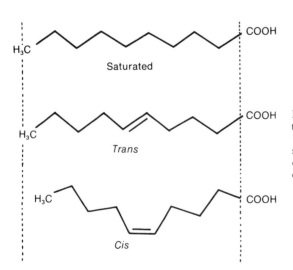

Figure 31–1 Creation of geometrical isomers by insertion of a double bond into a fatty acid. Note that in the "trans" configuration the terminal groups are on opposite sides of the molecule. (From Tietz, N. W.: Fundamentals of Clinical Chemistry. 2nd ed. Philadelphia, W. B. Saunders Co., 1976.)

their homologous saturated relative, while *trans* acids melt at a temperature in the range seen with saturated acids.

Variations of Structure on a Lipid Theme

To create larger lipid structures, organisms have turned to certain molecules bearing several functional groups that can serve as bridges for the lipid components (Fig. 31–2). Glycerol is the most frequently employed molecule serving this function. When all three of its OH groups are esterified by fatty acids, a *neutral fat* results. Simple triglycerides have fatty acids attached to glycerol that are all the same, while mixed triglycerides may contain two or three different acyl groups.

Often, only two of the hydroxyl groups are acylated, permitting the third hydroxyl group to become phosphorylated. This gives rise to a *phosphatidic acid,* the parent compound of a group of lipids that possess both polar and hydrophobic (amphipathic) characteristics. Such properties make them particularly suited for a role in cell membranes. Collectively, these are the *phosphoglycerides,* and they may be further modified by the substituents attached to a phosphate hydroxyl group.

When the free hydroxyl of glycerol forms a glycosidic linkage, usually with galactose, a *glycolipid* is the result. Such a compound also manifests amphipathic properties, but the polar character is not as pronounced as with the phosphatidic acids. Thus, by substituting a glycoside bond for a phosphoryl bond, a fine tuning of physicochemical properties of the resulting molecule is attained.

Sphingosine, a fatty acid amino alcohol, can also act as a bridging compound. In these compounds, a fatty acid molecule forms an amide with the NH_2 group (rather than an ester with the

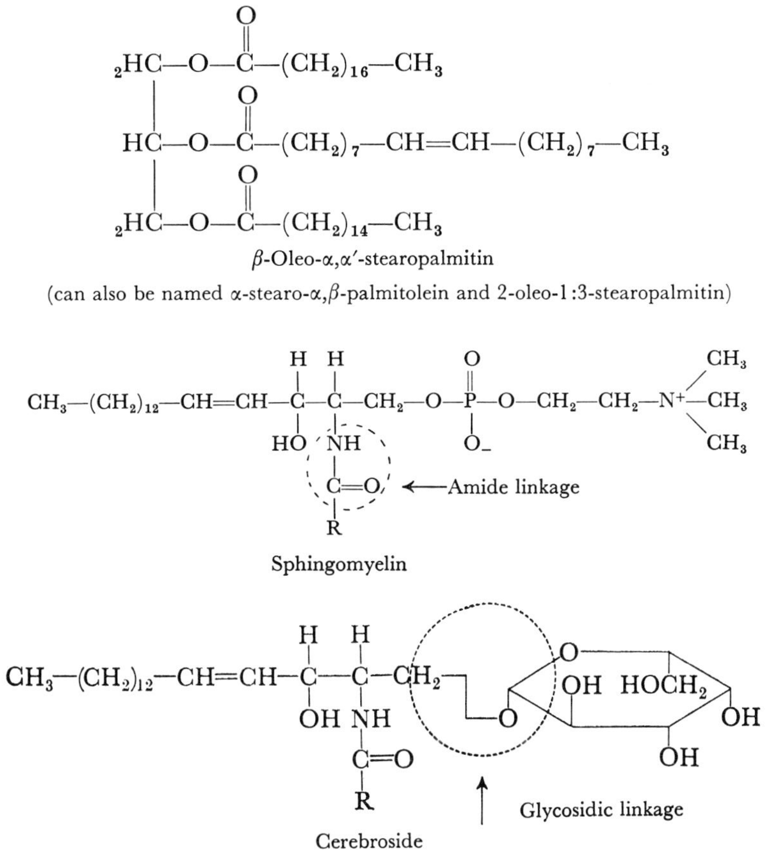

$$_2HC-O-\overset{\overset{\displaystyle O}{\|}}{C}-(CH_2)_{16}-CH_3$$

$$H\overset{}{C}-O-\overset{\overset{\displaystyle O}{\|}}{C}-(CH_2)_7-CH=CH-(CH_2)_7-CH_3$$

$$_2H\overset{}{C}-O-\overset{\overset{\displaystyle O}{\|}}{C}-(CH_2)_{14}-CH_3$$

β-Oleo-α,α'-stearopalmitin

(can also be named α-stearo-α,β-palmitolein and 2-oleo-1:3-stearopalmitin)

$$CH_3-(CH_2)_{12}-CH=CH-\overset{\overset{\displaystyle H}{|}}{C}-\overset{\overset{\displaystyle H}{|}}{C}-CH_2-O-\overset{\overset{\displaystyle O}{\|}}{P}-O-CH_2-CH_2-N^+\begin{matrix}CH_3 \\ -CH_3 \\ CH_3\end{matrix}$$

HO NH   O_

C=O ←—Amide linkage

R

Sphingomyelin

$$CH_3-(CH_2)_{12}-CH=CH-\overset{\overset{\displaystyle H}{|}}{C}-\overset{\overset{\displaystyle H}{|}}{C}-CH_2$$

OH NH

C=O

R

↑ Glycosidic linkage

Cerebroside

Figure 31–2 Functional groups of lipids. (From Masoro, E. J.: Physiological Chemistry of Lipids in Mammals. Philadelphia, W. B. Saunders, 1968.)

OH group as in the glycerides). The CH$_2$OH group of these compounds, called ceramides, can be phosphorylated, and the phosphate itself may undergo further substitution. These compounds are called *sphingolipids*. If instead of linking with a phosphoryl group, a carbohydrate is added, a compound called a *cerebroside* is formed. Sulfation of the galactose moiety, forming a *sulfatide*, can increase the polar properties of a glycolipid.

In the *gangliosides*, a neuraminic acid (sialic acid) is attached to the galactose of the carbohydrate chain attached to sphingosine. These compounds play an important role in the central nervous system (see Chapter 30).

LIPOPROTEIN COMPOSITION

There are four main classes of lipids in the blood, namely cholesterol and its esters, glycerides, phospholipids, and free or nonesterified fatty acids. Fatty acids employed in esterification with cholesterol, the glycerides, and the phospholipids vary in chain length between 16 and 24 carbon

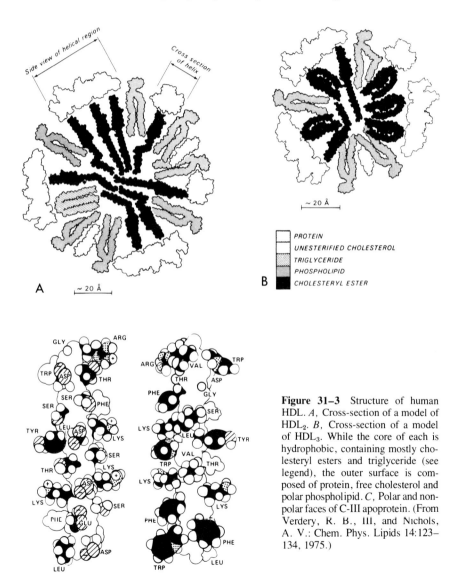

PROTEIN
UNESTERIFIED CHOLESTEROL
TRIGLYCERIDE
PHOSPHOLIPID
CHOLESTERYL ESTER

POLAR FACE   NON-POLAR FACE
C   *Apo C-III (VLDL)*

Figure 31–3 Structure of human HDL. *A,* Cross-section of a model of HDL$_2$. *B,* Cross-section of a model of HDL$_3$. While the core of each is hydrophobic, containing mostly cholesteryl esters and triglyceride (see legend), the outer surface is composed of protein, free cholesterol and polar phospholipid. *C,* Polar and nonpolar faces of C-III apoprotein. (From Verdery, R. B., III, and Nichols, A. V.: Chem. Phys. Lipids 14:123–134, 1975.)

Table 31–1 PHYSICAL AND CHEMICAL CHARACTERISTICS OF HUMAN LIPOPROTEINS

Class	Diameter (nm)	Density	M.W.	Components of Lipoprotein (Per Cent of Total)				
				TG	Cholesterol	Cholesterol Ester	Phospholipid	Protein
Chylomicrons	75–600	0.92–0.96	5×10^8	86	1	5	7	2 Apo C-II Apo B
VLDL	25–75	0.95–1.006	$5-10 \times 10^6$	50	7	13	20	10 Apo B (50%) Apo C (45%) Apo E (trace)
LDL	17–26	1.006–1.063	$2.2-2.3 \times 10^6$	8	10	30(37)	30(20)	22 Apo B (90%) Apo C-II (10%)
HDL	4–10	1.063–1.125	175,000–360,000	8	4	12	24	52 Apo A-I Apo A-II (80%) Apo C-II (15%)

atoms and include, in addition to saturated fatty acids, the polyunsaturated linoleic, linolenic, and arachidonic acids. Blood-borne lipids always exist in noncovalent combination with albumin or as emulsions (or vesicles), as in the complex entities termed lipoproteins. Such association permits these water-insoluble compounds to be maintained as stable colloids, thus utilizing the aqueous environment of the blood as a conduit serving the needs of the body. Lipoproteins as a group are the third most abundant plasma proteins after albumin and the immunoglobulins. They are supra-molecular complexes and are spherical (vesicular) in nature, ranging in size from 8 to 800 nm. Heterogeneity is the most distinctive feature of the composition of the different lipoprotein classes; nonetheless there are distinctive differences among the classes (VLDL, LDL, and HDL—Table 31–1). Lipoproteins manifest the following architectural features: a core, mainly composed of triglyceride and cholesteryl ester, which is hydrophobic, surrounded by a surface film of phospholipids, cholesterol, and specific proteins, which is amphipathic (Fig. 31–3).

Reference to Table 31–1 shows the composition of these serum lipoprotein fractions and demonstrates the relationship between electrophoretic and ultracentrifugal criteria. The lipoproteins range from very low density entities with high triglyceride content and low protein content to the high density moieties with low triglyceride content and high protein content. In between, phospholipid and cholesterol ester increase in content from the very low density lipoproteins (VLDL) to the high density lipoproteins (HDL). Hence, density varies inversely with triglyceride content and directly with protein content.

Apolipoproteins

Pending further investigation to clarify the relationship of specific apolipoproteins (protein components of the lipoproteins) to the parent lipoprotein class, several classification systems have

Table 31–2 FUNCTIONS OF SELECTED APOPROTEINS

A-I	Activates LCAT, structural component of HDL
A-II	Structural component of HDL
B	Component of chylomicrons and VLDL; almost totally absent in abetalipoproteinemia
C-I	Activates LCAT
C-II	Activates LPL
C-III	Major C apoprotein of VLDL
E	Transfer of cholesteryl ester from HDL to VLDL
LPL	Catalyzes hydrolysis of TG in VLDL and chylomicra
LCAT	Catalyzes esterification of HDL-bound cholesterol

been developed for the apoproteins. The simplest and most tentative is the A–E designation, which we employ here (Table 31–2), since it has the virtue of being widely used and the most easily amended as more definitive data are obtained.

Synthesis occurs predominantly in the liver, although apoprotein is also synthesized by intestinal cells. Hydrophobic interactions provide the major force by which these apoproteins "stick" to the lipid components of the various lipoproteins. Nonetheless, considerable hydrophilic segments of these proteins exist, presumably as these macromolecules serve to interact simultaneously with the lipid and aqueous environment so essential to the transport function of the lipoproteins.

We should note here that beyond their role in the stabilization of lipoprotein structure certain aproproteins function as well as cofactors (activators or specifiers) for certain enzymes involved in the metabolism of the lipoproteins. Seen in this light it should also be clear that it is somewhat simplistic to speak of one lipoprotein class in isolation from the others, since they all undergo lipid exchange, furnish cofactors, and in general interact in the blood, to provide for the energetic and structural needs of cells.

FORMATION AND FUNCTIONS OF THE SERUM LIPOPROTEINS

Nonesterified Fatty Acids

In contrast to most lipids in blood (which are part of the lipoproteins), some fatty acids exist alone, i.e., not as part of the more complex lipids. Rather they are carried mainly by albumin, which possesses two high-affinity reversible binding sites. This small pool (~ 0.5 mM or 10 to 15 mg/dl) has a half-life of approximately 2 minutes and serves as an energy source for the body, especially when glucose is in short supply (see Chapter 13). The source of plasma free fatty acids is adipose tissue; hence, palmitic and oleic acids (18:1) account for three quarters of the circulating pool. Skeletal muscle derives about half of its resting energy requirement from plasma free fatty acids.

Cardiac muscle utilizes free fatty acids as does liver, which utilizes them for energy, formation of ketone bodies, and incorporation into triglyceride, the last representing a component of lipoproteins secreted by hepatic parenchymal cells.

Chylomicrons

Chylomicrons are formed only by the mucosal cells of the small intestine (Fig. 31–4). Dietary triglyceride is emulsified in the small intestinal lumen in preparation for partial or complete enzymatic hydrolysis to its component fatty acids, monoglycerides, and free glycerol. Solubilization of these hydrolytic products with bile salts to form micelles is involved in preparing the lipid building blocks for absorption into the mucosal cells. Subsequently, resynthesis of triglycerides occurs in the mucosal cells, particularly from monoglycerides, and these are incorporated into chylomicrons. Formation of chylomicrons requires the combination of small amounts of cholesterol, phospholipids and protein, along with the predominant triglyceride.

At first glance this seems to be a roundabout way to absorb triglyceride, especially since biologic systems tend to function economically. Undoubtedly there must be a reason for this apparent profligacy. As noted above micellar solubilization of the components of hydrolyzed triglycerides is involved in preparing them for absorption by the mucosal cell. Moreover, the resynthesis of "custom-made" triglycerides, formed from endogenous fatty acids, can better serve the needs of the cells, which will obtain their lipid supplies via blood-borne chylomicrons (from lymph) and lipoproteins.

After formation, these bodies of approximately 0.5 to 1 μm diameter enter the lymph channels and flow from there into the blood. Chylomicrons can provide fatty acids for the energetic and synthetic needs of the body's cells. The fatty acids are liberated by the enzyme lipoprotein lipase

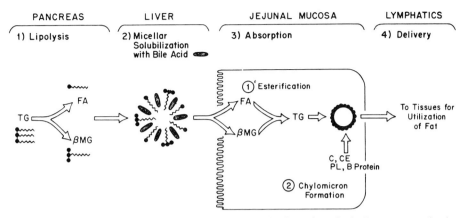

PANCREAS   LIVER   JEJUNAL MUCOSA   LYMPHATICS

1) Lipolysis   2) Micellar Solubilization with Bile Acid   3) Absorption   4) Delivery

(1) Esterification

To Tissues for Utilization of Fat

C, CE PL, B Protein

(2) Chylomicron Formation

Figure 31–4 Formation of chylomicrons. Note the role of bile in the formation of micelles, a supramolecular structure that facilitates absorption of lipid by intestinal cells. Chylomicron formation requires small amounts of cholesterol (C), cholesterol ester (CE), phospholipid (PL), and B-apoprotein (B-protein), in addition to the triglyceride (TG), which is resynthesized within the cell from fatty acid (FA) and β-monoglyceride (βMG). (From Wilson, F. A., and Dietschy, J. M.: Differential diagnostic approach to clinical problems of malabsorption. Gastroenterology 61:911, 1971.)

in capillary endothelium (see below). Chylomicrons are by far the largest of the lipid transport particles; they are virtually cleared within 12 hours after a fatty meal.

Very Low Density Lipoprotein (Prebeta-Lipoprotein)

Very low density lipoprotein (VLDL) is synthesized mainly within the liver, although the small intestine contributes a minor amount. In both organs cells responsible for VLDL synthesis are of endodermal origin. VLDL synthesized in liver appears to function by transporting endogenous triglyceride, while that provided by the intestine is composed of dietary fatty acids.

This macromolecular association is rich in triglyceride and poor in protein. Many feel that they represent a diminutive variant of the chylomicron. There is evidence that VLDL particle size is a function of underlying composition; smaller particles have a greater proportion of triglyceride and the C apoproteins.

Low Density Lipoprotein (Beta-Lipoprotein)

As opposed to chylomicrons and VLDL (formed by intestine and liver respectively), most low density lipoprotein (LDL) originates from catabolism of VLDL. The latter is converted into LDL when most of its triglycerides and apoprotein (apart from apo-β) are removed enzymatically. Lipid accounts for about three-quarters of LDL content, and LDL has a half-life of approximately 3 days. It appears to serve as the vehicle for cholesterol transport from tissues to the liver. Free exchange between the lipid of LDL and cell membrane lipid occurs, prompting the suggestion that it may serve a role in maintaining the integrity of cell membranes. Additionally there is considerable exchange between lipoproteins in the plasma, in a process that involves collision between the various particles. When collision occurs, it is probable that this is followed by partial coalescence of the lipid molecules, with transfer of components from one particle to another.

High Density Lipoprotein (Alpha-Lipoprotein)

This form of lipoprotein is produced mainly within the liver, contains about 50 per cent protein and 50 per cent lipid (cholesterol esters and phospholipids predominating), and has a half-life of approximately 4½ days. It appears to form complexes with the enzyme lecithin cholesterol acyl transferase (LCAT), which is responsible for the esterification of serum cholesterol (in the form of

HDL). HDL plays a central role in the mobilization of cholesterol from the tissues—in Tangier disease cholesterol storage in reticuloendothelial tissue is associated with virtual absence of HDL.

Precursor or nascent HDL, isolated from liver Golgi, is in the form of bilaminar discs. Similar discoidal particles are also found in the plasma of individuals with LCAT deficiency (see below). In both instances there is little esterified cholesterol in the HDL particle.

Normally plasma HDL exists as a spherical particle. Hence esterification of cholesterol appears to account for the transition of disc to sphere. LCAT transfers fatty acids from lecithin in HDL to cholesterol within the HDL particle. By so doing it produces lysolecithin and a cholesterol ester. The former binds to plasma albumin and is removed; the latter, unable to exist near the water interface, enters the interior of the HDL particle, splitting the lecithin-cholesterol layer. This transforms the disc into a vesicle.

Apoprotein Cycle

Normally, during the fasting state approximately 90 per cent of apoprotein A is associated noncovalently with HDL, 90 per cent of apoprotein B with LDL, and about half of plasma apoprotein C divided between VLDL and HDL.

After a fat-containing meal small intestinal cells manufacture apoproteins A and B as part of the chylomicrons formed there. Apoprotein C is a product of liver secretion and must be furnished to nascent chylomicrons from HDL, which serve as a readily available source. This apoprotein C can be recovered by HDL when triglycerides carried by chylomicrons are hydrolyzed in muscle and adipose tissue.

Lipoprotein Lipase and Triglyceride Transport

Triglyceride, as VLDL and chylomicrons, serves as a convenient supply of fatty acids for the energetic needs of multiple tissues. The surfeit persisting beyond oxidative requirements is stored. The triglyceride economy involves between 70 and 150 grams of dietary and synthesized (hepatic) triglyceride per day. Triglyceride-containing supramolecular entities are catabolized by lipoprotein lipase, which is localized to capillary endothelium, apparently bound there by electrostatic forces through glycosoaminoglycans (mucopolysaccharides). The first step in the process involves transfer of apoprotein C-II from circulating HDL particles to chylomicrons and VLDL. Once in place this apoprotein somehow facilitates interaction of lipoprotein lipase with the lipoprotein particles; there is consequent sequential removal of fatty acid groups from triglyceride, forming the diglyceride and monoglyceride. Liberated fatty acids are taken up by cells to provide a substrate for energetic needs and to be stored for future needs.

$$\text{Triglyceride} \begin{cases} \text{Chylomicron} \\ \text{VLDL} \end{cases} \xrightarrow{\text{LPL}} \text{Fatty Acids} + \text{Remnant chylomicrons and VLDL} \xrightarrow{\text{LPL}} \text{LDL}$$

Lipoprotein remnants undergo further catabolism in the liver as do monoglycerides. Glycerol is reutilized in gluconeogenesis or triglyceride synthesis.

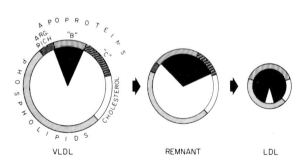

VLDL   REMNANT   LDL

Figure 31–5 Lipoprotein degradation. The relative proportions of constituents are shown for VLDL. As the remnant is formed, the mass of B-apoprotein remains constant, as is the mass of cholesteryl ester (black portion in core). The mass of triglyceride decreases progressively (white portion of core). Note that the LDL product has lost the "arginine-rich" and C-apoproteins entirely, while its core ratio of triglyceride to cholesteryl ester has been reversed. (From Havel, R. J., Goldstein, J. L., and Brown, M. S.: Lipoproteins and lipid transport. In Bondy, P. K., Rosenberg, L. E. (eds.): Metabolic Control and Disease. Philadelphia, W. B. Saunders Co., 1980.)

Progressive removal of lipid components eventuates in production of cholesterol-rich LDL (Fig. 31–5). These lipoprotein particles are removed by receptor-mediated endocytosis. This process involves ingestion of material intracellularly through the formation of invaginations in the plasma membrane, with eventual delivery to lysosomes for further catabolism. In the case of LDL this process furnishes cholesterol for membrane synthesis (see Familial Hypercholesterolemia).

Lipoprotein Disorders

Defects in lipoprotein metabolism run the gamut from gross elevation to profound deficiency; functionally inactive lipoproteins or defective cell receptors for lipoproteins have also been described. Generally clinical manifestations center around abnormalities of the cardiovascular system, with presentation in early adulthood. However, in some cases presentation occurs during infancy or childhood. Because of the central role of lipids in the energy economy of the body, conditions that lead to increased blood lipid transport may create secondary lipoprotein abnormalities, which sometimes masquerade on electrophoresis as the inherited defects. Careful history and physical examination should permit discrimination between primary (Table 31–3) and secondary causes. However, in between, there is a large group of individuals with lipid disorders that are probably polygenic in nature but that are very sensitive to environmental perturbations.

Lipoproteins and Serum Inspection

What follows is a description of plasma (in different hyperlipemic states) that has been allowed to stand overnight at 4°C. It is remarkable that the behavior of these lipoprotein moieties under the constraints of cold and gravity will provide data as useful (in most instances) as can be obtained by electrophoresis. As Figure 31–6 shows, the key factor in distinguishing the different states is accurate quantitation of plasma cholesterol and triglyceride.

1. Gross turbidity distributed uniformly through the sample ("colloid") indicates VLDL or broad-beta-lipoprotein (VLDL). Rarely a hypertriglyceridemic serum may appear clear because of a shift in VLDL particle size distribution toward smaller, less lipid-rich entities.

2. Dense creamy layer in the supernatant over lactescent serum usually indicates a type V pattern—increased chylomicrons and prebeta-lipoproteins. In broad-beta-hyperlipoproteinemia there is usually a slight chylomicronemia as well, but in this case there is a narrow dense layer of floating lactescence atop a diffusely opalescent serum.

Table 31–3 PRIMARY DYSLIPOPROTEINEMIAS—CLINICAL MANIFESTATIONS BY SYSTEMS

System	Symptom or Sign	Disorder (Type)
Skin	Eruptive xanthoma	I, V
	Palmar xanthoma	III
	Tuberous and tendinous xanthoma	II, III
Cardiovascular system	Atherosclerotic arterial degeneration	II, III, IV, V
	Aortic valvular disease	II (homozygous)
	Renovascular	II, III
Gastrointestinal system	Abdominal pain	I, V
	Hepatosplenomegaly	I, V, LCAT
	Malabsorption syndrome	Abetalipoproteinemia
Neuromuscular system	Ataxia	Abetalipoproteinemia
	Peripheral neuropathy	Tangier disease
Erythrocyte	Acanthocytosis	Abetalipoproteinemia
	Normocytic anemia ⎤	
Kidney	Glomerular disease ⎬	LCAT deficiency
Eye	Cataract ⎦	
	Arcus corneae	All
Oropharynx	Orange tonsils	Tangier disease
	Yellow buccal mucosal plaques	II

LIPOPROTEIN PHENOTYPE	CHARACTER OF LIPOPROTEIN ELEVATION	TOTAL PLASMA CHOLESTEROL	TOTAL PLASMA TRIGLYCERIDE	APPEARANCE OF PLASMA	
TYPE I	CHYLOMICRONS ↑↑↑	NORMAL TO MODERATELY ELEVATED	MARKEDLY ELEVATED	"CREAM LAYER" ABOVE CLEAR TO SLIGHTLY TURBID INFRANATE	
TYPE II-A	LDL ↑↑↑	ELEVATED	NORMAL	CLEAR, MAY HAVE INCREASED YELLOW-ORANGE TINT	
TYPE II-B	LDL ↑↑↑ VLDL ↑	ELEVATED	MODERATELY ELEVATED	SLIGHTLY TO MODERATELY TURBID	
TYPE III	B-VLDL, LDL OF ABNORMAL COMPOSITION	ELEVATED	MODERATELY TO MARKEDLY ELEVATED	TURBID TO FRANKLY OPAQUE "CREAM LAYER" ABOVE TURBID INFRANATE OCCASIONALLY PRESENT	
TYPE IV	VLDL ↑↑↑	NORMAL TO SLIGHTLY ELEVATED	MODERATELY TO MARKEDLY ELEVATED	TURBID TO FRANKLY OPAQUE	
TYPE V	CHYLOMICRONS ↑↑ VLDL ↑↑↑	MODERATELY ELEVATED	MARKEDLY ELEVATED	"CREAM LAYER" OVER TURBID TO OPAQUE INFRANATE	

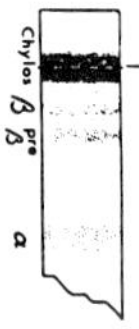

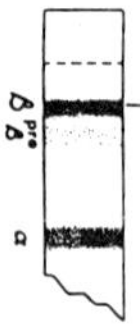

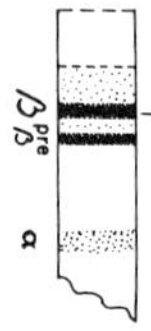

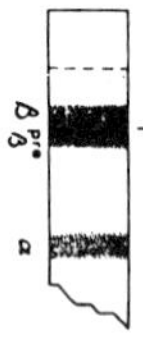

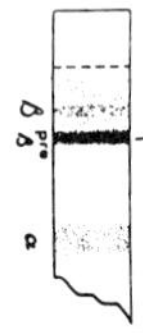

Figure 31–6 Principal biochemical characteristics of primary/secondary hyperlipoproteinemias. (From Tietz, N. W.: Fundamentals of Clinical Chemistry. 2nd ed. Philadelphia, W. B. Saunders, 1976, and Tamir, I., Rifkind, B. M., Levy, R. I.: Measurements of lipids and evaluation of lipid disorders. *In* Henry, J. B. (ed.): Clinical Diagnosis and Management by Laboratory Methods. 16th ed. Philadelphia, W. B. Saunders Co., 1979.)

3. A lactescent or creamy interface below a clear supernatant indicates the presence of chylomicrons, usually in a nonfasting sample and in exogenous hypertriglyceridemia.

4. While clear serum may be entirely normal, such an appearance is compatible with excess beta-lipoprotein, alpha-lipoprotein or lipoprotein X, and even a slight excess in prebeta-lipoprotein.

OVERVIEW OF TREATMENT OF LIPOPROTEIN DISORDERS

Fasting levels of serum lipid and lipoprotein are lowest during the newborn period, rising rapidly during the first week and reaching values on a par with those characteristic of later childhood by about the age of four months. Cholesterol seems to be the most sensitive of the serum lipids to dietary changes during the first year of life, but thereafter shows little fluctuation throughout childhood.

Like all inherited disease, the underlying biochemical defect exists for the lifetime of the individual. Considering the heightened risk for atherosclerotic heart disease in a number of these disorders, it would appear that attempts to lower lipid levels are justified. The earlier (in childhood) such therapy is initiated, the better the outcome will be. Data to support such an optimistic view are, however, sparse at present.

Diet represents the initial approach to therapy for these disorders and in the hypertriglyceridemic states can be very effective. It is not as efficacious in familial type 2a hypercholesterolemia.

Dietary Treatment

1. Even under normal circumstances calories, as fats and carbohydrates in excess of the liver's energetic needs and capacity for storage, will engender augmented triglyceride and VLDL synthesis. Weight reduction further ameliorates the situation by diminishing the state of insulin resistance that attends obesity. Triglyceride catabolism will increase in consequence, further diminishing VLDL levels.

2. By decreasing caloric intake VLDL synthesis can be diminished, and this can be expected to have a salutory effect on the tendency to develop atheromas. Elevated LDL concentrations will respond somewhat to restriction of cholesterol and saturated fats.

It has been known for some time that eating polyunsaturated fatty acids instead of saturated fatty acids can reduce LDL cholesterol levels, apparently by augmenting fecal excretion of cholesterol and bile acids. The mechanism of this effect is not clear; one possibility is decreased formation of triglycerides because of diminished availability of palmitate. As a result VLDL formation may fall, diminishing the pool from which LDL can arise.

Bile Acid Sequestrants

A group of nonabsorbable cationic polymers have been developed that sequester bile acids in the bowel and heighten their loss in the stool. Cholestyramine has gained wide popularity for this purpose. It seems that diminished bile acid absorption interrupts a negative feedback on cholesterol synthesis at the level of cholesterol 7-α-hydroxylase, so that sterol synthesis is enhanced. Coupled with increased loss this eventuates in continuing loss and negative balance. Since these agents are nonabsorbable, systemic effects are minimal.

Nicotinic Acid

Nicotinic acid is effective in diminishing plasma levels of both VLDL and LDL; its mechanism of action is not well understood. Side effects include cutaneous flushing, which can be annoying, and hepatocellular damage, which can be of more concern.

Plasma Exchange

Familial hypercholesterolemia has been treated successfully with repeated plasma exchange. The decreased levels of cholesterol will persist for three to four weeks before a repeat exchange is required.

Clofibrate

Clofibrate is an effective drug for the treatment of primary hypertriglyceridemia; it is less effective in hypercholesterolemia. Unfortunately, studies with rodents have disclosed a heightened propensity for the development of hepatic tumors. This has led the FDA to issue stringent guidelines for its possible use. In consequence, it ought not to be used before more conventional and less potentially deleterious therapies are employed.

LIPOPROTEIN DISORDERS

Abetalipoproteinemia

Clinical Features

Clinical manifestations of abetalipoproteinemia revolve around malabsorption, anemia (acanthocytosis), and neuromuscular symptoms, including involvement of posterior spinocerebellar tracts and retinal degeneration. Malabsorption of fat usually begins during the neonatal period and is associated with poor feeding, vomiting, and copious stools, all of which contribute to failure to thrive. While steatorrhea is lifelong, it appears to become milder as the child learns to avoid fatty foods. Psychomotor retardation begins during the infancy period; disorders of proprioception begin in the first decade, and all patients have ataxia by the end of the second decade. These latter findings are associated with a positive Romberg's sign and loss of position and vibratory sensation. Mental retardation occurs in about a third of patients. As the disease progresses, a picture resembling Friedreich's ataxia emerges: along with the neurological disturbances there develops the expected associated skeletal abnormalities—pes cavus, equinovarus, kyphoscoliosis, and lordosis. Cardiac findings occur as well, including arrhythmias, increased size, and murmurs. In contrast to Friedreich's ataxia, however, these patients rarely have diabetes mellitus.

Ocular findings are also quite common, being characterized by retinitis pigmentosa (with associated night blindness), nystagmus, and ophthalmoplegia. Interestingly, while cataracts are frequently associated with typical retinitis pigmentosa, this is not the case in abetalipoproteinemia.

Biochemical Defects

The defect in this disorder involves defective synthesis or secretion of apoprotein B, which consequently causes abnormalities in chylomicrons, VLDL, and HDL. How that causes the wide range of abnormalities seen in abetalipoproteinemia is at present obscure. Perhaps as a result of the lipoprotein abnormalities a generalized cell membrane defect occurs that involves the central nervous system and the red cell. Alternatively, some believe that the persistent malabsorption, which begins in infancy, permits vitamin E deficiency to develop, thus depriving the body of a membrane antioxidant. In either case, the sparing of certain membranes remains a puzzle. Clearly much work has to be done to rationalize the pathogenesis of this disorder.

Laboratory Findings

The most striking routine laboratory finding associated with this disorder is the presence of acanthocytes on a fresh, undiluted film of a peripheral smear. While they are not pathognomonic for this disorder (they have been described in some patients with alcoholic liver diseases and pyruvate kinase deficiency) their presence in a patient with neuromuscular findings, malabsorption, and retinal degeneration makes abetalipoproteinemia an essential diagnostic consideration. Although red cell survival is somewhat shortened in this disorder, anemia is usually the result of inadequate iron absorption and responds to iron supplementation. Serum is clear in abetalipoproteinemia, with decreased concentration of total lipid, cholesterol, phospholipid, and particularly triglyceride. Further studies are usually indicated on finding a triglyceride of less than 30 mg/dl and a cholesterol of less than 100 mg/dl. Because of the role of apoprotein B in chylomicrons, VLDL, and LDL, these three classes are greatly decreased or absent in plasma.

Treatment

No therapy thus far suggested appears to ameliorate the neurological manifestations. Restriction of long-chain fatty acids may improve malabsorption, but one must be careful not to prescribe an excess of medium-chain triglyceride, which may compound the malabsorption by competing for intestinal binding sites for long-chain fatty acids. Supplementation with fat-soluble vitamins is required because of steatorrhea. In addition it has been suggested that pharmacological doses of vitamin E (100 mg per kg per day) will benefit the neurological manifestations. In a recent report by Illingworth et al. (1980) two patients received high-dose vitamin E therapy with no progression of neurological symptoms. The arrest of what has hitherto been a progressive disorder bears careful scrutiny as a promising means of improving the outlook for these patients.

Tangier Disease

This is a rare disorder in which cholesterol ester storage occurs in the reticuloendothelial system. The most striking physical finding and the one that usually leads to the diagnostic investigation is abnormal tonsils. They are greatly enlarged and orange or yellowish-grey in color and have a peculiar odor arising from the cholesteryl esters stored there. This is associated with lymphadenopathy and hepatosplenomegaly. Neurological findings are less common but when present, manifest as mononeuritis multiplex with weakness, paresthesias, decreased deep tendon reflexes, and decreased strength. Ptosis, oculomuscular palsies, diplopia, and muscle atrophy are also seen. Symptoms are not usually apparent until after childhood.

Biochemical Defects

The primary gene defect appears to involve the synthesis of one of the major HDL proteins, apoprotein A. Since storage of cholesterol esters occurs in the reticuloendothelial system in this disorder, it seems that HDL is important in the transport of these esters from tissues to the blood. The pathogenesis of cholesteryl ester storage is undefined but appears to relate to the formation of abnormal chylomicron remnants, which are phagocytosed.

In consequence of the defect in apoprotein A of HDL, there is less HDL in plasma and commensurately less apoprotein C-II usually furnished by HDL. As apoprotein C-II is an activator of lipoprotein lipase, less chylomicrons and VLDL triglyceride will be hydrolyzed, accounting for the elevation of plasma triglyceride in association with the very low plasma cholesterol (40 to 120 mg/dl) characteristic of this disorder. Lipoprotein electrophoresis reveals absence of HDL, and on paper the LDL band is seen to be broader than usual.

Familial Lecithin Cholesterol Acyltransferase Deficiency

Clinical Features

This enzymatic abnormality results in an abnormally low amount of cholesterol ester being associated with each lipoprotein class. HDL is affected predominantly. Proteinuria beginning at around 3 to 4 years of age is the earliest clinical sign. The proteinuria may be static for years, but an increase in amount heralds the onset of worsening renal insufficiency. Indeed, renal failure is the major medical problem in this disorder. Anemia (normocytic, normochromic) and corneal opacities are also found, but there does not appear to be any central nervous system involvement.

Biochemical Defects

Lecithin cholesterol acyl transferase mediates the esterification of cholesterol bound to HDL. In the absence of this enzyme, the proportion of unesterified serum cholesterol increases. This leads to the loss of glomerular endothelial cells and the formation of abnormal glomerular membranes. How the gene defect leads to this accumulation and the consequent renal failure is not understood.

Laboratory Findings

As esterified cholesterol is present in low concentration, there seems to be a compensating increase in free cholesterol. Phosphorylcholine and triglycerides are also quite elevated. Electrophoretic mobility may vary from the expected distribution, since none of the lipoproteins possesses a normal complement of cholesterol esters. In consequence, VLDL manifests beta migration, and LDL and HDL also manifest abnormal migration.

Treatment

The use of a fat-restricted diet is being recommended in an attempt to forestall the onset of renal failure.

Familial Hyperchylomicronemia (Type I Hyperlipoproteinemia)
(Defect: lipoprotein lipase; Genetics: autosomal recessive)

Clinical Features

Although uncommon, this disorder is often first expressed during infancy by hepatosplenomegaly, lipemia retinalis, eruptive xanthomas over skin and mucous membranes, and foam cells in the bone marrow. In childhood, there may be attacks of colicky abdominal pain, which can be severe. Indeed, in adulthood, the pain may be so severe as to mimic an acute abdominal crisis (acute pancreatitis), with fever, nausea, vomiting, and leukocytosis. Conspicuous by its absence is any myocardial involvement, presumably because of the lack of atherogenic potential by chylomicrons.

Biochemical Defects

Familial hyperchylomicronemia is a result of a deficiency of lipoprotein lipase (extrahepatic triglyceride lipase), which catalyzes hydrolysis of the chylomicron and VLDL triglyceride. Normally, little enzyme activity is demonstrable in plasma, but heparin administration will cause release of the enzyme, accounting for the designation "postheparin lipolytic activity."

Reticuloendothelial uptake of uncatabolized chylomicrons accounts for the xanthoma and hepatosplenomegaly, which are the result of the storage of foam cells. Such cells also populate the bone marrow.

While the cause of pancreatitis is not known for sure, it has been speculated that clumping of chylomicrons in pancreatic acinar cells may lead to ischemia, with release of intracellular enzymes, including lipases. These may then hydrolyze fatty acids from chylomicron triglycerides, causing local inflammation.

Laboratory Findings

Observation of the fasting serum is quite useful, as it reveals gross turbidity, appearing variously as "cream of tomato soup" or "melted strawberry ice cream." If the plasma is kept in the refrigerator overnight, a creamy supernatant forms, the hallmark of this disorder. Triglycerides are greatly increased (often above 1000 mg/dl), but cholesterol and phospholipids are only moderately increased. By lipoprotein electrophoresis there is an enormous increase in the chylomicron fraction. A presumptive diagnosis of this disorder can be made by determining the response of the serum lipoprotein to a fat-free diet maintained for 4 to 5 days. On such a regimen the total serum triglycerides will decrease toward normal, and chylomicrons will disappear from plasma. Determination of postheparin lipolytic activity will confirm the diagnosis. Differential diagnosis of disorders that present the Type I pattern include lupus erythematosus, pancreatitis, uncontrolled diabetes, the use of oral contraceptives, hypothyroidism, and multiple myeloma (see Table 31–4).

Treatment

This disorder will usually respond to a low-fat diet, which will result in the disappearance of xanthomas within several weeks and the return of the liver and spleen to normal size. It appears

Table 31–4 SECONDARY HYPERLIPIDEMIAS

Lipoprotein Pattern	Underlying Clinical Condition	Mechanism for Hyperlipidemia
Type I: Chylomicronemia	Systemic lupus erythematosus	Immunoglobulin binds GAG at capillary endothelium, LPL activity ↓
Type IIa: ↑ LDL	Obstructive liver disease ⎫ Hypothyroidism ⎬	Decreased catabolism of LDL
	Nephrotic syndrome Dysglobulinemias	↑ secretion VLDL; ↓ catabolism VLDL and LDL
	Acute intermittent porphyria	Undefined
	Cushing's syndrome	↑ secretion VLDL→↑ formation LDL
Type IIb: ↑ LDL, ↑ VLDL	Nephrotic syndrome ⎫ Cushing's syndrome ⎬ Growth hormone deficiency ⎭	↑ secretion VLDL→↑ formation LDL
Type III: ↑ LP remnants (beta-migrating)	Monoclonal gammopathies ⎫	Immunoglobulins form immune complex with VLDL or remnants interfering with their catabolism
Type IV: ↑↑ VLDL	Monoclonal gammopathies ⎭	
	Diabetes mellitus	↑ secretion VLDL; ↓ LPL activity
	Lipodystrophies ⎫ Alcohol ⎬ Oral contraceptives ⎭	↑ secretion VLDL
	Hepatitis	↓ secretion LCAT
	Glucose-6-phosphatase deficiency	↑ secretion VLDL, ↓ LPL activity
	Uremia	↓ LPL activity
Type V: ↑↑ VLDL ↑↑ Chylomicrons	Diabetes mellitus Alcohol Oral contraceptives Glucose-6-phosphatase deficiency	
LP-X: ↑ Cholesterol and phospholipids	Cholestasis	Biliary cholesterol and lecithin diverted into blood

that intracellular lipases are able to mediate the hydrolysis of triglycerides sequestered by foam cells, bringing about a decrease in storage. Such patients benefit greatly from the coordinated efforts of a nutritional team associated with a metabolic clinic or lipid disorders group, since fat restrictions must be severe (15 to 30 g daily). Dietary fat should consist mainly of polyunsaturated fatty acids to avoid deficiency of essential fatty acids.

Familial Hypercholesterolemia (Hyperbetalipoproteinemia, Type II Hyperbetalipoproteinemia) (Defect: LDL cell receptor; Genetics: autosomal dominant)

Inheritance of familial hypercholesterolemia is autosomal dominant; the homozygous form is quite rare. However, the heterozygous form is the most common lipoprotein disorder presenting in childhood. It is often accompanied by xanthomatosis and precocious manifestations of atherosclerosis. Both tendinous or tuberous xanthomas may appear in childhood and indeed have been observed at birth. Manifestations of coronary insufficiency may also begin in the first decade, with worsening symptoms thereafter. Arcus cornea and arthritic changes may also be present. Heterozygotes will usually be affected as well, but clinical evidence of the disorder may not become apparent until adulthood. Nonetheless, hypercholesterolemia is present at birth in heterozygotes.

Biochemical Defects

Evidence reviewed by Brown et al. (1981) and Goldstein et al. (1979) supports the view that the LDL receptor is abnormal in this disorder. Three different defects have been described: absence of the receptor, defective binding activity for LDL, and inability to transport the bound LDL into the cytosol of the cell. As a consequence of this defect little cholesterol is available to regulate the key enzyme of cholesterol synthesis, HMG-CoA reductase; hence cholesterol levels are greatly elevated.

Normally two mechanisms are responsible for degradation of plasma LDL—the receptor pathway (which accounts for the bulk of removal) and a scavenger (macrophage) pathway. In the absence of the normal complement of receptors (actual or functional) the scavenger pathway must remove a greater quantity of LDL cholesterol. Presumably it is the storage of scavenger cells that accounts for the deposition of cholesterol in abnormal sites.

Laboratory Findings and Differential Diagnosis

In the fasting state the serum is clear, even when the cholesterol is greater than 1000 mg. per dl. As a general rule cholesterol levels are about 6 times normal in homozygotes and 2 times normal in heterozygotes. Coupled with triglycerides in the normal range, a cholesterol greater than 650 mg/dl in a nonjaundiced child is virtually pathognomonic of homozygous familial hypercholesterolemia.

Diagnosis of the heterozygous state represents a more difficult task. Clearly a pedigree analysis is central to making such a diagnosis in the absence of studies of LDL receptor activity in fibroblasts. Certain features tend to distinguish heterozygous familial hypercholesterolemia from combined hyperlipidemia or polygenic hypercholesterolemia. Familial hypercholesterolemic heterozygotes are more likely to have xanthomas, their cholesterol levels are usually higher (often over 400 mg/dl), and they do not have VLDL abnormalities. Secondary causes of isolated elevation of LDL include hypothyroidism, obstructive jaundice, nephrotic syndrome, acute intermittent porphyria, Cushing's syndrome, and dysglobulinemias (see Table 31–4).

Treatment

Therapy should begin with a diet that is low in cholesterol and high in polyunsaturated fats. Approximately 10 to 20 percent of children with Type II hyperlipidemia will experience near normalization of cholesterol on such a dietary regimen. Initiating therapy before age 2 and continuing it thereafter are likely to achieve normalization of plasma values in over 75 percent of patients.

Assuming a carefully devised and palatable diet has not been successful in lowering cholesterol, the anion exchange resin cholestyramine might then be employed. It acts by decreasing bile salt reabsorption from the bowel, a desirable effect on two counts: (1) cholesterol excretion is partly mediated through bile salt excretion and (2) a decrease in bile salt absorption evokes augmented LDL cholesterol catabolism to provide more bile salts, since the level of bile salts is under feedback regulation. Recently plasmaphoresis, on a continuing basis, has been shown to be effective in maintaining normal LDL cholesterol levels.

Familial Type III Hyperlipoproteinemia (Familial Dysbetalipoproteinemia, Broad-Beta)

Clinical Features

This is a rare, recessively inherited disorder that infrequently manifests clinically before childhood. Clinical suspicion should be high in any patient with xanthomas especially localized to palmar and digital creases and elbows. Tuberoeruptive xanthomas occur as well. Approximately one third of patients experience manifestations of atherosclerotic vascular disease, the major cause of infirmity in these individuals. In particular, intermittent claudication is an especially common manifestation of peripheral vascular involvement.

Biochemical Defects

While the underlying inherited defect is not yet understood, lipoprotein electrophoresis reveals an increase in plasma of a lipoprotein class of a density intermediate between VLDL and HDL.

This class has been termed broad-beta because of the difficulty encountered in separating beta and prebeta bands. The altered electrophoretic mobility seems to depend upon increased cholesteryl ester and decreased triglyceride in the hydrophobic core when compared with normal VLDL. As a result of modification of the core, surface components are also altered, resulting in the modified electrophoretic mobility. Subsequent studies have disclosed that there are two related protein abnormalities: apolipoprotein E (also called arginine-rich protein—ARP), which is composed of three proteins, is greatly increased; Apoprotein-E-III, one of the components of the three comprising ARP, is absent or significantly decreased. Increase in the total amount (by electrophoresis) is accounted for by increase in protein apoprotein E-II. With the demonstration of a protein abnormality, the alternative designation for this disorder, i.e., dysbetalipoproteinemia, more clearly defines the nature of the defect. Nonetheless the relationship of this protein defect to the syndrome is as yet unclear, since there are individuals with total absence of apoprotein E-III who do not have clinical manifestations of familial dysbetalipoproteinemia.

Laboratory Findings

In its most clear-cut manifestations both cholesterol and triglyceride levels are increased to approximately the same level, and lipoprotein electrophoresis will reveal an aberrant "broad beta" band. A useful maneuver is to observe the freshly separated plasma, which is usually clear; prolonged chilling will engender turbidity, which is caused by denaturation of lipoprotein owing to the temperature dependence of hydrophobic interactions.

Secondary causes of this abnormal electrophoretic pattern include hypothyroidism, systemic lupus erythematosus, and diabetic ketoacidosis, all of which can be diagnosed because of their characteristic clinical manifestations (see Table 31–4).

Treatment

Dietary therapy is usually quite effective. It involves weight loss followed by ingestion of a diet that provides 40 percent of calories as carbohydrate and 40 percent as fat, the latter preponderating in unsaturated fats.

Familial Endogenous Hypertriglyceridemia

Inherited and acquired disorders manifesting as hypertriglyceridemia as a consequence of accumulation of VLDL and/or chylomicrons in the blood are not as well understood as those previously discussed. Indeed the nosology for the inherited disorders of triglyceride transport is undergoing modification, so that the unwary reader may not always be sure what disorder is being spoken of. Part of the difficulty is that dietary and other environmental factors may impinge on the nature of the aggregates in the blood; electrophoretic separation has been the most useful laboratory means to discriminate among the disorders (different variants have been described). A consensus is now emerging that should permit a more logical classification until definitive understanding of the underlying defect is achieved.

Familial endogenous hypertriglyceridemia is inherited as an autosomal dominant trait manifesting usually as an isolated elevation of VLDL—the so-called Type IV pattern. Confusion can arise because, with elevation of plasma triglycerides above 1000 mg/dl, larger chylomicron-like particles may arise, giving the picture of a mixed hypertriglyceridemia (Type V pattern).

Rarely does the inherited disorder present in childhood. Clinical findings are variable but can include ischemic heart disease, xanthelasma, and arcus corneae.

Secondary Causes of Endogenous Hypertriglyceridemia

The Type IV pattern is the most commonly encountered lipoprotein pattern as a secondary manifestation of a variety of disorders apparently tied together by unavailability of glucose for the body's energy needs. These disorders include: uncontrolled diabetes mellitus, starvation, malabsorption, glycogen storage diseases (Types I, III, and IV), nephrotic syndrome, Cushing's syndrome, and total lipodystrophy.

The Type IV and V patterns are distinguished by the presence of chylomicrons in Type V in addition to the increased prebeta-band seen in both.

Treatment

Dietary manipulation along with weight reduction is often very helpful in normalizing triglyceride levels.

Familial Multiple Lipoprotein Type Hyperlipidemia (Combined Hyperlipidemia—IIA, IIB, IV)

Clinical Features

By definition variability of lipoprotein and lipid patterns characterizes the plasma findings in patients and their relatives. So wide can be the spectrum of findings that the patient and relatives may show, at any one time, one of three patterns: Type IIa, Type IIb, or Type IV. Without firm evidence as to the underlying inherited abnormality such diverse laboratory findings may delay recognition of the familial nature of the disorder unless it is sought vigorously.

As a group, clinical findings include obesity, premature myocardial insufficiency, and glucose intolerance. Xanthomata are absent. Inheritance appears to be as an autosomal dominant trait. The underlying biochemical defect still eludes investigators.

REFERENCES

Brown, M.S., Goldstein, J.L., and Fredrickson, D.S.: Familial type 3 hyperlipoproteinemia (dysbetalipoproteinemia). *In* Stanbury, J.B., Wyngaarden, J.B., Fredrickson, D.S., et al. (eds.): The Metabolic Basis of Inherited Disease. 5th ed. McGraw-Hill, New York, 1983, p. 655.

Brown, M.S., Kovanen, P.T., and Goldstein, J.L.: Regulation of plasma cholesterol by lipoprotein receptors. Science 212:628, 1981.

Cooper, R.A., Durocher, J.R., and Leslie, M.H.: Decreased fluidity of red cell membrane lipids in abetalipoproteinemia. J. Clin. Invest. 60:115, 1977.

Glomset, J.A., Norum, K.R., and Gjone, E.: Familial lecithin: cholesterol acyltransferase deficiency. *In* Stanbury, J.B., Wyngaarden, J.B., Fredrickson, D.S., et al. (eds.): The Metabolic Basis of Inherited Disease. 5th ed. McGraw-Hill, New York, 1983, p. 643.

Goldstein, J.L., and Brown, M.S.: Familial hypercholesterolemia. *In* Stanbury, J.B., Wyngaarden, J.B., Fredrickson, D.S., et al. (eds.): The Metabolic Basis of Inherited Disease, 5th ed. McGraw-Hill, New York, 1983, p. 672.

Goldstein, J.L., Anderson, R.G.W., and Brown, M.S.: Coated pits, coated vesicles, and receptor-mediated endocytosis. Nature 279:679, 1979.

Havel, R.J., Goldstein, J.L., and Brown, M.S.: Lipoproteins and lipid transport. *In* Bondy, P.K., and Rosenberg, L.E. (eds.): Metabolic Control and Disease. 8th ed. W. B. Saunders Co., Philadelphia, 1980, p. 393.

Herbert, P.N., Assmann, G., Gotto, A.M., and Frederickson, D.S.: Familial lipoprotein deficiency: abetalipoproteinemia, hypobetalipoproteinemia and Tangier disease. *In* Stanbury, J.B., Wyngaarden, J.B., Fredrickson, D.S., et al. (eds.): The Metabolic Basis of Inherited Disease. 5th ed. McGraw-Hill, New York, 1983, p. 589.

Illingworth, D.R., Connor, W.E., and Miller, R.G.: Abetalipoproteinemia: Report of two cases and a review of therapy. Arch. Neurol. 37:659, 1980.

Kane, J.P., Malloy, M.J., Tun, P., et al.: Normalization of low density lipoprotein levels in heterozygous familial hypercholesterolemia with a combined drug regimen. N. Engl. J. Med. 304:251, 1981.

Levy, R.I.: Cholesterol, lipoproteins, apoproteins and heart disease: Present status and future prospects. Clin. Chem. 27:653, 1981.

Low, P.A., Dyck, P.J., Okazaki, H., et al.: The splanchnic autonomic outflow in amyloid neuropathy and Tangier disease. Neurology 31:461, 1981.

Nicoll, A., Miller, N.E., and Lewis, B.: High density lipoprotein metabolism. Adv. Lipid Res. 17:54, 1980.

Nikkilä, E.A.: Familial lipoprotein lipase deficiency and related disorders of chylomicron metabolism. *In* Stanbury, J.B., Wyngaarden, J.B., Fredrickson, D.S., et al. (eds.): The Metabolic Basis of Inherited Disease. 5th ed. McGraw-Hill, New York, 1983, p. 622.

Nilsson-Ehle, P., Garfinkel, A.S., and Schotz, M.C.: Lipolytic enzymes and plasma lipoprotein metabolism. Ann. Rev. Biochem. 49:667, 1980.

Olivecrona, T., Bengtsson, G., Marklund, S., et al.: Heparin-lipoprotein lipase interactions. Fed. Proc. 36:60, 1977.

Scanu, A.M., Wissler, R.W., and Getz, G.S. (eds.): The Biochemistry of Atherosclerosis. Marcel Dekker, New York, 1979.

Soutar, A.K., and Myant, N.B.: Plasma lipoproteins. *In* International Review of Biochemistry. Vol. 25. Offord, R.E. (ed.): University Park Press, Baltimore, 1979, p. 55.

Tall, A.R., and Small, D.M.: Body cholesterol removal: Role of plasma high-density lipoproteins. Adv. Lipid Res. 17:1, 1980.

Tsang, R.C., and Glueck, C.J.: Atherosclerosis: A pediatric problem. Current Prob. Ped. 9:2, 1979.

Wenz, B., and Barland, P.: Therapeutic intensive plasmapheresis. Seminars in Hematol. 18:147, 1981.

32

Mucopolysaccharidoses

INTRODUCTION

The mucopolysaccharidoses involve the storage of polymeric carbohydrates, termed glycosaminoglycans (GAG's) or mucopolysaccharides, in various tissues of the body. Each disease results from a defect in a specific lysosomal hydrolase involved in the sequential degradation of these glycosaminoglycans. In these disorders, nearly all cells show intralysosomal storage of material.

In general these diseases are progressive, although they vary widely in severity. Coarse facial features are a feature of all, accounting for the use in the past of the stigmatizing designation "gargoylism." Skeletal abnormalities are represented by a wide spectrum of changes embraced by the term dysostosis multiplex. Joint changes are also found, often with limitation of motion. Owing to the wide distribution of GAG's, multiple organs are involved, including the liver and spleen, heart, and blood vessels. Several forms manifest clouding of the cornea.

All but one of the mucopolysaccharidoses, namely Morquio's syndrome, are due to an enzyme defect in the sequential degradation of dermatan sulfate and heparan (heparitin) sulfate, singly or in combination. In Morquio's syndrome the defect involves the catabolism of keratan sulfate. Degradation of each of the polysaccharides begins at the nonreducing end and occurs one bond at a time. A block at one step precludes the next enzyme in the sequence from carrying out its reaction. Hence the material will initially accumulate intracellularly, specifically within the lysosomes.

Glycosaminoglycans (GAG's)

In contrast to glycogen, which is a homogenous polymer of glucose units only, the glycosaminoglycans are heterogenous carbohydrate polymers and are composed of more than one type of simple building block (Fig. 32–1). These molecules are comprised of hexoses with amino and sulfate residues and are therefore polyanionic. These saccharide polymers occur in covalent association with protein, the combined entity being termed a proteoglycan. Combination of GAG's with protein produces a macromolecule with the higher order structure and binding ("lock and key") specificity of proteins and the mechanical strength of polysaccharides. GAG's represent the major component of the nonfibrous matrix of connective tissue occurring in large quantities in cartilage, bone, blood vessels, heart valves, skin, tendons, and cornea and in smaller amounts in liver and brain.

GAG's are heteropolysaccharides that are comprised of a carbohydrate backbone of alternating uronic acid and hexosamine residues. Figure 32–2 shows these monosaccharide components. The uronic acids, β-D-glucuronic acid and α-L-iduronic acid are C-5 epimers, while the amino sugars are acetylated derivatives of the parent hexoses, glucose (N-acetyl-β-D-glucosamine) and galactose (N-acetyl-β-D-galactosamine). In keratan sulfate un-derivatized D-galactose residues are present. Further modification of the amino sugars is provided by addition of sulfate residues at position 4 or 6. The result then is a polyanionic molecule that contains both acidic sulfate and carboxyl groups, thus permitting electrostatic interactions with other molecules (see Part I).

Distinction of each GAG is based both upon the constituent building blocks, the position and configuration of glycosidic linkages, and which substituents have sulfate residues. In contrast to the proteins, whose linear sequence is rigidly controlled by the base sequence in mRNA (see Part I), no such stringent control of the linear sequence of residues in the GAG's obtains. Hence these are

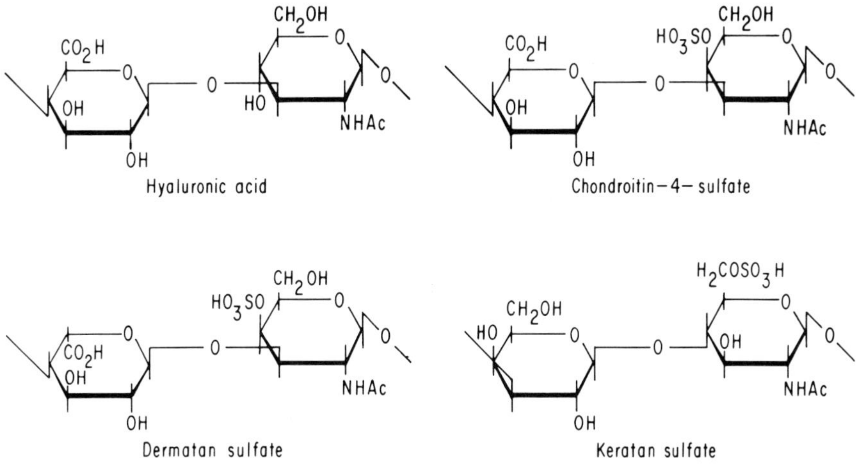

CH$_2$OH

CO$_2$H

OH

OH

HO

NHAc

Hyaluronic acid

CH$_2$OH

HO$_3$SO

CO$_2$H

OH

OH

NHAc

Chondroitin–4–sulfate

CH$_2$OH

HO$_3$SO

CO$_2$H
OH

OH

NHAc

Dermatan sulfate

H$_2$COSO$_3$H

CH$_2$OH

HO

OH

OH

NHAc

Keratan sulfate

Figure 32–1 The repeating disaccharide units of glycosaminoglycans. (From Bondy, P. K., and Rosenberg, L. E. (eds.): Duncan's Diseases of Metabolism. 7th ed. Philadelphia, W. B. Saunders, 1974.)

polydisperse structures, i.e., they evidence a high degree of heterogeneity in structure, since the sequence is controlled by enzymes, which, while operating in a sequential manner, must possess group rather than substrate specificity. This permits a degree of randomness in the selection of sugars to be added or sulfated. The additional chemical groups in these molecules introduce charges that alter their binding and steric properties. Hyaluronate and the chondroitin sulfates have relatively simple structures, but dermatan sulfate, heparan sulfate, and heparan species possess the bewilder-

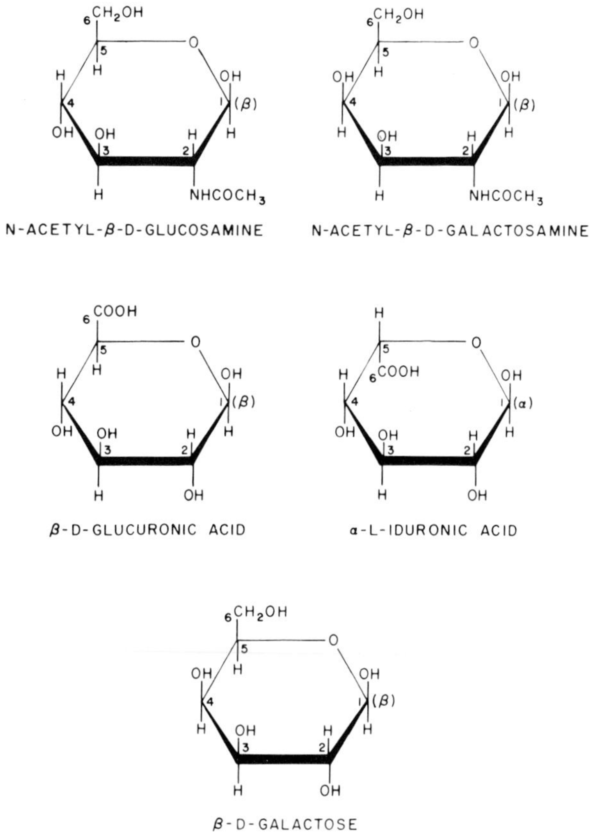

Figure 32–2 The monosaccharide units of glycosaminoglycans. (From Sly, W. S.: The mucopolysaccharidoses. *In* Bondy, P. K., and Rosenberg, L. E. (eds.): Metabolic Control and Disease. 8th ed. Philadelphia, W. B. Saunders Co., 1980.)

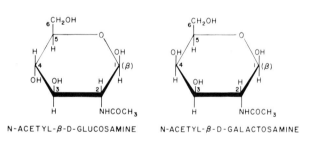

N-ACETYL-β-D-GLUCOSAMINE

N-ACETYL-β-D-GALACTOSAMINE

β-D-GLUCURONIC ACID

α-L-IDURONIC ACID

β-D-GALACTOSE

Table 32–1 COMPOSITION AND DISTRIBUTION OF THE MUCOPOLYSACCHARIDES*

	Synonyms	Hexose	Uronic Acid	Predominant Distribution	Remarks
Hyaluronic acid		N-Acetylglucosamine	D-Glucuronic acid	Vitreous humor Synovial fluid Umbilical cord Skin	
Chondroitin 4-sulfate	Chondroitin Sulfate A	N-Acetylgalactosamine -4-sulfate	D-Glucuronic acid	Cartilage Bone Aorta	Undersulfated forms exist
Chondroitin 6-sulfate	Chondroitin Sulfate C	N-Acetylgalactosamine -6-sulfate	D-Glucuronic acid	Cartilage Heart valves Aorta	Undersulfated forms exist
Dermatan sulfate	Chondroitin Sulfate B	N-Acetylgalactosamine -4-sulfate	L-Iduronic acid	Skin Heart valves Lung, tendon	Also contains D-glucuronic acid: variable additional sulfation
Keratan sulfate	Keratosulfate	Galactose N-Acetylglucosamine -6-sulfate	None	Cornea Cartilage Nucleus pulposus	Also contains galactosamine and galactose-6-sulfate; variable content of sialic acid
Heparan sulfate	Heparitin sulfate Heparin monosulfate	N-Acetylglucosamine N-Sulfate glucosamine	D-Glucuronic acid L-Iduronic acid	Aorta Liver Lung	Variable sulfation
Heparin		N-Sulfate glucosamine H-Acetylglucosamine	D-Glucuronic acid L-Iduronic acid	Liver Mast cells	Variable additional sulfation

*From Bondy, P. K., and Rosenberg, L. E.: Duncan's Diseases of Metabolism. Philadelphia, W. B. Saunders Co., 1974.

ing heterogenity spoken of above. Table 32–1 lists the main properties and biological distribution of these polymers in mammalian tissues.

GAG's play an essential role in maintaining the structural integrity of connective tissue. Indeed, the resiliency of cartilage appears to depend upon the ability of these polyanionic molecules to trap water and microions while excluding larger molecules in the fashion of a molecular sieve (dextran-like). GAG's fulfill these lubricating and load-bearing functions by virtue of their anionic charges (carboxyl and sulfate groups), which allow the trapping of water so that the polymers swell. Indeed, these heteropolysaccharides swell on undergoing dissolution in water, producing solutions of high viscosity and elasticity. For example, 1 gram of hyaluronic acid dissolves in an aqueous volume of approximately 1 liter, precluding the addition of any other macromolecule. Thus the GAG occupies a volume 1000 to 10,000 times larger than the volume that would be occupied by the same monosaccharide units were they to dissolve individually. Hence, when these units are formed by covalent linkage, cooperative interactions occur, which transform and amplify the range of physical phenomena that would be expected from the individual units. Such hierarchy of function also characterizes the interactions of amino acids in proteins. In both instances, water is the pivotal solvent necessary for the expression of these biological properties (see Part I).

Evidence is also accumulating that indicates an interaction of GAG's with cell-membrane components in such varied processes as cell growth, intercellular communication, and information reception. In addition, they play a role in organizing the extracellular matrix of connective tissue, in the coagulation process, and in the interaction of certain plasma proteins with the wall of blood vessels. The latter implicates them in the cardiovascular manifestations of some of the mucopolysaccharidoses and raises as well the larger question of the atherosclerotic process itself.

Mucopolysaccharides in the central nervous system are derived from proteoglycans, which turn over rapidly during the period in which the brain is forming. The formation of synapses is part of this process and probably is a major contributor of these compounds; surface glycoproteins at synaptic junctions are catabolized during the formation of these information transmission sites.

Pathogenesis of Mental Retardation in the Mucopolysaccharidoses

Under normal circumstances GAG's are found as a component of neuronal perikarya, myelinated axons, and glial elements of human brain. Expressed as a percentage of defatted dry weight of brain, they account for 0.3 percent. When these polymers were examined post-mortem in brains of patients with Hurler's syndrome, Hunter's syndrome and Sanfilippo's syndrome, GAG accounted for 1 to 1.5 percent of the defatted dry weight. In addition there was also a shift in size distribution to smaller partially degraded moieties, probably as a result of the action of nonspecific endoglycosidases.

Examination of the gangliosidic content and composition of these brains revealed striking abnormalities. Whereas GM_1, GD_{1a}, GD_{1b}, and GT_1 account for the preponderance of gangliosides in normal brain, in these patients dying with mucopolysaccharidoses, the minor gangliosides GM_3, GM_2, and GD_3 accounted for as much as 65 percent of ganglioside. Only in the gangliosidoses (see Chapter 30) are such abnormalities as these encountered. In both circumstances severe mental retardation is a key manifestation.

Several phenomena may conspire to produce the mental impairment characteristic of the mucopolysaccharidoses. GAG's, which have been found in higher concentration in myelinating axons in the brain of an 8-month-old normal infant than in the older individuals studied, may play a role in accretion and arborization of axons. Additionally, and potentially at least as important as the foregoing consideration, GAG accumulation leads to the accumulation of minor gangliosides. Excessive GAG in neurons and abnormal distribution of glycosphingolipids could disrupt neuronal geometry and synaptic interactions, particularly by altering the electrical properties of these excitable neural components.

MUCOPOLYSACCHARIDOSES (FIG. 32–3 AND TABLE 32–2)

Hurler's Syndrome

One of the puzzling discoveries in this area of lysosomal diseases is the finding that the severe Hurler's syndrome and relatively mild Scheie's syndrome are both due to deficiencies of the same enzyme, α-L-iduronidase. Autosomal recessive inheritance accounts for both syndromes and so a different allele must occur at the same structural locus for the enzyme. In vitro assays have shown some differences in thermal stability and affinity for the substrate, but until purified enzyme is available unequivocal differences (which would seem to be a necessary condition) between the enzymes or isozymes remain undefined.

Clinical Features

Hurler's syndrome, the most rapidly progressive of these disorders, usually results in the death of the child before the end of the first decade. Although the first year of life may be entirely uneventful, by the second year persistent nasal discharge, recurrent ear infections, or noisy breathing may cause parents to seek medical evaluation. Examination may also disclose lumbar lordosis, a chest deformity, or stiff joints, as well as a fall off in growth rate. Thereafter, delay in growth becomes quite obvious. Deterioration of psychomotor development proceeds relentlessly around this

Table 32–2 MUCOPOLYSACCHARIDOSES AND MUCOLIPIDOSES*

Disease		Enzyme Defect	Urinary GAG Excretion	Mental Retardation	Coarsened Features
Mucopolysaccharidoses					
IH Hurler		α-L-Iduronidase	DS:HS 3:1	3+	3+
IH/S Hurler-Scheie Compound		α-L-Iduronidase alleles	DS:HS	+	2+
IS Scheie		α-L-Iduronidase alleles	DS:HS 1:1	−	+
II Hunter		Iduronate sulfatase	DS:HS† 1:1	3+	2+
III Sanfilippo forms	A	N-Sulfamidase	HS	3+	+
(clinically	B	N-Acetylglucosamidase			
indistinguishable)	C	Acetyl CoA:α-glucosaminide-N-acetyltransferase			
IV Morquio		Gal-6-sulfate sulfatase	KS:CS† 1:1	−	+/−
V (unoccupied, currently classified as Scheie)					
VI Maroteaux-Lamy		N-Acetylgalactosamine-4-sulfatase (arylsulfatase-B)	DS:HS 4–5:1	−	3+
VII β-Glucuronidase Deficiency		β-Glucuronidase	HS,DS C-4/6-S	+ to 2+	2+
VIII		Glucosamine-6-sulfatase	KS:HS	2+ to 3+	−
Mucolipidoses					
I		Neuraminidase	Normal	+	3+
II I-Cell		Incorporation of hydrolases into lysosome	3+ Oligosaccharides	3+	3+
III Pseudo-Hurler		Milder variant of I-cell	Oligosaccharides	+ to 2+	+/−
IV		Not known	Normal	2+ to 3+	−
Mannosidosis		α-Mannosidase	3+ Oligosaccharides	3+	+ to 3+
Fucosidosis		α-Fucosidase	3+	3+	+ to 2+

*All are inherited as autosomal recessive traits except Hunter's syndrome, which is X-linked.
†Age-dependent.
+/− variable; + minimal; 2+ moderate; 3+ marked.

time but is not as profound or as rapidly progressive as with the neuronopathic sphingolipidoses (see Chapter 30). The features so characteristic of all of these children are the progressive coarsening of the face, with a large head, thickened lips, and hirsutism. Examination of the eyes reveals corneal clouding. Deafness is quite common, consisting of combined conductive and neurosensory causes. Storage of GAG's in the viscera leads to hepatosplenomegaly with abdominal distention, punctuated by hernias in various sites. Stiff joints and thickened skin, the latter often first appreciated because of difficulty in starting an intravenous drip, are almost invariant. Valvular changes with a predilection for the mitral and aortic valves are common, showing the same distribution as in rheumatic disease. A communicating hydrocephalus frequently develops. Repeated respiratory infections and worsening cardiac function are the usual causes of death.

X-rays of the skeleton reveal the gamut of dysostosis multiplex, with the most usual findings being widening of the medial end of the clavicle, spatulate ribs, claw hands, and a lumbar gibbus with anterior beaking of the vertebrae.

As discussed in more detail in the section on growth and development (see Chapter 10), bone growth and calcification depend upon coordinated physical and chemical interactions between GAG's, collagen, and hydroxyapatite. Hence interference with the timing, structure, or correct amount of any of these components can have far-reaching and permanent effects on the normal contours and size of bone.

Table 32–2 MUCOPOLYSACCHARIDOSES AND MUCOLIPIDOSES* *Continued*

Dysostosis multiplex	Hepatospleno-megaly	Cardiovascular Findings	Ocular Findings	Deafness	Survival
3+	2+ to 3+	2+ to 3+	3+	2+	5–10 years
2+	+	2+	3+	+/–	20's
+	+/–	Aortic valve	3+	–	50's
2+ to 3+	2+ to 3+	2+ to 3+	Corneal clouding rare	2+	10–15 years
+	+ to 2+	–	–	+	puberty
3+	+/–	+	+	+	20–40 years
3+	2+	2+	3+	+	adulthood
2+	2+	Aortic valve	Appear late +	–	variable
2+	+	–	–	+	unknown
3+	2+	–	Cherry-red macula	+ to 2+	10 years
2+	3+	3+	–	+/–	2–8 years
+ to 2+	+	Aortic valve	+	–	adulthood
–	–	–	3+	–	unknown
+ to 2+	2+	–	– to +	+	variable to adulthood
2+	+ to 2+	+ to 3+	+/–	+/–	

Biochemical Defects

The exoglycosidase α-L-iduronidase is deficient in Hurler's syndrome. Recalling that iduronic acid residues are found in both dermatan and heparan sulfate, sequential degradation of both of these GAG's is blocked at this step. The mucopolysacchariduria found in this disorder appears to be the result of the action of hepatic endoglycosidases, which can bring about a limited degradation of these polymers at internal points, generating fragments which accumulate and find their way into the urine.

Laboratory Findings

Mucopolysacchariduria involving both dermatan and heparan sulfate is marked in this disorder. Definitive diagnosis can be accomplished by measurement of α-L-iduronidase activity in cultured fibroblasts or leukocytes using phenyliduronide as substrate. Prenatal detection of an affected fetus can be accomplished during the second trimester by enzyme assay of cells cultured from amniotic fluid. Before enzyme diagnostic methods were available, attempts at prenatal diagnosis were pursued by evaluating the level or pattern of mucopolysaccharides in the amniotic fluid. Unfortunately, this method is not reliable, being fraught with considerable variability in level, which depends on the time of gestation that specimens are obtained.

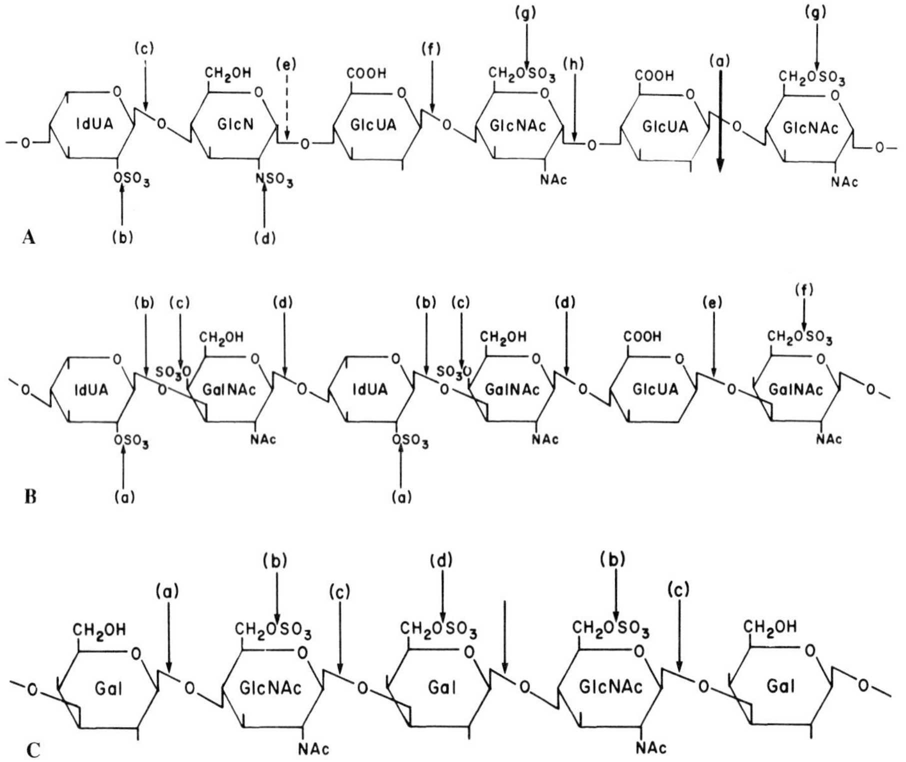

Figure 32–3 Mucopolysaccharide catabolism and its defects. *A,* Heparan sulfate. (a) = endoglucuronidase, (b) = L-sulfoiduronidate sulfatase (MPS II), (c) = α-L-iduronidase (MPS IH and MPS IS), (d) = heparan sulfate sulfaminidase (MPS IIIA), (e) = ?(h), (f) = β-D-glucuronidase (MPS VII), (g) = N-acetylglucosamine-6-sulfatase, (h) = N-acetyl-α-D-glucosaminidase (MPS III B). *B,* Dermatan sulfate. (a) = L-sulfoiduronidate sulfatase (MPS II), (b) = α-L-iduronidase (MPS IH and MPS IS), (c) = N-acetylgalactosamine-4-sulfatase (MPS VI), (d) = N-acetyl-β-hexosaminidase (Sandhoff's disease), (e) = β-glucuronidase (MPS VII), (f) = N-acetylgalactosamine-6-sulfatase (MPS IV). *C,* Keratan sulfate. (a) = β-galactosidase (GM₁ gangliosidosis and MPS IV), (b) = N-acetylglucosamine-6-sulfatase, (c) = N-acetyl-β-D-glucosaminidase (Sandhoff's disease), (d) = galactose-6-sulfatase = ?(b). (From Sly, W. S.: The mucopolysaccharidoses. *In* Bondy, P. K., and Rosenberg, L. E. (eds.): Metabolic Control and Disease. 8th ed. Philadelphia, W. B. Saunders Co., 1980.)

Treatment

Specific treatment is not yet available, but supportive care to the child and family is essential.

Scheie's Syndrome

As noted above, this disorder is allelic with Hurler's syndrome. It has been described in a number of adults, who manifested severe clouding of the cornea, somewhat coarsened facial features, and claw hands, but normal intelligence. In contrast to Hurler's syndrome, stature is normal. Involvement of the aortic valve with associated murmurs occurs.

Biochemical Defects

The enzyme defect is the same as that of the Hurler's syndrome, i.e., α-L-iduronidase. It would seem likely that this defect would manifest greater residual activity in vitro, to explain the mild clinical picture. However, this prediction has not yet been confirmed by in vitro fibroblast assays. This puzzling situation could result from the use of synthetic substrates or absence of a factor present in vivo.

Laboratory Diagnosis

Enzyme assay will show absence of α-L-iduronidase activity but will not distinguish Scheie's from Hurler's syndrome. The later onset and more benign course of Scheie's syndrome should make this distinction clear-cut.

Hurler-Scheie Type Mucopolysaccharidosis

With discovery that the Hurler's and Scheie's syndromes were allelic, further complexity was added by the possibility that a clinical variant, intermediate in severity, might exist. Such Hurler-Scheie compound individuals survive into their twenties but have more severe clinical findings than those with Scheie's syndrome. Structural and mental development are compromised, and bone and joint abnormalities are frequent. Hepatosplenomegaly and corneal opacification occur, as do cardiac abnormalities.

Hunter's Syndrome

Patients with this mucopolysaccharidosis survive longer than those with Hurler's syndrome and have a very low incidence of corneal clouding. It is the only one of these disorders inherited in an X-linked recessive manner. In general, the clinical features in this syndrome are similar to those characterizing Hurler's syndrome, but they are somewhat milder. The coarsened facial features, dwarfing, and stiff joints seen with Hurler's syndrome are seen here as well. Impairment of intellectual function does not occur as rapidly, but progressive deafness is universal. Slit-lamp examination is required to demonstrate the minimal corneal clouding as well as retinitis pigmentosa. Skeletal changes are not as severe, and the lumbar gibbus is less pronounced. Cardiac dysfunction occurs because of valvular, myocardial, and vascular involvement and is the usual cause of death. In particular, these patients are at an increased risk for arrhythmias during general anesthesia.

As with Hurler-Scheie type mucopolysaccharidosis there appear to be allelic forms of Hunter's syndrome that have milder clinical manifestations.

Biochemical Defects

The deficient enzyme in Hunter's syndrome is iduronate sulfatase, which removes sulfate residues from iduronic acid. Such groups occur in both dermatan sulfate and heparan sulfate, resulting in a cessation of the sequential hydrolysis of the two polymers. Action by some endoglycosidases can effect cleavage to smaller fragments which contribute to the mucopolysacchariduria.

Laboratory Findings

Mucopolysacchariduria (evaluated by electrophoresis) is marked, with excretion of approximately equal amounts of the affected polymers dermatan sulfate and heparan sulfate. The ratio may be skewed in favor of heparan sulfate however. Enzyme assay in leukocytes is the method of choice, and prenatal diagnosis can be accomplished using cultured amniotic cells.

Treatment

There is no specific treatment for this disorder.

Sanfilippo's Syndrome

Clinical Features

These mucopolysaccharidoses encompass the patients with the most severe progressive mental retardation. The relatively mild or absent somatic features present a stark contrast to the dementia.

Corneal clouding does not occur, and cardiovascular changes are unusual. Stature may be normal or only minimally affected. Joint involvement is not as severe as in Hurler's and Hunter's syndromes, and x-rays of the bone show only scant evidence of dysostosis multiplex. Posterior thickening of the calvarium may be the most characteristic skeletal finding in this disorder. Hepatosplenomegaly is usually not impressive.

Biochemical Defects

Absence of one of the enzymes mediating the sequential breakdown of heparan sulfate accounts for the Sanfilippo variants. Referring back to Figure 32–3, it can be seen that there are four linkages unique to this polymer, each of which should require a different enzyme for hydrolysis. To date, three of the four enzyme defects have been described. Clinically these three enzyme defects result in indistinguishable pictures.

In the A form, the enzyme heparan sulfate sulfamidase, which removes the nitrogen-bound sulfate residue, is deficient. In the next step, the α-glucosaminide residue resulting from the action of the sulfamidase must first be acetylated, forming α-N-acetylglucosaminide. Acetyl CoA:α-glucosaminide-N-acetyltransferase, the enzyme mediating this step, is deficient in Sanfilippo type C. In the third step, the N-acetylglucosamine group is removed by N-acetyl-α-glucosaminidase. It is this enzyme that is deficient in Sanfilippo type B.

Laboratory Findings

Mucopolysacchariduria is found by screening methods in most but not all patients. Cellulose acetate electrophoresis in those with urinary excretion will reveal heparan sulfate, but occasionally Hunter's syndrome patients as well will show this polymer only. Routine toluidine blue testing is likely to be negative in Sanfilippo's syndrome. Definitive diagnosis requires assay of enzymes in cultured fibroblasts or white cells. Prenatal diagnosis should also be possible.

Morquio's Syndrome

Clinical Features

This disorder affects the skeletal system predominantly, with secondary effects on the spinal cord. The physician may first notice a prominence of the lower ribs and somewhat coarsened facial features at the age of 12 to 18 months. Urine metabolic screen may reveal mucopolysacchariduria, and identification of the material as keratan sulfate will point to the diagnosis. As growth continues, further overt skeletal changes develop, including knock-knee, short trunk, pectus carinatum, and a very short neck. Corneal clouding is usually mild, but sensorineural deafness is almost universal. In contrast to stiff joints, found in many of the mucopolysaccharidoses, loose joints are more common in this syndrome. Hypoplasia or absence of the odontoid process of the second cervical vertebrae in combination with lax ligaments leads to atlantoaxial subluxation. While signs may be subtle, the knowledgeable physician will want to inquire into the history for evidence of cervical myelopathy. Not uncommonly, questioning will disclose that such children need to be carried from bed on awakening, being able to ambulate thereafter. Milder forms have been described.

Biochemical Defects

The defective enzyme in this syndrome is galactose-6-sulfatase, which splits a linkage peculiar to keratan sulfate. This glycosaminoglycan occurs in cartilage, nucleus pulposus, and cornea, accounting for the clinical manifestations.

Diagnosis depends upon identification of keratan sulfate in the urine and demonstration of the specific enzyme defect in fibroblasts or white cells. It is usual for the mucopolysacchariduria to decrease markedly by adolescence.

Treatment

Therapy is at present limited to orthopedic surgery and physical medicine.

Maroteaux-Lamy Syndrome

Clinical Features

This syndrome is distinguished by growth retardation and skeletal changes, but intellectual function is normal. Decrease in growth may not be appreciated until 2 to 3 years of age. Subsequently coarsening of facial features, knock-knees, a protuberant sternum, and limitation of joint movement ensue. Obvious corneal clouding and heart valve involvement with a propensity to cardiac failure are very common. Hydrocephalus and a picture similar to that seen in Morquio's syndrome occur frequently as a result of atlantoaxial subluxation.

With all of these syndromes, forms with attenuated severity, on the basis of presumed allelic or genetic-compound varieties, are being described with increased frequency as biochemical examination of children with skeletal abnormalities is becoming more widely employed. Thus far no patient with Maroteaux-Lamy syndrome has been described with normal stature, a point of distinction from Scheie's syndrome.

Biochemical Defects

The error is a defect in the enzyme arylsulfatase-β (*N*-acetylgalactosamine-4-sulfatase), which cleaves a sulfate group from residues occurring in dermatan sulfate. Diagnosis can be made by demonstrating dermatan sulfate in the urine and the specific enzyme defect in cells. Prenatal diagnosis is also possible.

β-Glucuronidase Deficiency

Several patients have been described with this disorder, evidencing a certain degree of clinical variability. The initial description included coarsened facial features, hepatosplenomegaly, and some skeletal abnormalities. Mental and physical development were somewhat slow. Another patient with characteristic facies had normal intelligence. Peripheral and bone marrow granulocytes show metachromatic granules.

Biochemical Defects

The deficient enzyme, β-glucuronidase, is required for the removal of glucuronic acid from both dermatan and heparan sulfate. As yet unexplained is the lack of excretion of fragments of chondroitin sulfate and hyaluronic acid, since these glycosaminoglycans also contain a substantial number of beta-linked glucuronic acid residues. The gene coding for this enzyme is on chromosome 7, and inheritance is autosomal recessive.

Diagnosis is suggested by finding dermatan and heparan sulfate in the urine and confirmed by enzyme assay showing deficient activity in fibroblasts, leukocytes, or serum.

REFERENCES

Chakrabarti, B., and Park, J.W.: Glycosaminoglycans: Structure and interaction. CRC Crit. Rev. Biochem. 8:225, 1980.
Comper, W.D., and Laurent, T.C.: Physiological function of connective tissue polysaccharides. Physiol. Rev. 58:255, 1978.
Constantopoulos, G., McComb, R.D., and Dekaban, A.S.: Neurochemistry of the mucopolysaccharidoses: brain glycosaminoglycans in normals and four types of mucopolysaccharidoses. J. Neurochem. 26:901, 1976.
Constantopoulos, G., Iqbal, K., and Dekaban, A.S.: Mucopolysaccharidoses types IH, IS, II and IIIA:Glycosaminoglycans and lipids of isolated brain cells and other fractions from autopsied tissues. J. Neurochem. 34:1399, 1980.

Hopwood, J.J., and Elliott, H.: The diagnosis of the Sanfilippo syndrome using monosaccharide and oligosaccharide substrates to assay acetyl-CoA: 2-amino-2-deoxy-α-glucoside N-acetyltransferase activity. Clin. Chim. Acta 112:67, 1981.

Kennedy, J.F.: Proteoglycans: Biological and Chemical Aspects in Human Life. Elsevier, Amsterdam, 1979.

Klein, U., Kresse, H., and von Figura, K.: Sanfilippo syndrome type C: Deficiency of acetyl-CoA: α-glucosaminide N-acetyltransferase in skin fibroblasts. Proc. Natl. Acad. Sci. USA. 75:5185, 1978.

Kresse, H., Paschke, E., von Figura, K., et al.: San Filippo disease type D: Deficiency of N-acetylglucosamine-6-sulfate sulfatase required for heparan sulfate degradation. Proc. Natl. Acad. Sci. USA. 77:6822, 1980.

Lindahl, U., and Hook, M.: Glycosaminoglycans and their binding to biological macromolecules. Ann. Rev. Biochem. 47:385, 1978.

Lowden, J.A., and O'Brien, J.S: Sialidosis: A review of human neuraminidase deficiency. Am. J. Hum. Genet. 31:1, 1979.

McKusick, V.A., and Neufeld, E.F.: The mucopolysaccharide storage diseases. *In* Stanbury, J.B., Wyngaarden, J.B., Fredrickson, D.S., et al. (eds.): The Metabolic Basis of Inherited Disease, 5th ed. McGraw-Hill, New York, 1983, p. 751.

Pennock, C.A.: A review and selection of simple laboratory methods used for the study of glycosaminoglycan excretion and the diagnosis of the mucopolysaccharidoses. J. Clin. Pathol. 29:111, 1976.

Rees, D.A: Polysaccharide Shapes. Chapman and Hall, Ltd. London, 1977.

Sly, W.S.: The mucopolysaccharidoses. *In* Bondy, P.K., and Rosenberg, L.E. (eds.): Metabolic Control and Disease. 8th ed. W.B. Saunders Co. Philadelphia, 1980, p. 545.

Steinman, L., Tharp, B.R., Dorfman, L.J., et al.: Peripheral neuropathy in the cherry-red spot myoclonus syndrome (sialidosis type I). Ann. Neurol. 7:450, 1980.

Stevenson, R.E., Howell, R.R., McKusick, V.A., et al.: The iduronidase-deficient mucopolysaccharidoses: Clinical and roentgenographic features. Pediatrics 57:111, 1976.

33

Inborn Errors Affecting Muscle

ENERGY SOURCES FOR MUSCLE

Elsewhere we have discussed the glycogen storage diseases as a group (see Chapter 28). In this chapter we want to concentrate only on those glycogen metabolic disorders with significant or solitary involvement of muscle.

Glucose (derived from muscle glycogen) and fatty acids serve the varying energy needs of muscle. During sedentary conditions fatty acids provide for the preponderance of the energy requirements. However, when muscles are stressed to the point of maximal exertion glycogen provides the energy needs under these relatively hypoxic conditions. Because of limitation of both glycogen stores and the capacity for gluconeogenesis, prolonged exercise (which is submaximal by definition) forces the carbohydrate muscle economy to give way to a lipid-based one.

Deficiency of muscle phosphorylase, the enzyme responsible for cleavage of 1-4 links in the glycogen polymer, is the underlying defect in McArdle's disease, described three decades ago. Generally these patients are not detected in childhood; retrospectively, a careful history reveals a child unable to keep up in activity with his peers. In adolescence, increasing exercise demands usually bring out easy fatigability associated with stiffness and painful cramps. These cramps are actually contractures, that is, they are electrically silent rather than true muscle cramps during which motor units fire repeatedly. Myoglobinuria, because of muscle damage, may be the consequence of maximal or prolonged exercise; fortunately acute renal failure as a result is decidedly uncommon.

Since resting muscle and "warmed-up" muscle use fatty acids as their main energy source, individuals with myophosphorylase deficiency are usually symptom free under such conditions. In contrast to the situation with normal individuals, such patients fail to demonstrate a rise in serum lactate after ischemic exercise. This biochemical finding serves as a useful test to evaluate the possibility of phosphorylase deficiency.

Clinically deficiency of muscle phosphofructokinase (Tarui's disease) presents in much the same manner as does McArdle's disease. Erythrocytes suffer a partial deficiency of phosphofructo-kinase activity, which is reflected by a decrease in red cell life span and an increase in serum bilirubin. Presently therapy for both disorders involves avoidance of maximal exercise.

Lipids assume importance in the energy economy of muscle during prolonged exercise and during rest. Long-chain fatty acyl CoA derivatives are the main lipids "burned" in the mitochondria by β-oxidation. They require covalent linkage to carnitine (β-hydroxy-γ-trimethylaminobutyric acid) in order to effect transfer into the mitochondrion. This linkage is mediated by the enzyme carnitine palmitoyltransferase I, situated on the outer surface of the inner membrane of the mitochondrion (see Chapter 13). Once inside the mitochondrion the fatty acyl CoA–carnitine bond is hydrolyzed by carnitine palymitoyltransferase II, liberating the fatty acyl CoA for catabolism and generation of ATP. This process is depicted in Figure 33–1.

Because of the limitation of glycogen stores in muscle, when exercise is prolonged beyond 40 minutes, fatty acids increasingly support the muscle's energy needs. Indeed, greater reliance on fatty acids and ketones, formed in liver from acetyl CoA emerging at the end of the β-oxidation sequence, characterizes the adaptation of muscle to exercise as well as to starvation.

351

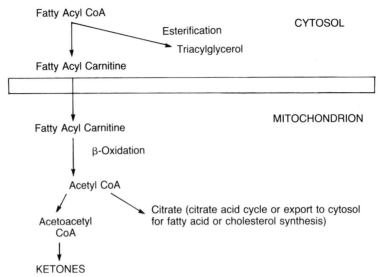

Figure 33–1 Scheme of conversion from fatty acid to ketone bodies in liver. Fatty acid entering the cell is "activated" by conversion to fatty acyl CoA; covalent linkage of fatty acyl CoA to carnitine is carried out by CAT I at the cystosolic surface of the mitochondrial membrane. The complex is transported into the mitochondrial matrix, where it is hydrolyzed to free the fatty acyl CoA by CAT II. Fatty acyl CoA then undergoes β-oxidation. In muscle the sequence proceeds through β-oxidation. Muscle cannot form ketones. When the carnitine system is defective, fat cannot be used to generate energy for muscle needs.

MUSCLE ENZYME DEFICIENCIES

Carnitine Palmitoyltransferase Deficiency

With the foregoing facts about the reliance of muscle on lipid substrates in mind, it is predictable that signs and symptoms of this disorder usually do not emerge until exercise is prolonged or is attempted under fasting conditions. Myalgias, episodic cramps, and myoglobinuria characterize the attacks, although the latter is rare before adolescence. In contrast to the defects in glycogenolysis or glycolysis, contractures do not occur with brief maximal exercise; serum lactate rises in association with ischemic exercise. Prolonged fasting results in a rise in serum CPK and myoglobinuria. Several of these patients were unable to mobilize ketones during fasting, further exacerbating the unavailability of substrates for energetic needs. Complementing this abnormality has been increased beta and prebeta-lipoproteins in several patients. Neither the lack of ketone mobilization nor the lipoprotein abnormalities are universal features however.

Deficiency of carnitine palmitoyltransferase can be demonstrated most easily in white cells as well as muscle, fibroblast, and liver. A diet rich in carbohydrate and low in fat associated with moderation in exercise is very helpful in avoiding symptoms. Because of the noxious effect of fasting on this condition, such a situation should be avoided.

Muscle Carnitine Deficiency

If a defect in the enzyme mediating the transfer of fatty acyl CoA's into mitochondria is responsible for muscle dysfunction, then it follows that limitation of the acceptor, i.e., carnitine, could produce similar results. In conformity with this expectation there is a form of carnitine deficiency limited to muscle as well as a more generalized form involving multiple organs These forms are termed myopathic and systemic, respectively.

Generalized progressive weakness characterizes the myopathic form. While limb and trunk muscles are involved predominantly, facial and pharyngeal muscles are occasionally involved as well. Myoglobinuria is not a feature of this disorder.

Carnitine is synthesized in liver and kidneys from lysine, with methionine serving as the methyl donor. In the myopathic form serum and liver levels are normal, but muscle concentrations are markedly decreased. A carnitine transport defect has been proposed.

Corticosteroids have improved the clinical condition of several patients, but the locus of their action is unknown. In several others carnitine replacement has been used with varying success. Considering the rationale for replacement with carnitine and its apparent lack of harmful side effects, it seems preferable to steroids.

Systemic Carnitine Deficiency

In this variant of carnitine deficiency liver dysfunction, often with a Reye's-like picture (hypoglycemia, hyperammonemia, enlarged fatty liver), is associated with myopathic features similar to those seen in the isolated muscle form. Muscle involvement is reflected by limb and trunk weakness. Indeed, cardiorespiratory failure has been the cause of death in a number of these patients.

Hypoglycemia has been reported in several of these patients and may be the consequence of two derangements in the energy economy of the individual. When fatty acid oxidation is compromised because of carnitine deficiency, it can no longer serve as the main energy source for the body, forcing the cells to utilize glucose preferentially. Compounding this forced dependence on glucose may be an inability of gluconeogenesis to satisfy these needs because of a lack of ATP normally generated by fatty acid oxidation. Together these two derangements may conspire to generate hypoglycemia.

Measurement of carnitine levels in serum, liver, and muscle showed a marked decrease. Since hepatic as well as serum levels were decreased the most likely defect is in the hepatic synthesis of carnitine. Supporting this contention has been the favorable response in patients administered carnitine by mouth in doses of 2 g/day.

Table 33-1 VARIANTS OF THE PERIODIC PARALYSES

	Hypokalemic	Hyperkalemic (Adynamia Episodica Hereditaria)	Periodic Paralysis With Cardiac Arrhythmia	Sodium-Responsive
Age of Onset	7–21 years	First decade	5–20 years	First decade
Genetics	AD	AD	?	AD
Clinical Features	Fluctuating periods of normal strength alternating with flaccid paralysis lasting hours to days. Cold or rest after exercise precipitates attacks, whereas continuation of mild exercise may prevent or abort attacks.			
	Oliguria	Myalgias		
Duration	Usually several hours (may last 4 days)	1–2 hours	2–3 days	Days to weeks
Time of Day	Paralyzed on awakening	Any time	Usually on awakening but can be any time	On awakening if N.P.O.
Severity	Complete quadriplegia frequent; muscles of respiration usually spared	Weakness of facial muscles; no respiratory involvement	Incomplete paresis; death from cardiac arrhythmias	Quadriplegia; respiratory muscles affected mildly
Precipitating Factors	Exercise followed by rest, high CHO meal, alcohol, salt, trauma, psychological stress	Exercise followed by rest, fasting, cold (paramyotonia); K rich food and drink	Exercise followed by rest, high sodium intake; premenstrual state	Usually exercise followed by rest; may occur at rest, however; alcohol; psychological stress
Treatment	Potassium salts	Epinephrine, calcium	Glucose and K^+; quinidine	Sodium
Prevention	Low sodium, high K diet, acetazolamide	Frequent CHO ingestion, inhalation of salbutamol at first sign of weakness	High CHO/K^+ diet	High Na^+ diet

Table 33-2 VARIANTS OF MUSCULAR DYSTROPHIES

	Duchenne's	Facioscapulohumeral	Limb Girdle	Oculopharyngeal	Myotonic Dystrophy
Onset	Usually before age 3	Late childhood or adolescence	20–45 years	Late adult life	Childhood to adulthood
Genetics	XLR	AD	AR	AD	AD
Muscle Groups	Pelvic and shoulder muscles, face usually spared	Facial and shoulder muscles	Proximal limb muscles	Levator palpebrae, pharyngeal lesser extent, facial, extraocular muscles	Facial, trunk, diaphragm, neck, smooth muscle ±
Symptoms and signs	Abnormal gait, fall frequently, difficulty climbing stairs, Gower's sign, pseudohypertrophy in most; unable to walk by end of first decade, never able to run; contractures	Cannot close eyes completely, cannot whistle, hands and feet spared, pseudohypertrophy uncommon, contracture rare	Pseudohypertrophy uncommon; feet, hands, and face uninvolved	Ptosis, myopathic facies, no myotonia	Myotonia, ptosis, frontal balding, hypogonadism
Cardiac Involvement	Minor arrhythmias, hypertrophy	EKG changes	No	No	Arrhythmias, heart block, heart failure
Progression	Steady deterioration	Slow	Slow with long remissions, progresses more rapidly than facioscapulohumeral	Slow	Slowly disabling
Prognosis	Rarely survive beyond 20 years	Good, occasionally severe disability, normal life span	Disability and death by 40 to 50	Usually normal life span	

354

EPISODIC MUSCLE WEAKNESS

In contrast to the disorders discussed above, certain disorders of muscle function manifest fluctuating weakness, so that between attacks the individual is normal or near normal. Pre-eminent among these are the periodic paralyses and myasthenia gravis. There are several forms of periodic paralytic disorders (see Table 33–1), all of which share certain features, which should suggest the category of disorders to the physician. Strikingly, paralysis occurs when exercise is followed by complete rest and can be aborted by continued mild exercise. During attacks, decreased tendon reflexes occur and return to normal during intercurrent periods. Cold is the primary provoking environmental factor.

Distinguishing clinical features of the four main syndromes are listed in Table 33–1. While the underlying biochemical defects in these disorders have not yet been defined, there is evidence that the sarcolemmal membrane calcium release-uptake system may malfunction as a consequence of the inherited defect.

MUSCULAR DYSTROPHIES

This group of disorders is bound together by their progressive nature and the fact that they are inherited. During the course of all of these disorders muscle fibers undergo gradual degeneration. Three general categories of abnormalities have been the focus of investigations to unravel the mystery of muscular dystrophy—microvascular supply, neuronal function, and muscle membrane, including the sarcotubular system. Recently, the pace of research into defects in membrane function has quickened, but it would be fair to say that as yet the fundamental defect is not established.

Table 33–2 provides information useful in distinguishing the majority of patients with variants of muscular dystrophy, with the caveat that variant forms exist that defy such neat distinctions.

REFERENCES

Appel, S.H., and Roses, A.D.: The muscular dystrophies. *In* Stanbury, J.B., Wyngaarden, J.B., Fredrickson, D.S., et al. (eds.): The Metabolic Basis of Inherited Disease. 5th ed. McGraw-Hill, New York, 1983, p. 1470.

Barchi, R.L.: Physical probes of biological membranes in studies of the muscular dystrophies. Muscle & Nerve 3:82, 1980.

Bertorini, T., Yeh, Y-Y., Trevisan, C., et al.: Carnitine palmitoyl transferase deficiency: Myoglobinuria and respiratory failure. Neurology 30:263, 1980.

Bosch, E.P., and Munsat, T.L.: Metabolic myopathies. Med. Clin. North Am. 63:759, 1979.

Chapoy, P.R., Angelini, C., Brown, W.J., et al.: Systemic carnitine deficiency—A treatable inherited lipid-storage disease presenting as Reye's syndrome. N. Engl. J. Med. 24:1389, 1980.

DiMauro, S., Trevisan, C., and Hays, A.: Disorders of lipid metabolism in muscle. Muscle & Nerve 3:369, 1980.

Engel, A.G.: Hypokalemic and hyperkalemic periodic paralyses. *In* Goldensohn, E.S., and Appel, S.H. (eds.): Scientific Approaches to Clinical Neurology. Lea & Febiger, Philadelphia, 1977, p. 1742.

Engel, W.K.: Introduction to the myopathies. *In* Goldensohn, E.S., and Appel, S.H. (eds.): Scientific Approaches to Clinical Neurology. Lea & Febiger, Philadelphia, 1977, p. 1602.

Rowland, L.P.: Biochemistry of muscle membranes in Duchenne muscular dystrophy. Muscle & Nerve 3:3, 1980.

Sweeny, P.R., and Brown, R.G.: The etiology of muscular dystrophy in mammals—A new perspective and hypothesis. Comp. Biochem. Physiol. 70B:27, 1981.

Symposium on Muscular Dystrophy: Brit. Med. Bull. 36:105–200, 1980.

Wang, P., and Clausen, T.: Treatment of attacks in hyperkalemic periodic paralysis by inhalation of salbutamol. Lancet I:221, 1976.

Ware, A.J., Burton, W.C., McGarry, J.D., et al.: Systemic carnitine deficiency. J. Pediatr. 93:959, 1978.

34

Disorders of Organic Acid Metabolism

INTRODUCTION

Many disorders of organic acid metabolism share with their prototype, maple syrup urine disease, a fulminant or catastrophic presentation in the neonatal period (Table 34–1). They should always be part of the work-up of *sepsis neonatorum* (see Chapter 1). Since both neonatal sepsis and inborn errors or organic acid metabolism manifest acidosis and central nervous system dysfunction, it is essential that urine and blood cultures, when obtained, be sent for metabolic studies as well. Of course, the use of the nose can sometimes provide the diagnosis of a specific organic acidemia. Nonetheless, these infants are often also infected because of bone marrow toxicity from metabolites, which accumulate as a result of the defect. As with the urea cycle defects, there are forms of these disorders that present after the neonatal period, presumably because of greater residual enzyme activity than in those presenting soon after birth. In these circumstances clinical manifestations occur later in the first year of life, with deterioration after an intercurrent infection, after dehydration, or following a minor operative procedure. After the first year of life, seizures may be the mode of presentation (Table 34–2). Calculation of the "anion gap" (see Chapter 3) is essential as a clue to early recognition. Ketonuria also supports the impression. Ancillary findings that may be helpful in directing attention toward an organic acidemia will be evidence of leukopenia, thrombocytopenia, and even profound anemia. Hypoglycemia and hyperammonemia are often associated with these disorders but may suggest a urea cycle defect as well. Elevation of blood ammonia appears to be the consequence of inhibition of formation of N-acetylglutamate, a key cofactor for carbamoyl phosphate synthetase (the first enzyme of the urea cycle). Hyperglycinemia is also commonly seen in these disorders. This has recently been ascribed by Hillman and associates to inhibition of the glycine-cleavage system by increased intracellular levels of thioester (R-CO-SCoA) compounds.

As a group the organic acidemias are usually defects of specific enzymes in the catabolism of the branched-chain amino acids, which act at a step after the initial transamination; hence, organic acids rather than amino acids accumulate. Although called organic acidemias, they are in the main disorders of leucine, isoleucine, or valine metabolism (Fig. 34–1). However, propionic acidemia and methylmalonic acidemia are caused by defects at points at which a number of different catabolic pathways converge and join the catabolism of the branched-chain amino acids. Thus, they manifest wide-reaching biochemical abnormalities.

Maple Syrup Urine Disease

Clinical Features

Affected infants usually appear normal for the first few days of life, symptoms arising somewhere between 3 and 5 days of age. As is characteristic of all the organic acidemias, symptoms are nonspecific, with the babies appearing listless and difficult to feed. The development of a high-pitched, unpleasant cry is indicative of CNS toxicity. Within short succession other neurological symptoms appear, including loss of tendon and Moro reflexes, wandering eye movement, and periods of extreme flaccidity and hypotonicity alternating with opisthotonos. Convulsions may appear

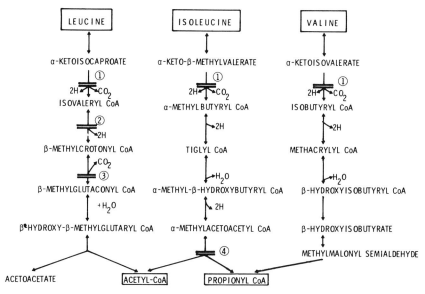

Figure 34–1 Enzyme defects in branched-chain amino acid catabolism. A defect in α-keto acid dehydrogenase (1) leads to maple syrup urine disease; isovaleryl CoA dehydrogenase deficiency (2) causes isovaleric acidemia; a putative defect of β-methyl-crotonyl CoA carboxylase (3) leads to β-methyl-crotonylglycinuria; and β-ketothiolase deficiency (4) results in α-methyl-β-hydroxybutyric and α-methylacetoacetic aciduria. (From Gompertz, D.: Inborn errors of organic acid metabolism. Clin. Endocrinol. Metab. 3:107, 1974.)

during this time, and respiratory disturbances and coma may supervene. The appearance of the odor that has given the disease its name occurs simultaneously with the earliest onset of neurological symptoms. It can be appreciated in urine, sweat, and ear wax and is so prominent that the discerning observer cannot help but perceive it. Hence, one cannot overstate the importance of smelling the urine and breath of any child appearing to have sepsis neonatorum. Warming a urine that has been refrigerated may be necessary to encourage volatilization of the acids and metabolites. Alternatively, smelling a frozen urine may facilitate appreciating the characteristic odor.

Biochemical Defects

The initial transamination step in the metabolism of the three branched-chain amino acids (leucine, isoleucine, and valine) occurs normally, but the second step, the oxidative decarboxylation, is defective. Recent work suggests that there is one multienzyme complex involved in the decarboxylation of the three branched-chain amino acids. As a result of the enzymatic defect the keto acid derivatives and the branched-chain amino acids accumulate in plasma, urine, red cells, and cerebrospinal fluid. Interesting but unexplained is the fact that the plasma leucine concentration is materially higher than is the concentration of the other branched-chain amino acids. In addition, alloisoleucine is often found in this disease, occurring as a result of enolization and subsequent reamination of alpha-keto-methylvaleric acid.

Laboratory Findings

As with the other catastrophic diseases presenting in the newborn period that mimic *sepsis neonatorum,* it is essential to consider the possibility of a metabolic disorder as the cause for the clinical findings. In that context we must emphasize again the "nose test" as part of the initial physical examination of these infants. In addition to smelling urine it is often useful to place a finger in the infant's mouth and leave it there for 15 to 30 seconds, since the offending acids may be secreted in the saliva and may then be most easily appreciated by smelling the finger. The ferric

Table 34-1 ORGANIC ACIDEMIAS

Condition	Genetics	Screening Tests	Amino Acid and Organic Acid Elevations in Plasma	Urinary Metabolites	Enzyme Defect	Treatment
Maple Syrup Urine Disease*	AR	Odor $FeCl_3$—grey-blue 2,4-DNP—yellow ppt.	3+ Leucine 2+ Isoleucine 2+ Valine	Ketoacids Alloisoleucine	α-Keto acid decarboxylases multienzyme complex	Severe form—peritoneal dialysis; special formula Thiamine 100 mg/day
Isovaleric* Acidemia	AR	Odor 2,4-DNP+	3+ Isovaleric acid 2+ Glycine BCAA—normal	+ Isovaleryl glycine—latent 3+ Isovaleryl glycine—overt β-Hydroisovaleric acid	Isovaleryl-CoA dehydrogenase	Glycine to form conjugate (250 mg/kg/day) Low protein diet
β-Methylcrotonyl Glycinuria*	AR	Odor	β-Methylcrotonyl glycine β-OH Isovalerate	β-Methylcrotonic acid β-Methylcrotonyl glycine β-Hydroxyisovaleric acid	β-Methylcrotonyl CoA carboxylase (putative)	Biotin
3-Hydroxy-3-methylglutaric Aciduria*	AR	Severe hypoglycemia and acidosis 2+ NH_3, odor 2,4-DNP—negative	Glutamine Alanine Lysine BCAA	3+ 3-Methylcrotonic acid 3-Methylglutaconic acid 3-OH-3-Methylglutaric acid + to 2+ 3-OH-3-Methylbutyric acid 3-Methylglutaric acid	3-Hydroxy-3-methylglutaryl-CoA lyase	High carbohydrate, protein-restricted diet
α-Methylacetoacetic Aciduria	AR	+ to 2+ NH_3 2,4-DNP+	Isoleucine and propionate levels normal	3+ − α-Methyl-β-OH butyric acid α-Methylacetoacetic acid Tiglylglycine n-Butanone	β-Ketothiolase	Protein restriction
Methylmalonic Aciduria*	AR	Anion gap p-Nitroaniline + to 2+ NH_3	3+ Methylmalonic acid 2+ Glycine	3+ Methylmalonic acid Long-chain ketones Propionic acid β-OH propionic acid Methylcitrate β-OH-n-valeric acid	Methylmalonyl racemase or mutase Abnormal adenosylcobalamin synthesis	Prenatal vitamin B_{12} to mother
Remethylation*→ Defect		p-Nitroaniline Nitroprusside No anion gap or ketones	Methionine decreased	Methylmalonic acid Homocystine Cystathionine	Abnormal synthesis of adenosylcobalamin and cobalamin	Vitamin B_{12}

Disorder	Inheritance	Clinical/Laboratory	Blood	Urine Organic Acids	Enzyme Defect	Treatment
Holocarboxylase Synthase (Mixed Carboxylase) Deficiency*	AR (probable)	Anion gap, Odor, 2,4-DNP+	Variable, often BCAA	β-methylcrotonic, β-methylcrotonyl-glycine, β-OH isovalerate, propionic, OH-propionic, methyl citrate	Holocarboxylase synthetase	Biotin
Propionic Acidemia* (Ketotic hyperglycinemia)	AR	+ to 2+ NH₃, Ketones + FeCl, Keto-stix, 2,4-DNP+	Propionic acid, Glycine	3-OH propionate, methylcitrate, propionate, propionyl-glycine, butanone, pentanone and hexanone	Propionyl-CoA carboxylase	Biotin, protein restriction
Multiple Acyl CoA Dehydrogenase Defect* (Glutaric Aciduria-II)	AR (probable)	Hypoglycemia, abnormal liver function tests, 3+ FFA		Glutaric, ethylmalonic, adipic, suberic, sebacic, isobutyric, isovaleric, and butyric acids	Multiple Acyl CoA dehydrogenase	
Formiminoglutamic Aciduria	AR (probable)	± Anemia, abnormal EEG, ventricular dilatation	Formiminoglutamic acid (FIGLU)	Formiminoglutamic acid (FIGLU), hydantoin-5-propionic acid	Glutamate formiminotransferase	Folate
D-Glyceric Acidemia* c̄ Hyperglycinemia	Unknown	No ketoacidosis	Glycine, Glyceric acid	Glycine, glyceric acid	D-Glyceric dehydrogenase	
s̄ Hyperglycinemia	Unknown	3+ Acidosis, - Ketones	Glyceric acid	Glyceric acid, lysine, cysteine	Unknown	Bicarbonate
α-Ketoadipic Aciduria	AR (probable)	Self-abusive	Phenylalanine, α-Aminoadipic acid	α-Aminoadipic acid, α-hydroxyadipate	?α-Ketoadipate dehydrogenase	None
Pyroglutamic Aciduria* (5-Oxoprolinuria)	AR	+ Hemolytic anemia, 2 to 3 + Acidosis	5-Oxoproline, Proline, Tyrosine	5-Oxoproline	Glutathione synthetase	Cystamine (?)
Hyperglycinemia c̄ Ketosis due to Defect in Isoleucine Metabolism	Unknown	Ketonuria, thrombocytopenia, neutropenia, hyperammonemia	Glycine, Threonine	Hyperglycinuria, butanone, hexanone	Unknown	Protein restriction
Glutaric Aciduria (Type I)	AR	Choreoathetosis + Acidosis	Glutaric, Glycine	Glutaric, glycine, β-OH-glutaric, glutaconic	Glutaryl-CoA-dehydrogenase	Protein restriction, Riboflavin, 4-amino-3 (4-chlorophenyl)-butyric acid

*May present as a neonatal catastrophe.
+ minimal elevation; 2+ moderate elevation; 3+ marked elevation; BCAA = branched-chain amino acids.

Table 34–2 MODE OF PRESENTATION OF ORGANIC
ACIDEMIAS

Neonatal Catastrophe
  Acidosis (anion gap)
  Ketosis and Ketonuria
  Tachypnea
  Neurological findings
  Neutropenia, anemia, and thrombocytopenia
Failure to Thrive and Vomiting During the First Year of Life
  Deterioration with infection or diarrhea
  Vomiting
  Progressive delay in psychomotor development
  Acidosis—usually seen with exacerbations but is occasionally persistent
  May be history of protein intolerance leading to symptoms
  Neurological symptoms with exacerbations
Onset After the First Year of Life
  Episodes of ketoacidosis following a minor infection
  May be lethargy, seizures, or coma with such attacks

chloride and 2,4-dinitrophenylhydrazine screening tests are often positive with this disorder. However, even in normal infants the 2,4-DNP test may sometimes be positive, and false positives may be encountered with ampicillin. Unequivocal diagnosis, however, will require gas chromatography. Assay of branched-chain decarboxylase activity in peripheral leukocytes will permit the differentiation of the variant forms of the disease but because of the time involved cannot be employed in initial diagnosis. Emergency therapy must be instituted if these infants are to recover from this catastrophe.

Treatment

These children represent true medical emergencies and in most instances are sufficiently ill by the time the diagnosis has been made that all protein has been stopped and intravenous feeding has been initiated. However, if this is not the case, cessation of protein and provision of calories by alternate routes are essential. When evidence of neurological involvement is present, therapy must move to a more aggressive plane, involving either repeated exchange transfusions or peritoneal dialysis. Either mode should only be employed in a major medical center; in the authors' hands, peritoneal dialysis is more easily accomplished, can remove a greater measure of the body's burden of the accumulated keto-acids and requires less specialized monitoring. In addition, unless repeated exchange transfusions are performed, the amelioration they furnish is only transitory.

While dialysis is being performed (usually for not more than 48 hours), it is essential to provide adequate calories (greater than 150 kcal/kg/day) to minimize the ongoing tissue catabolism; the use of intravenous fat preparations has been found to be particularly useful in this situation. Waisman et al. (1972) have reported the use of small nasogastric feeding of high fat content formula to accomplish this. Both Waisman et al. (1972) and Snyderman (1974) recommend that the oral administration of an amino acid solution deficient in the branched-chain amino acids also be instituted promptly even when dialysis is being carried out. This formula can be administered with small amounts at frequent intervals (Snyderman et al. suggest 5 ml every three hours).

When these children are admitted, the leucine level may be in the range of 40 to 60 mg per dl. After dialysis or multiple exchanges, a diminution of leucine levels to the range of 20 mg per dl can be accomplished; at that time the special formula alone may be sufficient to treat these children. It cannot be emphasized strongly enough that the therapy of this disease should be undertaken only in a center that is readily able to monitor amino acid and organic acid levels in blood and that has easy access to the specialized formulas. The reader, therefore, is encouraged to consider referral to such centers. The references should be consulted for definitive aspects of emergency therapy.

Isovaleric Acidemia (Defect: Isovaleryl CoA dehydrogenase; Inheritance: autosomal recessive; Prenatal diagnosis: not yet accomplished)

Clinical Features

The general symptoms associated with this disorder are those characteristic of all of the organic acidemias, save for the presence of the distinctive odor of "sweaty feet" imparted by isovaleric acid. While small amounts of this acid accumulate in these individuals, even during periods of apparent well-being, it is only during periods of clinical deterioration that large amounts are found in urine, blood, sweat, saliva, and cerumen. Ketoacidosis is the hallmark of this disease, with its associated vomiting and CNS depression, which progresses to coma. Milder, later-occurring cases may be associated with slow mental development rather than these acute symptoms; the spectrum of clinical presentation can vary widely.

Biochemical Defects

The defect in this disease is diminished or absent isovaleryl CoA dehydrogenase activity. As a consequence of the excessive accumulation of isovaleric acid (Fig. 34–1), a relatively minor pathway utilized for conjugation with glycine assumes major importance. Indeed, during periods of both well-being and acute exacerbations isovalerylglycine, which is rapidly cleared by the kidney, may be the most abundant compound in the urine. The central nervous system symptoms and bone marrow depression appear to be manifestations of the systemic toxicity of isovaleric acid.

Laboratory Findings

The critical laboratory findings are the odor of isovaleric acid, the ketoacidosis with anion gap, and hematological findings noted above in the organic acidemias. It should be emphasized that some of these children may have been treated with intravenous fluids and substantial amounts of alkalinizing agents. Hence, the acidosis may not be a prominent laboratory finding even though the odor of isovaleric acidemia is easily appreciated. Nonetheless, because of the CNS toxicity such infants are still likely to be neurologically depressed and the search for an odor should be carried out carefully.

Treatment

Children with this disorder should be maintained and managed at a center equipped to do so. While the general approach includes dietary restriction during the acute period of ketoacidosis and neurological depression, it is essential that glycine be administered to encourage the formation of the isovalerylglycine conjugate. During the acute phase glycine is usually administered by nasogastric tube at approximately 250 mg/kg/body weight. Administration requires monitoring of both organic acid and amino acid levels. Clinical reports of success both with late-onset isovaleric acidemia and with onset in the neonatal period are available; the interested reader may consult the references for full details of management. While biochemical improvement is prompt with glycine, clinical improvement lags behind, apparently because of the accumulation of this lipid-soluble acid in brain and other tissues. Neurological function may take an additional week to normalize and hematological abnormalities two weeks. Glycine therapy is continued after the patient recovers, and we believe it will permit these patients to lead a more normal existence than was hitherto possible.

Methylmalonic Acidemias

Clinical Features

Recognition of methylmalonic acidemia as a distinct entity followed initial investigations of the disease described as "ketotic hyperglycinemia"; the same is true of propionic acidemia. Such initial confusion underscores the fact that many of these diseases cannot be distinguished on clinical grounds alone.

There are several causes of the methylmalonic acidemias, but in general their presentation is as for the other organic acidemias (Table 34–1). Hepatomegaly is not uncommon and with later-onset varieties osteoporosis has been encountered, presumably because of bone buffering of acid.

Biochemical Defects

There are two primary enzyme deficiencies that may be associated with the accumulation of methylmalonic acid. One is a defect of methylmalonyl CoA racemase, and the other, of methylmalonyl CoA mutase activity (Fig. 34–2). The racemase defect appears to be most unusual; the mutase is associated with five separate defects that cause dysfunction of the enzyme. The first defect relates to an abnormality in the protein (apoenzyme) itself. Other defects impair catalytic activity by somehow preventing the synthesis of adenosylcobalamin (AdoCBl), the cofactor for the reaction. This group generally, but not invariably, responds to B_{12} administration. Vitamin B_{12} must enter the cell before it can undergo enzymatic conversion into either of two coenzyme forms: adenosyl-cobalamin necessary for the methylmalonyl mutase and methylcobalamin (MeCbl) essential for the remethylation pathway of homocystine. The biochemistry of these defects is both complicated and fascinating, and the interested reader is directed to the references at the end of this section, for further details.

Laboratory Findings

Laboratory studies will indicate the presence of a ketoacidosis, hyperammonemia, and hematological abnormalities. Hyperglycinemia is a variable finding. The definitive diagnosis requires the use of gas chromatography to isolate and identify methylmalonic acid. Normally urinary excretion is below 5 mg/dl, while in affected children excretion is greatly elevated to 50 to 1000 times that level. In the defect involving both the mutase and the enzyme in the homocystine remethylation pathway, there will be found in addition, high urinary levels of homocystine and cystathionine; methionine will not be found in high amounts. This variant form is described under homocystinuria (see Chapter 22).

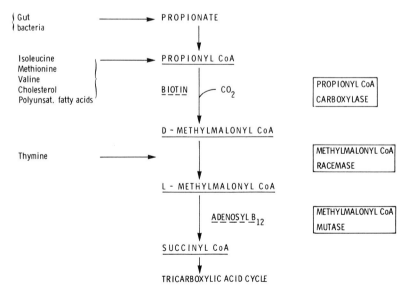

The propionate–methylmalonate pathway.

Figure 34–2 Scheme of propionate metabolism. (From Gompertz, D.: Inborn errors of organic acid metabolism. Clin. Endocrinol. Metab. 3:107, 1974.)

Treatment

Therapy for this disorder is as outlined for propionic acidemia with the additional consideration that vitamin B_{12} responsive forms have been found; hence, the physician should attempt a course of vitamin B_{12} administration. Adequate monitoring is essential.

Holocarboxylase Synthetase ("Mixed Carboxylase") Deficiency and Biotin Dependency

Clinical Features

This disease has only recently been recognized as distinct from what was initially described as β-methylcrotonylglycinuria. The clinical presentation is distinguished from that of other members of this group of diseases by an erythematous, exfoliative dermatitis, classically described by Sydenstricker et al. (1942) as the skin manifestations of biotin deficiency. Other findings include fulminant ketoacidosis, lactic acidemia, and thrombocytopenia. Hypoglycemia has not been described but is a potential problem. Indeed, the disorder may be due to multiple allelic mutations, since a more moderate presentation has been described in older infants and in association with immunological deficiencies. A recent report suggests a generalized cellular transport defect for biotin to account for the clinical variation.

Biochemical Defects

Four mammalian enzyme systems require biotin as a cofactor: pyruvate carboxylase, propionyl-CoA carboxylase, β-methylcrotonyl CoA carboxylase, and acetyl-CoA carboxylase—all CO_2-fixation reactions (Fig. 34–3). The first three carboxylases are mitochondrial enzymes; the latter is predominantly cytosolic. Normal function of these enzymes requires covalent attachment of biotin to the apoproteins—a reaction mediated by still another enzyme, holocarboxylase synthetase. Evidence for impairment of acetyl-CoA carboxylase function has recently been provided; there is firm documentation of deficiency of the mitochondrial carboxylases in affected individuals. The holocarboxylase synthetase itself has recently been shown to be deficient.

Pyruvate carboxylase normally carries out a key gluconeogenic step—conversion of pyruvate to oxaloacetate, so that these patients are at great potential risk for severe hypoglycemia. β-Methylcrotonyl CoA carboxylase is a key degradative step in production of acetoacetyl CoA and cho-

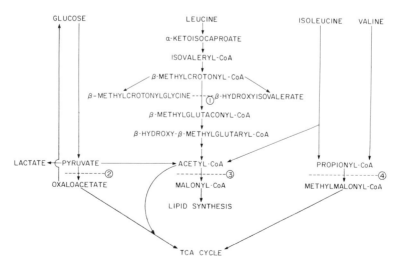

Figure 34–3 Sites of metabolic blocks in holocarboxylase synthetase deficiency. (From Roth, K. S., et al.: Holocarboxylase synthetase deficiency: a biotin responsive organic acidemia. J. Pediatr. 96:845–849, 1980.)

lesterol precursors from leucine. Failure of this enzyme results in accumulation of the glycine-conjugated intermediate, β-methylcrotonylglycine, and the reduced intermediate, β-hydroxyisovalerate. Propionyl-CoA carboxylase is of primary importance in degradation of isoleucine, methionine, threonine, cholesterol, and odd-chain fatty acids. Failure of this enzyme system leads to the severe ketoacidosis seen in infants with propionic acidemia. It is important to recognize, however, that in holocarboxylase synthetase deficiency the apoproteins are potentially normal in function but lack their cofactor, biotin. In contrast to propionic acidemia, in which the apoprotein is thought to be abnormal and thus biotin-unresponsive, in vitro and in vivo studies have clearly demonstrated restoration of normal mitochondrial carboxylase activity in the presence of large quantities of biotin.

Laboratory Findings

As with other such inborn errors, fulminant acidosis in a previously well infant should lead the physician to suspect holocarboxylase synthetase deficiency, among others, as a possible cause. The urine has been described as smelling like that of a cat, in several cases. Gas chromatographic analysis of the urine will reveal propionic acid and related metabolites (hydroxy-propionate and methylcitrate), β-methylcrotonate or its glycine conjugate, and β-hydroxyisovalerate; similar analysis of blood may show only large quantities of lactate, β-methylcrotonylglycine, and β-hydroxyisovalerate. Methylmalonic acid is conspicuously absent, and the p-nitroaniline spot test is therefore negative.

Diagnosis

Assay of mitochondrial carboxylase activities in leukocytes and fibroblasts should be carried out on all patients suspected of having propionic acidemia, in order to rule out the possibility of a holocarboxylase synthetase defect. Prenatal diagnosis is possible and prenatal therapy, permitting a normal neonatal course, has been accomplished.

Treatment

A dramatic response to biotin has been demonstrated in this disease. A daily dose of 10 mg in 4 divided doses administered either by mouth or by nasogastric tube is sufficient to achieve normalization of deranged biochemistry and physical growth. Chronic administration of biotin should be provided as a single 10 mg per day dose.

Propionyl-CoA Carboxylase Deficiency (Propionic Acidemia)

Clinical Features

Affected infants are generally normal at birth but develop vomiting, lethargy, and hypertonia, progressing to coma within the first week or so of life. As in most of the members of this family of diseases, there is a predictably severe ketoacidosis. Respiratory compensation with hyperventilation is often a prominent finding. Subsequent neurological deterioration may result in seizures and apneic episodes.

Occasionally, infants and older children present with a somewhat different clinical picture. In such cases, failure to thrive, hypertonia, and occasional seizures are the prominent findings, and the acidosis is variable and peripheral in importance. Indeed, an older sibling of a severely affected baby has been described whose fibroblasts manifest the biochemical defect but who is clinically normal.

Thus, there is a wide spectrum of clinical presentation in this disease, demanding its consideration in the differential diagnosis of any infant or older child with seizures or acidosis accompanied by failure to thrive.

Biochemical Defects

Discovery of propionyl-CoA carboxylase (Fig. 34–2) deficiency followed shortly after the recognition of methylmalonic acidemia as a cause for ketotic hyperglycinemia. During investigation of patients with "ketotic hyperglycinemia," Hsia et al. (1970) demonstrated large amounts of propionate with a virtual absence of methylmalonate in the urine of one such child. These observations led to the study of propionate metabolism in peripheral leukocytes from this child: propionate-^{14}C oxidation was deficient, while methylmalonate and succinate oxidation were normal, thus localizing the defect to the conversion of propionyl CoA to methylmalonyl CoA.

Variation in clinical presentation raised the obvious question of genetic heterogeneity. The in vitro genetic complementation studies with cultured skin fibroblasts have delineated at least three types of genetic mutants. However, the precise nature of the molecular defect is still unknown, and no statement can be made regarding correlation of a patient's genetic complement with severity of his disease. Recent work suggests that the mutant enzyme is both cold- and heat-labile to a greater degree than the normal enzyme and that the active site of the normal enzyme contains essential arginine residues.

Propionyl-CoA is generated from a number of sources—methionine, isoleucine, threonine, odd-chain fatty acids, and cholesterol. Further metabolism of this compound is entirely dependent upon the ability to incorporate CO_2 into the molecule to produce methylmalonyl-CoA. Failure to carry out this reaction results in accumulation of propionyl-CoA, which is hydrolyzed to propionic acid and then partially converted to β-hydroxypropionate. In addition, ketones (butanone, pentanone and hexanone) accumulate as metabolic by-products.

Laboratory Findings

Propionic acidemia, methylmalonic acidemia, and α-methylacetoacetyl CoA-β-ketothiolase deficiency share in common features generally associated with the so-called ketotic hyperglycinemia syndrome. As noted before, hyperammonemia may be found in these conditions as well. Routine spot tests will reveal positive ferric chloride, Keto-stix, and 2,4-DNP. These three disorders are not usually associated with a characteristic odor, although some investigators have suggested that propionate may be appreciated on the breath and urine in some patients. The definitive diagnosis will require gas chromatography.

Treatment

The reports in the literature have been misleading with regard to the biotin-responsiveness of this disease. The patient originally reported to be biotin-responsive was later found to have multiple carboxylase deficiencies (Sweetman et al., 1977) and finally shown to have an identical genetic complement with a patient with holocarboxylase synthetase deficiency (Saunders et al., 1979). It must, therefore, be assumed that biotin supplementation is unsuccessful in all cases of propionyl-CoA deficiency. Recent evidence supports this, since the molecular defect in the apoprotein cannot be corrected in vitro by large quantities of biotin. Nonetheless the acute management of any patient manifesting propionic acidemia should include biotin administration in addition to the measures outlined below.

The acute episode should be treated by cessation of all protein intake, with provision of adequate calories as glucose and even chain-length fatty acids to attenuate body protein catabolism. High fluid volumes may also assist the kidneys in removing toxic metabolites. As clinical improvement develops, protein should be reintroduced cautiously, using a low (0.5 to 1.0 g/kg/day) protein diet. Methionine, threonine, and branched-chain amino acids should be held to minimal allowable daily levels. For chronic management, protein intake ought not to exceed 1.5 g/kg/day in order to allow for growth. Close monitoring is vital, since ketoacidosis may recur, owing to mild upper respiratory infection, so that management at a fully staffed center for metabolic disease is essential.

β-Methylcrotonyl-CoA Carboxylase Deficiency (β-Methylcrotonylglycinuria)

The original description of this disease included a Werdnig-Hoffman-type picture in an infant who gave off a "cat-urine" odor. Two patients described thereafter presented with quite different clinical findings and at different ages. The fourth patient (Roth et al., 1976) was eventually found to have holocarboxylase synthetase deficiency (Saunders et al., 1979), and the fifth patient, originally reported as a biotin-responsive propionic acidemic, also was shown to have a holocarboxylase synthetase deficiency.

Thus, the existence of an isolated β-methylcrotonyl-CoA carboxylase defect is merely speculative at this time, since laboratory studies in the earliest two reported patients did not include assessment of the other mitochondrial carboxylases. Nonetheless, the disease should be looked for, since an isolated defect in this enzyme is as likely a deficiency as propionyl CoA carboxylase.

α-Methylacetoacetyl-CoA β-Ketothiolase Deficiency

α-Methylacetoacetyl-CoA β-ketothiolase deficiency is a very rare disease, with symptoms that appear to be characteristic of the other organic acidemias, namely, neonatal onset with vomiting and neurological findings and laboratory findings typical of ketoacidosis with hyperglycinemia, hyperammonemia and hematologic findings. The defect is apparently a block in isoleucine metabolism occurring prior to the formation of propionic acid. Management appears to involve successful use of a restricted protein diet.

Multiple Acyl CoA Dehydrogenase Defects (previously termed Glutaric Aciduria Type II)

Clinical Features

Four patients with this disorder have now been reported with enormous disparity in their clinical presentation. The first patient became ill within two hours after birth, presenting with tachypnea and a severe metabolic acidosis. A significant hypoglycemia accompanied these findings. By 30 hours of age the blood glucose was less than 5 mg/dl and shortly thereafter respiratory and cardiac arrest occurred. Resuscitation was successful, but the severe metabolic acidosis persisted, followed by a generalized convulsion at the age of 40 hours. By 44 hours of age a disagreeable, sweaty-foot odor was noted. The infant died at the age of 70 hours with a blood pH of 6.6.

The second patient reported was a 19-year-old woman who presented with episodic vomiting, severe hypoglycemia, and fatty infiltration of the liver. This individual was the oldest of 5 children from a non-consanguineous marriage. Her developmental milestones were normal. During childhood she experienced episodic mild weakness and easy fatigability with occasional nausea. Two of the other four siblings had died, one in a hypoglycemic coma and the second in her sleep. The latter sibling had a bout of jaundice and hepatomegaly two weeks after an acute febrile illness. Laboratory findings in this patient were generally indicative of severe liver disease. The SGOT rose to 1220 milli-IU/liter, while the SGPT reached 650 milli-IU/liter. Strikingly, plasma ammonia levels remained normal throughout. There was also jaundice, with the maximum bilirubin level reaching 21.5 mg/dl. The other noteworthy clinical feature in this individual was weakness and wasting of the proximal muscles, particularly in the upper limbs.

A notable chemical finding in this patient was that during apparent clinical normality she had a significant elevation in the free fatty acids of the plasma, while during hypoglycemic coma upon her initial admission she showed free fatty acids in the plasma greater than 4000 microequivalents/liter, corresponding to at least a fourfold increase over normal.

Recently, two more patients have been reported with a catastrophic presentation in the neonatal period. Their presentation was similar to the first patient save that a pungent odor was noted in one and both had significant hyperammonemia.

Gas chromatographic analysis of the urinary organic acids revealed large amounts of glutaric,

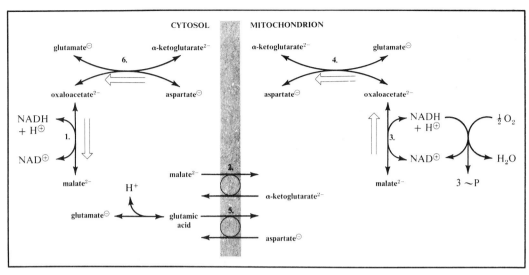

Figure 34–4 Malate-aspartate shuttle. The numbers indicate the sequence of reactions leading from cytosolic oxaloacetate through malate to mitochondrial oxaloacetate, with exchange for a mitochondrial α-ketoglutarate; this exchange requires no energy. (From McGilvery, R. W.: Biochemistry: A Functional Approach. 2nd ed. Philadelphia, W. B. Saunders Co., 1979.)

ethylmalonic, octenedioic, suberic, decenedioic, and sebacic acids and isovalerylglycine and hexanoylglycine. Correspondingly, gas chromatographic analysis of the urine from the first patient reported contained large amounts of glutaric, lactic, isobutyric, isovaleric and alphamethylbutyric acids. In addition, there was also an elevation of the following: adipic, ethylmalonic, alpha-hydroxybutyric, alpha-hydroxyglutaric, beta-hydroxybutyric, sebacic, suberic, propionic, alpha-hydroxyisovaleric, and hexanoic acids. This urinary organic acid excretion pattern bears a striking resemblance to that seen in Jamaican vomiting sickness. In this latter disorder the accumulation of the urinary organic acids results from the inhibition by hypoglycin of several of the acyl CoA dehydrogenases. Impaired oxidation of fatty acids is thought to result in decreased hepatic gluconeogenesis. In addition, glutaryl-CoA and ethylmalonic acid have been shown to be in vitro inhibitors of mitochondrial transport of malate, which is a pivotal step in transferring intramitochondrial oxaloacetate (as malate the key intermediate in gluconeogenesis) into the cytosol, where it is reoxidized to oxaloacetate (Fig. 34–4). A combination of these two effects might well explain the severe hypoglycemia seen in this disorder.

Treatment

Treatment of glutaric aciduria types I and II depends exclusively upon the limitation of dietary protein intake. Protein intake should not exceed 1.5 g/kg/day of protein. No significant effect on disordered mentation or upon the dystonic movements has been demonstrated in patients who have been so treated. However, there appears to be a significant decrease in the incidence of acidosis in those patients in whom this has been a problem. In addition, a recent report on treatment of glutaric aciduria type I with riboflavin and the α-aminobutyric acid analogue 4-amino-3-(4-chlorophenyl)butyric acid resulting in regression of neurological symptoms is encouraging.

REFERENCES

Brandt, N.J., Gregersen, N., Christensen, E., and Rasmussen, K.: Treatment of glutaryl-CoA dehydrogenase deficiency (glutaric aciduria). J. Pediatr. 94:669, 1979.

Cohn, R.M., Yudkoff, M., Rothman, R., and Segal, S.: Isovaleric acidemia: Use of glycine therapy in neonates. N. Engl. J. Med. 299:996, 1978.

Goodman, S.I., and Markey, S.P. (eds.): Diagnosis of Organic Acidemias by Gas Chromatography. Mass Spectrometry. A. Liss, New York, 1981.

Hillman, R.E.: Secondary modulation by accumulated thioesters in the branched-chain amino acid pathways. In Walser, M., and Williamson, J.R. (eds.): Metabolism and Clinical Implications of Branched Chain Amino and Ketoacids. Elsevier, North Holland, New York, 1981.

Hsia, Y.E., Scully, K.J., and Rosenberg, L.E.: Inherited propionyl-CoA carboxylase deficiency in ketotic hyperglycinemia. Pediatr. Res. 4:439, 1970.

Larsson, A., Mattsson, B., Wauters, E.A.K., et al.: 5-Oxoprolinuria due to hereditary 5-oxoprolinase deficiency. A new inborn error of the γ-glutamyl cycle. Acta Pediatr. Scand. 70:301, 1981.

Marstein, S., Jellum E., Nesbakken, R. and Perry, T.L.: Biochemical investigations of biopsied brain tissue and autopsied organs from a patient with pyroglutamic acidemia (5-oxoprolinemia). Clin. Chem. Acta 111:219, 1981.

Meister, A.: 5-oxoprolinuria (pyroglutamic aciduria): In Stanbury, J.B., Wyngaarden, J.B., and Fredrickson, D.S. (eds.): The Metabolic Basis of Inherited Disease. 4th ed. McGraw-Hill, New York, 1978, p. 328.

Packman, S., Sweetman, L., Yoshino, M., et al.: Biotin-responsive multiple carboxylase deficiency of infantile onset. J. Pediatr. 99:421, 1981.

Rhead, W., Mantagos, S., and Tanaka, K.: Glutaric aciduria type II: In vitro studies on substrate oxidation, acyl-CoA dehydrogenases, and electron-transferring flavoprotein in cultured skin fibroblasts. Pediatr. Res. 14:1339, 1980.

Rosenberg, L.E.: Disorders of propionate and methylmalonate metabolism. In Stanbury, J.B., Wyngaarden, J.B., Fredrickson, D.S., et al. (eds.): The Metabolic Basis of Inherited Disease. 5th ed. McGraw-Hill, New York, 1983, p. 474.

Roth, K.S.: Biotin in clinical medicine: A review. Am. J. Clin. Nutr. 34:1967, 1981.

Roth, K.S., and Yang, W.: Prenatal therapy of multiple carboxylase deficiency. Pediatr. Res., in press, 1982.

Roth, K.S., Cohn, R.M., Yandrasitz, J., et al.: Beta-methylcrotonic aciduria associated with lactic acidosis. J. Pediatr. 88:229, 1976.

Roth, K.S., Yang, W., Foreman, J.W., et al.: Holocarboxylase synthetase deficiency: A biotin-responsive organic acidemia. J. Pediatr. 96:845, 1980.

Saunders, M., Sweetman, L., Robinson, B., et al.: Biotin responsive organic aciduria. Multiple carboxylase defects and complementation studies with propionic acidemia in cultured fibroblasts. J. Clin. Invest. 64:1695, 1979.

Snyderman, S.E.: Maple syrup urine disease. In Nyhan, W.L. (ed.): Heritable Disorders of Amino Acid Metabolism: Patterns of Clinical Expression and Genetic Variation. J. Wiley & Sons, Inc., New York, 1974, p. 17.

Stokke, O., Goodman, S.I., and Moe, P.G.: Inhibition of brain glutamate decarboxylase by glutarate, glutaconate, and β-hydroxy-glutarate: Explanation of the symptoms in glutaric aciduria? Clin. Chim. Acta 66:411, 1976.

Sweetman, L., Bates, S.P., Hull, D., and Nyhan, W.L.: Propionyl-CoA carboxylase deficiency in a patient with biotin-responsive 3-methylcrotonyl glycinuria. Pediatr. Res. 11:1144, 1977.

Sydenstricker, V.P., Singal, S.A., Briggs, A.P., et al.: Observations on the "egg white injury" in man and its cure with biotin concentrate. J. Am. Med. Assn. 118:1199, 1942.

Tanaka, K., and Rosenberg, L.E.: Disorders of branched chain amino acid and organic acid metabolism. In Stanbury, J.B., Wyngaarden, J.B., Fredrickson, D.S., et al. (eds): The Metabolic Basis of Inherited Disease. 5th ed. McGraw-Hill, New York, 1983, p. 440.

Waisman, H.A., Smith, B.A., Brown, E.S., and Gerritsen, T.: Treatment of branched chain ketoaciduria (BCKA) during acute illness. Clin. Pediatr. 11:360, 1972.

Wolf, B., Hsia, Y.E., Sweetman, L., et al.: Propionic acidemia: A clinical update. J. Pediatr. 99:835, 1981.

Wolf, B., Paulsen, E.P., and Hsia, Y.E.: Asymptomatic propionyl CoA carboxylase deficiency in a 13-year-old girl. J. Pediatr. 95:563, 1979.

35

Porphyria

FORMATION OF HEME

Reflecting for a moment on the pivotal roles of photosynthesis, oxygen transport, and oxidative metabolism in the life process, it is impossible to overestimate the importance of chlorophyll and heme-containing proteins. Chlorophyll and heme are both porphyrins, i.e., tetrapyrrole molecules that form chelates with a variety of metal ions, most notably magnesium and iron. Magnesium is the metal in chlorophyll, while iron serves in the hemes: ferric (Fe^{3+}) ion in hematin and ferrous (Fe^{2+}) in heme.

Multicellular organisms could not exist without capabilities for oxygen transport (hemoglobin), oxygen storage (myoglobin), electron transport and synthesis of ATP (mitochondrial cytochromes), catabolism of fatty acids, steroids, foreign chemicals, including drugs (microsomal cytochromes) and removal of toxic oxidants, e.g., H_2O_2 (catalase, peroxidase). Indeed, interference with the normal conduct of oxidative metabolism at any one of these steps can have grave, if not lethal, consequences for the organism.

Correspondingly, we would therefore expect that any derangement in the formation of heme could have far-reaching effects on body function. Not only is such an expectation realized in the porphyrias, but, as our discussion unfolds we will discover that environmental factors often play the decisive role in determining whether or not the disorder is latent or overt, depending upon the nature and site of porphyrin storage and exposure to sun or certain drugs, among other factors.

Biosynthesis of Porphyrins

Consonant with a theme discussed in Part I of this book, the biosynthetic pathway for porphyrin synthesis exemplifies the economical usage of simple precursors to make complex structures, so essential to the conduct of the life process. Indeed, not only does this theme find expression with the porphyrins, but it does so as well with the purines and pyrimidines. While the theme may be simple, the variation as regards the porphyrins is actually quite complex. We must assume that this is because of the advantages for control that such multistep and compartmentalized processes afford the cell. Porphyrin synthesis involves enzymes located both in the mitochondria and in the cytosol. However, before we embark upon a discussion of porphyrin biosynthesis, a review of certain aspects of porphyrin chemistry and nomenclature is necessary.

The term porphyrin derives from the Greek word for purple; in fact, in acid solution porphyrins are red-purple, while in organic solvents or alkaline solution they tend to be red or brown in color. Undoubtedly, one of their most striking properties is their intense red fluorescence when irradiated with ultraviolet light of approximately 400 nm, the so-called Soret band. This fluorescence serves both to detect erythrodontia (fluorescent staining of teeth) in patients with congenital erythropoietic porphyria as well as to document the presence of fluorescent erythrocytes and excessive porphyrins in feces. As noted above, porphyrins are composed of four pyrrole rings (tetrapyrrole) in which the four rings are joined by methene bridges (Fig. 35–1). Such ring structures possess a high degree of chemical stability because of resonance stabilization (electron delocalization) resulting from the conjugated double bond system (see Part I).

Two other points are worthy of note. While the final product of this biosynthetic scheme is the porphyrin ring, in which the bridge atoms are partially oxidized, the intermediates leading to for-

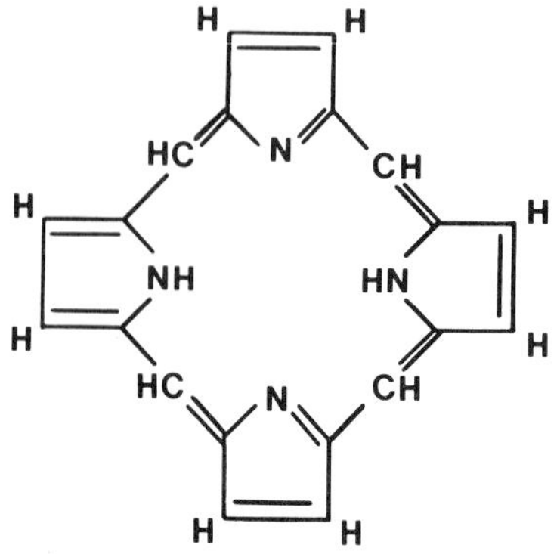

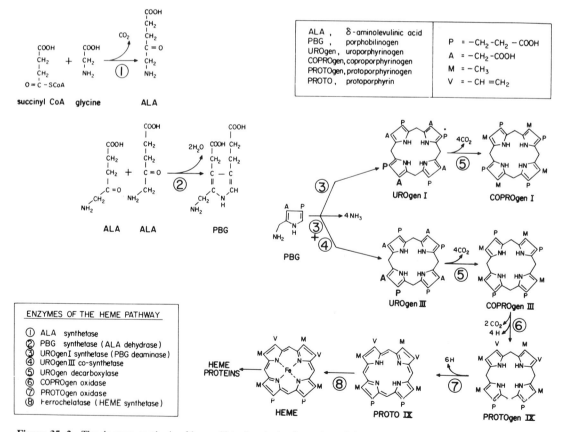

Figure 35–1 The basic porphin structure. Porphin is an unsubstituted ring compound composed of four pyrrole rings joined by methene rings. (From Woo, J., Treuting, J. J., Cannon, D. C.: Metabolic intermediates and inorganic ions. *In* Henry, J. B. (ed.): Clinical Diagnosis and Management by Laboratory Methods. 16th ed. Philadelphia, W. B. Saunders Co., 1979.)

mation of heme are the reduced forms of the porphyrins, termed porphyrinogens. In contrast to the porphyrins, they are colorless and nonfluorescent; in the laboratory they may be oxidized readily, utilizing light (the basis of the so-called "window-sill test," to be described subsequently) or weak oxidizing agents.

Finally, during the course of the formation of heme the specific intermediates are uroporphyrinogen, coproporphyrinogen, and protoporphyrinogen (Fig. 35–2). These intermediates of the biosynthetic pathway undergo facile oxidation being converted to uroporphyrin and coproporphyrin. While protoporphyrinogen can be converted to protoporphyrin nonenzymatically, there is substantial evidence that in the cell enzyme mediation is required. The biosynthetic sequence involves the

Figure 35–2 The de novo synthesis of heme. Note that during formation of the tetrapyrrole ring two isomers (uroporphyrinogen I and III) are formed, only one of which contributes to heme formation. (Wright, R., et al. (eds.): Liver and Biliary Disease. Philadelphia, W. B. Saunders Co., 1979.)

sequential removal of carboxylic acid side chains; uroporphyrin, which contains eight carboxy residues, is the most water soluble and is excreted in the urine. Coproporphyrin with four carboxylic acid residues is of intermediate water solubility and is excreted primarily in the bile, with some excretion in the urine as coproporphyrinogen. Protoporphyrin, possessing only two carboxylic acid residues, is the least water soluble and is excreted in the bile. Hence, under normal circumstances porphyrins are removed from the body via the feces, which accounts for about 2.0 to 3.0 mg/day; only 0.2 mg per day are found in the urine.

Biosynthetic Pathway

Studies initiated by Shemin and Rittenberg (1946) at the end of World War II and continued by Shemin and others have shown that glycine and intermediates of the citric acid cycle are the precursors of the porphyrin ring. The final product of this pathway is the heme moiety, which serves such variegated functions in the cell. The pathway is shown in Figure 35–2. In the first step, which occurs intramitochondrially, glycine condenses with succinyl-CoA to form δ-aminolevulinic acid (ALA). The enzyme requires pyridoxal phosphate as a cofactor. The ALA formed diffuses out of mitochondria into the cytosol, where the next enzyme, ALA dehydrase, condenses two molecules of ALA to form porphobilinogen (PBG). Porphobilinogen, as a monopyrrole, occupies a crucial role in this pathway, since it is the precursor for all of the tetrapyrroles. In the next step, which again occurs in the cytoplasm, two enzymes are apparently necessary to condense four molecules of PBG to form uroporphyrinogen III. They are uroporphyrinogen I synthase (PBG deaminase) and uroporphyrinogen III cosynthase (uroporphyrinogen III isomerase), which must act in concert to form the III isomer of uroporphyrinogen, the true intermediate of the heme biosynthetic pathway. When uroporphyrinogen III cosynthase activity is decreased, the predominant metabolite is the I isomer. This protein appears to act as a "specifier," conferring a unique stereospecificity on the reaction sequence. The next step also occurs in the cytosol and involves the stepwise decarboxylation of uroporphyrinogen III to coproporphyrinogen III, as four acetic acid side-chains are converted to methyl groups.

The coproporphyrinogen III formed re-enters the mitochondria, where the enzyme coproporphyrinogen oxidase converts it to protoporphyrinogen by oxidative decarboxylation of propionic acid side-chains of rings A and B. This reaction also has distinct stereospecificity, since the substituents present on rings C and D of the tetrapyrrole do not undergo enzymatic alteration. In the penultimate step of this pathway, protoporphyrinogen IX, the only isomer that acts as a precursor to heme, is converted to protoporphyrin IX by the mitochondrial enzyme, protoporphyrinogen oxidase. The final step of this pathway is catalyzed by the enzyme ferrochelatase (heme synthetase), which is responsible for the insertion of ferrous iron into the ring to form heme.

As with so many metabolic processes, the liver occupies a central role in the biosynthesis of heme, which will be incorporated into the cytochromes and other heme-containing enzymes. Normally heme incorporation is delicately balanced with the needs caused by degradation of these proteins; in the porphyrias this dynamic equilibrium is severely disordered in favor of excessive and gratuitous stimulation of the heme biosynthetic sequence. The site of this stimulation is the enhanced activity of ALA synthase, the rate-limiting enzyme of this pathway. Review of Table 35–1 will disclose that the various porphyric syndromes are each the result of a different enzymatic defect. Notably, the one enzyme missing from that list is the first enzyme of the pathway, i.e., ALA synthetase. Because this enzyme is the one most subject to control by both feedback inhibition and repression by the final product (heme), enhanced activity of ALA synthase due to diminished feedback further aggravates metabolite accumulation.

ALA Synthetase

In Part I of this book, we discussed the role of feedback inhibition in controlling the flux through a biosynthetic pathway. As regards the heme biosynthetic pathway, ALA synthase occupies

Table 35–1 PORPHYRIA VARIANTS

	Acute Intermittent		Variegate		Hereditary Coproporphyria	
Genetics	AD		AD		AD	
Onset	After puberty		10–30 years		Any age	
Symptoms and Signs	Abdominal pain, nausea, vomiting; hypertension Neuropsychiatric findings No skin findings		Variable pattern of expression Neurological findings similar to AIP Skin-fragility >> photosensitivy		Acute attacks are sporadic—drugs may precipitate Neurological findings similar to AIP Skin findings rare	
Lab Findings						
Urine	*Latent*	*Overt*	*Latent*	*Overt*	*Latent*	*Overt*
Color	N*	Red*	N*	N* or red	N*	N* or red*
ALA	+ to 3+	2+ to 3+	N to 2+	2+ to 3+	N to 2+	3+
PBG	+ to 3+	2+ to 3+	N to 2+	+ to 3+	N to 2+	3+
Uroporphyrin	N to 2+	2+ to 3+	N to 2+	3+	N to 2+	2+
Coproporphyrin	+	+	+ to 2+	3+	N to 2+	2+ to 3+
Feces						
Coproporphyrin	N	+	3+	3+	+ to 3+	3+
Protoporphyrin	N	+	3+	3+	N to +	N to +
Uroporphyrin	+	+ to 2+	N	2+	N	N
Erythrocyte						
Uroporphyrin						
Coproporphyrin	All Normal		All Normal		All Normal	
Protoporphyrin						
Enzyme Defect						
	Uroporphyrinogen I synthetase		Ferrochelatase (or protoporphyrin oxidase)—RBC		Coproporphyrinogen oxidase—RBC	
Treatment:	Avoid provocative drugs, glucose, hematin		Acute attacks as for AIP Skin—sun screen		Acute attacks as for AIP	

* Color may change to deep brown-red or black on standing.
0 absent; N normal; + increased; 2+ moderately increased; 3+ greatly increased.

such a crucial role. Ferrochelatase, the final enzyme of this pathway, is believed to be located in the immediate environment of ALA synthase so that heme, the final product of the pathway, is able to exert an inhibitory effect on the latter enzyme. Apparently, heme has two effects on ALA synthase: Intramitochondrial heme is believed to act as a classical allosteric inhibitor of the enzyme, while extramitochondrial heme appears to exert its effect by repressing synthesis of ALA synthase. The result, then, is exquisite control on the pathway for heme synthesis in liver and probably erythrocyte and adrenal gland.

What happens if an enzyme distal to ALA synthase is deficient in a particular individual? As we might expect, since heme synthesis is decreased, feedback inhibition and repression of ALA synthase is diminished and metabolites occurring proximal to the inherited enzymatic defect will build up, seeking alternative routes of metabolism. Other tissues that manifest the inherited defect in any of the porphyrias will not experience the same degree of overproduction of compounds proximal to the block because ALA synthase does not undergo induction in most extrahepatic sites.

From a therapeutic point of view, it has been known for some time that glucose feeding is able to repress the activity of hepatic ALA synthase. Thus, despite the fact that synthesis of heme is curtailed in these patients, it is possible to decrease the activity of ALA synthase by this effect of glucose. Unfortunately a convincing explanation of the mechanism of action of glucose in mediating this effect is not yet available.

With what has been said about this pathway and its control, it may occur to the reader that provision of heme exogenously to such patients might decrease ALA synthase activity. Fortunately, such is the case: I.V. hematin can reduce the frequency and severity of the manifestations of certain of the hepatic porphyrias. We are now ready to embark upon a discussion of the porphyrias.

Table 35–1 PORPHYRIA VARIANTS *continued*

Porphyria Cutanea Tarda	Congenital Erythropoietic (CEP)	Erythrohepatic Protoporphyria (EPP)
AD	AR	AD
ge—usually after 35	0–5	0–5
manifestations	Skin—severe photosensitivity	Early-onset photosensitivity—milder
urological findings	Hemolytic anemia, splenomegaly	than in CEP
tes mellitus in 1/4	No neurological findings	No neurological findings
iated liver disease determines	Erythrodontia, dark urine	Liver damage
gnosis—alcohol ingestion		
	Red*	N
+	N	
	N	
	3+	
3+	2+ to 3+	
2+	3+	N to +
+	N to variable	N to 3+
	2+	N to 2+
	←——— Fluorocytes on blood smear ———→	
ormal	3+	N
	2+	+
	+	3+
orphyrinogen decarboxylase (er and RBC)	Uroporphyrinogen I synthetase and/or uroporphyrinogen III cosynthetase	Ferrochelatase—RBC
otomy, oral chloroquine	Splenectomy, oral beta-carotene, hematin	Oral beta-carotene

THE PORPHYRIAS

While it has been the practice in the past to divide the porphyrias into the hepatic and erythropoietic forms, such a distinction is faulted on biochemical grounds because the enzyme defect is present in more than one tissue. Nonetheless, from a clinical point of view such a distinction permits certain useful generalizations. Neurological manifestations are the hallmark of the so-called hepatic forms (with the exception of porphyria cutanea tarda), while skin manifestations are usually more severe in the so-called erythropoietic forms (congenital erythropoietic and erythrohepatic protoporphyria). The hepatic porphyrias that manifest neurological disturbances (acute intermittent porphyria, variegate porphyria, and hepatic coproporphyria) share the marked overproduction of the porphyrin (nonpyrrole) precursors, ALA and PBG. Those porphyric states manifesting cutaneous lesions (of which the erythropoietic forms are the most notable) do so because of deposition of porphyrins in the skin. Owing to their photodynamic action with strong absorption at around 400 nm, they cause peroxidative damage to membrane lipids, the lysosome apparently being one of the preferred sites of damage. In addition, membrane proteins have been shown to suffer direct photooxidative damage as well. Table 35–1 presents much of the important clinical and laboratory information necessary to distinguish these forms. In what follows, we shall attempt to highlight some of these differences.

Acute Intermittent Porphyria

We begin our discussion of the hepatic porphyrias with a consideration of acute intermittent porphyria (AIP) because of the striking neuropsychiatric manifestations of this disorder. These represent a major form of presentation of this disorder, as well as of variegate and hereditary copro-porphyria. Over a half century ago Waldenström referred to acute intermittent porphyria as the "little imitator" and the gamut of symptoms that may be found in any one patient can provide a bewildering puzzle for the physician. Of even greater consequence, some of the attacks may involve paralysis of muscles served by the bulbar ganglia, with episodes that may end fatally with respiratory failure.

Clinical Features

Acute intermittent porphyria is inherited as an autosomal dominant trait and is the result of a defect in the enzyme uroporphyrinogen I synthase. The defect has been demonstrated in liver, fibroblasts, red cells, and amniotic cells. The biochemical consequence of the block of this enzyme is the accumulation of the porphyrin precursors ALA and PBG. Despite the block in this key pathway, it is rare for the symptoms of the disease to be present before puberty; the peak incidence of the disease occurs well into the third decade. Deranged function at multiple levels of the nervous system accounts for the symptomatology of this bizzare disorder. Most patients present with abdominal pain, vomiting, and constipation. Not infrequently the pain is so severe and the other clinical findings (including fever and leukocytosis) so suggestive of a surgical abdomen that these patients undergo exploratory laparotomy. The abdominal pain is a manifestation of autonomic neuropathy; other manifestations involving the autonomic system include hypertension as well as coronary and retinal artery spasm. Peripheral neuropathy is very common in this disease and bulbar manifestations affecting swallowing and respiration can be life threatening. The hypothalamus has been implicated in this disorder, one manifestation being hyponatremia as a consequence of inappropriate secretion of ADH. A further contributing factor to the hyponatremia is believed to be sodium loss from the gastrointestinal tract. Added to the variegated spectrum of neurological findings there may be hysteria, depression, psychosis, and even coma. It is noteworthy that skin manifestations are not a part of this disease. This is so because the metabolites that accumulate (ALA and PBG) are not photosensitizing agents.

It is essential to appreciate the role of certain drugs, infection, and starvation in the causation of acute attacks. Barbiturates, sulfonamides, and griseofulvin are contraindicated in these patients, since they may lead to exacerbation of latent disease. Induction by these drugs of the synthesis of ALA synthase and heme-containing proteins (e.g., cytochrome P-450) augments porphyrin precursor production. Starvation has been shown to uncover latent AIP, and the well-known glucose effect (decreasing the activity of ALA synthase) is the clinical correlate of the deleterious role of starvation.

Laboratory Findings

Certain abnormal routine laboratory tests, including bilirubin, cholesterol, triglycerides, and alkaline phosphatase, performed in an attempt to further define the etiology of the symptom complex, may suggest hepatic involvement. However, these are nonspecific and a high index of suspicion will be necessary to make this diagnosis. The wary physician will obtain a specimen of urine from the patient, sending a portion to the lab for the Watson-Schwartz test. This test qualitatively demontrates the presence of ALA and PBG. A portion of the urine should be placed on the windowsill to see whether the sunlight will turn the urine dark red from polymerization of PBG into porphyrins. Indeed, the patient may well have noted the presence of discolored urine in the past and, on questioning, may communicate this important fact to the physician. Since the defect in this disorder resides in a step prior to the formation of tetrapyrroles, there is no accumulation of porphyrins in urine, stool, or erythrocytes, as shown in Table 35–1. Details of isolation and quantitation of porphyrin in urine, blood, and feces can be found in the references at the end of the section.

Biochemical Defects

The reader may be wondering about the cause of the bizarre involvement of the central nervous system. At the present time, we can only give a tentative answer. Two major possibilities exist, neither of which is mutually exclusive. The first suggests that the neurological manifestations result from a toxic effect of these porphyrin precursors on the functioning of the central nervous system and the liver. The other theory suggests that the diminished formation of heme, so crucial to the oxidative strategy of metabolism of all cells, might either impair central nervous system function or, through a deleterious effect on the cytochrome P-450 system in the liver, lead to the formation of toxic compounds. Whatever the biochemical causation of the nervous system defect, there are pathological findings in the brain that confirm the proclivity of the nervous system to damage.

Treatment

So complicated may be the problems presented by a patient with an acute attack of porphyria that the concerned physician will wish to consult the major discussions on this disorder listed in the references for specific details of therapy. Clearly, the most important factor in the therapy of any of the porphyrias associated with acute attacks of neurological and autonomic dysfunction is the avoidance of any drugs or chemicals known to precipitate conversion of latent to overt disease. Phenothiazines have been found to be useful in treating the abdominal manifestations of this disorder, presumably by inhibiting autonomic outflow. Generous provision of glucose or other carbohydrate can often be of significant benefit to the patient. Nonetheless, as noted earlier in our discussion, the recently introduced infusion of hematin into such patients has apparently opened up a new dimension in the treatment of these unfortunate individuals. The review by Lamon et al. (1979) is an important resource for anyone considering such therapy.

Variegate Porphyria

The odd name for this autosomal dominant disorder underscores the fact that neuropsychiatric and cutaneous manifestations may occur together or at different times in an affected patient. While the neurological manifestations are the same as those encountered in AIP, they occur in only about one half of individuals with variegate porphyria (VP). Cutaneous manifestations are very common in the patients described from South Africa, but patients residing in more northern zones do not have the same frequency of skin manifestations; their absence may mislead the unsuspecting physician, who may anticipate a preponderance of skin manifestations.

At present, it is not known with certainty whether ferrochelatase or the preceding step (protoporphyrinogen oxidase) is the defective enzyme responsible for this disorder, although recent evidence favors the latter. Nonetheless, metabolites that accumulate would be substantially the same regardless of which enzyme is ultimately implicated.

Laboratory Findings

As seen in Table 35–1, fecal coproporphyrin (tetracarboxylic) and protoporphyrin (dicarboxylic) are greatly increased during latent and overt stages of this disorder. This pattern contrasts sharply with any of the other hepatic porphyrias. Moreover, during overt stages of the disease urinary ALA and PBG are elevated to levels seen in AIP, as are uroporphyrin and coproporphyrin. The latter elevations serve to distinguish the variegate form from AIP. Generally, during periods of latency the porphyrin precursors are in the normal range, although this is variable, particularly depending on the proximity of specimen collection to a preceding overt episode. A simple screening test in this disorder is to shine a Wood's light over a stool specimen; the stool will fluoresce because of the presence of coproporphyrin, protoporphyrin, and uroporphyrin.

Treatment

Acute attacks are treated as in AIP, including avoidance of provocative drugs and administration of glucose and I.V. hematin. Cutaneous manifestations may be diminished by the use of sun screen agents (such as beta-carotene) and of resins (in particular cholestyramine), which bind uroporphyrin and coproporphyrin.

Hepatic Coproporphyria

This autosomal dominant trait apparently results in a 50% decrease in the activity of coproporphyrinogen oxidase. Clinical manifestations, including neurological and cutaneous findings, resemble those occurring in variegate porphyria. Drugs have a role in the triggering of acute attacks. As shown in Table 35–1, quantitation of fecal porphyrins reveals elevation of coproporphyrin only. Urinary porphyrin precursors are elevated during the overt stage of this disorder and may be normal to moderately elevated during the latent stage. Definitive enzymatic diagnosis can be made using erythrocytes.

Treatment

Acute neuropsychiatric attacks may be treated as in AIP. Skin manifestations, which are rare in this disorder, should benefit from sun screen agents.

Porphyria Cutanea Tarda

For some time, there was doubt as to whether or not this form of porphyria was acquired or inherited. However, there is now substantial evidence to support the view that this is a dominantly inherited trait affecting the activity of hepatic uroporphyrinogen decarboxylase. While this disorder can occur at any age, generally it does not present until after age 35. This form of porphyria shares with congenital erythropoietic porphyria and erythrohepatic protoporphyria the lack of neurological manifestations. Cutaneous manifestations predominate, with bullae, vesicles, and ulcers being associated with hypertrichosis and pigment changes. A striking finding in this disorder is the proclivity to skin damage with minor trauma, a characteristic that porphyria cutanea tarda (PCT) shares with VP.

A number of authors have commented upon the role of pre-existing liver disease, often on the basis of excessive alcohol ingestion and iron accumulation acting upon the defective enzyme to provoke overt expression of the underlying defect. Indeed, long-term survival of these patients depends upon the progression of the liver disease and coexisting, exacerbating elements such as alcoholism and drug ingestion.

Laboratory Findings

As shown in Table 34–1, urinary uroporphyrin and coproporphyrin are increased, as are isomers with four to eight carboxyl groups. PCT can be distinguished from VP by the elevated urinary uroporphyrin and the normal to only minimally elevated fecal protoporphyrin. In a laboratory that carries out thin-layer chromatographic analysis of porphyrins, demonstration of high fecal isocoproporphyrin levels is usually diagnostic.

Treatment

Phlebotomy has been shown to be effective in treating the skin manifestations of this disorder, achieving this end despite continued ingestion of alcohol. Indeed, remissions may be reasonably long-standing once a successful course of phlebotomy has been accomplished. To achieve a remission, it may be necessary to remove as much as 7 liters of blood. For further details regarding phlebotomy the reader is directed to the major discussions on these disorders. Chloroquine has also been used successfully in treating the cutaneous manifestations.

Congenital Erythropoietic Porphyria

This rare disorder of porphyrin metabolism is characterized by striking and severe cutaneous manifestations. Indeed, because of the intense proclivity to photosensitization in this disorder some have suggested that individuals afflicted with CEP during the 19th century may well have been the so-called wolf-man, since a forest would have provided an effective sun screen.

The fundamental defect in this disorder is complicated; it appears to involve an imbalance of the activities of uroporphyrinogen I synthase and urophyrinogen III cosynthase. It is the combined activity of these two enzymes that directs the synthesis of the III porphyrin series. In the absence of the cosynthase, I isomers are formed; these are not intermediates in heme synthesis and are deposited in tissues instead. As seen in Table 35–1, there is a great increase in the excretion of uroporphyrin in the urine of such patients. In fact, the first sign, often appearing in the neonatal or infancy period, is the excretion of reddish urine. Photosensitivity will not become apparent until the infant or child is exposed to sunlight. The acute effects of sunlight include the formation of vesicles, bullae, and hyperpigmentation. With the propensity to secondary infection, scarring and ulceration occur, leading in some to loss of parts of digits and facial appendages. Hypertrichosis, which is extremely common, coupled with the unusual finding of erythrodontia (fluorescing of the teeth), presents a mental picture at least in keeping with the features of the so-called wolf-man, as inculcated by the cinema.

Hemolytic anemia may also begin in infancy and is apparently caused by sensitization of the red cells because of accumulation of intracellular porphyrins. In a number of patients compensation for this defect is accomplished by increased red cell production. In other individuals, however, a normochromic normocytic anemia is found. In these patients, there is also evidence for ineffective erythropoiesis.

In CEP and EPP, erythrocyte fluorescence is a striking finding on microscopy. Erythrodontia and the presence of increased urinary porphyrins distinguish CEP from EPP, as shown in Table 35–1.

Treatment

Sun screen agents, avoidance of sunlight, transfusions, and I.V. hematin therapy have all been used with success in this disorder.

Erythrohepatic Protoporphyria (EPP)

With this disorder we come to the end of our discussion of the major variants of the porphyrias. This abnormality of porphyrin metabolism is much more common than CEP but may be difficult to diagnose because of the lack of excretion of urinary porphyrins or porphyrin precursors, as in the other porphyrias. The defect involves the enzyme ferrochelatase and has been demonstrated in bone marrow, peripheral blood reticulocytes, erythrocytes, liver, and fibroblasts. While previously categorized as an erythropoietic porphyria, the wide distribution of the defect and the presence of liver damage make it appropriate that it be categorized as an erythrohepatic form of porphyria.

Onset of this disorder is usually early in childhood, with manifestations of photosensitivity being the initial finding. In general, cutaneous manifestations are not as severe as in CEP. Acute manifestations include edema, redness, purpura; chronic manifestations include scarring and thickening of areas exposed to the sun. It is particularly interesting that patients may experience itching, burning, or stinging while standing in front of a window or when wearing light clothes. In contrast to CEP there is no splenomegaly and no hemolytic anemia. However, serious and often fatal liver disease associated with gallstones is not uncommon in this disorder. Indeed, ultimately it is the course of the hepatobiliary disease that will determine the prognosis for the patient.

Laboratory Findings

The absence of urinary porphyrin and porphyrin precursors, coupled with the demonstration of fluorocytes on blood smear and greatly increased erythrocyte protoporphyrin should go a long way to substantiate the diagnosis. Definitive diagnosis can be accomplished by assay of the enzyme in red cells.

Treatment

As with the other porphyric disorders manifesting cutaneous findings, protection from sunlight with clothing and sun screen agents can be very effective.

REFERENCES

Benedetto, A.V., Kushner, J.P., and Taylor, J.S.: Porphyria cutanea tarda in three generations of a single family. N. Engl. J. Med. 298:358, 1978.

Bonkowsky, H.L., Sinclair, P.R., and Sinclair, J.F.: Hepatic heme metabolism and its control. Yale J. Biol. Med. 52:13, 1979.

Brenner, D.A., and Bloomer, J.R.: The enzymatic defect in variegate porphyria. N. Engl. J. Med. 302:765, 1980.

Brodie, J.J., Thompson, G.G., Moore, M.R., et al.: Hereditary coproporphyria. Demonstration of the abnormalities in haem biosynthesis in peripheral blood. Quart. J. Med. 46:229, 1977.

Dolphin, D. (ed.): The Porphyrins-Biochemistry, Part A. Vol. VI, Acad. Press, New York, 1979.

Kappas, A., Sassa, S., and Anderson, K.E.: The porphyrias. *In* Stanbury, J.B., Wyngaarden, J.B., Fredrickson, D.S., et al. (eds.): The Metabolic Basis of Inherited Disease. 5th ed. McGraw-Hill, New York, 1983, p. 1301.

Lamon, J.M., Frykholm, B.C., Hess, R.A., and Tschudy, D.P.: Hematin therapy for acute porphyria. Medicine 58:252, 1979.

Lamon, J.M., Frykholm, B.C., and Tschudy, D.P.: Screening tests in acute porphyria. Arch. Neurol. 34:709, 1977.

Mustajoki, P.: Variegate porphyria. Quart. J. Med. 49:191, 1980.

Gigli, I, Schothorst, A.A., Soter, N.A., and Pathak, M.A.: Erythropoietic protoporphyria: Photoactivation of the complement system. J. Clin. Invest. 66:517, 1980.

Grossman, M.E., and Poh-Fitzpatrick, M.B.: Porphyria cutanea tarda: Diagnosis and management. Med. Clin. North Am. 64:807, 1980.

Sassa, S., and Kappas, A.: Genetic, metabolic, and biochemical aspects of the porphyrias. Adv. Hum. Genetics 11:121, 1981.

Shemin, D.: On the synthesis of heme. Naturwissen. 57:185, 1970.

Shemin, D., and Rittenberg, D.: The biological utilization of glycine for the synthesis of the protoporphyrin of hemoglobin. J. Biol. Chem. 166:621, 1946.

Symposium: Porphyrins and Porphyrias: Etiopathogenesis, clinics and treatment. Int. J. Biochem. 12:671, 1980.

Tschudy, D.P., and Lamon, J.M.: Porphyrin metabolism and the porphyrias. *In* Bondy, P.K., and Rosenberg, L.E. (eds.): Metabolic Control and Disease. 8th ed. W.B. Saunders, Co. Philadelphia, 1980, p. 939.

With, T.K.: A short history of porphyrins and the porphyrias. Int. J. Biochem. 11:189, 1980.

36

Disorders of Purine and Pyrimidine Metabolism

GOUT

Gout is the result of various biochemical derangements, both inherited and acquired, that cause hyperuricemia and that are manifested by recurrent attacks of acute arthritis and tophaceous deposits of sodium urate. Life-threatening nephrolithiasis and parenchymatous renal disease develop in a substantial number of patients during the course of the persistent hyperuricemia.

Gout, like anemia or hypocalcemia, is the result of a heterogeneous group of biochemical and physiological abnormalities (Table 36–1). These abnormalities include inherited states with excessive synthesis of the purine precursors of uric acid. In others purine synthesis is normal, but renal excretion of uric acid is decreased, causing hyperuricemia. It appears that the majority of hyperuricemic patients manifest both abnormalities; each contributes to a different degree in any given individual.

Uric Acid

Uric acid, the end-product of purine metabolism in man, is the most highly oxidized purine. When subjected to further oxidation under neutral or alkaline conditions, carbon dioxide is eliminated at carbon 6 with formation of allantoin (Fig. 36–1). As with cystine and oxalate, limited solubility of uric acid and its salts is responsible for precipitation of uric acid throughout the body.

At body pH urate is ionized; hence, the solubility properties of its salt, monosodium urate, determine the propensity to precipitation. Monosodium urate is soluble to the extent of 120 mg/dl, while the acid is sparingly soluble (6.5 mg/dl).

Table 36–1 CAUSES OF HYPERURICEMIA

Metabolic	Secondary
Increased Production	
Hypoxanthine-guanine phosphoribosyl transferase (partial or Lesch-Nyhan [complete])	Glucose-6-phosphatase deficiency
Phosphoribosylpyrophosphate synthetase	Hereditary fructose intolerance
Glutamine phosphoribosylpyrophosphate amido transferase	Myeloproliferative disease
Xanthine oxidase	
Glutathione reductase	
Decreased Excretion	
Renal tubular defect in excretion of uric acid	*Competition for uric acid secretion*
Hemolytic disorders	Defects of gluconeogenesis and other conditions associated with lactic acidemia
Psoriasis	Elevations of β-hydroxybutyrate and acetoacetate
Sickle cell disease	*Renal Disease and Fluid Contraction*
	Renal failure
	Lead intoxication
	Dehydration (diuretics, diabetes insipidus)

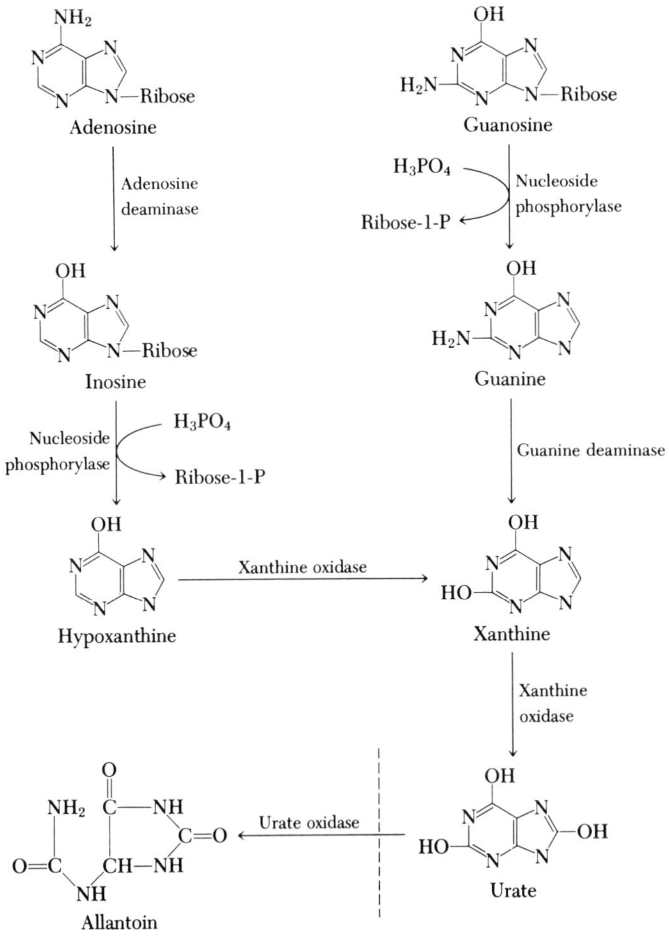

Figure 36–1 Purine catabolism and formation of uric acid. (From Cantarow, H., and Schepartz, B.: Biochemistry. 4th ed. Philadelphia, W. B. Saunders Co., 1967.)

Pathogenesis of Gout

Absence of the enzyme uricase, which converts urate to allantoin, a far more soluble molecule, dictates that uric acid become a "dead-end" metabolite requiring removal by the kidney. Matters then would be quite straightforward were it not for the fact that the kidney has a limited ability to clear the blood of urate. In consequence, humans have a normal serum urate of 3.0 to 7.0 (males), which is precariously poised around the solubility limit of monosodium urate in water. Nonetheless, gout is far less common than is moderate hyperuricemia. What factors diminish the liability to develop gout in individuals with high normal serum urate are not well understood.

Like any substrate in the body, plasma urate levels are the result of rates of production and intake balanced against metabolism and elimination. The production side includes oxidation of dietary and biosynthetically formed purines, while the elimination side includes the kidney (which predominates) as well as loss through gastrointestinal secretions. Theoretically, enhanced gastrointestinal absorption could contribute to hyperuricemia. This does not seem to be the case, however. Rather, as noted at the outset, endogenous overproduction or defects in renal excretion are the main culprits, often conspiring to upset the delicate balance discussed above.

PURINE NUCLEOTIDE BIOSYNTHESIS

The reaction that commits the cell to the biosynthesis of purines is catalyzed by amidophosphoribosyl transferase and involves the formation of alpha-phosphoribosyl-l-amine and inorganic pyrophosphate from PRPP and glutamine.

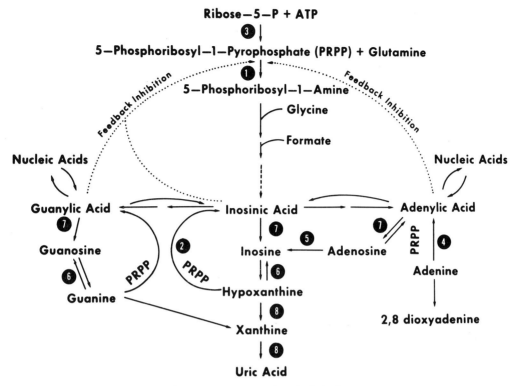

Figure 36–2 Scheme of purine synthesis. Numbers correspond to the following enzymes: (1) amidophosphoribosyltransferase, (2) hypoxanthine-guanine phosphoribosyltransferase. (3) phosphoribosyl-pyrophosphate synthetase, (4) adenine phosphoribosyltransferase, (5) adenosine deaminase, (6) purine nucleoside phosphorylase, (7) 5'-nucleotidase, (8) xanthine oxidase. Feedback control on reaction (1) is indicated by dotted lines. (From Kelley, W. N., et al. (eds.): Textbook of Rheumatology. Philadelphia, W. B. Saunders Co., 1981.)

$$\alpha\text{--PP--ribose--P} + \text{glutamine} + H_2O \xrightarrow{Mg^{++}} \beta\text{--}H_2N\text{--ribose--P} + \text{glutamic acid} + PP_i$$

Such a pivotal reaction should be under control to modulate purine synthesis. Adenine and guanine, the end-products of the pathway, exert feedback (allosteric) control of this enzyme. In addition, the availability of PRPP and glutamine is also an important determinant of activity of the enzyme. The purine synthetic pathway is shown in Figure 36–2.

Purine Reutilization

An additional mechanism exists that can utilize adenine and guanine (of endogenous or dietary origin) and convert them into their respective ribonucleotides. This conversion is mediated by two different phosphoribosyl transferases—adenine phosphoribosyl transferase (APRT), which reacts with adenine, and hypoxanthine (guanine) phosphoribosyltransferase (HPRT), which reacts with hypoxanthine or guanine. Inherited deficiency of APRT has been associated with urinary calculi composed of 2,8-dihydroxyadenine.

Hypoxanthine Phosphoribosyltransferase Deficiency

Complete deficiency of HPRT is the cause of the Lesch-Nyhan syndrome, characterized by severe neurological disease and urate nephrolithiasis. This inherited disease provides persuasive evidence that this enzyme is intimately involved in the purine economy of human cells and that it probably provides supplemental nucleotides for bone marrow and brain. When as little as 1 per cent of activity remains, neurological dysfunction does not occur; hyperuricemia is still present but is not as great as in the Lesch-Nyhan syndrome.

Lesch-Nyhan disease is characterized by choreoathetosis, spasticity, mental dysfunction, and a striking, compulsive self-mutilation. Inheritance is sex-linked; hence, males only are affected. These infants are clinically normal at birth, but they may pass crystals of uric acid, which are noted in the diaper as an orange discoloration. Often this is not appreciated until more overt symptoms appear at around 4 to 6 months of age.

In some infants excessive irritability, vomiting, febrile episodes, and seizures are encountered before that time; the most common presentation is developmental delay, with difficulty holding the head upright at around 4 to 6 months. Muscle tone increases dramatically and by the end of the first year choreiform and athetoid movements are present, along with increased deep tendon reflexes and scissoring of the lower extremities.

As noted above the most remarkable feature is compulsive aggressiveness and self-mutilation to a degree that leads these patients to bite away lips, tongue, and ends of their fingers when they are not restrained. This behavior does not begin until the second or third year of life. Placing restraints on hands or elbows will prevent this behavior and assuage the agitation and even terror that these patients experience as they proceed to carry out self-destructive activity that is beyond their control.

While not as remarkable as self-mutilation, these children can also lash or strike out at nurses, physicians, and other individuals in their environment. However, they really wish to please and are very contrite if they hurt someone. Throughout such behavior, either directed against self or others, they are fully aware of their lack of control.

Biochemical Defects

When enzyme activity is measured in washed erythrocytes, less than 1 per cent residual activity is present. It is important to understand how a defect in HPRT leads to heightened purine synthesis. One explanation would be release of feedback inhibition on the purine synthetic pathway because of diminished levels of adenine or guanine nucleotides. However, when concentrates of these intracellular nucleotides were measured, this expected difference was not found. On the other hand, intracellular concentrations of PRPP were elevated manyfold in mutant cells. Since PRPP is a substrate for the amidotransferase, effects on that enzyme of elevated levels of PRPP were examined, and an additional means of control uncovered. The inactive form of the enzyme is favored by purines, which cause binding of a subunit that diminishes enzymatic activity; binding of PRPP favors disaggregation to the active monomer. Under circumstances of elevated PRPP levels, the amidotransferase reaction is enhanced.

Another finding related to the increased intracellular PRPP levels is an increase of APRT activity in erythrocyte lysates of these patients. This is apparently a result of stabilization of this enzyme by PRPP.

Pathogenesis of Neurological Dysfunction

Conventional and electron microscopic examination of brains of children succumbing to the Lesch-Nyhan syndrome has failed to reveal any structural abnormalities. This has led investigators to pursue a possible neurotoxicity role of urate as well as other purines. To date evidence incriminating any of these compounds is not persuasive.

An intriguing finding is decreased levels of enzymes involved in dopamine synthesis in the extrapyramidal system of these patients. This has been interpreted to reflect a disruption in the normal arborization of dopaminergic neurons, which is inferred to be responsible for the movement disorder. How the purine defect causes the abnormality in this population of neurons is the fascinating question that must be answered.

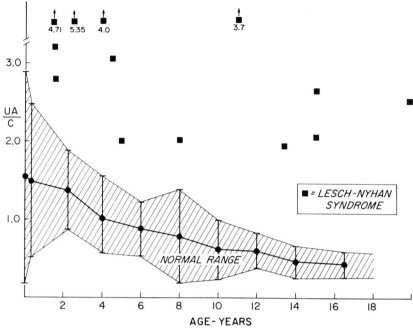

Figure 36–3 Urinary urate/creatinine ratio plotted as a function of age. The mean ratio ± 2 standard deviations is shown for 171 normal children and for infants in the first week of life (point on the abscissa). Patients with Lesch-Nyhan syndrome are seen to fall uniformly outside the normal values for age. (From Kaufman, J. M., Greene, M. L., and Seegmiller, J. E.: Urine uric acid to creatinine ratio. A screening test for inherited disorders of purine metabolism. J. Pediatr. 73:583, 1968.)

Diagnosis

As a screening test for a patient suspected of having HPRT deficiency, quantitation of urinary urate will document enhanced urate production. This is most readily accomplished on a spot urine, since these children will rarely cooperate for a timed (24 hour or less) collection. When the uric acid to creatinine ratio is determined in such individuals in the first years of life it will be greater than 3 (greater than 2 thereafter). The normal ratio is graphed in Figure 36–3 along with that seen in affected patients. Blood urate should also be measured in such an individual.

In any patient suspected of having complete or partial deficiency of HPRT enzyme, assay on washed red cell lysates is essential, since patients with myeloproliferative disorders and von Gierke's disease will also have an abnormal uric acid to creatinine ratio.

Treatment

As noted above, if restraints are placed on these children and their hands protected, they will become less agitated. Capping of teeth to eliminate cutting edges also improves their psychological state and renders them less at risk for self-mutilation. Diazepam (Valium) has improved the spasticity and athetosis.

Allopurinol, the xanthine oxidase inhibitor, at doses up to 10 mg/kg body weight can control the hyperuricemia, thus improving the prognosis for kidney function. Unfortunately, this therapy does not affect the neurological manifestations.

Hereditary Xanthinuria

Xanthinuria is an inherited defect of purine metabolism and is the result of a deficiency of xanthine oxidase. Its acquired counterpart occurs with the use of allopurinol. In both instances

Table 36–2   CAUSES OF HYPOURICEMIA

Excessive dosage with allopurinol
Deficiency of
    Purine nucleoside phosphorylase
    PRPP synthetase
Transport defects
    For urate
    Fanconi syndrome—inherited or acquired
Extensive liver disease
Syndrome of hypouricemia, hypercalciuria, and decreased bone density
Xanthinuria

hypoxanthine and xanthine, instead of uric acid, become the end products of purine metabolism. As a consequence serum urate levels are among the lowest encountered in clinical medicine—the tipoff to the possibility of xanthinuria. Indeed, while individuals with this defect are at risk for stone formation, only a small minority ever develop renal calculi.

Other causes of hypouricemia are listed in Table 36–2.

Xanthine oxidase is an aerobic dehydrogenase that mediates the step-wise oxidation converting hypoxanthine to xanthine and xanthine to uric acid.

Diagnosis

If quantitation of urate on a 24-hour urine, in a patient with hypouricemia, documents hypouricosuria as well, the next step should be qualitative or quantitative evaluation of xanthine excretion.

Treatment

Since xanthine stone formation is unusual, most individuals with the enzyme defect do not require therapy. Those, however, who have suffered from stones should imbibe large amounts of fluids (as for cystinuria) and restrict their intake of purines.

Hereditary Orotic Aciduria

Orotic aciduria is a rare, recessively inherited deficiency of two enzymes of pyrimidine metabolism, orotate phosphoribosyl transferase and orotidine 5′-phosphate decarboxylase (ODC), which renders these children dependent upon external sources of uridine. Fewer than 10 cases have been described. These children are normal at birth; during the first year of life they develop a severe megaloblastic anemia. Other rapidly growing tissues are also dependent on a ready source of pyrimidines; hence, these children show growth and mental retardation. Orotic aciduria is a consequence of the enzyme defect and is responsible for heavy crystalluria, which can lead to stone formation.

Biochemical Defects

Diminished activity of two sequential enzymes in the pyrimidine biosynthetic pathway makes such patients uridine auxotrophs, i.e., they require addition of uridine in their diet to provide this key building block. Hence, rapidly growing tissues deprived of uridine will not grow and divide normally.

Deficiency of two enzymes in a biosynthetic pathway is a distinct rarity—copurification of the two enzyme activities together suggests either that the two enzyme activities are associated with the same protein or that the two enzymes share the same subunit as part of their overall structure. A defect in genetic regulation preventing synthesis of two enzymes, as has been shown in bacteria, is highly unlikely as the cause.

Diagnosis

Orotic aciduria is manifested by a hypochromic megaloblastic anemia presenting in the latter part of the first year of life that is resistant to replacement therapy with iron, folic acid, and vitamin B_{12}. Leukopenia and retardation in growth and mental development should suggest this rare disorder of pyrimidine biosynthesis. A simple screening test performed by the suspicious clinician, or perhaps noted by the clinical laboratory, is the precipitation of orotic acid crystals on the walls of the refrigerated urine container. Quantitation will confirm the diagnosis.

Treatment

Uridine, approximately 150 mg/kg body weight, will improve the anemia and the growth disturbance. A good outcome for mental development seems to depend upon early recognition before irreversible changes occur.

IMMUNODEFICIENCY STATES CAUSED BY INHERITED DISORDERS OF PURINE METABOLISM

Introduction

The developing embryo is protected by its mother's immunological system from most bacterial and viral infections. In addition, some degree of maternal humoral antibody is passively conferred upon the fetus in the latter part of gestation. Nonetheless, passive immunization involves the transfer of protein molecules, which, as discussed in Part I, have a finite life span. Thus, the fetus must make preparations to defend itself against a wide variety of environmental pathogens upon departure from the intrauterine milieu. These preparations are directed towards the development of four primary immune system components: (1) antibody production; (2) cell-mediated immunity; (3) phagocytosis; and (4) production of complement.

The initial step in this process, which occurs before the 20th gestational week, involves the differentiation of a stem cell, probably originating in the fetal liver or bone marrow, into two primary cell types, the T-cell and the B-cell. The T-cell is so named because of its derivation from stem cells that have migrated to the thymus gland and subsequently differentiated. At birth, about 75 per cent of circulating lymphocytes are T-cells; they have also been disseminated widely throughout the lymphoreticular system. The B-cell derives its name from the fact that it originates by differentiation of stem cells within fetal bone marrow. The newborn has a 20 to 30 per cent B-cell population in its circulating lymphocytes.

There is a cooperativity between these two lymphocyte populations, reflecting their origins in a common stem cell. The B-cell is, in a sense, the "worker," responsible for maintenance of long-term humoral antibody levels following initial exposure to an antigen. T-cells may be characterized as the "brains" of the system, comprising the memory and regulatory factors. After initial sensitization to an antigen, the T-cell responds on subsequent exposure by destroying the cell carrying the antigen, either by direct cytotoxicity or by release of a variety of substances termed "lymphokines." An example of the latter is migration-inhibition factor, discussed in Chapter 37 with regard to its role in malnutrition-induced immunoincompetence. This T-cell response permits recognition and destruction of foreign cells (tumor, graft, and so on). Other subgroups of T-cells interact with B-cells to enhance (helper T-cells) or inhibit (suppressor T-cells) antibody production. In her typical frugal fashion, Nature has designated production of specific antibodies to specific B-cells; thus response to a specific antigen derives from the interaction of the subgroups of T-cells with a subgroup of B-cells capable of production of the necessary antibody. The T-cells are also necessary to the proliferation of B-cells and the latter's ability to further differentiate into fixed plasma cells.

Underlying all of the activities of T-cells and B-cells referred to above is a huge capacity for cell reproduction. Normal rates of cell death must be balanced by cell division, while every exposure to an environmental pathogen will occasion an increase in absolute cell number. As discussed in Part I, nucleic acids (DNA and RNA) are the repositories of all information stored in cells, so that the rate of nucleic acid breakdown and synthesis (turnover) must be "mother" to the "daughter" of cellular division. It is this tremendous demand for nucleic acid synthesis in the defense of host survival that has led to the discovery of specific genetic defects in purine metabolism and immunocompetence. In turn, discovery of these defects has contributed greatly to our understanding of regulation of purine metabolism.

Purine Degradation

The enormous size of the nucleic acid molecule would reasonably lead one to the conclusion that breakdown of such a molecule should result in a great number of end products in large amounts. However, as pointed out earlier in this chapter, in characteristic fashion, Nature has avoided such biological extravagance. The purine nucleotide monophosphates that comprise approximately half of the nucleic acid molecule are all degraded by a final common pathway, through hypoxanthine, to uric acid (Fig. 36–1). Interposed between the latter two compounds, however, is a reclamation pathway, which is subject to complex regulation and results in "recycling" of a major fraction of hypoxanthine back to purine nucleotides.

While a defect in this reclamation pathway has been recognized for some time (see discussion of the Lesch-Nyhan syndrome) only in the last 8 years have we become aware that other enzymatic abnormalities in purine degradation exist and lead to clinically detectable disease states. These disorders can be classified as defects in the degradation process or those resulting in increased degradation. Of primary interest to us in this chapter are those defects inhibiting degradation, and only these will be discussed here. The reader is referred to Table 36–1 and to the pertinent sections of this book in which the other entities listed are discussed.

Adenosine Deaminase (ADA) Deficiency

Clinical Features

A constant clinical feature of this autosomal recessive disease is severe combined immunodeficiency. There is a greater and earlier loss of T-cell function, although eventually B-cell functional impairment becomes equally apparent. There are, as a direct result, severe, recurrent infections beginning shortly after birth. These may be due to common pathogens as well as to opportunistic organisms normally not seen in a healthy individual. In addition, one sees gastrointestinal symptoms, including intractable diarrhea, malabsorption, and failure to thrive; these are thought to be independent features and not secondary to enteral infection. Bony abnormalities resembling rachitic changes have been described in about 50 per cent of affected individuals, and neurological defects such as nystagmus, spasticity, athetosis, and developmental lag appear in about 10 to 15 per cent.

Laboratory Findings

There is an absolute lymphopenia involving both species of lymphocytes; those few present fail to respond to phytohemagglutinin (PHA) in vitro. Immunoglobulins IgA, IgM, and IgG are very low or absent in serum, and there is a failure of specific antibody response following immunization. Increased levels of adenosine and deoxyadenosine are found in plasma and red cells.

Biochemical Defects

ADA is the enzyme responsible for the deamination of adenosine and deoxyadenosine in production of inosine or deoxyinosine. Among all organs of the body, thymus tissue contains the highest specific activity (defined as enzymatically active units per milligram of tissue protein) of ADA, although all human tissues contain detectable levels of the enzyme. While in affected individuals erythrocyte ADA levels are less than 1 per cent of control, some residual ADA activity is

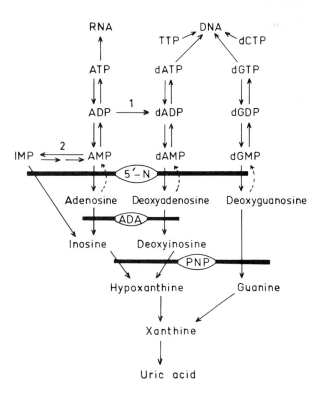

Figure 36–4 Scheme of purine catabolism, showing inborn errors associated with immune deficiency states. ADA = adenosine deaminase, PNP = purine nucleoside phosphorylase and 5'-N = 5'-nucleotidase. Dotted arrows denote steps catalyzed by d-nucleoside kinases. (From Raivio, K. O.: The biochemical basis of immunodeficiency disease. Eur. J. Pediatr. 135:13–20, 1980.)

generally present in other tissues. Study of this residual activity has resulted in demonstration of a structurally altered enzyme molecule. There is also a secondary deficiency of erythrocyte S-adenosylhomocysteine hydrolase, although the significance of this is presently unknown.

Absence of ADA activity will result (Fig. 36–4) in accumulation of adenosine and deoxyadenosine, reflected in high urinary and plasma levels seen in these patients. In a wide variety of in vitro systems, cytotoxicity or immunosuppression results following addition of adenosine or deoxyadenosine to the culture medium. If ADA is specifically inhibited in these systems, using coformycin, for example, these adverse effects of adenosine or deoxyadenosine are potentiated. Studies of the relative potency of the latter two compounds have shown that deoxyadenosine is the more effective as an inhibitor. However, deoxyadenosine could not be demonstrated intracellularly in ADA-deficient cell lines, although deoxyadenosine-mediated cytotoxicity was accompanied by an increase in intracellular deoxyATP. Thus, through the action of a deoxynucleoside kinase, deoxyadenosine is converted by successive phosphorylation steps to dATP. The enzyme ribonucleotide reductase, which converts the diphosphorylated purine nucleotides to their corresponding deoxy forms (Fig. 36–5), is subjected to feedback inhibition. As a result, the deoxynucleotides essential to DNA synthesis cannot be synthesized. Thus, abnormal amounts of a single compound lead to total disarray of normal control mechanisms and cell death.

Diagnosis

ADA deficiency should be a part of the differential diagnosis in any infant with a family or personal history of recurrent severe infection, failure to thrive, chronic diarrhea, and malabsorption. Absolute lymphopenia and low or absent levels of all immunoglobulins are strongly suggestive of this disorder. Definitive diagnosis rests upon demonstration of an ADA deficiency in the red cell.

Treatment

In about 50 per cent of ADA-deficient patients, administration of packed, irradiated red cells will occasion an increased absolute lymphocyte and PHA response, together with a decrease in

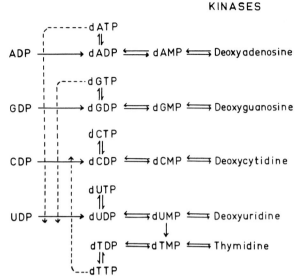

RIBONUCLEOTIDE
REDUCTASE

DEOXYNUCLEOSIDE
KINASES

Figure 36–5 Scheme of d-ribonucleotide synthesis. Steps catalyzed by ribonucleotide reductase which are believed to be inhibited by d-ribonucleoside triphosphates are shown by dashed lines and arrows. (From Raivio, K. O.: The biochemical basis of immunodeficiency disease. Eur. J. Pediatr. 135:13–20, 1980.)

urinary excretion of adenosine/deoxyadenosine. A low purine diet may be of added benefit in these individuals. However, bone marrow transplantation offers the only permanent form of treatment in this disease and is thus the treatment of choice.

Purine Nucleoside Phosphorylase (PNP) Deficiency

Clinical Features

Patients afflicted with this autosomal recessive disorder begin to manifest increased susceptibility to severe infections in the latter half of the first year of life or later. Some patients have had anemia, either hemolytic (autoimmune) or megaloblastic. No other clinical features of the 9 patients thus far reported have been common enough to be considered representative of the enzyme defect. Viral infections are a particular problem in affected individuals.

Laboratory Findings

An absolute and age-related degree of lymphopenia is typical of this disorder; it is due to a marked reduction in circulating T-cells, while B-cells are present in normal numbers. In accordance with the role of the T-cell as a regulator of B-cell antibody production, immunoglobulin levels in blood are normal or elevated, although PHA stimulation of peripheral blood lymphocytes is either diminished or absent. There is also hypouricemia (a finding that is highly relevant to the biochemical aberration in this disorder), together with increased excretion of the nucleosides inosine/deoxyinosine and guanosine/deoxyguanosine.

Biochemical Defects

The hypouricemia seen in this disease implies a block in purine degradation, while the urinary excretion of inosine/deoxyinosine and guanosine/deoxyguanosine point to PNP as the defective enzyme step. Erythrocytes of the initial patient showed virtually no PNP activity, while the parents had levels that were 50 per cent of control. In subsequent patients there has been considerable variation in residual enzyme activity, paralleling the heterogeneous clinical presentations.

Interestingly, there is a massive increase in total purine synthesis, with elevations of phosphoribosylpyrophosphate in red cells to levels approximating those seen in patients with a deficiency of hypoxanthine-guanine phosphoribosyltransferase. This can be related to the fact that hypoxanthine cannot be produced in significant amounts, since it is distal to the affected enzyme step. Thus, the purine reclamation pathway is rendered inoperative, and the compounds must be synthesized de novo. The mechanism accounting for the high intracellular levels of dGTP seen is the same as the one discussed earlier for the accumulation of dATP in ADA deficiency (see p. 387). Also in common with ADA deficiency, there is a defect in erythrocyte S-adenosylhomocysteine hydrolase activity in PNP deficient red cells. The significance of this observation in this disorder as well remains unclear.

Diagnosis

Severe, recurrent infections with an onset in late infancy should awaken suspicion to an immunodeficiency disease. The presence of absolute lymphopenia with normal serum immunoglobulin levels points to a PNP deficiency. Hypouricemia and increased urinary levels of inosine/deoxyinosine and guanosine/deoxyguanosine are strongly suggestive of this defect. Definitive diagnosis rests upon demonstration of absent or very low activity of PNP in the patient's erythrocytes.

Treatment

Enzyme replacement by transfusion of irradiated, packed red cells has met with only moderate success. Incomplete and short-lived response to thymus transplant has been reported. Bone marrow transplant is of no help, since the defect is primarily expressed in the T-cell lymphocyte. Recent studies in vitro indicate that toxicity induced by d-adenosine or d-guanosine can be reversed with d-cytidine; this agent remains to be tested in vivo. Thus, only palliative therapy is available at this time.

The final question remains: why are these enzyme deficiencies expressed more or less selectively in lymphoid tissue function? We have attempted to give a partial answer by pointing out that the turnover of these cells is enormous in view of the frequency of normal exposure to environmental pathogens, but this cannot be the sole reason. Other theories have been advanced, such as the relative activities of certain of the enzymes to others in lymphoid tissue as compared with other organs of the body. However, the precise answer to this question has eluded investigators up to the present time.

REFERENCES

Borkowsky, W., Gershon, A.A., Shenkman, L., and Hirschhorn, R.: Adenosine deaminase deficiency without immunodeficiency: Clinical and metabolic studies. Pediatr. Res. 14:885, 1980.

Fox, I.H.: Metabolic basis for disorders of purine nucleotide degradation. Metabolism 30:616, 1981.

Holmes, E.W., and Wyngaarden, J.B.: Hereditary xanthinuria. In Stanbury, J.B., Wyngaarden, J.B., Fredrickson, D.S. et al. (eds.): The Metabolic Basis of Inherited Disease. 5th ed. McGraw-Hill, New York, 1983, p. 1192.

Hurst, D.T.: An Introduction to the Chemistry and Biochemistry of Pyrimidines, Purines and Pteridines. J. Wiley & Sons, Chicester, 1980.

Jones, M.F.: Pyrimidine nucleotide biosynthesis in animals: Genes, enzymes and regulation of UMP biosynthesis. Ann. Rev. Biochem. 49:253, 1980.

Kaufman, J.M., Greene, M.L., and Seegmiller, J.E.: Urine uric acid to creatinine ratio—A screening test for inherited disorders of purine metabolism. J. Pediatr. 73:583, 1968.

Kelley, W.N.: In Stanbury, J.B., Wyngaarden, J.B., Fredrickson, D.S. et al. (eds.): The Metabolic Basis of Inherited Disease. 5th ed. McGraw-Hill, New York, 1983, p. 1202.

Kelley, W.N., and Wyngaarden, J.B.: Clinical syndromes associated with hypoxanthin-guanine phosphoribosyltransferase deficiency. In Stanbury, J.B., Wyngaarden, J.B., Fredrickson, D.S. et al. (eds.): The Metabolic Basis of Inherited Disease. 5th ed. McGraw-Hill, New York, 1983, p. 1115.

Kredich, N.M., and Hershfield, M.S.: Immunodeficiency diseases caused by adenosine deaminase deficiency and purine nucleoside phosphorylase deficiency. *In* Stanbury, J.B., Wyngaarden, J.B., Fredrickson, D.S. et al. (eds.): The Metabolic Basis of Inherited Disease. 5th ed. McGraw-Hill, New York, 1983, p. 1157.

Lloyd, K.G., Hornykiewicz, O., Davidson, L., et al.: Biochemical evidence of dysfunction of brain neurotransmitters in the Lesch-Nyhan syndrome. N. Engl. J. Med. 305:1106, 1981.

Mitchell, B.S., and Kelley, W.N.: Purinogenic immunodeficiency diseases: Clinical features and molecular mechanisms. Ann. Intern. Med. 92:826, 1980.

Musick, W.D.L.: Structural features of the phosphoribosyltransferases and their relationship to the human deficiency disorders of purine and pyrimidine metabolism. CRC Crit. Rev. Biochem. 11:1, 1981.

Osborne, W.R.A.: Inherited absences of purine recycling enzymes associated with defects of immunity. Trends Biochem. Sci. 6:80, 1981.

Raivio, K.O.: The biochemical basis of immunodeficiency disease. Eur. J. Pediatr. 135:13, 1980.

Seegmiller, J.E.: Disorders of purine and pyrimidine metabolism. *In* Freinkel, N. (ed.): Contemporary Metabolism. Plenum, New York, 1979, p. 1.

Seegmiller, J.E.: Diseases of purine and pyrimidine metabolism. *In* Bondy, P.K., and Rosenberg, L.E. (eds.): Metabolic Control and Disease. 8th ed. W.B. Saunders Co., Philadelphia, 1980, p. 777.

Shin-Buehring, Y.S., Osang, M., Wirtz, A., et al.: Prenatal diagnosis of Lesch-Nyhan syndrome and some characteristics of hypoxanthine-guanine phosphoribosyltransferase and adenine phosphoribosyltransferase in human tissues and cultivated cells. Pediatr. Res. 14:825, 1980.

Wilson, J.M., Baugher, B.W., Mattes, P.M., et al.: Human hypoxanthine-guanine phosphoribosyltransferase. Demonstration of structural variants in lymphoblastoid cells derived from patients with a deficiency of the enzyme. J. Clin. Invest. 69:706, 1982.

Wyngaarden, J.B., and Kelley, W.N.: Gout. *In* Stanbury, J.B., Wyngaarden, J.B., Fredrickson, D.S. et al. (eds.): The Metabolic Basis of Inherited Disease. 5th ed. McGraw-Hill, New York, 1983, p. 1043.

37

Nutritional Disorders

INTRODUCTION

In various sections of this book, we have emphasized the high degree of order required for the conduct of life's processes. Such a concept suggests that maintenance of life in any organism requires a constant expenditure of energy to resist the natural tendency of all ordered systems to revert toward chaos with the inevitable increase in *entropy* (see Part I). This energy cost to the body is equivalent to the more widely used term "basal metabolic rate" (BMR). It may be defined as the number of kcal per day required to maintain overall metabolic homeostasis in the absence of significant physical activity. A straightforward analogy would be the number of gallons of gasoline per day required to keep an automobile engine idling in a car completely still. Clearly, just as one will inevitably have to refill the gas tank, an organism will have to replenish its energy supply.

The "Engine" At Rest

At rest, the organism processes metabolic fuel through the myriad reactions designed to utilize these substances in a maximally efficient fashion. In keeping with the economical nature of biochemical processes, which proceed under the constraints (pH and temperature) of the living state, uncontrolled direct combustion is scrupulously avoided. Oxidation is accomplished by stepwise (ordered) degradation of the carbon skeleton, through decarboxylations and dehydrogenations. As the protons and electrons join with oxygen to form water at the end of the electron transport chain, ATP is formed in a closely coupled process to store the energy released from this combustion. Release of CO_2 and H_2O as end products is in conformity both with the constraints of the laws of thermodynamics as well as with the need to limit formation of toxic products. The measurement of the oxygen consumed in this process can be used to quantitate the basal metabolic rate.

For a BMR measurement to be meaningful, we must standardize the "grade" of metabolic fuel and the tissues that are contributing to the use of this energy source. Thus, the assumption is made that in an otherwise normal individual, the fuel utilized after an 8-hour sleep and a 12-hour fast will be the same as in all other similar normal individuals. In addition, a standardized measure of "engine" size must be utilized, such as body surface area or fat-free body mass. The measurement of BMR is, therefore, expressed as milliliters of O_2 (equivalent to kcal) per minute consumed per m^2 surface area or per kg lean body mass.

What processes are actually measured in the resting organism by a BMR? Although no external work is being performed, energy must nonetheless be expended to support muscular movements of breathing, myocardial contractions, maintenance of muscle tone, and the maintenance of overall metabolic homeostasis. This last expenditure predominantly involves the maintenance of transmembrane ionic potential (see Chapter 8). More than 90 per cent of the O_2 consumed by the cells involved in these processes is reduced to H_2O via the mitochondrial electron transport system. Thus, a properly performed BMR measurement can be a fairly accurate gauge of basic energy consumption required to preserve the high degree of order of the human organism.

Nutritional Support of Growth

The first law of thermodynamics states that matter can neither be created nor destroyed, yet clearly the human organism achieves a huge increase in mass throughout its growth period. We

Table 37-1 BODY PROTEIN HOMEOSTASIS

Total Body Protein (70 kg man)   10,000 g
Daily Intake   100 g
Daily Loss
Stool   10 g
Urine   80 g
Skin   2 g
Total Daily Protein Synthesis $\sim$ 300 g
Muscle   75 g
GI secretions   70 g
Leukocytes   20 g
Plasma proteins (albumin, fibrinogen, γ-globulins)   20 g
Hemoglobin   8 g
Other (enzymes, connective tissue, cell regeneration, etc.)   95–110 g

have already discussed (see Chapter 10) the hyperplastic and hypertrophic phases of the growth process, pointing out the distinguishing aspects of each. According to the principle inherent in the first law of thermodynamics, it should be clear that basic to growth is a supply of raw materials quantitatively adequate to explain this increase in body mass. For this reason, infants and children require significantly more kcal/kg body weight than do adults.

Equally important to the support of growth, the nature of which implies net synthesis, is the qualitative aspect of the calories ingested. Lipid and carbohydrate can be stored as triglycerides and glycogen, respectively, when ingested in excess. Protein, on the other hand, is not stored to any extent by the body and must be continually supplied if growth is to persist (Table 37–1). While any of these three basic nutritional components can be oxidized to provide energy, the body's capacity to interconvert amino acids is limited. Indeed, certain fatty and amino acids that cannot be derived from endogenous transformations and that are necessary for synthesis are known as "essential" compounds and must be provided in the diet. For example, in the absence of adequate quantities of any one of the essential amino acids, protein synthesis does not proceed normally. Instead the bulk of dietary intake will be degraded to generate energy or will be wasted, since synthesis cannot proceed.

An additional aspect of the synthesis vital to growth is the energy cost of this process of accretion of new tissue. Since amino acids must be converted to more active derivatives, in an ATP-requiring step prior to utilization, it is not hard to see what a very large energy cost is necessitated by biosynthetic processes. Generation of energy for this purpose is partially accounted for by carbohydrate oxidation and is known as the "protein-sparing effect" of ingested glucose.

In summary, because protein synthesis and the growth of tissues are energy-requiring processes overall energy requirements must be met before protein synthesis can occur. When insufficient carbohydrate and lipid are ingested to provide for these needs, amino acids will be catabolized to substrates, which can be oxidized through the citric acid cycle to make up the energy deficit in preference to their role in protein synthesis. Thus, the nutritional demands for growth are large, requiring sufficient quantities of carbohydrates and lipids to meet the prodigious needs of the resting organism plus the protein necessary for cell restoration. Additional amounts of sugar and fat are needed to balance the energy cost of new protein synthesized from dietary proteins. All of this is reflected in the greater caloric requirement of the infant and its higher dietary protein requirement.

Effects of Stress on the System

Intercurrent, usually mild, illness is an inescapable part of infancy and childhood. As a general rule, illnesses are accompanied by loss of appetite. From all that has already been said about the energy requirements of the growing organism it is clear that this has metabolic consequences for the infant. Further complicating the situation are the almost inevitable qualitative dietary changes that accompany illness in the infant. These generally include decreases in protein content and caloric density, creating in themselves a condition of partial acute protein-calorie deprivation. Furthermore, a leading type of illness in infancy is diarrheal disease, either primary or secondary, resulting in decreased absorption and availability of ingested nutrients. For these and other reasons, it has been difficult for investigators to determine precisely the direct effects of illness on energy metabolism and growth.

Many discussions of the metabolic responses to illness take a "balance sheet" approach, placing heavy emphasis on the catabolic aspects of the response to trauma or infection. Nonetheless we should never lose sight of the fact that the metabolic response to stress has evolved over millions of years into a highly integrated process directed at survival of the organism. Tissue catabolism must, in this light, be considered only a means toward an end. We will try to underscore this principle in the following discussion.

Keeping in mind the fact that hormones are messengers permitting communications between cells of various body tissues, it would be reasonable to expect a hormonal response to stress. Indeed, among the first responses to stress is a sympathetic impulse, mediated through the hypothalamus, resulting in release from the pituitary of TSH, ACTH, ADH, and growth hormone. Among the many known effects of the hormonal secretions elicited by TSH and ACTH are increased metabolic rate, increased cellular uptake of amino acids, increased rate of peripheral protein breakdown, and decreased peripheral response to insulin. The primary function of the first three alterations mentioned may be the facilitation of synthesis of leukocytes, acute phase reactants, and specific antibodies by reutilization of endogenous amino acids. The primary function of the latter may actually lie in conservation of glucose for use by glucose-dependent tissues, such as erythrocytes and brain. The lactate produced as a consequence of decreased glucose utilization provides valuable substrate for myocardial metabolism and gluconeogenesis, facilitated by elevated levels of glucagon. Further, we have already seen that glucagon is ketogenic (Chapter 13), facilitating production of acetyl CoA units from β-oxidation, thus by-passing the decreased flux of glucose through the pyruvate dehydrogenase step of glycolysis. Thus, the orchestrated general metabolic response to stress mediated by a number of hormones can be appreciated.

Increased granulocytopoiesis with consequent enhanced phagocytic activity causes a rise in blood levels of two other hormone-like substances, leukocyte endogenous mediator (LEM) and endogenous pyrogen released by these phagocytes. The effect of LEM is directed upon the liver and bone marrow: hepatic uptake of amino acids, zinc, and iron is stimulated; stimulation of RNA, polyribosomes, acute phase reactants, and ceruloplasmin synthesis takes place; hepatic levels of some inducible enzymes related to amino acid metabolism (tyrosine transaminase, tryptophan oxygenase) increase; and, in addition, bone marrow production of leukocytes is stimulated. Thus, the organism's response to stress is anabolic in the sense that it is directed toward meeting the challenge of an external or internal stress instead of carrying out the usual incessant renewal of body tissues. It is this trade-off in the face of "clear and present danger" that renders the process catabolic from the point of view of a body balance sheet.

The effect of pyrogen is to act on the hypothalamus to increase body temperature; the precise role of fever in the overall response to stress remains undefined. The onset of fever coincides with the secretion of aldosterone in addition to that of ADH, mentioned earlier. The combined effects of these two hormones result in retention of water and Na^+, with an increased distal tubular conservation of the latter in exchange for K^+, derived from muscle catabolism. Nonetheless, serum Na^+ levels may fall slightly during acute illness, due to a dilutional effect of ADH-induced water retention. The reason for the H_2O retention is not clear, but we may speculate that it is integrated with the febrile response; increased total body water may help keep body temperature within physiological limits by "buffering" the shunting of energy expenditure into heat production. Such a mechanism would prevent abrupt increases and decreases in temperature by absorption of the heat (1 kcal = the amount of heat energy required to raise one kg of H_2O 1°C).

Finally, we ought to discuss the concept of nitrogen balance in relationship to the phenomena we have just discussed. It is imperative that the BMR be maintained at all costs, irrespective of the stress, if the organism is to survive. Part of the energy expended in maintaining the BMR is involved in the activation of amino acids and the synthesis of protein. If there is a deficit of the essential components necessary for this process, the requisite amino acids will be drawn from pre-existing body protein. Other amino acids will be converted to body protein, while still other amino acids will be converted to pyruvate or Krebs cycle intermediates for energy production. Thus, adequate exogenous protein must be supplied to offset these losses, producing a zero net nitrogen balance. If provision of this quantity of protein is not possible, the organism exists in a state of negative nitrogen balance. In view of the tremendous caloric requirements and synthetic response to stress, superimposed upon those necessary for BMR maintenance (in the face of anorexia typical of most stress), it can be seen that a negative nitrogen balance is characteristic of a stressed organism. On the other hand, a positive nitrogen balance is the characteristic state of the growing organism. As might be expected, growth is affected during periods of stress, thus accounting for the poor growth observed in chronically ill infants and children (see Chapter 10).

Starvation and Protein Calorie Malnutrition

We have already examined the body's response to hypoglycemia (see Chapter 12). Our task here is to outline the means by which the organism adjusts to more prolonged periods of metabolic fuel deprivation. The overall response to starvation appears to be one of preservation of essential body protein and (within that one constraint) making the transition from exogenous to endogenous nutrient dependency as smooth and parsimonious as possible.

On a caloric basis the vast bulk of body energy stores are in lipid form. Nonetheless at the onset of starvation, in a previously well-fed individual, the first few days of fasting are marked by a reliance upon carbohydrate as the predominant fuel. Several of the body's tissues (e.g., erythrocytes) have an absolute dependency on glucose, so that total reliance upon glucose by the rest of the body would be self-defeating. Once again, the need for integration and coordination of metabolic responses in various organs is illustrated, the prime communicators being, naturally, the hormones (see Chapter 2). In the initial stage of starvation, the sequence of events is rather complex and seems to be triggered by a slight but significant fall in blood glucose levels. There is an immediate pancreatic response to this, with decreasing insulin and increasing glucagon secretion. Decreased insulin slows amino acid uptake and carbohydrate utilization by peripheral tissues, while increased glucagon stimulates gluconeogenesis and ketogenesis (see Chapter 13).

The net result of these pancreatic responses is to create a metabolic environment in which glucose is simultaneously synthesized and spared, the latter occurring because of the lipolysis and ketogenesis induced by the combination of insulinopenia and glucagonemia. Thus, glucose derived from amino acid skeletons can supply the brain, erythrocytes, and so on, while the body's major energy supply becomes fat. There is a problem inherent in this response, however: the derivative increase in ketone bodies as a result of fatty acid breakdown represents a large amount of potential energy, which cannot be entirely utilized by muscle, while gluconeogenesis demands a concurrent proteolysis, which cannot be tolerated for long. This situation is resolved by increased utilization by the brain of ketone bodies, thus reducing its dependence upon glucose as a major fuel and decreasing the need for gluconeogenesis significantly. The phenomena thus far described constitute the initial phase of the body's response to fasting and permit survival for prolonged periods, using depot lipid as a primary fuel source. This is reflected in a more rapid rate of body fat loss than that of lean muscle mass.

However, the nature of enzyme protein as an ordered structure implies also a finite life span. Thus, there is a need for renewal of these enzymes on a continuous basis in viable cells. Since no system is perfectly efficient, there is bound to be some amino acid loss persisting throughout starvation and, as the period of fasting continues and lipid stores become depleted, the body must inevitably draw upon protein for energy needs. There is a premorbid phase of starvation during which time nitrogen excretion is seen to increase, signaling the use of amino acids for energy supply. At this stage the body is faced with a dilemma: amino acids must be used for energy supply through oxidation and they are also necessary for resynthesis of the enzymes facilitating both their own oxidation and those of other vital metabolic reactions. This is, however, a paradox to which the body has no answer. Such an answer would defy the laws of thermodynamics in any case and is therefore not possible. Thus, at this stage death is not far off, the entire process having taken 2 to 3 months in an adult. Nonetheless, the time required to reach this irreversible state is a monument to the tenacity with which life processes resist disorder.

A variation on this theme is protein-calorie malnutrition, a term applied to a spectrum of disorders, all having in common some degree of oral intake with inadequate protein content (Table 37–2). For obvious reasons, this type of energy deficit is more common by far, on a world-wide basis, than the phenomenon of total starvation. It is, therefore, important to understand the biochemical events that are a result of a chronic partial energy and protein deficit. Clinically, such patients very often exhibit a superimposed infectious process, the stress of which causes decompensation of the very tenuous metabolic state in which they exist.

As discussed above, the triggering event in the body's adaptation to cessation of caloric intake is a slight fall in blood glucose, evoking insulinopenia and glucagonemia. Gluconeogenesis is stimulated, the glucose thus synthesized supporting the energy requirements of the glucose-dependent body tissues. Simultaneously, lipolysis and ketogenesis commence, the energy yield from these processes being used to support the needs of peripheral tissues such as muscle. The overall design is directed at body protein conservation. However, intake of protein-deficient calories, primarily as carbohydrate, has an undesirable effect upon this adaptive mechanism by stimulating insulin release.

The presence of normal, rather than low, circulating insulin levels slows both gluconeogenesis and lipolysis. Because of the "protein-sparing" effect of dietary carbohydrate the release of amino acids from muscle is inhibited, causing a severe depletion of glucose as well as essential amino acids in plasma. The resulting decrease in hepatic protein synthesis produces hypoalbuminemia and hypolipoproteinemia, the former helping to account for the severe edema that is often seen in these patients. The excess carbohydrate and hypolipoproteinemia combine to accelerate hepatic fatty acid synthesis and increased hepatic fat content, accounting for the hepatic fatty infiltration of severe malnutrition (see Chapter 15). In addition, the decreased circulating levels of lipoproteins lead to decreased levels of plasma lipids. Underlying all of this is the chronic deficiency of protein necessary for replacement and synthesis which constitutes the basis for growth. Thus, while growth

Table 37–2 COMPARISON OF MARASMUS AND KWASHIORKOR

	Marasmus	Kwashiorkor
Dietary Etiology	Partial nutritional deprivation of all components in normal proportion	Diminished protein intake with relatively normal caloric increment
Duration Prior to Clinical Presentation	Months to years, dependent on degree of deprivation	Weeks to months, dependent upon relative protein intake and superimposed stress (infection)
Clinical Features	↓ Growth rate (both weight and height), ↓ physical activity, apathy, weight/height for age < 80% of normal, sunken cheeks, monkey-like facies, hair sparse and brittle, nails slow in growth, hypoglycemia, hypothermia	Appear fairly well-nourished, irritable, anorectic, hepatomegaly with fatty infiltration, mild-severe edema, hyperkeratotic skin lesions with superficial ulceration, petechiae, ecchymosis, hair loss, rapid decompensation in face of infection
Laboratory Findings	Hb 8–10 g/dl, serum IgD 4.0 ± 1.1 mg/dl, serum albumin > 2.8 g/dl, total WBC normal to mildly elevated	Hb < 8 g/dl, serum IgD 13.5 ± 4.3 mg/dl, serum albumin < 2.8 g/dl, absolute lymphocytopenia, anergic response
Clinical Course	Ravenous appetite, frequent constipation, relatively resistant to intercurrent infection, rickets, terminal signs are depression of vital signs, hypoglycemia, hypothermia	Anorectic, diarrhea common, diminished ability to resist infection, rapid decompensation and death due to secondary infection
Therapy and Mortality	Small, frequent feedings, initially meeting only maintenance requirements and gradually increasing in concentration and volume; mortality generally low	Reintroduction of protein must be cautious, overload may result in cardiac failure; mortality is generally high

Table 37–3 ORGAN DYSFUNCTION IN CYSTIC FIBROSIS CAUSED BY VISCOUS SECRETIONS AND OBSTRUCTION

Organ	Clinical Manifestations
Gastrointestinal tract	Meconium ileus, meconium peritonitis Obstruction in older individuals
Pancreas	Deficiency of pancreatic hydrolytic enzymes
Liver	Focal biliary cirrhosis Occasionally multilobular biliary cirrhosis with portal hypertension
Lungs	Chronic obstructive pulmonary disease—bronchiectasis, peribronchial fibrosis and airway obstruction
Sweat glands	Elevated sodium and chloride concentrations in sweat (98 per cent)

slows, the total body protein pool slowly decreases in size, so that it may be difficult to determine clinically that there has been a loss of lean body mass except in severe cases.

At this point, it can be clearly appreciated that the metabolic effects of stress superimposed upon those of protein calorie malnutrition may be disastrous. In addition to those problems already mentioned, deficient protein intake very likely implies deficiencies of trace metals and vitamins as well, with their attendant consequences (see below). Therefore, despite the body's ability to withstand nutrient depletion for prolonged periods of time, this process takes its toll and is a leading cause of morbidity in this country and of both morbidity and mortality throughout the world.

CYSTIC FIBROSIS

This disorder, which used to be considered a lethal or semilethal disease, has over the years displayed a remarkable heterogeneity of clinical manifestations and severity, which permit a tempering of the original bleak outlook. While far more common in Caucasians (about 1:2000) it does occur in Blacks (about 1:17,000) but is very rare in American Indians and Orientals.

The fundamental inherited defect is still unknown but results in the elaboration of abnormally thick secretions by all exocrine glands. Clinical manifestations arise from the obstruction of organ ducts by these secretions, leading to infection.

These manifestations (Table 37–3) revolve around chronic obstructive pulmonary disease, insufficiency of pancreatic enzymes and secretions, with malabsorption and failure to thrive. The diagnosis depends upon demonstration of abnormal sweat chloride (> 60 mEq/l) and sodium concentrations. Because of increasing recognition of milder forms presenting in adolescence and adulthood the indications for sweat testing are fairly broad—hence older individuals with chronic cough and bronchitis or minimal malabsorption findings deserve a consideration of cystic fibrosis in their differential diagnosis. Several diseases are also associated with abnormal sweat electrolytes, but

Table 37–4 WHEN TO CONSIDER CYSTIC FIBROSIS

Neonate and Infant
    Meconium ileus; rectal prolapse
    Steatorrhea
    Recurrent pulmonary infections
All Ages
    Siblings of patients with cystic fibrosis or child of a patient with cystic fibrosis
    Failure to thrive
    Chronic cough
    Recurrent pulmonary infections and complications
    Intestinal obstruction
    Nasal polyps
    Liver disease
    Salty taste to skin
    Undue sensitivity to heat exposure

they should be clearly distinguishable from cystic fibrosis. They include Addison's disease, nephrogenic diabetes insipidus, glucose-6-phosphatase deficiency, hypothyroidism, fucosidosis, and ectodermal dysplasia. Clinical situations that warrant quantitation of sweat electrolytes are listed in Table 37–4.

So variegated are the manifestations of this disease that a team approach to therapy becomes necessary—this is best accomplished in a regional center. Details of therapy are quite involved, so that the reader is directed to the references for the exhaustive coverage not possible here.

TRACE METAL METABOLISM

Introduction

Presently, chromium, copper, cobalt, manganese, molybdenum, selenium, and zinc are considered to be essential trace elements in human nutrition. The general physiological role of trace elements has so far been found to reside in their association with enzyme systems in living cells, although other functions are possible. The multivalent property of the trace elements has been utilized to add stability to the polyionic protein molecule; hence both increased longevity and reactivity are conferred. In cases in which the metal is firmly bound to specific sites on the protein and cannot be removed without denaturing the molecule, the complex is termed a metalloenzyme. The metal may constitute a part of the active site or may only serve to maintain a three-dimensional structure necessary for enzymatic activity; in either case, loss of the metal seriously or totally impairs the activity of the protein.

A larger and less well-understood group of enzyme proteins are the metal-enzyme complexes. Here the adaptability of biological systems is well illustrated, since in many cases, one metal may substitute for another, the only criterion being activation of the enzyme's catalytic function. In a metal-enzyme complex, the metal can be readily removed and replaced without denaturation of the protein, a primary distinction from a metalloenzyme. Notably, some metal-enzymes retain catalytic activity in the absence of the metal component; regrettably such observations do little to augment our understanding of the role of metal-enzyme complexes in vivo.

A relatively recent development in knowledge of the biological role of trace metals is the discovery of substantial quantities of nickel, chromium, cobalt, and manganese firmly bound to ribonucleic acids. The precise role they play with respect to RNA remains to be determined, but it is thought that they serve to stabilize the three-dimensional structure of the molecule. In such a capacity trace metals would, therefore, be vital to the synthesis of all proteins.

Endogenous Handling of Trace Metals

The average dietary intake of the trace metals is small, ranging from 5 μg for cobalt to 15 mg for zinc per day (Table 37–5). Quantitatively, this range overlaps that of the vitamins but is far from comparable to the dietary requirements for carbohydrate, protein, and fat. The major implication of this is that dietary aberrations or inadequacies can lead to trace metal deficiencies almost as quickly as to the better-known dietary vitamin deficiencies such as scurvy and beri-beri. However, the area of trace metal metabolism is relatively new, and much information has yet to be learned regarding deficiencies of these substances.

The precise mechanisms by which the various trace elements are absorbed are only partially understood. Whether uptake of a given metal by intestinal epithelium is active is not known, although the widely variable and generally low fractional absorption of daily intake (Table 37–5) would suggest otherwise. On the other hand, a disease like acrodermatitis enteropathica, which appears to be a specific disorder of intestinal zinc absorption, is consistent with the possibility of a protein carrier molecule mediating, at least, facilitated diffusion (see Chapter 23). It is also possible that a small fraction of some metals, like copper, may be actively transported bound to amino acids. Once the metals reach the serosal surface of the intestinal epithelium, they must be carried by the

Table 37-5 NUTRITIONAL ASPECTS OF TRACE METALS

Element	MRDA	Dietary Source	Amount of Oral Intake Absorbed	Route of Excretion
Copper	Infants (< 1 year)—0.5 to 1.0 mg Children (< 12 years)— 1.0 to 3.0 mg Adults—2.0 to 3.0 mg	Whole grain cereals, organ meats, shellfish, nuts, legumes, cocoa, drinking water	40% (stomach, small intestine)	Bile (feces)
Zinc	Infants (< 1 year)—3.0 to 5.0 mg Children (< 12 years)—10.0 mg Adults—15.0 mg	Muscle meats, shellfish, nuts, cereals	20–30% (10–100%) Small intestine	Pancreatic juices (unabsorbed) Feces
Chromium	Infants (< 1 year)—0.01 to 0.06 mg Children (< 12 years)—0.02 to 0.2 mg Adults—0.05 to 0.2 mg	Meats, seafood, whole grains, Brewer's yeast	< 1% Cr^{+3} 10% GTF*G	Kidney
Manganese	Infants (< 1 year)—0.5 to 1.0 mg Children (< 12 years)—1.0 to 5.0 mg Adults—2.5 to 5.0 mg	Whole cereals, nuts, fruits, meats, poultry, fish, seafood, nonleafy vegetables	Poorly understood; appears to vary inversely with iron absorption	Bile
Cobalt (as vitamin B_{12})	Infants (< 1 year)—0.5 to 1.5 μg Children (< 12 years)—2.0 to 3.0 μg Adults—3.0 μg	Meats or pure vitamin B_{12} (not supplied by a strict vegetarian diet)	Active	Kidney
Molybdenum	Infants (< 1 year)—0.03 to 0.08 mg Children (< 12 years)—0.05 to 0.5 mg Adult—0.15 to 0.5 mg	Plant foods	Efficiency figures N/A	Kidney
Magnesium	Infants (< 1 year)—50 to 70 mg Children (< 12 years)—150 to 300 mg Adults—300 to 400 mg	Fish, seafood, meat, nuts, grains, spices, legumes	44% (24–76%)	Kidney
Selenium	Infants (< 1 year)—0.01 to 0.04 mg Children (< 12 years)—0.02 to 0.2 mg Adults—0.05 to 0.2 mg	Fish, seafood, protein-rich plant foods	44–70%	Kidney

*Glucose Tolerance Factor

blood to the body tissues. Again, this process is poorly characterized: a large percentage of plasma zinc and copper is bound to albumin, and some of each also binds to plasma transferrin. Specific transport proteins for the trace metals in the portal circulation have not been demonstrated.

Upon reaching the tissues, metals enter cells and are bound by low molecular weight proteins called thioneins. The true biological role of these proteins has not yet been defined, but it is thought that they function in metal storage, regulation of metal toxicity, and intracellular metabolism of the essential trace metals. Also unclear is whether or not all thioneins, irrespective of their bound metal, are identical in nature. However, one fascinating aspect of thionein production is the fact that it is inducible. Synthesis is known to occur in liver, kidney, and spleen and can be initiated by exposure of the animal to trace metals in slightly increased daily increments. Even such nonessential metals like silver can provoke this synthesis, thus bolstering the evidence for the role of thioneins in the regulation of metal toxicity. How this process of induction occurs is controversial; there are studies suggesting that new mRNA is synthesized in response to trace metals, while other observations indicate that the mRNA is always present and converted from an inactive to active form by the metals. Whatever the mechanism, the trace metals that are potentially toxic by virtue of their reactivity with biologically critical enzyme proteins are bound and thus sequestered intracellularly by thioneins. The essential trace elements are thus bound within the cell and utilized for synthesis as necessary. Release of the thionein-bound metal presumably occurs by mass-action between the plasma-bound metal, the intracellular free metal, and the saturation of the thionein binding sites by the element.

Excretory pathways differ for the various essential trace metals. Zinc is primarily excreted via the pancreatic secretions, although the major portion of fecal zinc is derived from dietary zinc. The main route for copper excretion is via the bile which contains more than 80 per cent of absorbed copper. Chromium, on the other hand, is removed primarily by the kidney.

ESSENTIAL TRACE METAL METABOLISM

Copper

Copper is known to be involved in diverse mammalian biochemical processes ranging from hemoglobin synthesis to function of the central nervous system. The widespread involvement of this trace metal in metabolism is a reflection of the large number of important proteins of which it is a constituent (Table 37–6). Notable among these is cytochrome oxidase, the final enzyme in the electron transport chain from which high energy bonds are generated by substrate oxidation. Another important cuproprotein is the plasma α_2 globulin, ceruloplasmin, which is synthesized in the liver and is associated with more than 90 per cent of total serum copper. Ceruloplasmin possesses significant oxidase activity and, in particular, can change the oxidation state of iron from the ferrous (Fe^{2+}) to the ferric (Fe^{3+}) form. This function is vital to the ability of transferrin to bind and transport iron, as well as to the uptake of iron by erythrocyte precursors in bone marrow.

The oxidation of certain compounds, such as xanthine by xanthine oxidase, results in production of the highly reactive free radical O_2^-. It is well known that free radicals are, in general, highly toxic to biological systems because of their reactivity. Hence, the presence of enzymes that can degrade free radicals is essential to the well-being of the organism. Indeed, it has been observed that obligate anaerobic microorganisms have no ability to convert O_2^- to a less toxic form. The enzyme responsible for this conversion, superoxide dismutase, was first identified in bovine erythrocytes and shown to contain 2 g atoms of copper and 2 g atoms of zinc per mole. The reaction catalyzed is as follows:

$$O_2^- + O_2^- + 2H^+ \rightarrow O_2 + H_2O_2$$

Although no human pathology due to a deficiency of the enzyme has been identified, its existence has only recently been demonstrated.

Table 37–6 BIOLOGIC ROLES OF TRACE METALS

Trace Element	Associated Molecule or Enzyme	Functions
Copper	Ceruloplasmin	(a) Oxidation of $Fe^{2+} \rightarrow Fe^{3+}$ (Ferroxidase)
		(b) Copper transport in blood
		(c) Oxidation of phenols (phenoloxidase)
	Tyrosinase	(a) Hydroxylation of tyrosine $\rightarrow$ DOPA
		(b) Oxidation of DOPA $\rightarrow$ quinone (ending in melanin)
	Lysyl Oxidase	Production of allysine in collagen formation:
		$HC\!-\!(CH_2)_3\!-\!C\!-\!NH_2 + O_2 + H_2O \rightarrow HC\!-\!(CH_2)_3\!-\!C\!=\!O + NH_3 + H_2O_2$
	Amine Oxidase	Oxidation of lysine $\epsilon\!-\!NH_2$ groups:
		$R\!-\!CH_2\!-\!NH_2 + O_2 \rightarrow R\!-\!C\!=\!O + H_2O_2 + NH_3$
	Dopamine β-Hydroxylase	Conversion of dopamine $\rightarrow$ norepinephrine
	Uricase	Oxidation of uric acid $\rightarrow$ allantoin
	Mitochondrocuprein	Found in liver lysosomes, may be sequestered storage form of cuprothionein
	Diamine Oxidase $\rbrace$ Spermine Oxidase Benzylamine Oxidase	Involved in establishment of cross-links in elastic and collagenous tissue
	Cytochrome c Oxidase (also contains heme)	Catalyzes transfer of electrons: reduced cytochrome c $+ O_2 \rightarrow$ oxidized cytochrome c $+ H_2O + O^-$
	Superoxide Dismutase (also contains zinc)	Catalyzes conversion of free radical: $O_2^- + O_2^- + 2H^+ \rightarrow O_2 + H_2O_2$
Zinc	Carbonic Anhydrase	Catalyzes formation of bicarbonate: $CO_2 + H_2O \rightleftharpoons H_2CO_3 \rightleftharpoons H^+ + HCO_3^-$
	Lactate Dehydrogenase	Conversion of pyruvate $\leftrightarrow$ lactate
	Alkaline Phosphatase	Nonspecific hydrolysis of phosphate esters:

$$R\!-\!O\!-\!\underset{\underset{OH}{|}}{\overset{\overset{O}{\|}}{P}}\!-\!OH + H_2O \rightleftharpoons ROH + HO\!-\!\underset{\underset{OH}{|}}{\overset{\overset{O}{\|}}{P}}\!-\!OH$$

Trace Element	Associated Molecule or Enzyme	Functions
	Carboxypeptidase A and B	Cleavage of C-terminal peptide bond
	Alcohol Dehydrogenase	NAD-dependent oxidation of alcohol:

$$RC\!-\!OH + NAD^+ + O_2 \rightarrow RC\!-\!OH + NADH + H^+$$

Trace Element	Associated Molecule or Enzyme	Functions
	Leucine Aminopeptidase	Cleavage of N-terminal leucine from peptides
	L-Aminolevulinate Dehydrogenase	Condensation of 2-aminolevulinates to form porphobilinogen
	Glutamate Dehydrogenase	Ammonia detoxification
	Retinene Reductase	Conversion of retinol $\rightarrow$ retinaldehyde
	Aldolase	Cleavage of fructose-1-phosphate $\rightarrow$ glyceraldehyde and dihydroxyacetone phosphate
	Malate Dehydrogenase	Oxidation of malate $\rightarrow$ oxaloacetate in Krebs cycle
	Pyridoxal Phosphokinase	Phosphorylation of dietary pyridoxine
	RNA Polymerase DNA Polymerase Reverse Transcriptase $\rbrace$ Thymidine Kinase	Replication and transcription of genetic code
	Superoxide Dismutase (see Copper)	
Manganese	Pyruvate Carboxylase	Conversion of pyruvate $\rightarrow$ oxaloacetate
	Pyruvate Kinase	Removal of phosphate from PEP and transfer to ADP

Table 37–6   BIOLOGIC ROLES OF TRACE METALS *Continued*

Trace Element	Associated Molecule or Enzyme	Functions
Manganese (*Continued*)	PEP Carboxykinase	Conversion of oxaloacetate → PEP
	Creatine Kinase	Transfer of phosphate from ATP → creatine
	Adenylate Kinase	Conversion of 2ADP → ATP + AMP
	Enolase	Conversion of 2-phosphoglycerate → PEP
	Histidase	Conversion of histidine → urocanate
	Acetyl CoA Carboxylase	Conversion of acetyl CoA → malonyl CoA
	Palmitate-Synthesizing System	Synthesis of palmitate from acetyl CoA
	N-Acetylgalactosamine Transferase	Transfer of N-acetylgalactosamine from UDP to glycolipid
	Galactose Transferase	Transfer of galactose from UDP to glycolipid
	Serine Hydroxymethyl Transferase	Conversion of serine → glycine
	Glycylglycine Dipeptidase	Cleavage of Gly-Gly peptide bond → 2 GLY
	NADP-Specific Isocitrate Dehydrogenase	Production of reducing equivalents: Isocitrate + NADP $\rightleftharpoons$ NADPH + H$^+$ + oxalosuccinate $\rightleftharpoons$ αKG
	Phosphatidylinositol Kinase	Synthesis of phosphatidylinositol: CDP-diacylglycerol + inositol → phosphatidyl-inositol + CMP
	6-Phosphogluconate Dehydrogenase	Decarboxylation of 6-phosphogluconate to form CO$_2$ + D-ribulose-5-phosphate
Magnesium	Acyl CoA Synthetase	Conversion of fatty acid → fatty acyl CoA
	Argininosuccinate Synthetase	Conversion of citrulline and aspartate to form ASA (urea cycle)
	Kinases (in glycolysis)	Phosphate group transfer reactions
	Mevalonate Kinase	
	Phosphomevalonate Kinase	De novo cholesterol synthesis from acetyl CoA
	Pyrophosphomevalonate Kinase	
	Sialyl Transferase	Transfer of N-acetylneuraminic acid from CMP to lactosylceramide
	Glutamine Synthetase	Conversion of glutamate + NH$_3$ + ATP → glutamine + ADP + P$_i$
	γ-Glutamylcysteine Synthetase	First step in glutathione synthesis
	Actomyosin ATPase	Muscle contraction
	5-Oxoprolinase	Conversion 5-oxoproline → glutamate in γ-glutamyl cycle
	Propionyl-CoA Carboxylase	Carboxylation of propionyl-CoA → methylmalonyl CoA
	Transketolase	Conversion of D-xylulose-5-phosphate + ribose-5-phosphate $\rightleftharpoons$ D-sedoheptulose-7-phosphate + D-glyceraldehyde-3-phosphate
Molybdenum	Xanthine Oxidase (Also contains iron)	Conversion of hypoxanthine → xanthine → uric acid
	Aldehyde Oxidase	Oxidation of acetaldehyde → acetic acid
	Sulfite Oxidase (Also contains heme)	Oxidation of $-SH \rightarrow SO_3^{-2} \rightarrow SO_4^{-2}$
Chromium	Glucose Tolerance Factor	? Enhances binding of insulin to cell surface receptor
Cobalt (as vitamin B$_{12}$)	Methylmalonyl CoA Mutase	Isomerization of methylmalonyl CoA to succinyl CoA
	S-Adenosylmethionine Methyl-Transferase	Regeneration of methionine from homocysteine by methyl group transfer
Selenium	Glutathione Peroxidase	Protection of tissues from oxidative damage by converting H$_2$O$_2$ → H$_2$O

Human whole blood contains approximately 100 μg/dl of copper. Distribution is roughly equal between plasma and erythrocytes. Owing to a lower concentration of serum ceruloplasmin, serum copper concentrations in newborns are low compared with those of adults. A normal daily copper intake is estimated to be 2.5 to 5 mg; this amount is adequate for maintenance of a positive copper balance. On a body weight basis, infants require more copper than adults; a premature infant needs approximately 0.1 mg/kg daily. Older children require about 0.04 mg/kg per day.

Although hypocupremia has been described in a variety of conditions, it has not been recognized as indicative of an isolated copper deficiency in otherwise well-nourished subjects. However, with the advent of intravenous hyperalimentation on a wide basis, particularly in the distressed neonate, clinical features of isolated trace metal deficiencies have now been described. The earliest and most consistent features of copper deficiency are anemia of a hypochromic, microcytic nature and osteoporosis (Table 37–7). The anemia is a consequence of diminished ferroxidase activity in plasma attributable to decreased ceruloplasmin and disruption of normal incorporation of iron into erythrocyte precursors. The osteoporosis derives from deficient activities of copper *amine oxidases* (Table 37–6), responsible for establishing normal collagen cross-linking during osteogenesis (see Chapter 27).

Menkes' disease can be included among the copper-deficiency states, since the weight of the evidence favors a defect in gastrointestinal absorption of copper. The CNS findings of isolated copper deficiency, including hypotonia, mental retardation, cortical blindness and apnea are mimicked in this disease, resulting in a fatal outcome. These, as well as the severe hypothermia to which affected individuals are prone, may be attributed to defective activity of a number of cuproenzymes, including cytochrome oxidase. Arterial tortuosity, also characteristic of the disease, is probably due to faulty elastin synthesis resulting from deficient amine oxidase activity.

Hypercupremia is seen in association with a variety of disorders but is unusual as an isolated finding. The symptoms and signs of acute copper toxicity include nausea, vomiting, diarrhea, headache, dizziness, tachycardia, hypertension, hemolytic anemia, hemoglobinuria, uremia and death. This spectrum of clinical findings is fairly representative of heavy metal toxicity, in general.

Wilson's disease exemplifies the clinical results of chronic copper intoxication, in which cop-

Table 37–7 CLINICAL ABNORMALITIES OF TRACE METAL DISTURBANCES

	Copper	Zinc	Magnesium	Chromium	Selenium	Cadmium
Deficiency	Neutropenia Hypochromic, microcytic anemia Osteoporosis Periosteal changes Pathological fractures Tortuosity of arterial vessels Hypotonia	Growth retardation Anorexia Hypogeusia Skin lesions Diarrhea Lethargy Irritability Alopecia Delayed puberty	Muscle wasting Apathy Diaphoresis Tachycardia Numbness Convulsions Delirium PVC, ventricular fibrillation Tachycardia, ventricular fibrillation Coma Death	Impaired glucose tolerance Relative insulin resistance		
Toxicity	Nausea Vomiting Diarrhea Headache Dizziness Tachycardia Hypertension Hemolytic anemia Hemoglobinuria Uremia Death	Vomiting Dehydration Electrolyte imbalance Abdominal pain Dizziness Muscular incoordination Acute renal failure	CNS depression Hypotonia Hypothermia Heart block Coma Death		Nausea Vomiting Skin depigmentation Alopecia Lassitude ? Abortion	Growth retardation Anemia Osteoporosis Anosmia Dyspnea Emphysema Fanconi syndrome Pathological fractures

per deposition occurs in various body tissues. Serum copper, however, is typically low in these individuals as a result of decreased ceruloplasmin levels. The precise biochemical basis for this disease is unknown. Wilson's disease is discussed more extensively later in this chapter.

Zinc

Zinc, like copper, is involved in diverse biochemical processes, reflected in the numerous enzyme proteins with which zinc is associated (Table 37–6). One such critical process is conversion of CO_2 and H_2O to H_2CO_3 by carbonic anhydrase in red cells and kidney (see Chapter 14). Another is metabolic conversion of —C—OH groups to —C=O groups by activity of pyridine nucleotide-dependent dehydrogenases. Proper digestion of dietary proteins and peptides by pancreatic carboxypeptidases A and B depends upon zinc as a contributor to the catalytic activity of these enzymes.

The total body content of zinc is close to that of iron and 10 to 100 times that of copper. Like copper, however, zinc requirements are higher for infants and children on a body weight basis than for adults (Table 37–5). Human plasma normally contains about 80 μg/dl zinc; most plasma zinc is protein bound, distributed between albumin and an α_2-macroglobulin, now known to be a zinc metalloprotein. Erythrocyte zinc is almost entirely associated with carbonic anhydrase, and that in leukocytes with alkaline phosphatase.

Since the dietary requirements and total body content of zinc is similar to that of iron, it is realistic to expect isolated dietary zinc deficiency much as one sees iron deficiency. This is made all the more likely because the nature of the diet will influence the extent of zinc absorption. Indeed, a unique form of dwarfism in Iran includes severe iron-deficiency anemia, hepatosplenomegaly, and hypogonadism and has been attributed to zinc deficiency. It is thought to derive from the high phytate and fiber content of the diet, which interferes with intestinal zinc absorption. The most severe type of zinc deficiency is illustrated by the disease known as acrodermatitis enteropathica. Affected infants suffer from intermittent diarrhea, dermatitis, and alopecia. The dermatitic lesions are typically distributed around body orifices and extremities and are progressive, sometimes ending in death due to supervening infection. Studies of intestinal radiolabeled zinc have shown impaired absorption in affected individuals.

Compared with other metals, zinc is relatively nontoxic. Industrial exposure produces an acute illness consisting of fever, cough, leukocytosis and pulmonary infiltrates. As with other trace elements, widespread use of intravenous hyperalimentation can be relied upon to produce acute toxicity in the future. In lambs, high zinc doses produced hemolytic anemia and hematuria, a toxicity picture common to the trace metals.

Manganese

Although manganese is widely distributed, both in nature and in human tissues, its function as a trace element appears to be less specific than those of copper and zinc. The association of manganese with enzyme proteins generally falls into the category of metal-enzyme complexes. In this role, other metals, particularly magnesium, may substitute for manganese. Nonetheless, manganese is normally associated with a wide variety of enzyme proteins (Table 37–6).

Human whole blood contains about 13 μg/dl of manganese, with an estimated daily intake of approximately 3 to 4 mg. The manganese intake of children necessary for normal growth is estimated to be between 0.2 and 0.3 mg/kg body weight per day. However, since other trace metals may substitute for manganese in metabolic functions, determination of a minimal daily requirement is difficult and has not been established. This same functional substitution probably explains the fact that no isolated manganese deficiency in humans has been reported.

Manganese toxicity has been described in an industrial setting in miners who chronically inhale manganese-containing dust. This results in an encephalitis-like clinical syndrome, initially characterized by asthenia, headache, impotence, and speech disturbance, progressing to hepatolenticular degeneration resembling Parkinson's disease.

Cobalt

The major known function of cobalt in human metabolism is as a component of cobalamin, or vitamin B_{12}. In this form, it functions as a coenzyme for two key metabolic steps (Table 37–6). Normal absorption of vitamin B_{12} depends upon secretion by gastric mucosa of intrinsic factor, normal pancreatic exocrine function, and normal ileal function. Normal human whole blood contains about 0.08 μg/dl of vitamin B_{12}. The daily requirement decreases with age, on a body weight basis ranging from 1.5 μg/day in neonates to 0.3 μg/day in adults.

The central role of vitamin B_{12} in human metabolism is best illustrated by the congenital methylmalonic acidemias deriving from abnormal cellular transport and activation of the vitamin. These diseases are discussed in Chapter 34. Either inadequate dietary intake or ileal absorption will result in the well-known syndrome of pernicious anemia, with attendant peripheral neuropathy and/or multisystem disease.

Other Trace Metals

A variety of other trace metals subserve important biological functions (Table 37–6). Selenium, whose role has recently been highlighted by discussions of radioactive selenium in cow's milk, is thought to have an important antioxidant function along with vitamin E in maintenance of membrane integrity. Chromium has been known for years to enhance the activity of insulin, possibly by facilitating insulin binding to cell membranes. Molybdenum is a constituent of complex metalloenzymes that are involved in the process of oxidation-reduction and electron transfer. Cadmium, an element that is found to increase in concentration in human tissues with age, has no known biological function. It activates certain enzymes but is not specific in this role, since other metals can perform the same function.

Of these several trace metals, only a deficiency of chromium and toxicity of selenium and cadmium are described. These are exceedingly rare entities, for descriptions of which the reader is directed to the references at the end of this chapter.

Wilson's Disease (Hepatolenticular Degeneration)

Clinical Features

Wilson's disease, like acute intermittent porphyria, can present in one of several ways, often taxing the diagnostic acumen of the physician. Biochemically, Wilson's disease is a copper storage disease involving all tissues but affecting particularly liver, brain, cornea, and kidney. The underlying cause is still unknown.

The three predominant modes of presentation involve signs and symptoms indicative of hepatic, neurological, or psychiatric disease. When abnormalities suggesting two of the foregoing categories are part of the presentation, it is not difficult to consider Wilson's disease. Compounding the difficulty in clinical recognition is the fact that different systems may seem to be involved at different times and to varying degrees. Because of the great variability in clinical manifestations and because it is a treatable inborn error of metabolism the physician must be on the alert for its protean manifestations.

Onset is usually in the latter part of the first decade. Dystonic manifestations were the first recognized by Wilson but are not the most common mode of presentation. In this form the patient comes to attention because of evidence of spasticity, rigidity, drooling, dysarthria, and dysphagia. Deterioration of handwriting or of playing an instrument may be the tip-off here.

Another form of the disease, which is probably more frequent, is pseudosclerosis. Here flapping tremors of the wrist and shoulders predominate, with the rigidity and spasticity of the dystonic form being infrequent. In clinical practice hybrid forms are likely to be most common. Occasionally, one sees seizures, but neuropsychiatric manifestations with aggressive behavior are not at all uncommon. In some series psychiatric deterioration, with puerile, neurotic, or even schizoid behavior, is the first manifestation of Wilson's disease. Such a presentation may be missed because it appears to be part of the adolescent adjustment to school stress; deterioration in school performance may be the first clue to the diagnosis.

In childhood, hepatic dysfunction, usually manifesting between 6 and 14 years of age, is the most usual mode of clinical presentation. While there are rare patients who present with a fulminant hepatitis, the usual presentation is more subtle; it is reminiscent of a chronic active hepatitis with weakness, lassitude, easy exhaustion, jaundice, anorexia, splenomegaly, and abnormal liver chemistries. Of course, Wilson's disease must be considered in any child in whom hepatic cirrhosis is suspected.

Finally, renal tubular acidosis and aminoaciduria (see Chapter 23) may be uncovered on laboratory evaluation but rarely are these findings of clinical significance in determining the ultimate prognosis of the patient. Nonetheless, on an acute basis hyperchloremic acidosis can cause clinical deterioration.

The pathognomonic physical finding, i.e., greenish-brown discoloration at the limbus of the cornea (termed Kayser-Fleischer rings) is not usually present before 7 years. Two remarkable features attend the presence of the Kayser-Fleischer rings. On the one hand the physical finding itself is striking and should always be sought. On the other hand, by the time they are present there will usually be other evidence of basal ganglia involvement. Yet save for the Kayser-Fleischer rings there is no evidence of nystagmus or cranial nerve abnormality. Hence, the paucity of other ocular findings in a patient with basal ganglia involvement should alert one to search for the Kayser-Fleischer rings and perform laboratory tests to evaluate the possibility of Wilson's disease.

Biochemical Defects

Total body copper in the normal adult is in the range of 50 to 150 mg, with the highest concentrations in liver, brain, kidney, and heart. Copper serves a role in the structure and function of several enzymes, including cytochrome c oxidase, tyrosinase, monoamine oxidase, and superoxide dismutase (see page 400). As with most trace elements, accumulation beyond that necessary for enzyme function causes toxicity. In contrast to the situation with iron, the gastrointestinal tract does not play a decisive role in copper homeostasis. Albumin serves as the initial transport protein for copper after absorption from the gastrointestinal tract, whereby the complex is brought to the liver. There the copper is incorporated into ceruloplasmin, which is synthesized in the liver. One possibility in Wilson's disease is a defect in the manner by which copper is incorporated into this glycoprotein. Alternatively the defect may lie with the excretion of copper into the bile.

Ceruloplasmin is one of a family of proteins found in the serum that increase in response to infection and are termed "acute phase reactants." Recently it has been demonstrated that ceruloplasmin can carry out the detoxification of superoxide anion radicals (O_2^-) to H_2O_2 and O_2, a reaction hitherto shown to be mediated by the intracellular enzyme superoxide dismutase. This catalytic action by ceruloplasmin has led to the suggestion that, in serum, it may scavenge highly reactive superoxide anions circulating there.

In consequence of the retention of copper in the body in Wilson's disease the first line of defense appears to be sequestration in the cytoplasm of liver parenchymal cells. So efficient is this mechanism that other tissues usually evince no evidence of storage. Of course, after several years have elapsed, the liver (which now contains copper in the range of 500 to 2000 μg/g dry weight), can no longer confine this tremendous burden. Cell necrosis ensues, with uptake into hepatic lysosomes and "spillover" into the blood stream. Lysosomal uptake probably serves to protect the hepatocyte from the ravages of copper accumulation but dispersal through the blood now makes other tissues of the body liable to damage from copper accumulation. Paramount among those cells bearing the burden of this release are those in brain, cornea, and kidney. In addition the erythrocyte is often affected acutely—a hemolytic anemia resulting from the uptake of copper by the red cell. Several red cell glycolytic enzymes appear to be affected in copper toxicity, clinically causing an acquired hemolytic anemia analogous to that encountered with the inherited defects of red cell enzymes.

Laboratory Findings

An evaluation of liver function in an older child with hepatomegaly should generate an assessment of urinary amino acid excretion as well. Patients with Wilson's disease will demonstrate a Fanconi picture with generalized aminoaciduria associated with glucose, uric acid, calcium, and phosphate in increased amounts in the urine. Despite these findings, rarely are there any symptoms referable to renal dysfunction in Wilson's disease. More specific abnormalities referable to Wilson's disease include a low serum copper (normal = 108 μg/dl) and decreased serum ceruloplasmin levels. The latter findings, although not universal, are observed in well over 90 per cent of patients with this disease. Nonetheless, decreased serum copper and ceruloplasmin are found in all normal newborns and in some patients with severe malnutrition (including malabsorption) and nephrosis. Urinary copper excretion is excessive in patients with symptoms, the normal value being less than 40 μg per 24 hours. Copper overloading (found in severe liver disease as well) can be uncovered with a penicillamine load, which will augment copper excretion. Quantitation of copper on a closed liver biopsy specimen should help in diagnosis, but heterozygotes and patients with liver disease may have values in the gray zone of 100 to 250 μg/g dry weight. The latter may well have levels that exceed that value, putting them in the range usually assumed to point to Wilson's disease. Of course, if Kayser-Fleischer rings are seen, the diagnosis is assured.

Treatment

D-Penicillamine, an effective chelating agent for stored copper, has made this hitherto fatal disease eminently treatable. This is especially so when therapy can be initiated early, as can happen in siblings of a previously diagnosed case. For further details of therapy, the physician should consult the references at the end of this section.

Menkes' Disease (Kinky Hair Syndrome)

As with many of the disorders appearing in the neonatal period the earliest manifestations of Menkes' disease are relatively nonspecific. They include a premature male who feeds poorly and slowly and suffers from temperature instability. These findings are followed in about a month by drowsiness, lethargy, and even greater difficulty feeding. Myoclonic seizures, associated with hypotonia or hypertonia, then ensue. Progressive neurological deterioration with increasing seizure frequency becomes obvious thereafter, and these infants become prone to pneumonia and sepsis. These infants have been described by Danks et al. (1974) as having the following facial characteristics: puffed out cheeks, an upper lip shaped like a cupid-bow, and tangled eye brows.

The characteristic hair findings that have given this copper deficiency disease its name include washed out color, with strands that fracture easily, producing short stubbles that look and feel like kinky or steely hair. Indeed the hair is reminiscent of a well-used pad of steel wool. On microscopic examination one sees pili torti. Abnormalities in collagen and elastin, because of defects in cross-linking, are manifested as osteoporosis (see Chapter 27). Deficient cross-link formation is related to the copper dependency of lysyl oxidase (see Chapter 27).

The defect appears to be in the gastrointestinal absorption of copper, leading to severe copper deficiency. Since the uptake of copper into the mucosal cell is not disturbed, the abnormality must then lie either in the second phase involving intracellular transport or in the third, transport through the serosal face of the membrane.

This is a diagnosis that requires a high degree of suspicion on the part of the physician and that depends on history and physical findings. The hair findings may not appear for several weeks, and it may be necessary to follow serum copper and ceruloplasmin serially, since they fluctuate in neonates. Needle biopsy of liver and quantitation of diminished copper stores should permit the diagnosis to be made during this period, since hepatic copper is increased in normal neonates.

As this is a copper deficiency disease resulting from abnormal gastrointestinal absorption, parenteral administration of copper should be corrective, with the proviso that therapy be started early in infancy. Delay is not likely to result in a favorable outcome.

NUTRITIONAL THERAPY OF INBORN ERRORS OF METABOLISM

In order to properly design the therapeutic regimen for a given inborn error it is vital to understand the nature of the molecular defect as well as its effect on normal biochemical processes. Just how important these two factors are may be illustrated by a brief review of some basic principles of molecular genetics and protein structure.

The basic concepts of polypeptide synthetic mechanisms are illustrated in Figure 37–1. Messenger RNA, synthesized at the direction of the DNA molecule, joins with the ribosome. Transfer RNA is bound to a free amino acid in an energy-requiring reaction. At the ribosomal site the tRNA

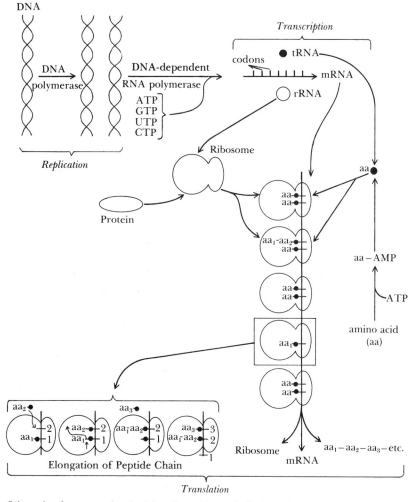

Figure 37–1 Schematic of processes involved in polypeptide synthesis, including DNA replication, formation of mRNA from the DNA template, and translation of the information in the triplet nucleotide code into the linear sequence of amino acids. (From Villee, D. B.: Human Endocrinology: A Developmental Approach. Philadelphia, W. B. Saunders Co., 1975.)

attaches to the mRNA by hydrogen bonding between complementary bases, with the bound amino acid 'dangling free' from the ribosome. As the peptide bond is formed between neighboring amino acid residues, by the peptidyl transferase activity associated with the ribosome, the tRNA is released from the ribosome. Any change in the base sequence of the parent DNA will be reflected in a corresponding change in the messenger RNA sequence (transcription), which will eventuate in a change in the linear sequence of amino acid residues in the polypeptide chain.

As we have noted before, when placed in water, a polypeptide assumes a three-dimensional conformation and is then a protein (see Part I). Depending upon the specific amino acid residues present in the chain, certain portions will be highly polar with a tendency to form hydrogen bonds with surrounding water molecules, and some will be nonpolar or hydrophobic. The variation in polar and nonpolar regions of the peptide molecule, as well as the spatial orientations of the amino acid residue side-chains, will force the chain to bend upon itself. The final configuration will be quite specific for the individual protein, tending to orient the polar groups towards the surrounding polar medium—in the final analysis it will depend entirely upon the DNA base sequence from which it is derived.

In Chapter 2 we reviewed the details of protein structure, emphasizing that many proteins are composed of more than one polypeptide chain. Hemoglobin, a tetramer, is the prime example of this subunit principle in construction. The same basic forces governing the three-dimensional folding of the polypeptide chain also determine the relationship of protein subunits to each other. That is to say, the nonpolar areas of each folded polypeptide subunit will associate, excluding water from the interior of the complex molecule. Oppositely charged amino acid residues on each of the subunits will attract each other and be oriented towards the surrounding medium. In this context, it is important to understand that substitution of one amino acid residue for another may alter the surface charge of a folded polypeptide subunit in such a way that it will not complement that of a second polypeptide subunit. Under these circumstances, association of the monomer units of a complex protein will be abnormal, possibly being reflected in the function of this complex molecule.

In summary, from what we have seen, an alteration in the DNA base sequence can cause a number of significant defects in the structure of the protein whose synthesis is directed by that sequence. These effects may include abnormal amino acid sequences in the area of the active site of an enzyme, abnormal folding of a polypeptide chain that results in sequestration of an important amino acid side-chain within the molecule, or abnormal association of polypeptide monomers due to improper folding, and so on.

Now let us turn to a consideration of some general principles of therapy. The goals of any therapy are as follows: (1) preserve integrity of the CNS; (2) permit normal physical growth; and (3) normalize affected biochemical parameters. There are a variety of means, both practical and theoretical, that may be utilized to achieve these ends. Table 37–8 is a list of these various modes of therapy. Clearly, genetic engineering represents the ultimate means of therapy in any inborn error in which an enzyme is either defective or absent. This alternative, however, remains to be realized. Enzyme replacement has been attempted in a small number of inborn errors without major success at this time. Organ transplantation represents a poor alternative, at best, even in these advanced times of organ transplant technique. We are therefore left with the first three options as practical means to approach the therapy of inborn errors of metabolism. The choice of a therapeutic

Table 37–8
TREATMENT OF INHERITED
METABOLIC DISEASE

1. Diet manipulation	4. Organ transplantation
2. Vitamin therapy	5. Enzyme replacement
3. Drug administration	6. Genetic engineering

Table 37–9 CIRCUMSTANCES DICTATING CHOICE OF THERAPY

The nature of the gene defect, reflected by the altered state of the enzyme protein, will be a prime determinant of the therapeutic approach. The characteristics of the normal molecule, especially cofactor dependence, are also important.

1. **Dietary Therapy Alone**
   a. Enzyme protein absent (CRM−)
   b. Enzyme protein present but totally inactive (CRM+)
   c. Enzyme partially active, normal protein not cofactor dependent
2. **Dietary Therapy and Cofactor**
   a. Enzyme partially active, normal protein cofactor dependent
   b. Enzyme normally active but present in decreased amount due to structural alteration with increased degradation rate, normal protein cofactor dependent
3. **Cofactor Therapy Only (Normal Enzyme Cofactor Dependent)**
   a. Apoprotein normal, cofactor interaction defective due to failure to convert the latter to active form
   b. Apoprotein normal, cofactor interaction normal, inadequate supply of latter due to transport defect

modality will be dictated by the nature of the defect and its biochemical consequences, as we have said earlier. Table 37–9 lists the possible situations that will dictate the choices of therapy. It is clear that if the DNA alterations result in absent or totally inactive enzyme, no feasible therapeutic maneuver can restore enzyme activity. Hence, dietary therapy alone should be the first consideration. When the defective enzyme is cofactor dependent, megavitamin therapy alone or in conjunction with dietary therapy may be of help.

As more and more patients with a given disease have been described, it has become clear that factors other than the enzyme defect itself contribute to variability in clinical manifestations. This illustrates that while the biochemical abnormality may be related to the pathology, clinical manifestations of the disease may vary widely from patient to patient. An example of this situation is the report by Wolf et al. (1979) of two siblings, each with no detectable propionyl-CoA carboxylase activity in the peripheral leukocytes; one of the siblings is retarded and the other, 10 years older, is normal without treatment. Thus, one cannot always be certain that the apparent success of a therapy is, in fact, related to a direct effect on the enzyme defect.

Choices of Therapeutic Modalities

Some situations permit relatively simple forms of therapy. Simple elimination of the offending dietary component or the substrate for the defective enzyme is feasible in cases in which this compound is nonessential, i.e., can be endogenously synthesized. The metabolic relationships of glucose with the other carbohydrate components of the diet are such that it is possible, in cases in which either galactose or fructose metabolic abnormalities exist, to eliminate completely from the diet one or the other sugar (see Chapter 26). In cases such as this, the body is capable of synthesizing from glucose the necessary quantities of these two hexoses to provide for the carbohydrate components of cell membranes and other structural elements of the body.

Another option is the provision of a nontoxic analogue of the parent compound; this approach can be useful in a number of disorders of the urea cycle (see Chapter 22). The major difficulty with this approach is our present poor understanding of the relationship between abnormal quantities of a compound and the compound's CNS toxicity. Indeed, one might reasonably state that it is equally possible that CNS toxicity results from a deficiency of the product of the defective enzyme rather than abnormal increases in the quantity of the substrate for the enzyme. However, in the urea cycle disorders hyperammonemia appears to be a major factor contributing to the CNS toxicity. Reduction of dietary nitrogen loading by feeding alpha-keto analogues of the amino acids has successfully lowered plasma ammonia levels. The biochemical principles upon which this alpha-keto analogue therapy is based are discussed in Chapter 22. Unfortunately, the biochemical efficacy of this therapy has not always resulted in a clinical response of equal measure.

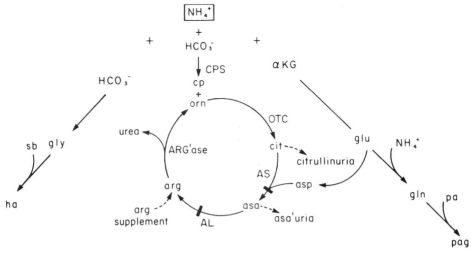

Figure 37–2 Rationale for dietary therapy of urea cycle disorders. Abbreviations are as follows: ha = hippuric acid; sb = sodium benzoate; pag = phenylacetylglutamine; pa = phenylacetic acid; cp = carbamyl phosphate; asa = argininosuccinic acid. (From Batshaw, M. L., Thomas, G. H., and Brusilow, S. W.: New approaches to the diagnosis and treatment of inborn errors of urea synthesis. Pediatrics 68:290, 1981. Copyright American Academy of Pediatrics 1981.)

Two other approaches to therapy of the urea cycle disorders have recently been proposed. Figure 37–2 illustrates the biochemical basis for the approaches. Glycine, the most abundant amino acid in the body, can be conjugated in liver with benzoic acid to form hippurate. Hippurate is excreted, as well as secreted, in the urine very efficiently and therefore constitutes an excretory sink for glycine nitrogen. The other therapy, administration of arginine, provides large amounts of ornithine through the action of arginase. This provides increased substrate for detoxification of ammonia through synthesis and excretion of citrulline or argininosuccinic acid.

The treatment of isovaleric acidemia with glycine is a variation on the same theme that we have just discussed. This therapeutic approach takes advantage of the hepatic detoxification reaction linking glycine to the toxic compound. Unfortunately, this approach cannot be applied in all of the organic acidemias because of the relative lack of conjugating ability of the enzyme glycine-N-acylase with the other organic acids. Much more isovaleric acid can be conjugated through this pathway than any of the other organic acids. We should distinguish between the approach outlined in the previous paragraph, utilizing benzoate in the urea cycle disorders, and the use of glycine administration in isovaleric acidemia. In the former, glycine (as the sink for otherwise toxic ammonia nitrogen) is the toxin to be conjugated by the reaction, while in the latter, glycine accelerates the detoxification of isovalerate, the toxic compound. Nonetheless, each of the two approaches utilizes the same enzyme reaction.

Certain disorders involve cofactor-dependent enzyme pathways, a subgroup of which are "vitamin-responsive disorders." The relationship between a vitamin and a cofactor in substance consists of the enzymatic conversion of a nutritional molecule (vitamin) to an "activated" molecule (coenzyme). A mutation may so alter the three-dimensional conformation of a cofactor-dependent enzyme protein that the avidity of binding to the cofactor is severely decreased. This in turn results in failure of formation of the holoenzyme. Normally vitamin concentrations are extremely low, depending upon high affinity for binding of the apoprotein to its cofactor. In cases such as these, supplying enormous amounts of dietary vitamin may permit binding of the cofactor to the defective protein, with the net result of increased enzyme activity. Table 37–10 is a partial list of enzyme defects known to respond to cofactor therapy.

Like all dietary components, vitamins must proceed through a number of processing steps prior to achieving their ultimate destination. Again, as with all dietary components, the complicated digestive, absorptive, and activating processes present numerous loci for potential inherited disor-

Table 37–10   COFACTOR RESPONSIVE INHERITED DISORDERS

Cofactor	MRDA	Disease	Daily Therapeutic Dose	Deficient Enzyme
Biotin	50–300 μg	Multiple carboxylase deficiency	10 mg 10–100 mg	Holocarboxylase synthetase ?Biotin transport protein
		?Propionic acidemia	10 mg	Propionyl CoA carboxylase
		?Congenital lactic acidosis	10 mg	Pyruvate carboxylase
Vitamin B$_{12}$	2.5–5.0 μg	Methylmalonic aciduria	250–500 μg	Deficient conversion of B$_{12}$ to adenosylcobalamin form
		Juvenile pernicious anemia	< 5 μg	Intrinsic factor
		Methylmalonic aciduria homocystinuria and hypomethioninemia	500 μg	Deficient conversion of B$_{12}$ to methyl- and adenosylcobalamin forms
		Megaloblastic anemia	> 100 μg	Transcobalamin II
Ascorbate	35–60 μg	Neonatal tyrosinemia	50–100 mg	p-Hydroxyphenylpyruvate oxidase
Folate	0.05–0.1 mg	Forminotransferase deficiency	5 mg	Forminotransferase
		Homocystinuria and hypomethioninemia	10–20 mg	N^5, N^{10}-Methylenetetrahydrofolate reductase
		Congenital megaloblastic anemia	0.1–0.2 mg	Dihydrofolate reductase
		Phenylketonuria	0.8 μmol/kg tetrahydrobiopterin	Dihydropteridine reductase
		THF methyltransferase deficiency	15 mg	THF methyltransferase
Nicotinamide	6–22 mg	Tryptophanuria	100 mg	Tryptophan pyrrolase
		Hartnup	50–200 mg	?
Pyridoxine	0.4–2.0 mg	β-Alaninemia	10–50 mg	β-Alanine transaminase
		Cystathioninuria	100–500 mg	Cystathionase
		Homocystinuria	25–500 mg	Cystathionine β-synthetase
		Infantile convulsions	10–50 mg	Glutamate decarboxylase
		Xanthurenicaciduria	5–10 mg	Kynureninase
		Hyperoxaluria	100–500 mg	Glyoxylate: α-ketoglutarate carboligase
Thiamine	0.4–1.4 mg	Congenital lactic acidosis	5–20 mg	Pyruvate carboxylase
		MSUD	5–10 mg	α-Keto acid decarboxylase
		Megaloblastic anemia	20 mg	?
		Pyruvic acidemia	5–20 mg	Pyruvate decarboxylase
Vitamin D	200–400 I.U.	Vitamin D-dependent rickets	25,000–40,000 I.U.	?Calcium transport protein

ders. Presently a small number of diseases have been defined that are considered to be due to impairment of a step in vitamin transport rather than a defect in apoprotein. Clinically, these disorders resemble closely the disorders that are due to enzyme abnormalities. The complex nature of absorption and blood transport of vitamin B$_{12}$ is indicative of the potential for genetically determined disorders of vitamin transport. Intrinsic factor, a glycoprotein synthesized by gastric mucosa, complexes with dietary cobalamine in the upper gastrointestinal tract. In the presence of Ca^{++}, the protein moiety of this macromolecular complex binds to specific receptor sites in the ileum, where dissociation and transport of the vitamin across the intestinal barrier subsequently occurs. At the serosal surface, the vitamin is bound to an α-globulin (transcobalamin I) and a β-globulin (transcobalamin II); the latter is the specific transport protein for cobalamin as evidenced by the rapid turnover of the bound vitamin. It is believed that the TCII-B$_{12}$ complex binds to specific cell surface receptors and is absorbed intact by endocytosis. Subsequent fusion of the resulting vacuole with the lysosome and protease degradation of the protein moiety permits release of free B$_{12}$ into the cytosol.

In addition to the complexities of vitamin transport and activation just discussed, we should review some of the ways in which a cofactor may potentially interact with an enzyme protein. The cofactor may provide certain groups that foster a favorable binding energy that can be used to accelerate catalysis. It may increase the enzyme's capacity for substrate binding either by providing a portion of the substrate binding site on the enzyme or by altering the configuration of the protein to facilitate substrate binding. In some cases (e.g., glycogen phosphorylase and pyridoxal phosphate) it may link differing subunits of the enzyme to create the complete active site. As a general rule coenzymes provide chemical groupings (particularly conjugated bonds) that facilitate electron delocalization during transition-state formation. Such possibilities are not furnished by the amino acid residues that remain after peptide bond formation.

In addition, there is another alternative in development of an inborn error; this derives from the fact that for a vitamin to become metabolically active it must be "activated." Throughout this book we have discussed the fact that energy expenditure by the body requires an enzymatic mediation, and this process is no exception. Therefore, a genetic mutation of the enzyme that mediates activation may impair the binding of apoenzyme with its cofactor, since the cofactor is not in the proper chemical form.

Finally, we have the situation in which the apoenzyme is abnormal in two different individuals with similar clinical presentations, yet one responds to vitamin therapy and the other does not. It appears that some mutations affect the cofactor binding site but not the active site. Thus cofactor binding to the apoenzyme produces a normally active enzyme despite the fact that this binding may be somewhat less efficient than normal. Such a situation can be remedied with pharmacological doses of vitamin. The unresponsive patient may have a genetic mutation resulting in an abnormality of the enzymatically active site, in which case binding of cofactor to apoenzyme will not enhance the enzyme's activity. Thus, in these two cases one is presented with two patients with a clinically and apparently biochemically identical disease, yet one patient will respond to megavitamin doses while the other patient must be treated with diet alone.

While this discussion of the design of nutritional therapy in approaching metabolic disorders has not been extensive, it is hoped that sufficient consideration has been given to the various major possibilities and alternatives in molecular defects to give the reader a basis for therapeutic design. In the final analysis, it will be important for the physician to measure the success of this therapy in light of the criteria listed on page 408. This is a particularly difficult thing to do in the situation in which the major consequence of the inborn error is CNS damage. This is clearly due to the fact that by the time CNS impairment (particularly in the areas of mentation) has occurred it may be too late to reverse the process. We need modalities of evaluation that permit early recognition of CNS dysfunction. This has traditionally been a problem in the evaluation of PKU therapy, for example.

Specific therapies have been discussed earlier in the relevant sections of this book. For more extensive discussions of the design of therapeutic modalities and evaluation of therapeutic successes, the reader is referred to the references listed at the end of this chapter.

REFERENCES

Nutrition

Alfin-Slater, R.B., and Kritchevsky, D. (eds.). Human Nutrition. A Comprehensive Treatise. 5 Vols. Plenum Press, New York, 1979 and 1980.
Caldwell, M.D., and Kennedy-Caldwell, C.: Normal nutritional requirements. Surg. Clin. North Am. 61:487, 1981.
Danks, D.S.: Hereditary disorders of copper metabolism in Wilson's disease and Menkes' disease. In Stanbury, J.B., Wyngaarden, J.B., Fredrickson, D.S. et al. (eds.): The Metabolic Basis of Inherited Disease. 5th ed. McGraw-Hill, New York, 1983, p. 1251.
Danks, D.S., Stevens, B.J., Campbell, P.E., et al.: Menkes' kinky-hair syndrome. An inherited defect in the intestinal absorption of copper with widespread effects. Birth Defects, Orig. Artic. Ser. 10:(10), 132, 1974.
Desnick, R.J., and Grabowski, G.A.: Advances in the treatment of inherited metabolic diseases. Adv. Human Genet. 11:281, 1981.
Glass, A.R., Burman, K.D., Dahms, W.T., and Boehm, T.M.: Endocrine function in human obesity. Metabolism 30:89, 1981.
Goldstein, I.M., Kaplan, H.B., Edelson, H.S., and Weissman, G.: Ceruloplasmin: A scavenger of superoxide anion radicals. J. Biol. Chem. 254:4040, 1979.
Kerr, D.S., Stevens, M.C.G., and Robinson, H.M.: Fasting metabolism in infants. I. Effect of severe undernutrition on energy and protein utilization. Metabolism 27:411, 1978.

Mertz, W.: The essential trace elements. Science 213:1332, 1981.

Moran, J.R., and Greene, H.L.: The B vitamins and vitamin C in human nutrition. Am. J. Dis. Child. 133:192, 308, 1979.

Sternlieb, I.: Copper and the liver. Gastroenterology 78:1615, 1980.

Suskind, R.M. (ed.): Textbook of Pediatric Nutrition. Raven Press, New York, 1981.

Versieck, J., and Cornelis, R.: Normal levels of trace elements in human blood plasma or serum. Anal. Chim. Acta 116:217, 1980.

Waterlow, J.C., Garlich, P.J., and Millward, D.J.: Protein Turnover in Mammalian Tissues and in the Whole Body. North-Holland Pub. Co., Amsterdam, 1978.

Symposium on Impact of Infection on the Nutritional Status of the Host. Am. J. Clin. Nutr. 30:1203–1566, 1977.

Wolf, B., Paulsen, E.P., and Hsia, Y.E.: Asymptomatic propionyl CoA carboxylase deficiency in a 13 year old girl, J. Pediatr. 95:563, 1979.

Wolfe, B.M., and Chock, E.: Energy sources, stores and hormonal controls. Surg. Clin. North Am. 61:509, 1981.

Cystic Fibrosis

Breslow, J.L., McPherson, J., and Epstein, J.: Distinguishing homozygous and heterozygous cystic fibrosis fibroblasts from normal cells by differences in sodium transport. N. Engl. J. Med. 304:1, 1981.

Chase, H.P., Long, M.A., and Lavin, M.H.: Cystic fibrosis and malnutrition. J. Pediatr. 95:337, 1979.

Davis, P.B., and DiSant'Agnese, P.A.: A review. Cystic fibrosis at forty—Quo vadis? Pediatr. Res. 14:83, 1980.

Davis, P.B., Hubbard, V.S., and DiSant'Agnese, P.A.: Low sweat electrolytes in a patient with cystic fibrosis. Am. J. Med. 69:643, 1980.

DiSant'Agnese, P.A., and Davis, P.B.: Cystic fibrosis in adults: 75 cases and a review of 232 cases in the literature. Am. J. Med. 66:121, 1979.

Park, R.W., and Grand, R.J.: Gastrointestinal manifestations of cystic fibrosis. A review. Gastroenterology 81:1143, 1981.

Talamo, R.C., Rosenstein, B.J., and Berninger, R.W.: Cystic fibrosis. *In* Stanbury, J.B., Wyngaarden, J.B., Fredrickson, D.S. et al. (eds.): The Metabolic Basis of Inherited Disease. 5th ed. McGraw-Hill, New York, 1983, p. 1889.

Wood, R.E., Boat, T.F., and Doershuk, C.F.: Cystic fibrosis. Am. Rev. Resp. Dis. 113:833, 1976.

IV

LABORATORY EVALUATION OF METABOLIC DISORDERS

38

Metabolic Screening Tests

Peter Jezyk

The purpose of metabolic screening is to identify abnormal components or quantitate abnormal amounts of metabolites appearing in the body fluids of a patient suspected of having an inherited metabolic disorder. There are a number of alternative routes to arriving at an unequivocal identification of an abnormal metabolite. The methods utilized by different laboratories will vary according to personal preferences and areas of expertise of the personnel. What methods are used makes little difference as long as the end result, i.e., identification or quantification of the compound of interest, is accurate and expeditious. In what follows we stress submission of properly obtained samples to the laboratory, as they are the bulwark of the laboratory's approach to diagnosis. Indeed a less than optimal specimen can lead to uncertain or even incorrect results.

The most generally useful sample for evaluation of a suspected metabolic disorder is an accurately timed and measured urine sample. There are several reasons for this choice. Among the most important is that most compounds of pathological significance in the blood will be filtered through the glomerulus and remain in the urine owing to failure of specific tubular resorption. As a consequence, the amount of such compounds in a given volume of urine is therefore often several times greater than in blood or plasma. Defects in normal tubular transport mechanisms have the same effect. Timed samples allow estimates of the amount of metabolite being produced. Twenty-four–hour collections allow direct calculation of daily output and obviate the effect of known diurnal variations in excretion of many substances.

Considering the difficulty in collecting such samples from very young or severely retarded children, an accurate sample from a 4- to 8-hour period will usually suffice for diagnosis, even though the data will be less reflective of total production and excretion than a 24-hour collection. Random urine samples can be utilized for screening purposes, but are not as useful as a timed collection. Not infrequently we receive a random sample with inadequate volume, which renders it impossible to perform all necessary screening tests. Urines are best collected with no preservatives and kept refrigerated or frozen during and after collection.

Plasma or serum samples serve a limited purpose in diagnosis of most metabolic disorders, are essential in a very few, and useless in some. If a metabolic disease is diagnosed or suspected, the reference laboratory will usually request further samples, indicating the proper samples and mode of collection.

Information that should be provided with the samples will vary with the laboratory, but we have found that the more information provided, the easier it is to reach a final laboratory diagnosis. As many of the tests require subjective evaluation, recognition of subtle abnormalities is aided by an increased index of suspicion. As important as a description of clinical features may be in this regard, it is essential that the laboratory know what medications a patient is receiving or has recently received, as many drugs or their metabolites interfere with some tests. Specific examples of commonly encountered problems in this regard will be given as the various tests are described and discussed. The scheme of analysis outlined below is that currently utilized in our laboratory. However, we modify this scheme as improved methods and/or equipment become available.

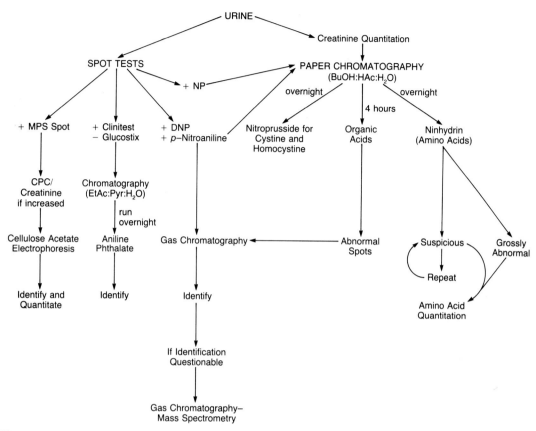

Figure 38–1 Diagram of procedures used in screening urine samples for metabolic disorders at Children's Hospital of Philadelphia. All samples are submitted to the initial battery of tests. Any with putative abnormalities are then further investigated by methodologies outlined until an identification and/or quantitation of the abnormal components are made. After the metabolites are identified, the enzymatic defect is determined when feasible.

The overall flow-chart for sample handling is shown in Figure 38–1. Each component of this chart will now be dealt with more specifically in terms of relevance and interpretation. Spot tests are useful in screening because they are simple to perform, rapid, and aid the laboratory in directing their efforts toward rapid diagnosis of life-threatening conditions. When large quantities of certain metabolites are present, these tests are reliable and straightforward in interpretation. With lesser quantities of these metabolites interpretation often requires some expertise. Each test detects the presence of certain metabolites. Those tests used in our laboratory are:

Ketones

This test utilizes commercially available forms of a nitroprusside reaction for ketones; i.e., Acetest tablets or Keto-stix. Ketones may be present in urine for a variety of reasons. The most common cause of ketosis is fasting. More serious are other altered metabolic states causing ketoacidosis, for example, diabetes mellitus (Table 38–1).

Ketonuria is also associated with some organic acidurias, for example, isovaleric acidemia, methylmalonic acidemia, and holocarboxylase synthase deficiency. α-Keto acids or other compounds with oxo groups that are capable of reaction with dinitrophenylhydrazine reagent form dinitrophenylhydrazones, which are insoluble and yield a yellow precipitate (Table 38–2). This test has been most useful in detection of the branched-chain ketoacids present in the urine of patients with maple syrup ruine disease, although other compounds are detected. A positive test in a child suspected

Table 38–1 CONDITIONS ASSOCIATED WITH KETONURIA

Fasting and starvation
Diabetic ketoacidosis
Organic acidemias
Glycogen storage disease Type I (variable, often nutrition dependent)
Glycogen storage disease Type III
Disorders associated with lactic acidosis (variable)

of having maple syrup urine disease (particularly because of the presence of the characteristic odor) is sufficient to initiate therapy while awaiting further confirmatory results. There are relatively few interfering substances in this test. The major problem we have experienced is submission of urines shortly after the patient has had a radiology procedure involving a contrast dye. Some dyes form heavy precipitates with this reagent immediately upon mixing with the urine.

p-Nitroaniline Reaction

The para-nitroaniline reaction is specific for methylmalonic, ethylmalonic, and malonic acids. Methylmalonic acidemia is a relatively common metabolic disorder and is probably best detected by the use of this specific test. Ethylmalonic acid is excreted by patients with glutaric aciduria type 2 in amounts sufficient to be detected by this test as well. The color given by these metabolites in this reaction is emerald green. Valproic acid and/or its metabolites also yield a green color with this reagent. However, this color is best described as avocado green and is readily distinguishable from the emerald green. As many children who have urine submitted for metabolic screening have seizure disorders that are difficult to control, the use of valproic acid is quite common in this group of patients. When this test is performed, a normal urine with added methylmalonic acid should be run so that the color of the urine being tested may be compared against a standard.

Ferric Chloride Test

The ferric chloride test (Table 38–3) is one of the most easily performed but perhaps most difficult tests to interpret. Addition of ferric chloride to a normal urine usually results in the formation of a brown precipitate. This precipitate consists primarily of phosphates. A large number of compounds react with ferric chloride to give various colors. The classic reaction is a green to blue-green color given by phenylpyruvate in the urine of patients with phenylketonuria. Parahydroxy-phenylpyruvate in the urine of patients with tyrosinemia also gives a green color, which tends to fade more rapidly than that from phenylpyruvate. The most common cause of a green color in this reaction, however, is the presence of bilirubin in the urine. This produces a deep green that

Table 38–2 CONDITIONS ASSOCIATED WITH A POSITIVE 2,4-DINITROPHENYLHYDRAZINE

Maple syrup urine disease
Phenylketonuria
Hereditary tyrosinemia } with heavy excretion
Ketosis
Radio-opaque dyes

Table 38–3 CONDITIONS ASSOCIATED WITH A POSITIVE FERRIC CHLORIDE

Condition	Color
Phenylketonuria	Green
Hereditary tyrosinemia	Green
Homogentisic acid	Transient blue green
Melanoma	Gray turning black
Icterus	Green
Ketones (heavy excretion)	Purple
Salicylate	Purple
Phenothiazines	Purple

persists for long periods of time. All urines with a positive ferric chloride are, therefore, checked for bilirubin with one of the commercially available dipsticks.

The branched-chain ketoacids present in maple syrup urine disease have been reported to give a gray-green color in this reaction. Notwithstanding such reports, we have not observed this reaction in the urines of any of our patients with MSUD. The most common color reaction that we see with ferric chloride is a purple, due to the presence of salicylates in the urine. A purple reaction has also been reported in patients with oasthouse disease due to the presence of alpha-hydroxybutyric acid. We have had one patient with excessive excretion of alpha-hydroxybutyric acid; no purple coloration was noted with urine from this patient. Large amounts of acetoacetic acid in urine from patients with diabetic ketoacidosis have been reported to give a cherry-red color with ferric chloride. We have also failed to observe this reaction in urine from such patients. The ferric chloride reaction has also been incorporated into a dipstick and is available from the Ames Corporation, marketed as Phenistix. This is a convenient form for the occasional user, or for use when only small amounts of sample are available, but must be interpreted with caution, as the limits of detection are considerably higher than using the conventional reaction.

Clinitest Reaction

The Clinitest reaction is a test for reducing substances. It is basically designed to detect reducing sugars in the urine. There are relatively few false positive reactions with this test. However, when large amounts of ampicillin or similar penicillin derivatives are present in the urine, a weakly positive test is obtained. Drugs that are excreted as glucuronides may also give positive reactions with this reagent.

Clinistix Reaction

This dipstick reaction is based on glucose oxidase and is specific for glucose in the urine. All urines with a positive Clinitest reaction are checked with the Clinistix reagent. Any urines giving a positive Clinitest reaction that is not explained by the Clinistix are investigated further by paper chromatography for the presence of other reducing sugars, such as galactose.

Nitroprusside Reaction

The cyanide-nitroprusside reaction is a test for sulfhydryl-containing compounds. The most common substances giving a positive reaction are cystine and homocystine. The silver nitroprusside reaction has been suggested as a means of differentiating homocystine from cystine. We, however, have not found this test to be a reliable means of differentiating these two amino acids and have substituted paper chromatography, with subsequent nitroprusside staining, to effect this distinction. We have also encountered some urines that give a false-positive reaction with this reagent immediately after addition of cyanide and before the addition of nitroprusside. The cause of this false-positive reaction has not yet been identified. The color of the product of this reaction, like that of the para-nitroaniline reaction, is extremely important. A positive reaction yields a magenta-colored product. High concentrations of creatinine in the urine give a salmon-pink–colored product in this reaction. A control urine with added cystine should always be run along with patient specimens.

Nitrosonaphthol Reaction

The nitrosonaphthol reaction is a test for the presence of tyrosine and tyrosine metabolites. False-positives in this reaction are often found with urines from patients with gastrointestinal disorders. This reaction is apparently due to the presence of parahydroxyphenylacetic acid and similar metabolites produced by intestinal bacteria and it is most common in those conditions in which bacterial overgrowth exists.

Chromatographic Identification of Compounds of Metabolic Significance

Spot tests, by their very nature, may be performed rapidly. The tradeoff for this speed is a lack of specificity and relative insensitivity to compounds below a threshold value. Consequently, while a positive test may be indicative of an inborn error, a negative test (in a clinically suspicious situation) should never be taken as adequate proof that a metabolic disorder does not exist. In our experience even with the use of the more sensitive and definitive methods outlined below, many of the disorders of intermediary metabolism are relatively silent (in terms of urine studies) except during periods of overt clinical deterioration. The organic acidemias are a prime example of this observation. Furthermore, the fact that performance of the spot tests appears so simple ought not be construed as support for careless technique. Unless the lab performing such studies is expert in the whole gamut of metabolic studies, one can be misled as to the clinical implications.

As a supplement to spot tests we routinely perform one-dimensional amino acid and organic acid paper chromatography as outlined in Figure 38–1. When the nitroprusside test is positive, we run an additional chromatogram for staining with nitroprusside reagent to distinguish homocystine and cystine. These chromatographic methods date from World War II and enjoy a widespread popularity in metabolic laboratories because of the minimal sample preparation required and the easy reproducibility of results in experienced hands. Since all amino acids are not separated by this system and quantitation is not possible, we resort to ion exchange chromatography to accomplish both ends. We do so when the results of our other studies are abnormal or equivocal or the patient is so gravely ill that no delay can be tolerated.

Organic acid paper chromatography does not discriminate the myriad organic acids in urine as well as amino acid paper chromatography separates amino acids. In the absence of an odor (the presence of which often provides the diagnosis) or positive spot tests we routinely employ paper chromatography and dimethylaminodiphenyl carbinol overspray to identify those samples that require further investigation. Again, we abbreviate our preliminary work-up for the catastrophically ill patient.

In the past, quantitation and identification of organic acids required gas chromatography and mass spectrometry. However, as more information has been accumulated on the behavior of organic acids on columns of differing selectivity it has often been possible (with the well-described organic acidemias) to make a diagnosis using dual-column studies (see Table 34–1). Extraction of organic acids possessing differing degrees of lipid and aqueous solubility presents the methodological hurdle that often results in widely varying values for metabolites in these disorders. In the most severe forms of these disorders less than complete recovery from a biological fluid will not impair diagnosis and therapy; it may have implications for metabolic studies, however.

REFERENCES

Blazer-Yost, B., and Jezyk, P.: Free amino acids in the plasma and urine of dogs from birth to senescence. Am. J. Vet. Res. 40:832, 1979.

Chalmers, R.A., Purkiss, P., Watts, R.W.E., and Lawson, A.M.: Screening for organic acidurias and amino acidopathies in newborns and children. J. Inher. Metab. Dis. 3:27, 1980.

Cohn, R.M., Updegrove, S., Yandrasitz, J., et al.: Evaluation of continuous solvent extraction of organic acids from biological fluids. Clin. Biochem. 11:125, 1978.

Shih, V.E.: Laboratory Techniques for the Detection of Hereditary Metabolic Disorders. CRC Press, Cleveland, 1973.

Tanaka, K., Hine, D.G., West-Dull, H., and Lynn, T.B.: Gas-chromatographic method of analysis for urinary organic acids. I. Retention indices of 155 metabolically important compounds. Clin. Chem. 26:1839, 1980.

Tanaka, K., West-Dull, H., Hine, D.G., et al.: Description of the procedure, and its application to diagnosis of patients with organic acidurias. Clin. Chem. 26:1847, 1980.

Taniguchi, N., Korzumi, S., Masaki, K., and Kobayashi, Y.: Diagnosis of genetic mucopolysaccharidoses: Electrophoretic and enzymatic characterization of urinary glycosaminoglycans. Biochem. Med. 14:241, 1975.

Thomas, G.H., and Howell, R.R.: Selected screening tests for genetic metabolic diseases. Year Book Medical Publishers, Chicago, 1973.

39

Lysosomal Enzyme Studies

Michael Palmieri

As discussed in the chapter on neurodegenerative disorders (sphingolipidoses and mucopolysaccharidoses), the absence of a specific lysosomal hydrolase that removes a substituent group on a complex lipid or carbohydrate membrane component usually results in widespread storage of the undegraded material. Very often the central nervous system bears the brunt of this storage, which leads ultimately to progressive and irreversible mental deterioration. Another mode of clinical presentation spares the central nervous system but involves the viscera and skeletal system. These somewhat simplistic clinical distinctions are more fully discussed in the relevant chapters noted above. Suffice it to say that any child showing organ involvement, as noted here, deserves further evaluation for the possibility of a lysosomal storage disease. Without repeating the facets of the clinical work-up of such a patient, since it was discussed in Chapter 18, we want to consider here the nature of these enzymes and their substrates and how these considerations bear directly upon specimen preparation and transport.

PRINCIPLES OF LYSOSOMAL ENZYME ASSAYS

Lysosomes are subcellular organelles, which appear to serve a "garbage disposal" function for cellular constituents, which must be broken down into their simplest building blocks, i.e., monosaccharides, amino acids, fatty acids, and other simple components (see Chapter 30). Material to be broken down by the acid hydrolases contained within the lysosomes enters by means of endocytosis.

Most of these enzymes are exohydrolases: the component to be degraded is broken down in a sequential fashion from an external point of attachment. Hence, interruption of this stepwise degradative process results in the accumulation of material that cannot leave the lysosome—until such large amounts accumulate that they seriously impair lysosomal function and, ultimately, the economy of the whole cell. Generally, these enzymes manifest group specificity rather than substrate specificity. In the cell this means that several different compounds that possess groups with the appropriate configuration (e.g., α vs. β for a carbohydrate) may be subject to stepwise cleavage by a particular enzyme whose recognition capabilities depend on that particular group as well neighboring groups. This "group specificity" can be utilized in the laboratory by employing synthetic substrates that possess the crucial configuration (and often neighboring groups) but lack the rest of the groups that may be attached to the "natural substrate" within the cell.

Fluorogenic substrates and occasionally radioactively labeled substrates form the bulwark of the laboratory's approach to the enzymatic diagnosis of these disorders.

The major clinical disorders are listed in Table 39–1 along with the presumed natural substrate, synthetic substrate, and the principle of the assay. A few words underscoring problems or puzzles attending these assays are in order.

GM_1 gangliosidosis presents an enigma. By present assays using fluorimetric substrates it is

Table 39–1 LABORATORY EVALUATION OF LYSOSOMAL ENZYME DEFECTS

Disease	Enzyme Defect	Natural Compound	Synthetic Substrate	Principle of Assay
GM$_1$ gangliosidosis	β-Galactosidase	GM$_1$ ganglioside	4-MUB-β-D-galactoside	Fluorimetric
Tay-Sachs disease	Hexosaminidase A	GM$_2$ ganglioside	4-MUB-2-acetamido-2-deoxy-β-D-glucoside	Fluorimetric
Sandhoff's disease	Hexosaminidase A & B	GM$_2$ and GA$_2$ ganglioside; globoside	4-MUB-2-acetamido-2-deoxy-β-D-glucoside	Fluorimetric
Niemann-Pick disease	Sphingomyelinase	Sphingomyelin	2-N-(Hexadecanoyl)-amino-4-nitrophenylphosphorylcholine	Colorimetric
Gaucher's disease	Glucocerebroside-β-glucosidase	Glucocerebroside	4-MUB-β-D-glucoside	Fluorimetric
Metachromatic leukodystrophy	Arylsulfatase A	Sulfatide (galactose-3-sulfate)	p-Nitrocatechol sulfate	Colorimetric
Krabbe's disease	Galactocerebroside β-galactosidase	Galactocerebroside	—	Radioactive
Fabry's disease	α-Galactosidase	Ceramide trihexoside	4-MUB-α-D-galactoside	Fluorimetric
Farber's disease	Ceramidase	Ceramide	—	Radioactive
Wolman's disease	Acid lipase	Cholesterol esters; triglycerides	4-MUB-palmitate	Fluorimetric
Fucosidosis	α-Fucosidase	Fucose-containing sphingolipids and glycoproteins	4-MUB-α-L-fucoside	Fluorimetric
Mannosidosis	α-Mannosidase	Mannose-containing glycoproteins	4-MUB-α-D-mannoside	Fluorimetric

not possible to show a difference in activity, in white cells, between the infantile and juvenile onset forms that would account for the dramatically different clinical course.

Tay-Sachs screening programs have been developed in several urban communities that have large Ashkenazi Jewish populations. For ease of screening relatively large groups, one can make use of the presence of the enzyme in serum. The assay takes advantage of the thermal lability (at 60°C for 2½ minutes) of hexosaminidase A, one of the isozymic forms of the enzyme, while hex B, the other form, survives such treatment. In normal individuals total activity will be the sum of contributions of hex A and B, the A component being determined by the decrease in activity after heating. However, in patients with Tay-Sachs disease the activity after heating will be the same as the total activity prior to heating, since there is no contribution from hex A, and B is usually somewhat increased in such individuals. One can take advantage of the differential thermal lability in assaying the enzyme in white cells as well.

However, a problem arises during pregnancy: a third isozymic form that is more thermally stable than hex A is present in serum. This isozymic form (there may actually be several isozymes) increases the total activity assayed and at the same time the A/B ratio is decreased in pregnancy, suggesting that the mother may be a heterozygote. To avoid this incorrect diagnosis and its potential consequences, white cells (which do not have these intermediate forms) must be the source of enzyme for heterozygote determination during pregnancy.

While the A and B forms of Niemann-Pick disease exhibit a clear decrease in sphingomyelinase activity, the C and D forms do not present an unequivocal enzymatic defect. Despite the fact that sphingomyelin has been found in the spleen of several patients with type C, the universality of this finding remains to be demonstrated. Hence, for the moment the underlying defects in type C as well as D are unknown.

While patients with types A and B can be diagnosed enzymatically using white blood cells, heterozygote detection of these forms requires the use of cultured skin fibroblasts, which normally have 30 to 40 times the level of activity found in white cells.

The infantile or neuropathic form of Gaucher's disease should present no problem in diagnosis, as residual activity of β-glucocerebrosidase is in the range of 1 to 10 percent of normal. However, the adult form, which is the most common variant, manifests activity ranging from 10 to 25 percent of normal. This range of activity may account for some of the clinical heterogeneity seen in this disorder, but from a laboratory point of view, it may pose a real problem in detecting heterozygotes. This latter group may have activity overlapping the higher range of affected adults. Some help in arriving at this distinction comes from assaying serum acid phosphatase activity in the presence of 2-mercaptoethanol, which will be elevated in homozygotes. Although this elevation is also found in patients with cancer of the prostate, further discrimination can be achieved by assaying the enzyme in the presence of sodium tartrate, a compound that inhibits acid phosphatase activity in prostatic cancer patients.

SPECIMEN REQUIREMENTS AND PREPARATION

In our hospital we request that the metabolic service be consulted before a specimen for assay of lysosomal hydrolases is submitted. Specimen requirements for white cell assays are 8 ml of heparinized blood transported to the laboratory at room temperature (this specimen should never be placed on ice). We have isolated leukocytes from heparinized blood collected 10 to 12 hours earlier and found them to be suitable for all lysosomal enzyme assays. In certain cases, a serum sample will be requested in addition to the leukocyte specimen. This specimen is to be obtained in a red top tube and also maintained at room temperature. If the serum is isolated at an outlying hospital, then the specimen should be shipped frozen (on dry ice).

Leukocytes are isolated by the dextran procedure of Skoog and Beck (1956), which consists of precipitating the red cells with dextran and then collecting the white cells from the upper phase by low-speed centrifugation. Contaminating red cells are removed by lysing with water followed by restoration of isotonicity with saline solution. Subsequently, the white cells are collected and stored at $-40°C$. Most lysosomal enzymes are stable in this form for several months.

REFERENCES

Brady, R.O.: Sphingolipidoses. Ann. Rev. Biochem. 47:687, 1978.

Callahan, J.W., and Lowden, J.A. (eds.): Lysosomes and Lysosomal Storage Disease. Raven Press, New York, 1981.

Daniels, L.B., and Glew, R.H.: β-glucosidase assays in the diagnosis of Gaucher's disease. Clin. Chem. 28:569, 1982.

Glew, R.H., and Peters, S.P. (eds.): Practical Enzymology of the Sphingolipidoses. Alan R. Liss, Inc., New York, 1977.

Pentchev, P.G., and Barranger, J.A.: Molecular manifestations and biochemical strategies. J. Lip. Res. 19:401, 1978.

Skoog, W.A., and Beck, W.S.: Studies on the fibrinogen, dextran and phytohemagglutinin methods of isolating leukocytes. Blood 11:436, 1956.

INDEX

Page numbers in *italics* indicate illustrations; page numbers followed by (t) indicate tables.